The Principles
(Volum

Herbert Spencer

Alpha Editions

This edition published in 2024

ISBN 9789362514882

Design and Setting By
Alpha Editions
www.alphaedis.com
Email - info@alphaedis.com

Contents

PREFACE

TO THE REVISED AND ENLARGED EDITION.

Rapid in all directions, scientific progress has during the last generation been more rapid in the direction of Biology than in any other; and had this work been one dealing with Biology at large, the hope of bringing it up to date could not have been rationally entertained. But it is a work on the *Principles* of Biology; and to bring an exposition of these up to date, seemed not impossible with such small remnant of energy as is left me. Slowly, and often interrupted by ill-health, I have in the course of the last two years, completed this first volume of the final edition.

Numerous additions have proved needful. What was originally said about vital changes of matter has been supplemented by a chapter on "Metabolism." Under the title "The Dynamic Element in Life," I have added a chapter which renders less inadequate the conception of Life previously expressed. A gap in preceding editions, which should have been occupied by some pages on "Structure," is now filled up. Those astonishing actions in cell-nuclei which the microscope has of late revealed, will be found briefly set forth under the head of "Cell-Life and Cell-Multiplication." Further evidence and further thought have resulted in a supplementary chapter on "Genesis, Heredity, and Variation"; in which certain views enunciated in the first edition are qualified and developed. Various modern ideas are considered under the title "Recent Criticisms and Hypotheses." And the chapter on "The Arguments from Embryology" has been mainly rewritten. Smaller increments have taken the shape of new sections incorporated in pre-existing chapters. They are distinguished by the following section-marks:—§ 8*a*, § 46*a*, § 87*a*, § 100*a*, § 113*a*, § 127*a*, §§ 130*a*-130*d*. There should also be mentioned a number of foot-notes of some significance not present in preceding editions. Of the three additional appendices the two longer ones have already seen the light in other shapes.

After these chief changes have now to be named the changes necessitated by revision. In making them assistance has been needful. Though many of the amendments have resulted from further thought and inquiry, a much larger number have been consequent on criticisms received from gentlemen whose aid I have been fortunate enough to obtain: each of them having taken a division falling within the range of his special studies. The part concerned with Organic Chemistry and its derived subjects, has been looked through by Mr. W. H. Perkin, Ph.D., F.R.S., Professor of Organic Chemistry, Owens College, Manchester. Plant Morphology and Physiology have been overseen by Mr. A. G. Tansley, M.A., F.L.S., Assistant Professor of Botany, University College, London. Criticisms upon parts dealing with Animal Morphology, I owe to Mr. E. W. MacBride, M.A., Fellow of St. John's College, Cambridge, Professor of Zoology in the McGill University, Montreal, and Mr. J. T. Cunningham, M.A., late Fellow of University College, Oxford. And the statements included under Animal Physiology have been checked by Mr. W. B. Hardy, M.A., Fellow of Gonville and Caius College, Cambridge, Demonstrator of Physiology in the University. Where the discoveries made since 1864 have rendered it needful to change the text, either by omissions or qualifications or in some cases by additions, these gentlemen have furnished me with the requisite information.

Save in the case of the preliminary portion, bristling with the technicalities of Organic Chemistry (including the pages on "Metabolism"), I have not submitted the proofs, either of the new chapters or of the revised chapters, to the gentlemen above named. The abstention has resulted partly from reluctance to trespass on their time to a greater extent than was originally arranged, and partly from the desire to avoid complicating my own work. During the interval occupied in the preparation of this volume the printers have kept pace with me, and I have feared adding to the entailed attention the further attention which correspondence and discussion would have absorbed: feeling that it was better to risk minor inaccuracies than to leave the volume unfinished: an event which at one time appeared probable. I make this statement because, in its absence, one or other of these gentlemen might be held responsible for some error which is not his but mine.

Yet another explanation is called for. Beyond the exposition of those general truths constituting the Principles of Biology as commonly accepted, the original edition of this work contained sundry views for which biological opinion did not furnish any authority. Some of these have since obtained a certain currency; either in their original forms or in modified forms. Misinterpretations are likely to result. Readers who have met with them in other works may, in the absence of warning, suppose, to my disadvantage, that I have adopted them without acknowledgment. Hence it must be understood that where no indication to the contrary is given the substance is unchanged. Beyond the corrections which have been made in the original text, there are, in some cases, additions to the evidence or amplifications of the argument; but in all sections not marked as new, the essential ideas set forth are the same as they were in the original edition of 1864.

BRIGHTON,

August, 1898.

PREFACE.

The aim of this work is to set forth the general truths of Biology, as illustrative of, and as interpreted by, the laws of Evolution: the special truths being introduced only so far as is needful for elucidation of the general truths.

For aid in executing it, I owe many thanks to Prof. Huxley and Dr. Hooker. They have supplied me with information where my own was deficient;[1] and, in looking through the proof-sheets, have pointed out errors of detail into which I had fallen. By having kindly rendered me this valuable assistance, they must not, however, be held committed to any of the enunciated doctrines that are not among the recognized truths of Biology.

The successive instalments which compose this volume, were issued to the subscribers at the following dates:—No. 7 (pp. 1-80) in January, 1863; No. 8 (pp. 81-160) in April, 1863; No. 9 (pp. 161-240) in July, 1863; No. 10 (pp. 241-320) in January, 1864; No. 11 (pp. 321-400) in May, 1864; and No. 12 (pp. 401-476) in October, 1864.

London, September 29th, 1864.

PART I.
THE DATA OF BIOLOGY.

CHAPTER I.

ORGANIC MATTER.

§ 1. Of the four chief elements which, in various combinations, make up living bodies, three are gaseous under all ordinary conditions and the fourth is a solid. Oxygen, hydrogen, and nitrogen are gases which for many years defied all attempts to liquefy them, and carbon is a solid except perhaps at the extremely high temperature of the electric arc. Only by intense pressures joined with extreme refrigerations have the three gases been reduced to the liquid form.[2] There is much significance in this. When we remember how those redistributions of Matter and Motion which constitute Evolution, structural and functional, imply motions in the units that are redistributed; we shall see a probable meaning in the fact that organic bodies, which exhibit the phenomena of Evolution in so high a degree, are mainly composed of ultimate units having extreme mobility. The properties of substances, though destroyed to sense by combination, are not destroyed in reality. It follows from the persistence of force, that the properties of a compound are *resultants* of the properties of its components—*resultants* in which the properties of the components are severally in full action, though mutually obscured. One of the leading properties of each substance is its degree of molecular mobility; and its degree of molecular mobility more or less sensibly affects the molecular mobilities of the various compounds into which it enters. Hence we may infer some relation between the gaseous form of three out of the four chief organic elements, and that comparative readiness displayed by organic matters to undergo those changes in the arrangement of parts which we call development, and those transformations of motion which we call function.

Considering them chemically instead of physically, it is to be remarked that three out of these four main components of organic matter, have affinities which are narrow in their range and low in their intensity. Hydrogen, it is true, may be made to combine with a considerable number of other elements; but the chemical energy which it shows is scarcely at all shown within the limits of the organic temperatures. Of carbon it may similarly be said that it is totally inert at ordinary heats; that the number of substances with which it unites is not great; and that in most cases its tendency to unite with them is but feeble. Lastly, this chemical indifference is shown in the highest degree by nitrogen—an element which, as we shall hereafter see, plays the leading part in organic changes.

Among the organic elements (including under the title not only the four chief ones, but also the less conspicuous remainder), that capability of assuming different states called allotropism, is frequent. Carbon presents itself in the three unlike conditions of diamond, graphite, and charcoal. Under certain circumstances, oxygen takes on the form in which it is called ozone. Sulphur and phosphorus (both, in small proportions, essential constituents of organic matter) have allotropic modifications. Silicon, too, is allotropic; while its oxide, silica, which is an indispensable constituent of many lower organisms, exhibits the analogue of allotropism—isomerism. No other interpretation being possible we are obliged to regard allotropic change as some change of molecular arrangement. Hence this frequency of its occurrence among the components of organic matter is significant as implying a further kind of molecular mobility.

One more fact, that is here of great interest for us, must be set down. These four elements of which organisms are almost wholly composed, exhibit certain extreme unlikenesses. While between two of them we have an unsurpassed contrast in chemical activity; between one of them and the other three, we have an unsurpassed contrast in molecular mobility. While carbon, until lately supposed to be infusible and now volatilized only in the electric arc, shows us a degree of atomic cohesion greater than that of any other known element, hydrogen, oxygen, and nitrogen show the least atomic cohesion of all elements. And while oxygen displays, alike in the range and intensity of its affinities, a chemical energy exceeding that of any other substance (unless fluorine be considered an exception), nitrogen displays the greatest chemical inactivity. Now on calling to mind one of the general truths arrived at when analyzing the process of Evolution, the probable significance of this double difference will be seen. It was shown (*First Principles*, § 163) that, other things equal, unlike units are more easily separated by incident forces than like units are—that an incident force falling on units that are but little dissimilar does not readily segregate them; but that it readily segregates them if they are widely dissimilar. Thus, the substances presenting these two extreme contrasts, the one between physical mobilities, and the other between chemical activities, fulfil, in the highest degree, a certain further condition to facility of differentiation and integration.

§ 2. Among the diatomic combinations of the three elements, hydrogen, nitrogen and oxygen, we find a molecular mobility much less than that of these elements themselves; at the same time that it is much greater than that of diatomic compounds in general. Of the two products formed by the union of oxygen with carbon, the first, called carbonic oxide, which contains one atom[3] of carbon to one of oxygen (expressed by the symbol CO) is a gas condensible only with great difficulty; and the second, carbonic acid, containing an additional atom of oxygen (CO_2) assumes a liquid form also only under a pressure of about forty atmospheres. The several compounds of oxygen with nitrogen, present us with an instructive gradation. Nitrous oxide (N_2O), is a gas condensible only under a pressure of some fifty atmospheres; nitric oxide (NO) is a gas which although it has been liquefied does not condense under a pressure of 270 atmospheres at 46.4° F. (8° C.): the molecular mobility remaining undiminished in consequence of the volume of the united gases remaining unchanged. Nitrogen trioxide (N_2O_3) is gaseous at ordinary temperatures, but condenses into a very volatile liquid at the zero of Fahrenheit; nitrogen tetroxide (N_2O_4) is liquid at ordinary temperatures and becomes solid at the zero of Fahrenheit; while nitrogen pentoxide (N_2O_5) may be obtained in crystals which melt at 85° and boil at 113°. In this series we see, though not with complete uniformity, a decrease of molecular mobility as the weights of the compound molecules are increased. The hydro-carbons illustrate the same general truth still better. One series of them will suffice. Marsh gas (CH_4) is gaseous except under great pressure and at very low temperatures. Olefiant gas (C_2H_4) and ethane (C_2H_6) may be readily liquefied by pressure. Propane (C_3H_8) becomes liquid without pressure at the zero of Fahrenheit. Hexane (C_5H_{12}) is a liquid which boils at 160°. And the successively higher multiples, heptane (C_7H_{16}), octane (C_8H_{18}), and nonane (C_9H_{20}) are liquids which boil respectively at 210°, 257°, and 302°. Pentadecan ($C_{15}H_{32}$) is a liquid which boils at 270°, while paraffin-wax, which contains the still higher multiples, is solid. There are three compounds of hydrogen and nitrogen that have been obtained in a free state—ammonia (NH_3) is gaseous, but liquefiable by pressure, or by reducing its temperature to -40° F., and it solidifies at -112° F.; hydrazine (NH_2—NH_2) is liquid at ordinary temperatures, but hydrozoic acid (N_3H) has so far only been obtained in the form of a highly explosive gas. In cyanogen, which is composed of carbon and nitrogen, $(CN)_2$, we have a gas that becomes liquid at a pressure of four atmospheres and solid at -30° F. And in paracyanogen, formed of the same proportions of these elements in higher multiples, we have a solid which does not fuse or volatilize at ordinary temperatures. Lastly, in the most important member of this group, water (H_2O), we have a compound of two difficultly-condensible gases which assumes both the fluid state and the solid state within ordinary ranges of temperature; while its molecular mobility is still such that its fluid or solid masses are continually passing into the form of vapour, though not with great rapidity until the temperature is raised to 212°.

Considering them chemically, it is to be remarked of these diatomic compounds of the four chief organic elements, that they are, on the average, less stable than diatomic compounds in general. Water, carbonic oxide, and carbonic acid, are, it is true, difficult to decompose. But omitting these, the usual strength of union among the elements of the above-named substances is low considering the simplicity of the substances. With the exception of acetylene and possibly marsh gas, the various hydro-carbons are not producible by directly combining their elements; and the elements of most of them are readily separable by heat without the aid of any antagonistic affinity. Nitrogen and hydrogen do not unite with each other immediately save under very exceptional circumstances; and the ammonia which results from their union, though it resists heat, yields to the electric spark. Cyanogen is stable: not being resolved into its components below a bright red heat. Much less stable, however, are several of the oxides of nitrogen. Nitrous oxide, it is true, does not yield up its elements below a red heat; but nitrogen tetroxide cannot exist if water be added to it; nitrous acid is decomposed by water; and nitric acid not only readily parts with its oxygen to many metals, but when anhydrous, spontaneously decomposes. Here it will be well to note, as having a bearing on what is to follow, how characteristic of most nitrogenous compounds is this special instability. In all the familiar cases of sudden and violent decomposition, the change is due to the presence of nitrogen. The explosion of gunpowder results from the readiness with which the nitrogen contained in the nitrate of potash, yields up the oxygen combined with it. The explosion of gun-cotton, which also contains nitrogen, is a substantially parallel phenomenon. The various fulminating salts are all formed by the union with metals of a certain nitrogenous acid called fulminic acid; which is so unstable that it cannot be obtained in a separate state. Explosiveness is a property of nitro-mannite, and also of nitro-glycerin. Iodide of nitrogen detonates on the slightest touch, and often without any assignable cause. And the bodies which explode with the most tremendous violence of any known, are the chloride of nitrogen (NCl_3) and hydrazoic acid (N_3H). Thus these easy and rapid decompositions, due to the chemical indifference of nitrogen, are characteristic. When we come hereafter to observe the part which nitrogen plays in organic actions, we shall see the significance of this extreme readiness shown by its compounds to undergo changes. Returning from these facts parenthetically introduced, we have next to note that though among the diatomic compounds of the four chief organic elements, there are a few active ones, yet the majority of them display a smaller degree of chemical energy than the average of diatomic compounds. Water is the most neutral of bodies: usually producing little chemical alteration in the substances with which it combines; and being expelled from most of its combinations by a moderate heat. Carbonic acid is a relatively feeble acid: the carbonates being decomposed by the majority of other acids and by ignition. The various hydro-carbons are but narrow in the range of their comparatively weak affinities. The compounds formed by ammonia have not much stability: they are readily destroyed by heat, and by the other alkalies. The affinities of cyanogen are tolerably strong, though they yield to those of the chief acids. Of the several oxides of nitrogen, it is to be remarked that, while those containing the smaller proportions of oxygen are chemically inert, the one containing the greatest proportion of oxygen (nitric acid) though chemically active, in consequence of the readiness with which one part of it gives up its oxygen to oxidize a base with which the rest combines, is nevertheless driven from all its combinations by a red heat.

These diatomic compounds, like their elements, are to a considerable degree characterized by the prevalence among them of allotropism; or, as it is more usually called when displayed by compound bodies—isomerism. Professor Graham finds reason for thinking that a change in atomic arrangements of this nature, takes place in water, at or near the melting point of ice. In the various series of hydro-carbons, differing from each other only in the ratios in which the elements are united, we find not simply isomerism but polymerism occurring to an almost infinite extent. In some series of hydro-carbons, as, for example, the terpenes, we find isomerism and at the same time a great tendency to undergo polymerisation. And the relation between cyanogen and paracyanogen is, as we saw, a polymeric one.

There is one further fact respecting these diatomic compounds of the chief organic elements, which must not be overlooked. Those of them which form parts of the living tissues of plants and animals (excluding water which has a mechanical function, and carbonic acid which is a product of decomposition) belong for the most part to one group—the carbo-hydrates.[4] And of this group, which is on the average characterized by comparative instability and inertness, these carbo-hydrates found in living tissues are among the most unstable and inert.

§ 3. Passing now to the substances which contain three of these chief organic elements, we have first to note that along with the greater atomic weight which mostly accompanies their increased complexity, there is, on the average, a further marked decrease of molecular mobility. Scarcely any of them maintain a gaseous state at ordinary temperatures. One class of them only, the alcohols and their derivatives, evaporate under the usual atmospheric pressure; but not rapidly unless heated. The fixed oils, though they show that molecular mobility implied by an habitually liquid state, show this in a lower degree than the alcoholic compounds; and they cannot be reduced to the gaseous state without decomposition. In their allies, the fats, which are solid unless heated, the loss of molecular mobility is still more marked. And throughout the whole series of the fatty acids, in which to a fixed proportion of oxygen there are successively added higher equimultiples of carbon and hydrogen, we see how the molecular mobility decreases with the increasing sizes of the molecules. In the amylaceous and sugar-group of compounds, solidity is the habitual state: such of them as can assume the liquid form, doing so only when heated to 300° or 400° F.; and decomposing when further heated, rather than become gaseous. Resins and gums exhibit general physical properties of like character and meaning.

In chemical stability these triatomic compounds, considered as a group, are in a marked degree below the diatomic ones. The various sugars and kindred bodies, decompose at no very high temperatures. The oils and fats also are readily carbonized by heat. Resinous and gummy substances are easily made to render up some of their constituents. And the alcohols, with their allies, have no great power of resisting decomposition. These bodies, formed by the union of oxygen, hydrogen, and carbon, are also, as a class, chemically inactive. Formic and acetic are doubtless energetic acids; but the higher members of the fatty-acid series are easily separated from the bases with which they combine. Saccharic acid, too, is an acid of considerable power; and sundry of the vegetable acids possess a certain activity, though an activity far less than that of the mineral acids. But throughout the rest of the group, there is shown but a small tendency to combine with other bodies; and such combinations as are formed have usually little permanence.

The phenomena of isomerism and polymerism are of frequent occurrence in these triatomic compounds. Starch and dextrine are probably polymeric. Fruit-sugar and grape-sugar, mannite and sorbite, cane-sugar and milk-sugar, are isomeric. Sundry of the vegetal acids exhibit similar modifications. And among the resins and gums, with their derivatives, molecular re-arrangements of this kind are not uncommon.

One further fact respecting these compounds of carbon, oxygen and hydrogen, should be mentioned; namely, that they are divisible into two classes—the one consisting of substances that result from the destructive decomposition of organic matter, and the other consisting of substances that exist as such in organic matter. These two classes of substances exhibit, in different degrees, the properties to which we have been directing our attention. The lower alcohols, their allies and derivatives, which possess greater molecular mobility and chemical stability than the rest of these triatomic compounds, are rarely found in animal or vegetal bodies. While the sugars and amylaceous substances, the fixed oils and fats, the gums and resins, which have all of them much less molecular mobility, and are, chemically considered, more unstable and inert, are components of the living tissues of plants and animals.

§ 4. Among compounds containing all the four chief organic elements, a division analogous to that just named may be made. There are some which result from the decomposition of living tissues; there are others which make parts of living tissues in their state of integrity; and these two groups are contrasted in their properties in the same way as are the parallel groups of triatomic compounds.

Of the first division, certain products found in the animal excretions are the most important, and the only ones that need be noted; such, namely, as urea, kreatine, kreatinine. These animal-bases exhibit much less molecular mobility than the average of the substances treated of in the last section: being solid at ordinary temperatures, fusing, where fusible at all, at temperatures above that of boiling water, and having no power to assume a gaseous state. Chemically considered, their stability is low, and their activity but small, in comparison with the stabilities and activities of the simpler compounds.

It is, however, the nitrogenous constituents of living tissues, that display most markedly those characteristics of which we have been tracing the growth. Albumen, fibrin, casein, and their allies, are bodies in which that molecular mobility exhibited by three of their components in so high a degree is reduced to a minimum. These substances are known only in the solid state. That is to say, when deprived of the water usually mixed with them, they do not admit of fusion, much less of volatilization. To which add, that they have not even that molecular mobility which solution in water implies; since, though they form viscid mixtures with water, they do not dissolve in the same perfect way as do inorganic compounds. The chemical characteristics of these substances are instability and inertness carried to the extreme. How rapidly albumenoid matters decompose under ordinary conditions, is daily seen: the difficulty of every housewife being to prevent them from decomposing. It is true that when desiccated and kept from contact with air, they may be preserved unchanged for long periods; but the fact that they can be only thus preserved, proves their great instability. It is true, also, that these most complex nitrogenous principles are not absolutely inert, since they enter into combinations with some bases; but their unions are very feeble.

It should be noted, too, of these bodies, that though they exhibit in the lowest degree that kind of molecular mobility which implies facile vibration of the molecules as wholes, they exhibit in high degrees that kind of molecular mobility resulting in isomerism, which implies permanent changes in the positions of adjacent atoms with respect to each other. Each of them has a soluble and an insoluble form. In some cases there are indications of more than two such forms. And it appears that their metamorphoses take place under very slight changes of conditions.

In these most unstable and inert organic compounds, we find that the molecular complexity reaches a maximum: not only since the four chief organic elements are here united with small proportions of sulphur and sometimes phosphorus; but also since they are united in high multiples. The peculiarity which we found characterized even diatomic compounds of the organic elements, that their molecules are formed not of single equivalents of each component, but of two, three, four, and more equivalents, is carried to the greatest extreme in these compounds, which take the leading part in organic actions. According to Lieberkühn, the formula of albumen is $C_{72}H_{112}SN_{18}O_{22}$. That is to say, with the sulphur there are united seventy-two atoms of carbon, one hundred and twelve of hydrogen, eighteen of nitrogen, and twenty-two of oxygen: the molecule being thus made up of more than two hundred ultimate atoms.

§ 5. Did space permit, it would be useful here to consider in detail the interpretations that may be given of the peculiarities we have been tracing: bringing to their solution, the general mechanical principles which are now found to hold true of molecules as of masses. But it must suffice briefly to indicate the conclusions which such an inquiry promises to bring out.

Proceeding on these principles, it may be argued that the molecular mobility of a substance must depend partly on the inertia of its molecules; partly on the intensity of their mutual polarities; partly on their mutual pressures, as determined by the density of their aggregation; and (where the molecules are compound) partly on the molecular mobilities of their component molecules. Whence it is to be inferred that any three of these remaining constant, the molecular mobility will vary as the fourth. Other things equal, therefore, the molecular mobility of molecules must decrease as their masses increase; and so there must result that progression we have traced, from the high molecular mobility of the uncombined organic elements, to the low molecular mobility of those large-moleculed substances into which they are ultimately compounded.

Applying to molecules the mechanical law which holds of masses, that since inertia and gravity increase as the cubes of the dimensions while cohesion increases as their squares, the self-sustaining power of a body becomes relatively smaller as its bulk becomes greater; it might be argued that these large, aggregate molecules which constitute organic substances, are mechanically weak—are less able than simpler molecules to bear, without alteration, the forces falling on them. That very massiveness which renders them less mobile, enables the physical forces acting on them more readily to change the relative positions of their component atoms; and so to produce what we know as re-arrangements and decompositions.

Further, it seems a not improbable conclusion, that this formation of large aggregates of elementary atoms and resulting diminution of self-sustaining power, must be accompanied by a decrease of those dimensional contrasts to which polarity is ascribable. A sphere is the figure of equilibrium which any aggregate of units tends to assume, under the influence of simple mutual attraction. Where the number of units is small and their mutual polarities are decided, this proclivity towards spherical grouping will be overcome by the tendency towards some more special form, determined by their mutual polarities. But it is manifest that in proportion as an aggregate molecule becomes larger, the effects of simple mutual attraction must become relatively greater; and so must tend to mask the effects of polar attraction. There will consequently be apt to result in highly compound molecules like these organic ones, containing hundreds of elementary atoms, such approximation to the spherical form as must involve a less distinct polarity than in simpler molecules. If this inference be correct, it supplies us with an explanation both of the chemical inertness of these most complex organic substances, and of their inability to crystallize.

§ 6. Here we are naturally introduced to another aspect of our subject—an aspect of great interest. Professor Graham has published a series of important researches, which promise to throw much light on the constitution and changes of organic matter. He shows that solid substances exist under two forms of aggregation—the *colloid* or jelly-like, and the *crystalloid* or crystal-like. Examples of the last are too familiar to need specifying. Of the first may be named such instances as "hydrated silicic acid, hydrated alumina, and other metallic peroxides of the aluminous class, when they exist in the soluble form; with starch, dextrine and the gums, caramel, tannin, albumen, gelatine, vegetable and animal extractive matters." Describing the properties of colloids, Professor Graham says:—"Although often largely soluble in water, they are held in solution by a most feeble force. They appear singularly inert in the capacity of acids and bases, and in all the ordinary chemical relations." * * * "Although chemically inert in the ordinary sense, colloids possess a compensating activity of their own arising out of their physical properties. While the rigidity of the crystalline structure shuts out external impressions, the softness of the gelatinous colloid partakes of fluidity, and enables the colloid to become a medium of liquid diffusion, like water itself." * * * "Hence a wide sensibility on the part of colloids to external agents. Another and eminently characteristic quality of colloids is their mutability." * * * "The solution of hydrated silicic acid, for instance, is easily obtained in a state of purity, but it cannot be preserved. It may remain fluid for days or weeks in a sealed tube, but is sure to gelatinize and become insoluble at last. Nor does the change of this colloid appear to stop at that point; for the mineral forms of silicic acid, deposited from water, such as flint, are often found to have passed, during the geological ages of their existence, from the vitreous or colloidal into the crystalline condition (H. Rose). The colloid is, in fact, a dynamical state of matter, the crystalloidal being the statical condition. The colloid possesses *energia*. It may be looked upon as the primary source of the force appearing in the phenomena of vitality. To the gradual manner in which colloidal changes take place (for they always demand time as an element) may the characteristic protraction of chemico-organic changes also be referred."

The class of colloids includes not only all those most complex nitrogenous compounds characteristic of organic tissues, and sundry of the carbo-hydrates found along with them; but, significantly enough, it includes several of those substances classed as inorganic, which enter into organized structures. Thus silica, which is a component of many plants, and constitutes the spicules of sponges as well as the shells of many foraminifera and infusoria, has a colloid, as well as a crystalloid, condition. A solution of hydrated silicic acid passes in the course of a few days into a solid jelly that is no longer soluble in water; and it may be suddenly thus coagulated by a minute portion of an alkaline carbonate, as well as by gelatine, alumina, and peroxide of iron. This last-named substance, too—peroxide of iron—which is an ingredient in the blood of mammals and composes the shells of certain *Protozoa*, has a colloid condition. "Water containing about one per cent. of hydrated peroxide of iron in solution, has the dark red colour of venous blood." * * * "The red solution is coagulated in the cold by traces of sulphuric acid, alkalies, alkaline carbonates, sulphates, and neutral salts in general." * * * "The coagulum is a deep red-coloured jelly, resembling the clot of blood, but more transparent. Indeed, the coagulum of this colloid is highly suggestive of that of blood, from the feeble agencies which suffice to effect the change in question, as well as from the appearance of the product." The jelly thus formed soon becomes, like the last, insoluble in water. Lime also, which is so important a mineral element in living bodies, animal and vegetal, enters into a compound belonging to this class. "The well-known solution of lime in sugar forms a solid coagulum when heated. It is probably, at a high temperature, entirely colloidal."

Generalizing some of the facts which he gives, Professor Graham says:—"The equivalent of a colloid appears to be always high, although the ratio between the elements of the substance may be simple. Gummic acid, for instance, may be represented by $C^{12}H^{22}O^{11}$; but, judging from the small proportions of lime and potash which suffice to neutralize this acid, the true numbers of its formula must be several times greater. It is difficult to avoid associating the inertness of colloids with their high equivalents, particularly where the high number appears to be attained by the repetition of a small number. The inquiry suggests itself whether the colloid molecule may not be constituted by the grouping together of a number of smaller crystalloid molecules, and whether the basis of colloidality may not really be this composite character of the molecule."

§ 7. A further contrast between colloids and crystalloids is equally significant in its relations to vital phenomena. Professor Graham points out that the marked differences in volatility displayed by different bodies, are paralleled by differences in the rates of diffusion of different bodies through liquids. As alcohol and ether at ordinary temperatures, and various other substances at higher temperatures, diffuse themselves in a gaseous form through the air; so, a substance in aqueous solution, when placed in contact with a mass of water (in such way as to avoid mixture by circulating currents) diffuses itself through this mass of water. And just as there are various degrees of rapidity in evaporation, so there are various degrees of rapidity in diffusion: "the range also in the degree of diffusive mobility exhibited by different substances appears to be as wide as the scale of vapour-tensions." This parallelism is what might have been looked for; since the tendency to assume a gaseous state, and the tendency to spread in solution through a liquid, are both consequences of molecular mobility. It also turns out, as was to be expected, that diffusibility, like volatility, has, other things equal, a relation to molecular weight—other things equal, we must say, because molecular mobility must, as pointed out in § 5, be affected by other properties of atoms, besides their inertia. Thus the substance most rapidly diffused of any on which Professor Graham experimented, was hydrochloric acid—a compound which is of low molecular weight, is gaseous save under a pressure of forty atmospheres, and ordinarily exists as a liquid, only in combination with water. Again, "hydrate of potash may be said to possess double the velocity of diffusion of sulphate of potash, and sulphate of potash again double the velocity of sugar, alcohol, and sulphate of magnesia,"—differences which have a general correspondence with differences in the massiveness of their molecules.

But the fact of chief interest to us here, is that the relatively small-moleculed crystalloids have immensely greater diffusive power than the relatively large-moleculed colloids. Among the crystalloids themselves there are marked differences of diffusibility; and among the colloids themselves there are parallel differences, though less marked ones. But these differences are small compared with that between the diffusibility of the crystalloids as a class, and the diffusibility of the colloids as a class. Hydrochloric acid is seven times as diffusible as sulphate of magnesia; but it is fifty times as diffusible as albumen, and a hundred times as diffusible as caramel.

These differences of diffusibility manifest themselves with nearly equal distinctness, when a permeable septum is placed between the solution and the water. The result is that when a solution contains substances of different diffusibilities, the process of dialysis, as Professor Graham calls it, becomes a means of separating the mixed substances: especially when such mixed substances are partly crystalloids and partly colloids. The bearing of this fact on the interpretation of organic processes will be obvious. Still more obvious will its bearing be, on joining with it the remarkable fact that while crystalloids can diffuse themselves through colloids nearly as rapidly as through water, colloids can scarcely diffuse themselves at all through other colloids. From a mass of jelly containing salt, into an adjoining mass of jelly containing no salt, the salt spread more in eight days than it spread through water in seven days; while the spread of "caramel through the jelly appeared scarcely to have begun after eight days had elapsed." So that we must regard the colloidal compounds of which organisms are built, as having, by their physical nature, the ability to separate colloids from crystalloids, and to let the crystalloids pass through them with scarcely any resistance.

One other result of these researches on the relative diffusibilities of different substances has a meaning for us. Professor Graham finds that not only does there take place, by dialysis, a separation of *mixed* substances which are unlike in their molecular mobilities; but also that *combined* substances between which the affinities are feeble, will separate on the dialyzer, if their molecular mobilities are strongly contrasted. Speaking of the hydrochloride of peroxide of iron, he says, "such a compound possesses an element of instability in the extremely unequal diffusibility of its constituents;" and he points out that when dialyzed, the hydrochloric acid gradually diffuses away, leaving the colloidal peroxide of iron behind. Similarly, he remarks of the peracetate of iron, that it "may be made a source of soluble peroxide, as the salt referred to is itself decomposed to a great extent by diffusion on the dialyzer." Now this tendency to separate displayed by substances which differ widely in their molecular mobilities, though usually so far antagonized by their affinities as not to produce spontaneous decomposition, must, in all cases, induce a certain readiness to change which would not else exist. The unequal mobilities of the combined atoms must give disturbing forces a greater power to work transformations than they would otherwise have. Hence the probable significance of a fact named at the outset, that while three of the chief organic elements have the greatest atomic mobilities of any elements known, the fourth, carbon, has the least atomic mobility of known elements. Though, in its simple compounds, the affinities of carbon for the rest are strong enough to prevent the effects of this great difference from clearly showing themselves; yet there seems reason to think that in those complex compounds composing organic bodies—compounds in which there are various cross affinities leading to a state of chemical tension—this extreme difference in the molecular mobilities must be an important aid to molecular re-arrangements. In short, we are here led by concrete evidence to the conclusion which we before drew from first principles, that this great unlikeness among the combined units must facilitate differentiations.

§ 8. A portion of organic matter in a state to exhibit those phenomena which the biologist deals with, is, however, something far more complex than the separate organic matters we have been studying; since a portion of organic matter in its integrity, contains several of these.

In the first place no one of those colloids which make up the mass of a living body, appears capable of carrying on vital changes by itself: it is always associated with other colloids. A portion of animal-tissue, however minute, almost always contains more than one form of protein-substance: different chemical modifications of albumen and gelatine are present together, as well as, probably, a soluble and insoluble modification of each; and there is usually more or less of fatty matter. In a single vegetal cell, the minute quantity of nitrogenous colloid present, is imbedded in colloids of the non-nitrogenous class. And the microscope makes it at once manifest, that even the smallest and simplest organic forms are not absolutely homogeneous.

Further, we have to contemplate organic tissue, formed of mingled colloids in both soluble and insoluble states, as permeated throughout by crystalloids. Some of these crystalloids, as oxygen,[5] water, and perhaps certain salts, are agents of decomposition; some, as the saccharine and fatty matters, are probably materials for decomposition; and some, as carbonic acid, water, urea, kreatine, and kreatinine, are products of decomposition. Into the mass of mingled colloids, mostly insoluble and where soluble of very low molecular mobility or diffusive power, we have constantly passing, crystalloids of high molecular mobility or diffusive power, that are capable of decomposing these complex colloids, or of facilitating decompositions otherwise caused; and from these complex colloids, when decomposed, there result other crystalloids (the two chief ones extremely simple and mobile, and the rest comparatively so) which diffuse away as rapidly as they are formed.

And now we may clearly see the necessity for that peculiar composition which we find in organic matter. On the one hand, were it not for the extreme molecular mobility possessed by three out of the four of its chief elements; and were it not for the consequently high molecular mobility of their simpler compounds; there could not be this quick escape of the waste products of organic action; and there could not be that continuously active change of matter which vitality implies. On the other hand, were it not for the union of these extremely mobile elements into immensely complex compounds, having relatively vast molecules which are made comparatively immobile by their inertia, there could not result that mechanical fixity which prevents the components of living tissue from diffusing away along with the effete matters produced by decomposition.

§ 8*a*. Let us not omit here to note the ways in which the genesis of these traits distinguishing organic matter conforms to the laws of evolution as expressed in its general formula.

In pursuance of the belief now widely entertained by chemists that the so-called elements are not elements, but are composed of simpler matters and probably of one ultimate form of matter (for which the name "protyle" has been suggested by Sir W. Crookes), it is to be concluded that the formation of the elements, in common with the formation of all those compounds of them which Nature presents, took place in the course of Cosmic Evolution. Various reasons for this inference the reader will find set forth in the Addenda to an essay on "The Nebular Hypothesis" (see *Essays*, vol. I, p. 155). On tracing out the process of compounding and re-compounding by which, hypothetically, the elements themselves and afterwards their compounds and re-compounds have arisen, certain cardinal facts become manifest.

1. Considered as masses, the units of the elements are the smallest, though larger than the units of the primordial matter. Later than these, since they are composed of them, and since they cannot exist at temperatures so high as those at which the elements can exist, come the diatomic compounds—oxides, chlorides, and the rest—necessarily larger in their molecules. Above these in massiveness come the molecules of the multitudinous salts and kindred bodies. When associated, as these commonly are, with molecules of water, there again results in each case increase of mass; and unable as they are to bear such high temperatures, these molecules are necessarily later in origin than those of the anhydrous diatomic compounds. Within the general class of triatomic compounds, more composite still, come the carbohydrates, which, being able to unite in multiples, form still larger molecules than other triatomic compounds. Decomposing as they do at relatively low temperatures, these are still more recent in the course of chemical evolution; and with the genesis of them the way is prepared for the genesis of organic matter strictly so called. This includes the various forms of protein-substance, containing four chief elements with two minor ones, and having relatively vast molecules. Unstable as these are in presence of heat and surrounding affinities, they became possible only at a late stage in the genesis of the Earth. Here, then, in that chemical evolution which preceded the evolution of life, we see displayed that process of integration which is the primary trait of evolution at large.

2. Along with increasing integration has gone progress in heterogeneity. The elements, regarding them as compound, are severally more

heterogeneous than "protyle." Diatomic molecules are more heterogeneous than these elements; triatomic more heterogeneous than diatomic; and the molecules containing four elements more heterogeneous than those containing three: the most heterogeneous of them being the proteids, which contain two other elements. The hydrated forms of all these compounds are more heterogeneous than are the anhydrous forms. And most heterogeneous of all are the molecules which, besides containing three, four, or more elements, also exhibit the isomerism and polymerism which imply unions in multiples.

3. This formation of molecules more and more heterogeneous during terrestrial evolution, has been accompanied by increasing heterogeneity in the aggregate of compounds of each kind, as well as an increasing number of kinds; and this increasing heterogeneity is exemplified in an extreme degree in the compounds, non-nitrogenous and nitrogenous, out of which organisms are built. So that the classes, orders, genera, and species of chemical substances, gradually increasing as the Earth has assumed its present form, increased in a transcendent degree during that stage which preceded the origin of life.

§ 9. Returning now from these partially-parenthetic observations, and summing up the contents of the preceding pages, we have to remark that in the substances of which organisms are composed, the conditions necessary to that re-distribution of Matter and Motion which constitutes Evolution, are fulfilled in a far higher degree than at first appears.

The mutual affinities of the chief organic elements are not active within the limits of those temperatures at which organic actions take place; and one of these elements is especially characterized by its chemical indifference. The compounds formed by these elements in ascending grades of complexity, become progressively less stable. And those most complex compounds into which all these four elements enter, together with small proportions of two other elements which very readily oxidize, have an instability so great that decomposition ensues under ordinary atmospheric conditions.

Among these elements out of which living bodies are built, there is an unusual tendency to unite in multiples; and so to form groups of products which have the same chemical elements in the same proportions, but, differing in their modes of aggregation, possess different properties. This prevalence among them of isomerism and polymerism, shows, in another way, the special fitness of organic substances for undergoing re-distributions of their components.

In those most complex compounds that are instrumental to vital actions, there exists a kind and degree of molecular mobility which constitutes the plastic quality fitting them for organization. Instead of the extreme molecular mobility possessed by three out of the four organic elements in their separate states—instead of the diminished, but still great, molecular mobility possessed by their simpler combinations, the gaseous and liquid characters of which unfit them for showing to any extent the process of Evolution—instead of the physical properties of their less simple combinations, which, when not made unduly mobile by heat, assume the unduly rigid form of crystals; we have in these colloids, of which organisms are mainly composed, just the required compromise between fluidity and solidity. They cannot be reduced to the unduly mobile conditions of liquid and gas; and yet they do not assume the unduly fixed condition usually characterizing solids. The absence of power to unite together in polar arrangement, leaves their molecules with a certain freedom of relative movement, which makes them sensitive to small forces, and produces plasticity in the aggregates composed of them.

While the relatively great inertia of these large and complex organic molecules renders them comparatively incapable of being set in motion by the ethereal undulations, and so reduced to less coherent forms of aggregation, this same inertia facilitates changes of arrangement among their constituent molecules or atoms; since, in proportion as an incident force impresses but little motion on a mass, it is the better able to impress motion on the parts of the mass in relation to one another. And it is further probable that the extreme contrasts in molecular mobilities among the components of these highly complex molecules, aid in producing modifiability of arrangement among them.

Lastly, the great difference in diffusibility between colloids and crystalloids, makes possible in the tissues of organisms a specially rapid re-distribution of matter and motion; both because colloids, being easily permeable by crystalloids, can be chemically acted on throughout their whole masses, instead of only on their surfaces; and because the products of decomposition, being also crystalloids, can escape as fast as they are produced: leaving room for further transformations. So that while the composite molecules of which organic tissues are built up, possess that low molecular mobility fitting them for plastic purposes, it results from the extreme molecular mobilities of their ultimate constituents, that the waste products of vital activity escape as fast as they are formed.

To all which add that the state of warmth, or increased molecular vibration, in which all the higher organisms are kept, increases these various facilities for re-distribution: not only as aiding chemical changes, but as accelerating the diffusion of crystalloid substances.

CHAPTER II.

THE ACTIONS OF FORCES ON ORGANIC MATTER.

§ 10. To some extent, the parts of every body are changed in their arrangement by any incident mechanical force. But in organic bodies, and especially in animal bodies, the changes of arrangement produced by mechanical forces are usually conspicuous. It is a distinctive mark of colloids that they readily yield to pressures and tensions, and that they recover, more or less completely, their original shapes, when the pressures or tensions cease. Evidently without this pliability and elasticity, most organic actions would be impossible. Not only temporary but also permanent alterations of form are facilitated by this colloid character of organic matter. Continued pressure on living tissue, by modifying the processes going on in it (perhaps retarding the absorption of new material to replace the old that has decomposed and diffused away), gradually diminishes and finally destroys its power of resuming the outline it had at first. Thus, generally speaking, the substances composing organisms are modifiable by arrested momentum or by continuous strain, in far greater degrees than are inorganic substances.

§ 11. Sensitiveness to certain forces which are quasi-mechanical, if not mechanical in the usual sense, is seen in two closely-related peculiarities displayed by organic matter as well as other matter which assumes the same state of molecular aggregation.

Colloids take up by a power called "capillary affinity," a large quantity of water: undergoing at the same time great increase of bulk with change of form. Conversely, with like readiness, they give up this water by evaporation; resuming, partially or completely, their original states. Whether resulting from capillarity, or from the relatively great diffusibility of water, or from both, these changes are to be here noted as showing another mode in which the arrangements of parts in organic bodies are affected by mechanical actions.

In what is termed osmose, we have a further mode of an allied kind. When on opposite sides of a permeable septum, and especially a septum of colloidal substance, are placed miscible solutions of different densities, a double transfer takes place: a large quantity of the less dense solution finds its way through the septum into the more dense solution; and a small quantity of the more dense finds its way into the less dense—one result being a considerable increase in the bulk of the more dense at the expense of the less dense. This process, which appears to depend on several conditions, is not yet fully understood. But be the explanation what it may, the process is one that tends continually to work alterations in organic bodies. Through the surfaces of plants and animals, transfers of this kind are ever taking place. Many of the conspicuous changes of form undergone by organic germs, are due mainly to the permeation of their limiting membranes by the surrounding liquids.

It should be added that besides the direct alterations which the imbibition and transmission of water and watery solutions by colloids produce in organic matter, they produce indirect alterations. Being instrumental in conveying into the tissues the agents of chemical change, and conveying out of them the products of chemical change, they aid in carrying on other re-distributions.

§ 12. As elsewhere shown (*First Principles*, § 100) heat, or a raised state of molecular vibration, enables incident forces more easily to produce changes of molecular arrangement in organic matter. But besides this, it conduces to certain vital changes in so direct a way as to become their chief cause.

The power of the organic colloids to imbibe water, and to bring along with it into their substance the materials which work transformations, would not be continuously operative if the water imbibed were to remain. It is because it escapes, and is replaced by more water containing more materials, that the succession of changes is maintained. Among the higher animals and higher plants its escape is facilitated by evaporation. And the rate of evaporation is, other things equal, determined by heat. Though the current of sap in a tree is partly dependent on some action, probably osmotic, that goes on in the roots; yet the loss of water from the surfaces of the leaves, and the consequent absorption of more sap into the leaves by capillary attraction, must be a chief cause of the circulation. The drooping of a plant when exposed to the sunshine while the earth round its roots is dry, shows us how evaporation empties the sap-vessels; and the quickness with which a withered slip revives on being placed in water, shows us the part which capillary action plays. In so far, then, as the evaporation from a plant's surface helps to produce currents of sap through the plant, we must regard the heat which produces this evaporation as a part-cause of those re-distributions of matter which these currents effect. In terrestrial animals, heat, by its indirect action as well as by its direct action, similarly aids the changes that are going on. The exhalation of vapour from the lungs and the surface of the skin, forming the chief escape of the water that is swallowed, conduces to the maintenance of those currents through the tissues without which the functions would cease. For though the vascular system distributes nutritive liquids in ramified channels through the body; yet the absorption of these liquids into tissues, partly depends on the escape of liquids which the tissues already contain. Hence, to the extent that such escape is facilitated by evaporation, and this evaporation facilitated by heat, heat becomes an agent of re-distribution in the animal organism.[6]

§ 13. Light, which is now known to modify many inorganic compounds—light, which works those chemical changes utilized in photography, causes the combinations of certain gases, alters the molecular arrangements of many crystals, and leaves traces of its action even on substances that are extremely stable,—may be expected to produce marked effects on substances so complex and unstable as those which make up organic bodies. It does produce such effects; and some of them are among the most important that organic matter undergoes.

The molecular changes wrought by light in animals are of but secondary moment. There is the darkening of the skin that follows exposure to the Sun's rays. There are those alterations in the retina which cause in us sensations of colours. And on certain eyeless creatures that are semi-transparent, the light permeating their substance works some effects evinced by movements. But speaking generally, the opacity of animals limits the action of light to their surfaces; and so renders its direct physiological influence but small.[7] On plants, however, the solar rays that produce in us the impression of yellow, are the immediate agents of those molecular changes through which are hourly accumulated the materials for further growth. Experiments have shown that when the Sun shines on living leaves, they begin to exhale oxygen and to accumulate carbon and hydrogen—results which are traced to the decomposition, by the solar rays, of the carbonic acid and water absorbed. It is now an accepted conclusion that, by the help of certain classes of the ethereal undulations penetrating their leaves, plants are enabled to separate from the associated oxygen those two elements of which their tissues are chiefly built up.

This transformation of ethereal undulations into certain molecular re-arrangements of an unstable kind, on the overthrow of which the stored-up forces are liberated in new forms, is a process that underlies all organic phenomena. It will therefore be well if we pause a moment to consider whether any proximate interpretation of it is possible. Researches in molecular physics give us some clue to its nature.

The elements of the problem are these:—The atoms[8] of several ponderable matters exist in combination: those which are combined having strong affinities, but having also affinities less strong for some of the surrounding atoms that are otherwise combined. The atoms thus united, and thus mixed among others with which they are capable of uniting, are exposed to the undulations of a medium that is so rare as to seem imponderable. These undulations are of numerous kinds: they differ greatly in their lengths, or in the frequency with which they recur at any given point. And under the influence of undulations of a certain frequency, some of these atoms are transferred from atoms for which they have a stronger affinity, to atoms for which they have a weaker affinity. That is to say, particular orders of waves of a relatively imponderable matter, remove particular atoms of ponderable matter from their attachments, and carry them within reach of other attachments. Now the discoveries of Bunsen and Kirchoff respecting the absorption of particular luminiferous undulations by the vapours of particular substances, joined with Prof. Tyndall's discoveries respecting the absorption of heat by gases, show very clearly that the atoms of each substance have a rate of vibration in harmony with ethereal waves of a certain length, or rapidity of recurrence. Every special kind of atom can be made to oscillate by a special order of ethereal waves, which are absorbed in producing its oscillations; and can by its oscillations generate this same order of ethereal waves. Whence it appears that immense as is the difference in density between ether and ponderable matter, the waves of the one can set the atoms of the other in motion, when the successive impacts of the waves are so timed as to correspond with the oscillations of the atoms. The effects of the waves are, in such case, cumulative; and each atom gradually acquires a momentum made up of countless infinitesimal momenta. Note, further, that unless the members of a chemically-compound molecule are so bound up as to be incapable of any relative movements (a supposition at variance with the conceptions of modern science) we must conceive them as severally able to vibrate in unison or harmony with those same classes of ethereal waves that affect them in their uncombined states. While the compound molecule as a whole will have some new rate of oscillation determined by its attributes as a whole; its components will retain their original rates of oscillation, subject only to modifications by mutual influence. Such being the circumstances of the case we may partially understand how the Sun's rays can effect chemical decompositions. If the members of a diatomic molecule stand so related to the undulations falling on them, that one is thrown into a state of increased oscillation and the other not; it is manifest that there must arise a tendency towards the dislocation of the two—a tendency which may or may not take effect, according to the weakness or strength of their union, and according to the presence or absence of collateral affinities. This inference is in harmony with several significant facts. Dr. Draper remarks that "among metallic substances (compounds) those first detected to be changed by light, such as silver, gold, mercury, lead, have all high atomic weights; and such as sodium and potassium, the atomic weights of which are low, appeared to be less changeable." As here interpreted, the fact specified amounts to this; that the compounds most readily decomposed by light, are those in which there is a marked contrast between the atomic weights of the constituents, and probably therefore a marked contrast between the rapidities of their vibrations. The circumstance, too, that different chemical compounds are decomposed or modified in different parts of the spectrum, implies that there is a relation between special orders of undulations and special orders of molecules—doubtless a correspondence between the rates of these undulations and the rates of oscillation which some of the components of such molecules will assume. Strong confirmation of this view may be drawn from the decomposing actions of those longer ethereal waves which we perceive as heat. On contemplating the whole series of diatomic compounds, we see that the elements which are most remote in their atomic weights, as hydrogen and the noble metals generally, will not combine at all, or do so with great difficulty: their vibrations are so unlike that they cannot keep together under any conditions of temperature. If, again, we look at a smaller group, as the metallic oxides, we see that whereas those metals which have atoms nearest in weight to the atoms of oxygen, cannot be separated from oxygen by heat, even when it is joined by a powerful collateral affinity; those metals which differ more widely from oxygen in their atomic weights, can be de-oxidized by carbon at high temperatures; and those which differ from it most widely combine with it very reluctantly, and yield it up if exposed to thermal undulations of moderate intensity. Here indeed, remembering the relations among the atomic weights in the two cases, may we not suspect a close analogy between the de-oxidation of a metallic oxide by carbon under the influence of the longer ethereal waves, and the de-carbonization of carbonic acid by hydrogen under the influence of the shorter ethereal waves?

These conceptions help us to some dim notion of the mode in which changes are wrought in light in the leaves of plants. Among the several elements concerned, there are wide differences in molecular mobility, and probably in the rates of molecular vibration. Each is combined with one of the others, but is capable of forming various combinations with the rest. And they are severally in presence of a complex compound into which they all enter, and which is ready to assimilate with itself the new compound molecules they form. Certain of the ethereal waves falling on them when thus arranged, cause a detachment of some of the combined atoms and a union of the rest. And the conclusion suggested is that the induced vibrations among the various atoms as at first arranged, are so incongruous as to produce instability, and to give collateral affinities the power to work a rearrangement which, though less stable under other conditions, is more stable in the presence of these particular undulations. There seems, indeed, no choice but to conceive the matter thus. An atom united with one for which it has a strong affinity, has to be transferred to another for which it has a weaker affinity. This transfer implies motion. The motion is given by the waves of a medium that is relatively imponderable. No one wave of this imponderable medium can give the requisite motion to this atom of ponderable matter: especially as the atom is held by a positive force besides its inertia. The motion required can hence be given only by successive waves; and that these may not destroy each other's effects, it is needful that each shall strike the atom just when it has completed the recoil produced by the impact of previous ones. That is, the ethereal undulations must coincide in rate with the oscillations of the atom, determined by its inertia and the forces acting on it. It is also requisite that the rate of oscillation of the atom to be detached, shall differ from that of the atom with which it is united; since if the two oscillated in unison the ethereal waves would not tend to separate them. And, finally, the successive impacts of the ethereal waves must be accumulated until the resulting oscillations have become so wide in their sweep as greatly to weaken the cohesion of the united atoms, at the same time that they bring one of them within reach of other atoms with which it will combine. In this way only does it seem possible for such a force to produce such a transfer. Moreover, while we are thus enabled to conceive how light may work these molecular changes, we also gain an insight into the method by which the insensible motions propagated to us from the Sun, are treasured up in such ways as afterwards to generate sensible motions. By the accumulation of infinitesimal impacts, atoms of ponderable matter are made to oscillate. The quantity of motion which each of them eventually acquires, effects its transfer to a position of unstable equilibrium, from which it can afterwards be readily dislodged. And when so dislodged, along with other atoms similarly and simultaneously affected, there is suddenly given out all the motion which had been before impressed on it.

Speculation aside, however, that which it concerns us to notice is the broad fact that light is an all-important agent of molecular changes in organic substances. It is not here necessary for us to ascertain *how* light produces these compositions and decompositions. It is necessary only for us to observe that it *does* produce them. That the characteristic matter called chlorophyll, which gives the green colour to leaves, makes its appearance whenever the blanched shoots of plants are exposed to the Sun; that the petals of flowers, uncoloured while in the bud, acquire their bright tints as they unfold; and that on the outer surfaces of animals, analogous changes are induced; are wide inductions which are enough for our present purpose.

§ 14. We come next to the agency of chief importance among those that work changes in organic matter; namely, chemical affinity. How readily vegetal and animal substances are modified by other substances put in contact with them, we see daily illustrated. Besides the many compounds which cause the death of an organism into which they are put, we have the much greater number of compounds which work those milder effects termed medicinal—effects implying, like the others, molecular re-arrangements. Indeed, most soluble chemical compounds, natural and artificial, produce, when taken into the body, alterations that are more or less manifest in their results.

After what was shown in the last chapter, it will be manifest that this extreme modifiability of organic matter by chemical agencies, is the chief cause of that active molecular re-arrangement which organisms, and especially animal organisms, display. In the two fundamental functions of nutrition and respiration, we have the means by which the supply of materials for this active molecular re-arrangement is maintained.

The process of animal nutrition consists partly in the absorption of those complex substances which are thus highly capable of being chemically altered, and partly in the absorption of simpler substances capable of chemically altering them. The tissues always contain small quantities of alkaline and earthy salts, which enter the system in one form and are excreted in another. Though we do not know specifically the parts which these salts play, yet from their universal presence, and from the transformations which they undergo in the body, it may be safely inferred that their chemical affinities are instrumental in working some of the metamorphoses ever going on.

The inorganic substance, however, on which mainly depend these metamorphoses in organic matter, is not swallowed along with the solid and liquid food, but is absorbed from the surrounding medium—air or water, as the case may be. Whether the oxygen taken in, either, as by the lowest animals, through the general surface, or, as by the higher animals, through respiratory organs, is the immediate cause of those molecular changes which are ever going on throughout the living tissues; or whether the oxygen, playing the part of scavenger, merely aids these changes by carrying away the products of decompositions otherwise caused; it equally remains true that these changes are maintained by its instrumentality. Whether the oxygen absorbed and diffused through the system effects a direct oxidation of the organic colloids which it permeates, or whether it first leads to the formation of simpler and more oxidized compounds, which are afterwards further oxidized and reduced to still simpler forms, matters not, in so far as the general result is concerned. In any case it holds good that the substances of which the animal body is built up, enter it in either an unoxidized or in a but slightly oxidized and highly unstable state; while the great mass of them leave it in a fully oxidized and stable state. It follows, therefore, that, whatever the special changes gone through, the general process is a falling from a state of unstable chemical equilibrium to a state of stable chemical equilibrium. Whether this process be direct or indirect, the total molecular re-arrangement and the total motion given out in effecting it, must be the same.

§ 15. There is another species of re-distribution among the component matters of organisms, which is not immediately effected by the affinities of the matters concerned, but is mediately effected by other affinities; and there is reason to think that the re-distribution thus caused is important in amount, if not indeed the most important. In ordinary cases of chemical action, the two or more substances concerned themselves undergo changes of molecular arrangement; and the changes are confined to the substances themselves. But there are other cases in which the chemical action going on does not end with the substances at first concerned, but sets up chemical actions, or changes of molecular arrangement, among surrounding substances that would else have remained quiescent. And there are yet further cases in which mere contact with a substance that is itself quiescent, will cause other substances to undergo rapid metamorphoses. In what we call fermentation, the first species of this communicated chemical action is exemplified. One part of yeast, while itself undergoing molecular change, will convert 100 parts of sugar into alcohol and carbonic acid; and during its own decomposition, one part of diastase "is able to effect the transformation of more than 1000 times its weight of starch into sugar." As illustrations of the second species, may be mentioned those changes which are suddenly produced in many colloids by minute portions of various substances added to them—substances that are not undergoing manifest transformations, and suffer no appreciable effects from the contact. The nature of the first of these two kinds of communicated molecular change, which here chiefly concerns us, may be rudely represented by certain visible changes communicated from mass to mass, when a series of masses has been arranged in a special way. The simplest example is that furnished by the child's play of setting bricks on end in a row, in such positions that when the first is overthrown it overthrows the second, the second the third, the third the fourth, and so on to the end of the row. Here we have a number of units severally placed in unstable equilibrium, and in such relative positions that each, while falling into a state of stable equilibrium, gives an impulse to the next sufficient to make the next, also, fall from unstable to stable equilibrium. Now since, among mingled compound molecules, no one can undergo change in the arrangement of its parts without a molecular motion that must cause some disturbance all round; and since an adjacent molecule disturbed by this communicated motion, may have the arrangement of its constituent atoms altered, if it is not a stable arrangement; and since we know, both that the molecules which are changed by this so-called catalysis *are* unstable, and that the molecules resulting from their changes are *more* stable; it seems probable that the transformation is really analogous, in principle, to the familiar one named. Whether thus interpretable or not, however, there is good reason for thinking that to this kind of action is due a large amount of vital metamorphosis. Let us contemplate the several groups of facts which point to this conclusion.[9]

In the last chapter (§ 2) we incidentally noted the extreme instability of nitrogenous compounds in general. We saw that sundry of them are liable to explode on the slightest incentive—sometimes without any apparent cause; and that of the rest, the great majority are very easily decomposed by heat, and by various substances. We shall perceive much significance in this general characteristic when we join it with the fact that the substances capable of setting up extensive molecular changes in the way above described are all nitrogenous ones. Yeast consists of vegetal cells containing nitrogen,—cells that grow by assimilating the nitrogenous matter contained in wort. Similarly, the "vinegar-plant," which greatly facilitates the formation of acetic acid from alcohol, is a fungoid growth that is doubtless, like others of its class, rich in nitrogenous compounds. Diastase, by which the transformation of starch into sugar is effected during the process of malting, is also a nitrogenous body. So too is a substance called synaptase—an albumenous principle contained in almonds, which has the power of working several metamorphoses in the matters associated with it. These nitrogenized compounds, like the rest of their family, are remarkable for the rapidity with which they decompose; and the extensive changes produced by them in the accompanying carbo-hydrates, are found to vary in their kinds according as the decompositions of the ferments vary in their stages. We have next to note, as having here a meaning for us, the chemical contrasts between those organisms which carry on their functions by the help of external forces, and those which carry on their functions by forces evolved from within. If we compare animals and plants, we see that whereas plants, characterized as a class by containing but little nitrogen, are dependent on the solar rays for their vital activities; animals, the vital activities of which are not thus dependent, mainly consist of nitrogenous substances. There is one marked exception to this broad distinction, however; and this exception is specially instructive. Among plants there is a considerable group—the Fungi—many members of which, if not all, can live and grow in the dark; and it is their peculiarity that they are very much more nitrogenous than other plants. Yet a third class of facts of like significance is disclosed when we compare different portions of the same organism. The seed of a plant contains nitrogenous substance in a far higher ratio than the rest of the plant; and the seed differs from the rest of the plant in its ability to initiate, in the absence of light, extensive vital changes—the changes constituting germination. Similarly in the bodies of animals, those parts which carry on active functions are nitrogenous; while parts that are non-nitrogenous—as the deposits of fat—carry on no active functions. And we even find that the appearance of non-nitrogenous matter throughout tissues normally composed almost wholly of nitrogenous matter, is accompanied by loss of activity: what is called fatty degeneration being the concomitant of failing vitality. One more fact, which serves to make still clearer the meaning of the foregoing ones, remains—the fact, namely, that in no part of any organism where vital changes are going on, is nitrogenous matter wholly absent. It is common to speak of plants—or at least all parts of plants but the seeds—as non-nitrogenous. But they are only relatively so; not absolutely. The quantity of albumenoid substance in the tissues of plants, is extremely small compared with the quantity contained in the tissues of animals; but all plant-tissues which are discharging active functions have some albumenoid substance. In every living vegetal cell there is a certain part that includes nitrogen as a component. This part initiates those changes which constitute the development of the cell. And if it cannot be said that it is the worker of all subsequent changes undergone by the cell, it nevertheless continues to be the part in which the independent activity is most marked.

Looking at the evidence thus brought together, do we not get an insight into the actions of nitrogenous matter as a worker of organic changes? We see that nitrogenous compounds in general are extremely prone to decompose: their decomposition often involving a sudden and great evolution of energy. We see that the substances classed as ferments, which, during their own molecular changes, set up molecular changes in the accompanying carbo-hydrates, are all nitrogenous. We see that among classes of organisms, and among the parts of each organism, there is a relation between the amount of nitrogenous matter present and the amount of independent activity. And we see that even in organisms and parts of organisms where the activity is least, such changes as do take place are initiated by a substance containing nitrogen. Does it not seem probable, then, that these extremely unstable compounds have everywhere the effect of communicating to the less unstable compounds associated with them, molecular movements towards a stable state, like those they are themselves undergoing? The changes which we thus suppose nitrogenous matter to produce in the body, are clearly analogous to those which we see it produce out of the body. Out of the body, certain carbo-hydrates in continued contact with nitrogenous matter, are transformed into carbonic acid and alcohol, and unless prevented the alcohol is transformed into acetic acid: the substances formed being thus more highly oxidized and more stable than the substances destroyed. In the body, these same carbo-hydrates, in continued contact with nitrogenous matter, are transformed into carbonic acid and water: substances which are also more highly oxidized and more stable than those from which they result. And since acetic acid is itself resolved by further oxidation into carbonic acid and water; we see that the chief difference between the two cases is, that the process is more completely effected in the body than it is out of the body. Thus, to carry further the simile used above, the molecules of carbo-hydrates contained in the tissues are, like bricks on end, not in the stablest equilibrium; but still in an equilibrium so stable, that they cannot be overthrown by the chemical and thermal forces which the body brings to bear on them. On the other hand, being like similarly-placed bricks that have very narrow ends, the nitrogenous molecules contained in the tissues are in so unstable an equilibrium that they cannot withstand these forces. And when these delicately-poised nitrogenous molecules fall into stable arrangements, they give impulses to the more firmly-poised non-nitrogenous molecules, which cause them also to fall into stable arrangements. It is a curious and significant fact that in the arts, we not only utilize this same principle of initiating extensive changes among comparatively stable compounds, by the help of compounds much less stable, but we employ for the purpose compounds of the same general class. Our modern method of firing a gun is to place in close proximity with the gunpowder which we wish to decompose or explode, a small portion of fulminating powder, which is decomposed or exploded with extreme facility, and which, on decomposing, communicates the consequent molecular disturbance to the less-easily decomposed gunpowder. When we ask what this fulminating powder is composed of, we find that it is a nitrogenous salt.[10]

Thus, besides the molecular re-arrangements produced in organic matter by direct chemical action, there are others of kindred importance produced by indirect chemical action. Indeed, the inference that some of the leading transformations occurring in the animal organism, are due to this so-called catalysis, appears necessitated by the general aspect of the facts, apart from any such detailed interpretations as the foregoing. We know that various amylaceous and saccharine matters taken as food do not appear in the excreta, and must therefore be decomposed in their course through the body. We know that these matters do not become components of the tissues, but only of the contained liquids and solids; and that thus their metamorphosis is not a direct result of tissue-change. We know that their stability is such that the thermal and chemical forces to which they are exposed in the body, cannot alone decompose them. The only explanation open to us, therefore, is that the transformation of these carbo-hydrates into carbonic acid and water, is due to communicated chemical action.

§ 16. This chapter will have served its purpose if it has given a conception of the extreme modifiability of organic matter by surrounding agencies. Even were it possible, it would be needless to describe in detail the immensely varied and complicated changes which the forces from moment to moment acting on them, work in living bodies. Dealing with biology in its general principles, it concerns us only to notice how specially sensitive are the substances of which organisms are built up to the varied influences that act upon organisms. Their special sensitiveness has been made sufficiently manifest in the several foregoing sections.

CHAPTER III.

THE RE-ACTIONS OF ORGANIC MATTER ON FORCES.

§ 17. Re-distributions of Matter imply concomitant re-distributions of Motion. That which under one of its aspects we contemplate as an alteration of arrangement among the parts of a body, is, under a correlative aspect, an alteration of arrangement among certain momenta, whereby these parts are impelled to their new positions. At the same time that a force, acting differently on the different units of an aggregate, changes their relations to one another; these units, reacting differently on the different parts of the force, work equivalent changes in the relations of these to one another. Inseparably connected as they are, these two orders of phenomena are liable to be confounded together. It is very needful, however, to distinguish between them. In the last chapter we took a rapid survey of the re-distributions which forces produce in organic matter; and here we must take a like survey of the simultaneous re-distributions undergone by the forces.

At the outset we are met by a difficulty. The parts of an inorganic mass undergoing re-arrangement by an incident force, are in most cases passive—do not complicate those necessary re-actions that result from their inertia, by other forces which they themselves originate. But in organic matter the re-arranged parts do not re-act in virtue of their inertia only. They are so constituted that an incident force usually sets up in them other actions which are much more important. Indeed, what we may call the indirect reactions thus caused, are so great in their amounts compared with the direct re-actions, that they quite obscure them.

The impossibility of separating these two kinds of reaction compels us to disregard the distinction between them. Under the above general title, we must include both the immediate re-actions and those re-actions mediately produced, which are among the most conspicuous of vital phenomena.

§ 18. From organic matter, as from all other matter, incident forces call forth that re-action which we know as heat. More or less of molecular vibration necessarily results when, to the forces at work among the molecules of any aggregate, other forces are added. Experiment abundantly demonstrates this in the case of inorganic masses; and it must equally hold in the case of organic masses. In both cases the force which, more markedly than any other, produces this thermal re-action, is that which ends in the union of different substances. Though inanimate bodies admit of being greatly heated by pressure and by the electric current, yet the evolutions of heat, thus induced are neither so common, nor in most cases so conspicuous, as those resulting from chemical combination. And though in animate bodies there are certain amounts of heat generated by other actions, yet these are secondary to the heat generated by the action of oxygen on the substances composing the tissues and the substances contained in them. Here, however, we see one of the characteristic distinctions between inanimate and animate bodies. Among the first there are but few which ordinarily exist in a condition to evolve the heat caused by chemical combination; and such as are in this condition soon cease to be so when chemical combination and genesis of heat once begin in them. Whereas, among the second there universally exists the ability, more or less decided, thus to evolve heat; and the evolution of heat, in some cases very slight and in no cases very great, continues as long as they remain animate bodies.

The relation between active change of matter and re-active genesis of molecular vibration, is clearly shown by the contrasts between different organisms, and between different states and parts of the same organism. In plants the genesis of heat is extremely small, in correspondence with their extremely small production of carbonic acid: those portions only, as flowers and germinating seeds, in which considerable oxidation is going on, having decidedly raised temperatures. Among animals we see that the hot-blooded are those which expend much force and respire actively. Though insects are scarcely at all warmer than the surrounding air when they are still, they rise several degrees above it when they exert themselves; and in mammals, which habitually maintain a temperature much higher than that of their medium, exertion is accompanied by an additional production of heat.

This molecular agitation accompanies the falls from unstable to stable molecular combinations; whether they be those from the most complex to the less complex compounds, or whether they be those ultimate falls which end in fully oxidized and relatively simple compounds; and whether they be those of the nitrogenous matters composing the tissues or those of the non-nitrogenous matters diffused through them. In the one case as in the other, the heat must be regarded as a concomitant. Whether the distinction, originally made by Liebig, between nitrogenous substances as tissue-food and non-nitrogenous substances as heat-food, be true or not in a narrower sense, it cannot be accepted in the sense that tissue-food is not also heat-food. Indeed he does not himself assert it in this sense. The ability of carnivorous animals to live and generate heat while consuming matter that is almost exclusively nitrogenous, suffices to prove that the nitrogenous compounds forming the tissues are heat-producers, as well as the non-nitrogenous compounds circulating among and through the tissues: a conclusion which is indeed justified by the fact that nitrogenous substances out of the body yield heat, though not a large amount, during combustion. But most likely this antithesis is not true even in the more restricted sense. The probability is that the hydrocarbons and carbo-hydrates which, in traversing the system, are transformed by communicated chemical action, evolve, during their transformation, not heat alone but also other kinds of force. It may be that as the nitrogenous matter, while falling into more stable molecular arrangements, generates both that molecular agitation called heat and such other molecular movements as are resolved into forces expended by the organism; so, too, does the non-nitrogenous matter. Or perhaps the concomitants of this metamorphosis of non-nitrogenous matter vary with the conditions. Heat alone may result when it is transformed while in the circulating fluids, but partly heat and partly another force when it is transformed in some active tissue that has absorbed it; just as coal, though producing little else but heat as ordinarily burnt, has its heat partially transformed into mechanical motion if burnt in a steam-engine furnace. In such case the antithesis of Liebig would be reduced to this—that whereas nitrogenous substance is tissue-food *both* as material for building-up tissue and as material for its function; non-nitrogenous substance is tissue-food *only* as material for function.

There can be no doubt that this thermal re-action which chemical action from moment to moment produces in the body, is from moment to moment an aid to further chemical action. We before saw (*First Principles*, § 100) that a state of raised molecular vibration is favourable to those re-distributions of matter and motion which constitute Evolution. We saw that in organisms distinguished by the amount and rapidity of such re-distributions, this raised state of molecular vibration is conspicuous. And we here see that this raised state of molecular vibration is itself a continuous consequence of the continuous molecular re-distributions it facilitates. The heat generated by each increment of chemical change makes possible the succeeding increment of chemical change. In the body this connexion of phenomena is the same as we see it to be out of the body. Just as in a burning piece of wood, the heat given out by the portion actually combining with oxygen, raises the adjacent portion to a temperature at which it also can combine with oxygen; so, in a living animal, the heat produced by oxidation of each portion of organized or unorganized substance, maintains the temperature at which the unoxidized portions can be readily oxidized.

§ 19. Among the forces called forth from organisms by re-action against the actions to which they are subject, is Light. Phosphorescence is in some few cases displayed by plants—especially by certain fungi. Among animals it is comparatively common. All know that there are several kinds of luminous insects; and many are familiar with the fact that luminosity is a characteristic of various marine creatures.

Much of the evidence is supposed to imply that this evolution of light, like the evolution of heat, is consequent on oxidation of the tissues or of matters contained in them. Light, like heat, is the expression of a raised state of molecular vibration: the difference between them being a difference in the rates of vibration. Hence it seems inferable that by chemical action on substances contained in the organism, heat or light may be produced, according to the character of the resulting molecular vibrations. Some experimental evidence supports this view. In phosphorescent insects, the continuance of the light is found to depend on the continuance of respiration; and any exertion which renders respiration more active, increases the brilliancy of the light. Moreover, by separating the luminous matter, Prof. Matteucci has shown that its emission of light is accompanied by absorption of oxygen and escape of carbonic acid. The phosphorescence of marine animals has been referred to other causes than oxidation; but it may perhaps be explicable without assuming any more special agency. Considering that in creatures of the genus *Noctiluca*, for example, to which the phosphorescence most commonly seen on our own coasts is due, there is no means of keeping up a constant circulation, we may infer that the movements of aerated fluids through their tissues, must be greatly affected by impulses received from without. Hence it may be that the sparkles visible at night when the waves break gently on the beach, or when an oar is dipped into the water, are called forth from these creatures by the concussion, not because of any unknown influence it excites, but because, being propagated through their delicate tissues, it produces a sudden movement of the fluids and a sudden increase of chemical action.

Nevertheless, in other phosphorescent animals inhabiting the sea, as in the *Pyrosoma* and in certain *Annelida*, light seems to be produced otherwise than by direct re-action on the action of oxygen. Indeed, it needs but to recall the now familiar fact that certain substances become luminous in the dark after exposure to sunlight, to see that there are other causes of light-emission.

§ 20. The re-distributions of inanimate matter are habitually accompanied by electrical disturbances; and there is abundant evidence that electricity is generated during those re-distributions of matter that are ever taking place in organisms. Experiments have shown "that the skin and most of the internal membranes are in opposite electrical states;" and also that between different internal organs, as the liver and the stomach, there are electrical contrasts: such contrasts being greatest where the processes going on in the compared parts are most unlike. It has been proved by du Bois-Reymond that when any point in the longitudinal section of a muscle is connected by a conductor with any point in its transverse section, an electric current is established; and further, that like results occur when nerves are substituted for muscles. The special causes of these phenomena have not yet been determined. Considering that the electric contrasts are most marked where active secretions are going on—considering, too, that they are difficult to detect where there are no appreciable movements of liquids—considering, also, that even when muscles are made to contract after removal from the body, the contraction inevitably causes movements of the liquids still contained in its tissues; it may be that they are due simply to the friction of heterogeneous substances, which is universally a cause of electric disturbance. But whatever be the interpretation, the fact remains the same:—there is throughout the living organism, an unceasing production of differences between the electric states of different parts; and, consequently, an unceasing restoration of electric equilibrium by the establishment of currents among these parts.

Besides these general, and not conspicuous, electrical phenomena common to all organisms, vegetal as well as animal, there are certain special and strongly marked ones. I refer, of course, to those which have made the *Torpedo* and the *Gymnotus* objects of so much interest. In these creatures we have a genesis of electricity which is not incidental on the performance of their different functions by the different organs; but one which is itself a function, having an organ appropriate to it. The character of this organ in both these fishes, and its largely-developed connexions with the nervous centres, have raised in some minds the suspicion that in it there takes place a transformation of what we call nerve-force into the force known as electricity. Perhaps, however, the true interpretation may rather be that by nervous stimulation there is set up in these animal-batteries that particular transformation of molecular motion which it is their function to produce.

But whether general or special, and in whatever manner produced, these evolutions of electricity are among the reactions of organic matter called forth by the actions to which it is subject. Though these re-actions are not direct, but seem to be remote consequences of changes wrought by external agencies on the organism, they are yet incidents in that general re-distribution of motion which these external agencies initiate; and as such must here be noticed.

§ 21. To these known modes of motion, has next to be added an unknown one. Heat, Light, and Electricity are emitted by inorganic matter when undergoing changes, as well as by organic matter. But there is manifested in some classes of living bodies a kind of force which we cannot identify with any of the forces manifested by bodies that are not alive,—a force which is thus unknown, in the sense that it cannot be assimilated to any otherwise-recognized class. I allude to what is called nerve-force.

This is habitually generated in all animals, save the lowest, by incident forces of every kind. The gentle and violent mechanical contacts, which in ourselves produce sensations of touch and pressure—the additions and abstractions of molecular vibration, which in ourselves produce sensations of heat and cold, produce in all creatures that have nervous systems, certain nervous disturbances: disturbances which, as in ourselves, are either communicated to the chief nervous centre, and there arouse consciousness, or else result in mere physical processes set going elsewhere in the organism. In special parts distinguished as organs of sense, other external actions bring about other nervous re-actions, that show themselves either as special sensations or as excitements which, without the intermediation of distinct consciousness, beget actions in muscles or other organs. Besides neural discharges following the direct incidence of external forces, others are ever being caused by the incidence of forces which, though originally external, have become internal by absorption into the organism of the agents exerting them. For thus may be classed those neural discharges which result from modifications of the tissues wrought by substances carried to them in the blood. That the unceasing change of matter which oxygen and other agents produce throughout the system, is accompanied by production of nerve-force, is shown by various facts;—by the fact that nerve-force is no longer generated if oxygen be withheld or the blood prevented from circulating; by the fact that when the chemical transformation is diminished, as during sleep with its slow respiration and circulation, there is a diminution in the quantity of nerve-force; by the fact that an excessive expenditure of nerve-force involves excessive respiration and circulation, and excessive waste of tissue. To these proofs that nerve-force is evolved in greater or less quantity, according as the conditions to rapid molecular change throughout the body are well or ill fulfilled, may be added proofs that certain special molecular actions are the causes of these special re-actions. The effects of the vegeto-alkalies put beyond doubt the inference that the overthrow of molecular equilibrium by chemical affinity, when it occurs in certain parts, causes excitement in the nerves proceeding from those parts. Indeed, looked at from this point of view, the two classes of nervous changes—the one initiated from without and the other from within—are seen to merge into one class. Both of them may be traced to metamorphosis of tissue. The sensations of touch and pressure are doubtless consequent on accelerated changes of matter, produced by mechanical disturbance of the mingled fluids and solids composing the parts affected. There is abundant evidence that the gustatory sensation is due to the chemical actions set up by particles which find their way through the membrane covering the nerves of taste; for, as Prof. Graham points out, sapid substances belong to the class of crystalloids, which are able rapidly to permeate animal tissue, while the colloids which cannot pass through animal tissue are insipid. Similarly with the sense of smell. Substances which excite this sense are necessarily more or less volatile; and their volatility being the result of their molecular mobility, implies that they have, in a high degree, the power of getting at the olfactory nerves by penetrating their mucous investment. Again, the facts which photography has familiarized us with, show that those nervous impressions called colours, are primarily due to certain changes wrought by light in the substance of the retina. And though, in the case of hearing, we cannot so clearly trace the connexion of cause and effect, yet as we see that the auditory apparatus is one fitted to intensify those vibrations constituting sound, and to convey them to a receptacle containing liquid in which nerves are immersed, it can scarcely be doubted that the sensation of sound proximately results from molecular re-arrangements caused in these nerves by the vibrations of the liquid: knowing, as we do, that the re-arrangement of molecules is in all cases aided by agitation. Perhaps, however, the best proof that nerve-force, whether peripheral or central in origin, results from chemical change, lies in the fact that most of the chemical agents which powerfully affect the nervous system, affect it whether applied at the centre or at the periphery. Various mineral acids are tonics—the stronger ones being usually the stronger tonics; and this which we call their acidity implies a power in them of acting on the nerves of taste, while the tingling or pain following their absorption through the skin, implies that the nerves of the skin are acted on by them. Similarly with certain vegeto-alkalies which are peculiarly bitter. By their bitterness these show that they affect the extremities of the nerves, while, by their tonic properties, they show that they affect the nervous centres: the most intensely bitter among them, strychnia, being the most powerful nervous stimulant.[11] However true it may be that this relation is not a regular one, since opium, hashish, and some other drugs, which work marked effects on the brain, are not remarkably sapid—however true it may be that there are relations between particular substances and particular parts of the nervous system; yet such instances do but qualify, without negativing, the general proposition. The truth of this proposition can scarcely be doubted when, to the facts above given, is added the fact that various condiments and aromatic drugs act as nervous stimulants; and the fact that anæsthetics, besides the general effects they produce when inhaled or swallowed, produce local effects of like kind—first stimulant and then sedative—when absorbed through the skin; and the fact that ammonia, which in consequence of its extreme molecular mobility so quickly and so violently excites the nerves beneath the skin, as well as those of the tongue and the nose, is a rapidly-acting stimulant when taken internally.

Whether a nerve is merely a conductor, which delivers at one of its extremities an impulse received at the other, or whether, as some now think, it is itself a generator of force which is initiated at one extremity and accumulates in its course to the other extremity, are questions which cannot yet be answered. All we know is that agencies capable of working molecular changes in nerves are capable of calling forth from them manifestations of activity. And our evidence that nerve-force is thus originated, consists not only of such facts as the above, but also of more conclusive facts established by direct experiments on nerves—experiments which show that nerve-force results when the cut end of a nerve is either mechanically irritated, or acted on by some chemical agent, or subject to the galvanic current—experiments which prove that nerve-force is generated by whatever disturbs the molecular equilibrium of nerve-substance.

§ 22. The most important of the re-actions called forth from organisms by surrounding actions, remains to be noticed. To the various forms of insensible motion thus caused, we have to add sensible motion. On the production of this mode of force more especially depends the possibility of all vital phenomena. It is, indeed, usual to regard the power of generating sensible motion as confined to one out of the two organic sub-kingdoms; or, at any rate, as possessed by but few members of the other. On looking closer into the matter, however, we see that plant-life as well as animal-life, is universally accompanied by certain manifestations of this power; and that plant-life could not otherwise continue.

Through the humblest, as well as through the highest, vegetal organisms, there are ever going on certain re-distributions of matter. In Protophytes the microscope shows us an internal transposition of parts, which, when not immediately visible, is proved to exist by the changes of arrangement that become manifest in the course of hours and days. In the individual cells of many higher plants, an active movement among the contained granules may be witnessed. And well-developed cryptogams, in common with all phanerogams, exhibit this genesis of mechanical motion still more conspicuously in the circulation of sap. It might, indeed, be concluded *a priori*, that through plants displaying much differentiation of parts, an internal movement must be going on; since, without it, the mutual dependence of organs having unlike functions would be impossible. Besides keeping up these motions of liquids internally, plants, especially of the lower orders, move their external parts in relation to each other, and also move about from place to place. There are countless such illustrations as the active locomotion of the zoospores of many *Algæ*, the rhythmical bendings of the *Oscillatoræ*, the rambling progression of the *Diatomaceæ*. In fact many of these smallest vegetals, and many of the larger ones in their early stages, display a mechanical activity not distinguishable from that of the simplest animals. Among well-organized plants, which are never locomotive in their adult states, we still not unfrequently meet with relative motions of parts. To such familiar cases as those of the Sensitive plant and the Venus' fly-trap, many others may be added. When its base is irritated the stamen of the Berberry flower leans over and touches the pistil. If the stamens of the wild *Cistus* be gently brushed with the finger, they spread themselves: bending away from the seed-vessel. And some of the orchid-flowers, as Mr. Darwin has shown, shoot out masses of pollen on to the entering bee, when its trunk is thrust down in search of honey.

Though the power of moving is not, as we see, a characteristic of animals alone, yet in them, considered as a class, it is manifested to an extent so marked as practically to become their most distinctive trait. For it is by their immensely greater ability to generate mechanical motion, that animals are enabled to perform those actions which constitute their visible lives; and it is by their immensely greater ability to generate mechanical motion, that the higher orders of animals are most obviously distinguished from the lower orders. Though, on remembering the seemingly active movements of infusoria, some will perhaps question this last-named contrast, yet, on comparing the quantities of matter propelled through given spaces in given times, they will see that the momentum evolved is far less in the *Protozoa* than in the *Metazoa*. These sensible motions of animals are effected in sundry ways. In the humblest forms, and even in some of the more developed forms which inhabit the water, locomotion results from the oscillations of whip-like appendages, single or double, or from the oscillations of cilia: the contractility resides in these waving hairs that grow from the surface. In many *Cœlenterata* certain elongations or tails of ectodermal or endodermal cells shorten when stimulated, and by these rudimentary contractile organs the movements are effected. In all the higher animals, however, and to a smaller degree in many of the lower, sensible motion is generated by a special tissue, under a special excitement. Though it is not strictly true that such animals show no sensible motions otherwise caused, since all of them have certain ciliated membranes, and since the circulation of liquids in them is partially due to osmotic and capillary actions; yet, generally speaking, we may say that their movements are effected solely by muscles which contract solely through the agency of nerves.

What special transformations of force generate these various mechanical changes, we do not, in most cases, know. Those re-distributions of liquid, with the alterations of form sometimes caused by them, that result from osmose, are not, indeed, incomprehensible. Certain motions of plants which, like those of the "animated oat," follow contact with water, are easily interpreted; as are also such other vegetal motions as those of the Touch-me-not, the Squirting Cucumber, and the *Carpobolus*. But we are ignorant of the mode in which molecular movement is transformed into the movement of masses, in animals. We cannot refer to known causes the rhythmical action of a Medusa's disc, or that slow decrease of bulk which spreads throughout the mass of an *Alcyonium* when one of its component individuals has been irritated. Nor are we any better able to say how the insensible motion transmitted through a nerve, gives rise to sensitive motion in a muscle. It is true that Science has given to Art several methods of changing insensible into sensible motion. By applying heat to water we vaporize it, and the movement of its expanding vapour we transfer to solid matter; but evidently the genesis of muscular movement is in no way analogous to this. The force evolved in a galvanic battery or by a dynamo, we communicate to a soft iron magnet through a wire coiled round it; and it would be possible, by placing near to each other several magnets thus excited, to obtain, through the attraction of each for its neighbours, an accumulated movement made up of their separate movements, and thus mechanically to imitate a muscular contraction. But from what we know of organic matter there is no reason to suppose that anything analogous to this takes place in it. We can, however, through one kind of molecular change, produce sensible changes of aggregation such as possibly might, when occurring in organic substance, cause sensible motion in it. I refer to change that is allotropic or isomeric. Sulphur, for example, assumes different crystalline and non-crystalline forms at different temperatures, and may be made to pass backwards and forwards from one form to another, by slight variations of temperature: undergoing each time an alteration of bulk. We know that this allotropism, or rather its analogue isomerism, prevails among colloids—inorganic and organic. We also know that some of these metamorphoses among colloids are accompanied by visible re-arrangements: instance hydrated silicic acid, which, after passing from its soluble state to the state of an insoluble jelly, begins, in a few days, to contract and to give out part of its contained water. Now considering that such isomeric changes of organic as well as inorganic colloids, are often rapidly produced by very slight causes—a trace of a neutral salt or a degree or two rise of temperature—it seems not impossible that some of the colloids constituting muscle may be thus changed by a nervous discharge: resuming their previous condition when the discharge ceases. And it is conceivable that by structural arrangements, minute sensible motions so caused may be accumulated into large sensible motions.

§ 23. But the truths which it is here our business especially to note, are independent of hypotheses or interpretations. It is sufficient for the ends in view, to observe that organic matter *does* exhibit these several conspicuous reactions when acted on by incident forces. It is not requisite that we should know *how* these re-actions originate.

In the last chapter were set forth the several modes in which incident forces cause re-distributions of organic matter; and in this chapter have been set forth the several modes in which is manifested the motion accompanying this re-distribution. There we contemplated, under its several aspects, the general fact that, in consequence of its extreme instability, organic matter undergoes extensive molecular re-arrangements on very slight changes of conditions. And here we have contemplated, under its several aspects, the correlative general fact that, during these extensive molecular re-arrangements, there are evolved large amounts of energy. In the one case the components of organic matter are regarded as falling from positions of unstable equilibrium to positions of stable equilibrium; and in the other case they are regarded as giving out in their falls certain momenta—momenta that may be manifested as heat, light, electricity, nerve-force, or mechanical motion, according as the conditions determine.

I will add only that these evolutions of energy are rigorously dependent on these changes of matter. It is a corollary from the primordial truth which, as we have seen, underlies all other truths, (*First Principles*, §§ 62, 189,) that whatever amount of power an organism expends in any shape, is the correlate and equivalent of a power which was taken into it from without. On the one hand, it follows from the persistence of force that each portion of mechanical or other energy which an organism exerts, implies the transformation of as much organic matter as contained this energy in a latent state. And on the other hand, it follows from the persistence of force that no such transformation of organic matter containing this latent energy can take place, without the energy being in one shape or other manifested.

CHAPTER IIIA.

METABOLISM.

§ 23*a*. In the early forties the French chemist Dumas pointed out the opposed actions of the vegetal and animal kingdoms: the one having for its chief chemical effect the decomposition of carbon-dioxide, with accompanying assimilation of its carbon and liberation of its oxygen, and the other having for its chief chemical effect the oxidation of carbon and production of carbon-dioxide. Omitting those plants which contain no chlorophyll, all others de-oxidize carbon; while all animals, save the few which contain chlorophyll, re-oxidize carbon. This is not, indeed, a complete account of the general relation; since it represents animals as wholly dependent on plants, either directly or indirectly through other animals, while plants are represented as wholly independent of animals; and this last representation though mainly true, since plants can obtain direct from the inorganic world certain other constituents they need, is in some measure not true, since many with greater facility obtain these materials from the decaying bodies of animals or from their *excreta*. But after noting this qualification the broad antithesis remains as alleged.

How are these transformations brought about? The carbon contained in carbon-dioxide does not at a bound become incorporated in the plant, nor does the substance appropriated by the animal from the plant become at a bound carbon-dioxide. It is through two complex sets of changes that these two ultimate results are brought about. The materials forming the tissues of plants as well as the materials contained in them, are progressively elaborated from the inorganic substances; and the resulting compounds, eaten and some of them assimilated by animals, pass through successive changes which are, on the average, of an opposite character: the two sets being constructive and destructive. To express changes of both these natures the term "metabolism" is used; and such of the metabolic changes as result in building up from simple to compound are distinguished as "anabolic," while those which result in the falling down from compound to simple are distinguished as "katabolic." These antithetical names do not indeed cover all the molecular transformations going on. Many of them, known as isomeric, imply neither building up nor falling down: they imply re-arrangement only. But those which here chiefly concern us are the two opposed kinds described.

A qualification is needful. These antithetic changes must be understood as characterizing plant-life and animal-life in general ways rather than in special ways—as expressing the transformations in their totalities but not in their details. For there are katabolic processes in plants, though they bear but a small ratio to the anabolic ones; and there are anabolic processes in animals, though they bear but a small ratio to the katabolic ones.

From the chemico-physical aspect of these changes we pass to those distinguished as vital; for metabolic changes can be dealt with only as changes effected by that living substance called protoplasm.

§ 23*b*. On the evolution-hypothesis we are obliged to assume that the earliest living things—probably minute units of protoplasm smaller than any the microscope reveals to us—had the ability to appropriate directly from the inorganic world both the nitrogen and the materials for carbo-hydrates without both of which protoplasm cannot be formed; since in the absence of preceding organic matter there was no other source. The general law of evolution as well as the observed actions of *Protozoa* and *Protophyta*, suggest that these primordial types simultaneously displayed animal-life and plant-life. For whereas the developed animal-type cannot form from its inorganic surroundings either nitrogenous compounds or carbo-hydrates; and whereas the developed plant-type, able to form carbo-hydrates from its inorganic surroundings, depends for the formation of its protoplasm mainly, although indirectly, on the nitrogenous compounds derived from preceding organisms, as do also most of the plants devoid of chlorophyll—the fungi; we are obliged to assume that in the beginning, along with the expending activities characterizing the animal-type, there went the accumulating activities characterizing both of the vegetal types—forms of activity by-and-by differentiated.

Though the successive steps in the artificial formation of organic compounds have now gone so far that substances simulating proteids, if not identical with them, have been produced, yet we have no clue to the conditions under which proteids arose; and still less have we a clue to the conditions under which inert proteids became so combined as to form active protoplasm. The essential fact to be recognized is that living matter, originated as we must assume during a long stage of progressive cooling in which the infinitely varied parts of the Earth's surface were slowly passing through appropriate physical conditions, possessed from the outset the power of assimilating to itself the materials from which more living matter was formed; and that since then all living matter has arisen from its self-increasing action. But now, leaving speculation concerning these anabolic changes as they commenced in the remote past, let us contemplate them as they are carried on now—first directing our attention to those presented in the vegetal world.

§ 23*c*. The decomposition of carbon-dioxide (§ 13)—the separation of its carbon from the combined oxygen so that it may enter into one or other form of carbo-hydrate,—is not now ordinarily effected, as we must assume it once was, by the undifferentiated protoplasm; but is effected by a specialized substance, chlorophyll, imbedded in the protoplasm and operating by its instrumentality. The chlorophyll-grain is not simply immersed in protoplasm but is permeated throughout its substance by a protoplasmic network or sponge-work apparently continuous with the protoplasm around; or, according to Sachs, consists of protoplasm holding chlorophyll-particles in suspension: the mechanical arrangement facilitating the chemical function. The resulting abstraction of carbon from carbon-dioxide, by the aid of certain ethereal undulations, appears to be the first step in the building up of organic compounds—the first step in the primary anabolic process. We are not here concerned with details. Two subsequent sets of changes only need here to be noted—the genesis of the passive materials out of which plant-structure is built up, and the genesis of the active materials by which these are produced and the building up effected.

The hydrated carbon which protoplasm, having the chlorophyll-grain as its implement, produces from carbonic acid and water, appears not to be of one kind only. The possible carbo-hydrates are almost infinite in number. Multitudes of them have been artificially made, and numerous kinds are made naturally by plants. Though perhaps the first step in the reduction of the carbon from its dioxide may be always the same, yet it is held probable that in different types of plants different types of carbo-hydrates forthwith arise, and give differential characters to the compounds subsequently formed by such types: sundry of the changes being katabolic rather than anabolic. Of leading members in the group may be named dextrin, starch, and the various sugars characteristic of various plants, as well as the cellulose elaborated by further anabolism. Considered as the kind of carbo-hydrate in which the products of activity are first stored up, to be subsequently modified for divers purposes, starch is the most important of these; and the process of storage is suggested by the structure of the starch-grain. This consists of superposed layers, implying intermittent deposits: the probability being that the variations of light and heat accompanying day and night are associated now with arrest of the deposit and now with recommencement of it. Like in composition as this stored-up starch is with sugar of one or other kind, and capable of being deposited from sugar and again assuming the sugar form, this substance passes, by further metabolism, here into the cellulose which envelopes each of the multitudinous units of protoplasm, there into the spiral fibres, annuli, or fenestrated tubes which, in early stages of tissue-growth, form channels for the sap, and elsewhere into other components of the general structure. The many changes implied are effected in various ways: now by that simple re-arrangement of components known as isomeric change; now by that taking from a compound one of its elements and inserting one of another kind, which is known as substitution; and now by oxidation, as when the oxy-cellulose which constitutes wood-fibre, is produced.

Besides elaborating building materials, the protoplasm elaborates itself—that is, elaborates more of itself. It is chemically distinguished from the building materials by the presence of nitrogen. Derived from atmospheric ammonia, or from decaying or excreted organic matter, or from the products of certain fungi and microbes at its roots, the nitrogen in one or other combination is brought into a plant by the upward current; and by some unknown process (not dependent on light, since it goes on equally well if not better in darkness) the protoplasm dissociates and appropriates this combined nitrogen and unites it with a carbo-hydrate to form one or other proteid—albumen, gluten, or some isomer; appropriating at the same time from certain of the earth-salts the requisite amount of sulphur and in some cases phosphorus. The ultimate step, as we must suppose, is the formation of living protoplasm out of these non-living proteids. A cardinal fact is that proteids admit of multitudinous transformations; and it seems not improbable that in protoplasm various isomeric proteids are mingled. If so, we must conclude that protoplasm admits of almost infinite variations in nature. Of course *pari passu* with this dual process—augmentation of protoplasm and accompanying production of carbo-hydrates—there goes extension of plant-structure and plant-life.

To these essential metabolic processes have to be added certain ancillary and non-essential ones, ending in the formation of colouring matters, odours, essential oils, acrid secretions, bitter compounds and poisons: some serving to attract animals and others to repel them. Sundry of these appear to be excretions—useless matters cast out, and are doubtless katabolic.

The relation of these facts here sketched in rude outline to the doctrine of Evolution at large should be observed. Already we have seen how (§ 8*a*), in the course of terrestrial evolution, there has been an increasingly heterogeneous assemblage of increasing heterogeneous compounds, preparing the way for organic life. And here we may see that during the development of plant-life from its lowest algoid and fungoid forms up to those forms which constitute the chief vegetal world, there has been an increasing number of complex organic compounds formed; displayed at once in the diversity of them contained in the same plant and in the still greater diversity displayed in the vast aggregate of species, genera, orders, and classes of plants.

§ 23*d*. On passing to the metabolism characterizing animal life, which, as already indicated, is in the main a process of decomposition undoing the process of composition characterizing vegetal life, we may fitly note at the outset that it must have wide limits of variation, alike in different classes of animals and even in the same animal.

If we take, on the one hand, a carnivore living on muscular tissue (for wild carnivores preying upon herbivores which can rarely become fat obtain scarcely any carbo-hydrates) and observe that its food is almost exclusively nitrogenous; and if, on the other hand, we take a graminivorous animal the food of which (save when it eats seeds) contains comparatively little nitrogenous matter; we seem obliged to suppose that the parts played in the organic processes by the proteids and the carbo-hydrates can in considerable measures replace one another. It is true that the quantity of food and the required alimentary system in the last case, are very much greater than in the first case. But this difference is mainly due to the circumstance that the food of the graminivorous animal consists chiefly of waste-matter—ligneous fibre, cellulose, chlorophyll—and that could the starch, sugar, and protoplasm be obtained without the waste-matter, the required bulks of the two kinds of food would be by no means so strongly contrasted. This becomes manifest on comparing flesh-eating and grain-eating birds—say a hawk and a pigeon. In powers of flight these do not greatly differ, nor is the size of the alimentary system conspicuously greater in the last than in the first; though probably the amount of food consumed is greater. Still it seems clear that the supply of energy obtained by a pigeon from carbo-hydrates with a moderate proportion of proteids is not widely unlike that obtained by a hawk from proteids alone. Even from the traits of men differently fed a like inference may be drawn. On the one hand we have the Masai who, during their warrior-days, eat flesh exclusively; and on the other hand we have the Hindus, feeding almost wholly on vegetable food. Doubtless the quantities required in these cases differ much; but the difference between the rations of the flesh-eater and the grain-eater is not so immense as it would be were there no substitution in the physiological uses of the materials.

Concerning the special aspects of animal-metabolism, we have first to note those various minor transformations that are auxiliary to the general transformation by which force is obtained from food. For many of the vital activities merely subserve the elaboration of materials for activity at large, and the getting rid of waste products. From blood passing through the salivary glands is prepared in large quantity a secretion containing among other matters a nitrogenous ferment, ptyaline, which, mixed with food during mastication, furthers the change of its starch into sugar. Then in the stomach come the more or less varying secretions known in combination as gastric juice. Besides certain salts and hydrochloric acid, this contains another nitrogenous ferment, pepsin, which is instrumental in dissolving the proteids swallowed. To these two metabolic products aiding solution of the various ingested solids, is presently added that product of metabolism in the pancreas which, added to the chyme, effects certain other molecular changes—notably that of such amylaceous matters as are yet unaltered, into saccharine matters to be presently absorbed. And let us note the significant fact that the preparation of food-materials in the alimentary canal, again shows us that unstable nitrogenous compounds are the agents which, while themselves changing, set up changes in the carbo-hydrates and proteids around: the nitrogen plays the same part here as elsewhere. It does the like in yet another viscus. Blood which passes through the spleen on its way to the liver, is exposed to the action of "a special proteid of the nature of alkali-albumin, holding iron in some way peculiarly associated with it." Lastly we come to that all-important organ the liver, at once a factory and a storehouse. Here several metabolisms are simultaneously carried on. There is that which until recent years was supposed to be the sole hepatic process—the formation of bile. In some liver-cells are masses of oil-globules, which seem to imply a carbo-hydrate metamorphosis. And then, of leading importance, comes the extensive production of that animal-starch known as glycogen—a substance which, in each of the cells generating it, is contained in a plexus of protoplasmic threads: again a nitrogenous body diffused through a mass which is now formed out of sugar and is now dissolved again into sugar. For it appears that this soluble form of carbo-hydrate, taken into the liver from the intestine, is there, when not immediately needed, stored up in the form of glycogen, ready to be re-dissolved and carried into the system either for immediate use or for re-deposit as glycogen at the places where it is presently to be consumed: the great deposit in the liver and the minor deposits in the muscles being, to use the simile of Prof. Michael Foster, analogous in their functions to a central bank and branch banks.

An instructive parallelism may be noted between these processes carried on in the animal organism and those carried on in the vegetal organism. For the carbo-hydrates named, easily made to assume the soluble or the insoluble form by the addition or subtraction of a molecule of water, and thus fitted sometimes for distribution and sometimes for accumulation, are similarly dealt with in the two cases. As the animal-starch, glycogen, is now stored up in the liver or elsewhere and now changed into glucose to be transferred, perhaps for consumption and perhaps for re-deposit; so the vegetal starch, made to alternate between soluble and insoluble states, is now carried to growing parts where by metabolic change it becomes cellulose or other component of tissue and now carried to some place where, changed back into starch, it is laid aside for future use; as it is in the turgid inside leaves of a cabbage, the root of a turnip, or the swollen underground stem we know as a potato: the matter which in the animal is used up in generating movement and heat, being in the plant used up in generating structures. Nor is the parallelism even now exhausted; for, as by a plant starch is stored up in each seed for the subsequent use of the embryo, so in an embryo-animal glycogen is stored up in the developing muscles for subsequent use in the completion of their structures.

§ 23*e*. We come now to the supreme and all-pervading metabolism which has for its effects the conspicuous manifestations of life—the nervous and muscular activities. Here comes up afresh a question discussed in the edition of 1864—a question to be reconsidered in the light of recent knowledge—the question what particular metabolic changes are they by which in muscle the energy existing under the form of molecular motion is transformed into the energy manifested as molar motion?

There are two views respecting the nature of this transformation. One is that the carbo-hydrate present in muscle must, by further metabolism, be raised into the form of a nitrogenous compound or compounds before it can be made to undergo that sudden decomposition which initiates muscular contraction. The other is the view set forth in § 15, and there reinforced by further illustrations which have occurred to me while preparing this revised edition—the view that the carbo-hydrate in muscle, everywhere in contact with unstable nitrogenous substance, is, by the shock of a small molecular change in this, made to undergo an extensive molecular change, resulting in the oxidation of its carbon and consequent liberation of much molecular motion. Both of these are at present only hypotheses, in support of which respectively the probabilities have to be weighed. Let us compare them and observe on which side the evidence preponderates.

We are obliged to conclude that in carnivorous animals the katabolic process is congruous with the first of these views, in so far that the evolution of energy must in some way result solely from the fall of complex nitrogenous compounds into those simpler matters which make their appearance as waste; for, practically, the carnivorous animal has no carbo-hydrates out of which otherwise to evolve force. To this admission, however, it should be added that possibly out of the exclusively nitrogenous food, glycogen or sugar has to be obtained by partial decomposition before muscular action can take place. But when we pass to animals having food consisting mainly of carbo-hydrates, several difficulties stand in the way of the hypothesis that, by further compounding, proteids must be formed from the carbo-hydrates before muscular energy can be evolved. In the first place the anabolic change through which, by the addition of nitrogen, &c., a proteid is formed from a carbo-hydrate, must absorb an energy equal to a moiety of that which is given out in the subsequent katabolic change. There can be no dynamic profit on such part of the transaction as effects the composition and subsequent decomposition of the proteid, but only on such part of the transaction as effects the decomposition of the carbo-hydrate. In the second place there arises the question—whence comes the nitrogen required for the compounding of the carbo-hydrates into proteids? There is none save that contained in the serum-albumen or other proteid which the blood brings; and there can be no gain in robbing this proteid of nitrogen for the purpose of forming another proteid. Hence the nitrogenizing of the surplus carbo-hydrates is not accounted for. One more difficulty remains. If the energy given out by a muscle results from the katabolic consumption of its proteids, then the quantity of nitrogenous waste matters formed should be proportionate to the quantity of work done. But experiments have proved that this is not the case. Long ago it was shown that the amount of urea excreted does not increase in anything like proportion to the amount of muscular energy expended; and recently this has been again shown.

On this statement a criticism has been made to the following effect:—Considering that muscle will contract when deprived of oxygen and blood and must therefore contain matter from which the energy is derived; and considering that since carbonic acid is given out the required carbon and oxygen must be derived from some component of muscle; it results that the energy must be obtained by decomposition of a nitrogenous body. To this reasoning it may be objected, in the first place, that the conditions specified are abnormal, and that it is dangerous to assume that what takes place under abnormal conditions takes place also under normal ones. In presence of blood and oxygen the process may possibly, or even probably, be unlike that which arises in their absence: the muscular substance may begin consuming itself when it has not the usual materials to consume. Then, in the second place, and chiefly, it may be replied that the difficulty raised in the foregoing argument is not escaped but merely obscured. If, as is alleged, the carbon and oxygen from which carbonic acid is produced, form, under the conditions stated, parts of a complex nitrogenous substance contained in muscle, then the abstraction of the carbon and oxygen must cause decomposition of this nitrogenous substance; and in that case the excretion of nitrogenous waste must be proportionate to the amount of work done, which it is not. This difficulty is evaded by supposing that the "stored complex explosive substance must be, in living muscle, of such nature" that after explosion it leaves a "nitrogenous residue available for re-combination with fresh portions of carbon and oxygen derived from the blood and thereby the re-constitution of the explosive substance." This implies that a molecule of the explosive substance consists of a complex nitrogenous molecule united with a molecule of carbo-hydrate, and that time after time it suddenly decomposes this carbo-hydrate molecule and thereupon takes up another such from the blood. That the carbon is abstracted from the carbo-hydrate molecule can scarcely be said, since the feebler affinities of the nitrogenous molecule can hardly be supposed to overcome the stronger affinities of the carbo-hydrate molecule. The carbo-hydrate molecule must therefore be incorporated bodily. What is the implication? The carbo-hydrate part of the compound is relatively stable, while the nitrogenous part is relatively unstable. Hence the hypothesis implies that, time after time, the unstable nitrogenous part overthrows the stable carbo-hydrate part, without being itself overthrown. This conclusion, to say the least of it, does not appear very probable.

The alternative hypothesis, indirectly supported as we saw by proofs that outside the body small amounts of change in nitrogenous compounds initiate large amounts of change in carbonaceous compounds, may in the first place be here supported by some further indirect evidences of kindred natures. A haystack prematurely put together supplies one. Enough water having been left in the hay to permit chemical action, the decomposing proteids forming the dead protoplasm in each cell, set up decomposition of the carbo-hydrates with accompanying oxidation of the carbon and genesis of heat; even to the extent of producing fire. Again, as shown above, this relation between these two classes of compounds is exemplified in the alimentary canal; where, alike in the saliva and in the pancreatic secretion, minute quantities of unstable nitrogenous bodies transform great quantities of stable carbo-hydrates. Thus we find indirect reinforcements of the belief that the katabolic change generating muscular energy is one in which a large decomposition of a carbo-hydrate is set up by a small decomposition of a proteid.[12]

§ 23*f.* A certain general trait of animal organization may fitly be named because its relevance, though still more indirect, is very significant. Under one of its aspects an animal is an apparatus for the multiplication of energies—a set of appliances by means of which a minute amount of motion initiates a larger amount of motion, and this again a still larger amount. There are structures which do this mechanically and others which do it chemically.

Associated with the peripheral ends of the nerves of touch are certain small bodies—*corpuscula tactus*—each of which, when disturbed by something in contact with the skin, presses on the adjacent fibre more strongly than soft tissue would do, and thus multiplies the force producing sensation. While serving the further purpose of touching at a distance, the *vibrissæ* or whiskers of a feline animal achieve a like end in a more effectual way. The external portion of each bristle acts as the long arm of a lever, and the internal portion as the short arm. The result is that a slight touch at the outer end of the bristle produces a considerable pressure of the inner end on the nerve-terminal: so intensifying the impression. In the hearing organs of various inferior types of animals, the otolites in contact with the auditory nerves, when they are struck by sound-waves, give to the nerves much stronger impressions than these would have were they simply immersed in loose tissue; and in the ears of developed creatures there exist more elaborate appliances for augmenting the effects of aerial vibrations. From this multiplication of molar actions let us pass to the multiplication of molecular actions. The retina is made up of minute rods and cones, so packed together side by side that they can be separately affected by the separate parts of the images of objects. As each of them is but 1/10,000th of an inch in diameter, the ethereal undulations falling upon it can produce an amount of change almost infinitesimal—an amount probably incapable of exciting a nerve-centre, or indeed of overcoming the molecular inertia of the nerve leading to it. But in close proximity are layers of granules into which the rods and cones send fibres, and beyond these, about 1/100th of an inch from the retinal layer, lie ganglion-cells, in each of which a minute disturbance may readily evolve a larger disturbance; so that by multiplication, single or perhaps double, there is produced a force sufficient to excite the fibre connected with the centre of vision. Such, at least, judging from the requirement and the structure, seems to me the probable interpretation of the visual process; though whether it is the accepted one I do not know.

But now, carrying with us the conception made clear by the first cases and suggested by the last, we shall appreciate the extent to which this general physiological method, as we may call it, is employed. The convulsive action caused by tickling shows it conspicuously. An extremely small amount of molecular change in the nerve-endings produces an immense amount of molecular change, and resulting molar motion, in the muscles. Especially is this seen in one whose spinal cord has been so injured that it no longer conveys sensations from the lower limbs to the brain; and in whom, nevertheless, tickling of the feet produces convulsive actions of the legs more violent even than result when sensation exists: clearly proving that since the minute molecular change produced by the tickling in the nerve-terminals cannot be equivalent in quantity to the amount implied by the muscular contraction, there must be a multiplication of it in those parts of the spinal cord whence issue the reflex stimuli to the muscles.

Returning now to the question of metabolism, we may see that the processes of multiplication above supposed to take place in muscle, are analogous in their general nature to various other physiological processes. Carrying somewhat further the simile used in § 15 and going back to the days when detonators, though used for small arms, were not used for artillery, we may compare the metabolic process in muscle to that which would take place if a pistol were fired against the touch-hole of a loaded cannon: the cap exploding the pistol and the pistol the cannon. For in the case of the muscle, the implication is that a nervous discharge works in certain unstable proteids through which the nerve-endings are distributed, a small amount of molecular change; that the shock of this causes a much larger amount of molecular change in the inter-diffused carbo-hydrate, with accompanying oxidation of its carbon; and that the heat liberated sets up a transformation, probably isomeric, in the contractile substance of the muscular fibre: an interpretation supported by cases in which small rises and falls of temperature cause alternating isomeric changes; as instance Mensel's salt.

Ending here this exposition, somewhat too speculative and running into details inappropriate to a work of this kind, it suffices to note the most general facts concerning metabolism. Regarded as a whole it includes, in the first place, those anabolic or building-up processes specially characterizing plants, during which the impacts of ethereal undulations are stored up in compound molecules of unstable kinds; and it includes, in the second place, those katabolic or tumbling-down changes specially characterizing animals, during which this accumulated molecular motion (contained in the food directly or indirectly supplied by plants), is in large measure changed into those molar motions constituting animal activities. There are multitudinous metabolic changes of minor kinds which are ancillary to these—many katabolic changes in plants and many anabolic changes in animals—but these are the essential ones.[13]

CHAPTER IV.[14]

PROXIMATE CONCEPTION OF LIFE.

§ 24. To those who accept the general doctrine of Evolution, it need scarcely be pointed out that classifications are subjective conceptions, which have no absolute demarcations in Nature corresponding to them. They are appliances by which we limit and arrange the matters under investigation; and so facilitate our thinking. Consequently, when we attempt to define anything complex, or make a generalization of facts other than the most simple, we can scarcely ever avoid including more than we intended, or leaving out something which should be taken in. Thus it happens that on seeking a definite idea of Life, we have great difficulty in finding one that is neither more nor less than sufficient. Let us look at a few of the most tenable definitions that have been given. While recognizing the respects in which they are defective, we shall see what requirements a more satisfactory one must fulfil.

Schelling said that Life is the tendency to individuation. This formula, until studied, conveys little meaning. But we need only consider it as illustrated by the facts of development, or by the contrast between lower and higher forms of life, to recognize its significance; especially in respect of comprehensiveness. As before shown, however (*First Principles*, § 56), it is objectionable; partly on the ground that it refers not so much to the functional changes constituting Life, as to the structural changes of those aggregates of matter which manifest Life; and partly on the ground that it includes under the idea Life, much that we usually exclude from it: for instance—crystallization.

The definition of Richerand,—"Life is a collection of phenomena which succeed each other during a limited time in an organized body,"—is liable to the fatal criticism, that it equally applies to the decay which goes on after death. For this, too, is "a collection of phenomena which succeed each other during a limited time in an organized body."

"Life," according to De Blainville, "is the two-fold internal movement of composition and decomposition, at once general and continuous." This conception is in some respects too narrow, and in other respects too wide. On the one hand, while it expresses what physiologists distinguish as vegetative life, it does not indicate those nervous and muscular functions which form the most conspicuous and distinctive classes of vital phenomena. On the other hand, it describes not only the integrating and disintegrating process going on in a living body, but it equally well describes those going on in a galvanic battery; which also exhibits a "two-fold internal movement of composition and decomposition, at once general and continuous."

Elsewhere, I have myself proposed to define Life as "the co-ordination of actions."[15] This definition has some advantages. It includes all organic changes, alike of the viscera, the limbs, and the brain. It excludes the great mass of inorganic changes; which display little or no co-ordination. By making co-ordination the specific character of vitality, it involves the truths, that an arrest of co-ordination is death, and that imperfect co-ordination is disease. Moreover, it harmonizes with our ordinary ideas of life in its different grades; seeing that the organisms which we rank as low in their degrees of life, are those which display but little co-ordination of actions; and seeing that from these up to man, the recognized increase in degree of life corresponds with an increase in the extent and complexity of co-ordinations. But, like the others, this definition includes too much. It may be said of the Solar System, with its regularly-recurring movements and its self-balancing perturbations, that it, also, exhibits co-ordination of actions. And however plausibly it may be argued that, in the abstract, the motions of the planets and satellites are as properly comprehended in the idea of life as the changes going on in a motionless, unsensitive seed: yet, it must be admitted that they are foreign to that idea as commonly received, and as here to be formulated.

It remains to add the definition since suggested by Mr. G. H. Lewes—"Life is a series of definite and successive changes, both of structure and composition, which take place within an individual without destroying its identity." The last fact which this statement brings into view—the persistence of a living organism as a whole, in spite of the continuous removal and replacement of its parts—is important. But otherwise it may be argued that, since changes of structure and composition, though concomitants of muscular and nervous actions, are not the muscular and nervous actions themselves, the definite excludes the more visible movements with which our idea of life is most associated; and further that, in describing vital changes as *a series*, it scarcely includes the fact that many of them, as Nutrition, Circulation, Respiration, and Secretion, in their many subdivisions, go on simultaneously.

Thus, however well each of these definitions expresses the phenomena of life under some of its aspects, no one of them is more than approximately true. It may turn out that to find a formula which will bear every test is impossible. Meanwhile, it is possible to frame a more adequate formula than any of the foregoing. As we shall presently find, these all omit an essential peculiarity of vital changes in general—a peculiarity which, perhaps more than any other, distinguishes them from non-vital changes.

Before specifying this peculiarity, however, it will be well to trace our way, step by step, to as complete an idea of Life as may be reached from our present stand-point; by doing which we shall both see the necessity for each limitation as it is made, and ultimately be led to feel the need for a further limitation.

And here, as the best mode of determining what are the traits which distinguish vitality from non-vitality, we shall do well to compare the two most unlike kinds of vitality, and see in what they agree. Manifestly, that which is essential to Life must be that which is common to Life of all orders. And manifestly, that which is common to all forms of Life, will most readily be seen on contrasting those forms of Life which have the least in common, or are the most unlike.[16]

§ 25. Choosing assimilation, then, for our example of bodily life, and reasoning for our example of that life known as intelligence; it is first to be observed, that they are both processes of change. Without change, food cannot be taken into the blood nor transformed into tissue; without change, there can be no getting from premisses to conclusion. And it is this conspicuous display of changes which forms the substratum of our idea of Life in general. Doubtless we see innumerable changes to which no notion of vitality attaches. Inorganic bodies are ever undergoing changes of temperature, changes of colour, changes of aggregation; and decaying organic bodies also. But it will be admitted that the great majority of the phenomena displayed by inanimate bodies, are statical and not dynamical; that the modifications of inanimate bodies are mostly slow and unobtrusive; that on the one hand, when we see sudden movements in inanimate bodies, we are apt to assume living agency, and on the other hand, when we see no movements in living bodies, we are apt to assume death. Manifestly then, be the requisite qualifications what they may, a true idea of Life must be an idea of some kind of change or changes.

On further comparing assimilation and reasoning, with a view of seeing in what respect the changes displayed in both differs from non-vital changes, we find that they differ in being not simple changes; in each case there are *successive* changes. The transformation of food into tissue involves mastication, deglutition, chymification, chylification, absorption, and those various actions gone through after the lacteal ducts have poured their contents into the blood. Carrying on an argument necessitates a long chain of states of consciousness; each implying a change of the preceding state. Inorganic changes, however, do not in any considerable degree exhibit this peculiarity. It is true that from meteorologic causes, inanimate objects are daily, sometimes hourly, undergoing modifications of temperature, of bulk, of hygrometric and electric condition. Not only, however, do these modifications lack that conspicuousness and that rapidity of succession which vital ones possess, but vital ones form an *additional* series. Living as well as not-living bodies are affected by atmospheric influences; and beyond the changes which these produce, living bodies exhibit other changes, more numerous and more marked. So that though organic change is not rigorously distinguished from inorganic change by presenting successive phases; yet vital change so greatly exceeds other change in this respect, that we may consider it as a distinctive character. Life, then, as thus roughly differentiated, may be regarded as change presenting successive phases; or otherwise, as a series of changes. And it should be observed, as a fact in harmony with this conception, that the higher the life the more conspicuous the variations. On comparing inferior with superior organisms, these last will be seen to display more rapid changes, or a more lengthened series of them, or both.

On contemplating afresh our two typical phenomena, we may see that vital change is further distinguished from non-vital change, by being made up of many *simultaneous* changes. Nutrition is not simply a series of actions, but includes many actions going on together. During mastication the stomach is busy with food already swallowed, on which it is pouring out solvent fluids and expending muscular efforts. While the stomach is still active, the intestines are performing their secretive, contractile, and absorbent functions; and at the same time that one meal is being digested, the nutriment obtained from a previous meal is undergoing transformation into tissue. So too is it, in a certain sense, with mental changes. Though the states of consciousness which make up an argument occur in series, yet, as each of them is complex, a number of simultaneous changes have taken place in establishing it. Here as before, however, it must be admitted that the distinction between animate and inanimate is not precise. No mass of dead matter can have its temperature altered, without at the same time undergoing an alteration in bulk, and sometimes also in hygrometric state. An inorganic body cannot be compressed, without being at the same time changed in form, atomic arrangement, temperature, and electric condition. And in a vast and mobile aggregate like the sea, the simultaneous as well as the successive changes outnumber those going on in an animal. Nevertheless, speaking generally, a living thing is distinguished from a dead thing by the multiplicity of the changes at any moment taking place in it. Moreover, by this peculiarity, as by the previous one, not only is the vital more or less clearly marked off from the non-vital; but creatures possessing high vitality are marked off from those possessing low vitality. It needs but to contrast the many organs cooperating in a mammal, with the few in a polype, to see that the actions which are progressing together in the body of the first, as much exceed in number the actions progressing together in the body of the last, as these do those in a stone. As at present conceived, then, Life consists of simultaneous and successive changes.

Continuance of the comparison shows that vital changes, both visceral and cerebral, differ from other changes in their *heterogeneity*. Neither the simultaneous acts nor the serial acts, which together constitute the process of digestion, are alike. The states of consciousness comprised in any ratiocination are not repetitions one of another, either in composition or in modes of dependence. Inorganic processes, on the other hand, even when like organic ones in the number of the simultaneous and successive changes they involve, are unlike them in the relative homogeneity of these changes. In the case of the sea, just referred to, it is observable that countless as are the actions at any moment going on, they are mostly mechanical actions that are to a great degree similar; and in this respect differ widely from the actions at any moment taking place in an organism. Even where life is nearly simulated, as by the working of a steam-engine, we see that considerable as is the number of simultaneous changes, and rapid as are the successive ones, the regularity with which they soon recur in the same order and degree, renders them unlike those varied changes exhibited by a living creature. Still, this peculiarity, like the foregoing ones, does not divide the two classes of changes with precision; since there are inanimate things presenting considerable heterogeneity of change: for instance, a cloud. The variations of state which this undergoes, both simultaneous and successive, are many and quick; and they differ widely from one another both in quality and quantity. At the same instant there may occur change of position, change of form, change of size, change of density, change of colour, change of temperature, change of electric state; and these several kinds of change are continuously displayed in different degrees and combinations. Yet when we observe that very few inorganic objects manifest heterogeneity of change comparable to that manifested by organic objects, and further, that in ascending from low to high forms of life, we meet with an increasing variety in the kinds of changes displayed; we see that there is here a further leading distinction between vital and non-vital actions. According to this modified conception, then, Life is made up of heterogeneous changes both simultaneous and successive.

If, now, we look for some trait common to the nutritive and logical processes, by which they are distinguished from those inorganic processes that are most like them in the heterogeneity of the simultaneous and successive changes they comprise, we discover that they are distinguished by the *combination* among their constituent changes. The acts which make up digestion are mutually dependent. Those composing a train of reasoning are in close connection. And, generally, it is to be remarked of vital changes, that each is made possible by all, and all are affected by each. Respiration, circulation, absorption, secretion, in their many sub-divisions, are bound up together. Muscular contraction involves chemical change, change of temperature, and change in the excretions. Active thought influences the operations of the stomach, of the heart, of the kidneys. But we miss this union among non-vital activities. Life-like as may seem the action of a volcano in respect of the heterogeneity of its many simultaneous and successive changes, it is not life-like in respect of their combination. Though the chemical, mechanical, thermal, and electric phenomena exhibited have some inter-dependence, yet the emissions of stones, mud, lava, flame, ashes, smoke, steam, take place irregularly in quantity, order, intervals, and mode of conjunction. Even here, however, it cannot be said that inanimate things present no parallels to animate ones. A glacier may be instanced as showing nearly as much combination in its change as a plant of the lowest organization. It is ever growing and ever decaying; and the rates of its composition and decomposition preserve a tolerably constant ratio. It moves; and its motion is in immediate dependence on its thawing. It emits a torrent of water, which, in common with its motion, undergoes annual variations as plants do. During part of the year the surface melts and freezes alternately; and on these changes depend the variations in movement, and in efflux of water. Thus we have growth, decay, changes of temperature, changes of consistence, changes of velocity, changes of excretion, all going on in connexion; and it may be as truly said of a glacier as of an animal, that by ceaseless integration and disintegration it gradually undergoes an entire change of substance without losing its individuality. This exceptional instance, however, will scarcely be held to obscure that broad distinction from inorganic processes which organic processes derive from the combination among their constituent changes. And the reality of this distinction becomes yet more manifest when we find that, in common with previous ones, it not only marks off the living from the not-living, but also things which live little from things which live much. For while the changes going on in a plant or a zoophyte are so imperfectly combined that they can continue after it has been divided into two or more pieces, the combination among the changes going on in a mammal is so close that no part cut off from the rest can live, and any considerable disturbance of one chief function causes a cessation of the others. Hence, as we now regard it, Life is a combination of heterogeneous changes, both simultaneous and successive.

When we once more look for a character common to these two kinds of vital action, we perceive that the combinations of heterogeneous changes which constitute them, differ from the few combinations which they otherwise resemble, in respect of *definiteness*. The associated changes going on in a glacier, admit of indefinite variation. Under a conceivable alteration of climate, its thawing and its progression may be stopped for a million years, without disabling it from again displaying these phenomena under appropriate conditions. By a geological convulsion, its motion may be arrested without an arrest of its thawing; or by an increase in the inclination of the surface it slides over, its motion may be accelerated without accelerating its rate of dissolution. Other things remaining the same, a more rapid deposit of snow may cause great increase of bulk; or, conversely, the accretion may entirely cease, and yet all the other actions continue until the mass disappears. Here, then, the combination has none of that definiteness which, in a plant, marks the mutual dependence of respiration, assimilation, and circulation; much less has it that definiteness seen in the mutual dependence of the chief animal functions; no one of which can be varied without varying the rest; no one of which can go on unless the rest go on. Moreover, this definiteness of combination distinguishes the changes occurring in a living body from those occurring in a dead one. Decomposition exhibits both simultaneous and successive changes, which are to some extent heterogeneous, and in a sense combined; but they are not combined in a definite manner. They vary according as the surrounding medium is air, water, or earth. They alter in nature with the temperature. If the local conditions are unlike, they progress differently in different parts of the mass, without mutual influence. They may end in producing gases, or adipocire, or the dry substance of which mummies consist. They may occupy a few days or thousands of years. Thus, neither in their simultaneous nor in their successive changes, do dead bodies display that definiteness of combination which characterizes living ones. It is true that in some inferior creatures the cycle of successive changes admits of a certain indefiniteness—that it may be suspended for a long period by desiccation or freezing, and may afterwards go on as though there had been no breach in its continuity. But the circumstance that only a low order of life can have its changes thus modified, serves but to suggest that, like the previous characteristics, this characteristic of definiteness in its combined changes, distinguishes high vitality from low vitality, as it distinguishes low vitality from inorganic processes. Hence, our formula as further amended reads thus:—Life is a definite combination of heterogenous changes, both simultaneous and successive.

Finally, we shall still better express the facts if, instead of saying *a* definite combination of heterogeneous changes, we say *the* definite combination of heterogeneous changes. As it at present stands, the definition is defective both in allowing that there may be *other* definite combinations of heterogeneous changes, and in directing attention to the heterogeneous changes rather than to the definiteness of their combination. Just as it is not so much its chemical elements which constitute an organism, as it is the arrangement of them into special tissues and organs; so it is not so much its heterogeneous changes which constitute Life, as it is the co-ordination of them. Observe what it is that ceases when life ceases. In a dead body there are going on heterogeneous changes, both simultaneous and successive. What then has disappeared? The definite combination has disappeared.

Mark, too, that however heterogeneous the simultaneous and successive changes exhibited by such an inorganic object as a volcano, we much less tend to think of it as living than we do a watch or a steam-engine, which, though displaying changes that, serially contemplated, are largely homogeneous, displays them definitely combined. So dominant an element is this in our idea of Life, that even when an object is motionless, yet, if its parts be definitely combined, we conclude either that it has had life, or has been made by something having life. Thus, then, we conclude that Life is—*the* definite combination of heterogeneous changes, both simultaneous and successive.

§ 26. Such is the conception at which we arrive without changing our stand-point. It is, however, an incomplete conception. This ultimate formula (which is to a considerable extent identical with one above given—"the co-ordination of actions;" seeing that "definite combination" is synonymous with "co-ordination," and "changes both simultaneous and successive" are comprehended under the term "actions;" but which differs from it in specifying the fact, that the actions or changes are "heterogeneous")—this ultimate formula, I say, is after all but a rude approximation. It is true that it does not fail by including the growth of a crystal; for the successive changes this implies cannot be called heterogeneous. It is true that the action of a galvanic battery is not comprised in it; since here, too, heterogeneity is not exhibited by the successive changes. It is true that by this same qualification the motions of the Solar System are excluded, as are also those of a watch and a steam-engine. It is true, moreover, that while, in virtue of their heterogeneity, the actions going on in a cloud, in a volcano, in a glacier, fulfil the definition; they fall short of it in lacking definiteness of combination. It is further true that this definiteness of combination distinguishes the changes taking place in an organism during life from those which commence at death. And beyond all this it is true that, as well as serving to mark off, more or less clearly, organic actions from inorganic actions, each member of the definition serves to mark off the actions constituting high vitality from those constituting low vitality; seeing that life is high in proportion to the number of successive changes occurring between birth and death; in proportion to the number of simultaneous changes; in proportion to the heterogeneity of the changes; in proportion to the combination subsisting among the changes; and in proportion to the definiteness of their combination. Nevertheless, answering though it does to so many requirements, this definition is essentially defective. *The definite combination of heterogeneous changes, both simultaneous and successive*, is a formula which fails to call up an adequate conception. And it fails from omitting the most distinctive peculiarity—the peculiarity of which we have the most familiar experience, and with which our notion of Life is, more than with any other, associated. It remains now to supplement the conception by the addition of this peculiarity.

CHAPTER V.

THE CORRESPONDENCE BETWEEN LIFE AND ITS CIRCUMSTANCES.

§ 27. We habitually distinguish between a live object and a dead one, by observing whether a change which we make in the surrounding conditions, or one which Nature makes in them, is or is not followed by some perceptible change in the object. By discovering that certain things shrink when touched, or fly away when approached, or start when a noise is made, the child first roughly discriminates between the living and the not-living; and the man when in doubt whether an animal he is looking at is dead or not, stirs it with his stick; or if it be at a distance, shouts, or throws a stone at it. Vegetal and animal life are alike primarily recognized by this process. The tree that puts out leaves when the spring brings increase of temperature, the flower which opens and closes with the rising and setting of the sun, the plant that droops when the soil is dry and re-erects itself when watered, are considered alive because of these induced changes; in common with the acorn-shell which contracts when a shadow suddenly falls on it, the worm that comes to the surface when the ground is continuously shaken, and the hedgehog that rolls itself up when attacked.

Not only, however, do we look for some response when an external stimulus is applied to a living organism, but we expect a fitness in the response. Dead as well as living things display changes under certain changes of condition: instance, a lump of carbonate of soda that effervesces when dropped into sulphuric acid; a cord that contracts when wetted; a piece of bread that turns brown when held near the fire. But in these cases, we do not see a connexion between the changes undergone and the preservation of the things that undergo them; or, to avoid any teleological implication—the changes have no apparent relations to future events which are sure or likely to take place. In vital changes, however, such relations are manifest. Light being necessary to vegetal life, we see in the action of a plant which, when much shaded, grows towards the unshaded side, an appropriateness which we should not see did it grow otherwise. Evidently the proceedings of a spider which rushes out when its web is gently shaken and stays within when the shaking is violent, conduce better to the obtainment of food and the avoidance of danger than were they reversed. The fact that we feel surprise when, as in the case of a bird fascinated by a snake, the conduct tends towards self-destruction, at once shows how generally we have observed an adaptation of living changes to changes in surrounding circumstances.

A kindred truth, rendered so familiar by infinite repetition that we forget its significance, must be named. There is invariably, and necessarily, a conformity between the vital functions of any organism and the conditions in which it is placed—between the processes going on inside of it and the processes going on outside of it. We know that a fish cannot live long in air, or a man under water. An oak growing in the ocean and a seaweed on the top of a hill, are incredible combinations of ideas. We find that each kind of animal is limited to a certain range of climate; each kind of plant to certain zones of latitude and elevation. Of the marine flora and fauna, each species is found only between such and such depths. Some blind creatures flourish in dark caves; the limpet where it is alternately covered and uncovered by the tide; the red-snow alga rarely elsewhere than in the arctic regions or among alpine peaks.

Grouping together the cases first named, in which a particular change in the circumstances of an organism is followed by a particular change in it, and the cases last named, in which the constant actions occurring within an organism imply some constant actions occurring without it; we see that in both, the changes or processes displayed by a living body are specially related to the changes or processes in its environment. And here we have the needful supplement to our conception of Life. Adding this all-important characteristic, our conception of Life becomes—The definite combination of heterogeneous changes, both simultaneous and successive, *in correspondence with external co-existences and sequences.* That the full significance of this addition may be seen, it will be necessary to glance at the correspondence under some of its leading aspects.[17]

§ 28. Neglecting minor requirements, the actions going on in a plant pre-suppose a surrounding medium containing at least carbonic acid and water, together with a due supply of light and a certain temperature. Within the leaves carbon is being appropriated and oxygen given off; without them, is the gas from which the carbon is taken, and the imponderable agents that aid the abstraction. Be the nature of the process what it may, it is clear that there are external elements prone to undergo special re-arrangements under special conditions. It is clear that the plant in sunshine presents these conditions and so effects these re-arrangements. And thus it is clear that the changes which primarily constitute the plant's life, are in correspondence with co-existences in its environment.

If, again, we ask respecting the lowest protozoon how it lives; the answer is, that while on the one hand its substance is undergoing disintegration, it is on the other hand absorbing nutriment; and that it may continue to exist, the one process must keep pace with, or exceed, the other. If further we ask under what circumstances these combined changes are possible, there is the reply that the medium in which the protozoon is placed, must contain oxygen and food—oxygen in such quantity as to produce some disintegration; food in such quantity as to permit that disintegration to be made good. In other words—the two antagonistic processes taking place internally, imply the presence externally of materials having affinities that can give rise to them.

Leaving those lowest animal forms which simply take in through their surfaces the nutriment and oxygenated fluids coming in contact with them, we pass to those somewhat higher forms which have their tissues slightly specialized. In these we see a correspondence between certain actions in the digestive sac, and the properties of certain surrounding bodies. That a creature of this order may continue to live, it is necessary not only that there be masses of substance in the environment capable of transformation into its own tissue, but also that the introduction of these masses into its stomach, shall be followed by the secretion of a solvent fluid which will reduce them to a fit state for absorption. Special outer properties must be met by special inner properties.

When, from the process by which food is digested, we turn to the process by which it is seized, the same general truth faces us. The stinging and contractile power of a polype's tentacle, correspond to the sensitiveness and strength of the creatures serving it for prey. Unless that external change which brings one of these creatures in contact with the tentacle, were quickly followed by those internal changes which result in the coiling and drawing up of the tentacle, the polype would die of inanition. The fundamental processes of integration and disintegration within it, would get out of correspondence with the agencies and processes without it, and the life would cease.

Similarly, when the creature becomes so large that its tissue cannot be efficiently supplied with nutriment by mere absorption through its lining membrane, or duly oxygenated by contact with the fluid bathing its surface, there arises a need for a distributing system by which nutriment and oxygen may be carried throughout the mass; and the functions of this system, being subsidiary to the two primary functions, form links in the correspondence between internal and external actions. The like is obviously true of all those subordinate functions, secretory and excretory, that facilitate oxidation and assimilation.

Ascending from visceral actions to muscular and nervous actions, we find the correspondence displayed in a manner still more obvious. Every act of locomotion implies the expenditure of certain internal forces, adapted in amounts and directions to balance or out-balance certain external forces. The recognition of an object is impossible without a harmony between the changes constituting perception, and particular properties co-existing in the environment. Escape from enemies implies motions within the organism, related in kind and rapidity to motions without it. Destruction of prey requires a special combination of subjective actions, fitted in degree and succession to overcome a group of objective ones. And so with those countless automatic processes constituting instincts.

In the highest order of vital changes the same fact is equally manifest. The empirical generalization that guides the farmer in his rotation of crops, serves to bring his actions into concord with certain of the actions going on in plants and soil. The rational deductions of the educated navigator who calculates his position at sea, form a series of mental acts by which his proceedings are conformed to surrounding circumstances. Alike in the simplest inferences of the child and the most complex ones of the man of science, we find a correspondence between simultaneous and successive changes in the organism, and co-existences and sequences in its environment.

§ 29. This general formula which thus includes the lowest vegetal processes along with the highest manifestations of human intelligence, will perhaps call forth some criticisms which it is desirable here to meet.

It may be thought that there are still a few inorganic actions included in the definition; as, for example, that displayed by the mis-named storm-glass. The feathery crystallization which, on a certain change of temperature, takes place in its contained solution, and which afterwards dissolves to reappear in new forms under new conditions, may be held to present simultaneous and successive changes that are to some extent heterogeneous, that occur with some definiteness of combination, and, above all, occur in apparent correspondence with external changes. In this case vegetal life is simulated to a considerable extent; but it is *merely* simulated. The relation between the phenomena occurring in the storm-glass and in the atmosphere respectively, is not a correspondence at all, in the proper sense of the word. Outside there is a thermal change; inside there is a change of atomic arrangement. Outside there is another thermal change; inside there is another change of atomic arrangement. But subtle as is the dependence of each internal upon each external change, the connexion between them does not, in the abstract, differ from the connexion between the motion of a straw and the motion of the wind that disturbs it. In either case a change produces a change, and there it ends. The alteration wrought by some environing agency on this or any other inanimate object, does not tend to induce in it a secondary alteration which anticipates some secondary alteration in the environment. But in every living body there is a tendency towards secondary alterations of this nature; and it is in their production that the correspondence consists. The difference may be best expressed by symbols. Let A be a change in the environment, and B some resulting change in an inorganic mass. Then A having produced B, the action ceases. Though the change A in the environment is followed by some consequent change *a* in it; no parallel sequence in the inorganic mass simultaneously generates in it some change *b* that has reference to the change *a*. But if we take a living body of the requisite organization, and let the change A impress on it some change C; then, while in the environment A is occasioning *a*, in the living body C will be occasioning *c*; of which *a* and *c* will show a certain concord in time, place, or intensity. And while it is *in* the continuous production of such concords or correspondences that Life consists, it is *by* the continuous production of them that Life is maintained.

The further criticism to be expected concerns certain verbal imperfections in the definition, which it seems impossible to avoid. It may fairly be urged that the word *correspondence* will not include, without straining, the various relations to be expressed by it. It may be asked:—How can the continuous *processes* of assimilation and respiration correspond with the *co-existence* of food and oxygen in the environment? or again:—How can the act of secreting some defensive fluid correspond with some external danger which may never occur? or again:—How can the *dynamical* phenomena constituting perception correspond with the *statical* phenomena of the solid body perceived? The only reply is, that we have no word sufficiently general to comprehend all forms of this relation between the organism and its medium, and yet sufficiently specific to convey an adequate idea of the relation; and that the word *correspondence* seems the least objectionable. The fact to be expressed in all cases is that certain changes, continuous or discontinuous, in the organism, are connected after such a manner that in their amounts, or variations, or periods of occurrence, or modes of succession, they have a reference to external actions, constant or serial, actual or potential—a reference such that a definite relation among any members of the one group, implies a definite relation among certain members of the other group.

§ 30. The presentation of the phenomena under this general form, suggests that our conception of Life may be reduced to its most abstract shape by regarding its elements as relations only. If a creature's rate of assimilation is increased in consequence of a decrease of temperature in the environment, it is that the relation between the food consumed and the heat produced, is so re-adjusted by multiplying both its members, that the altered relation in the environment between the quantity of heat absorbed from, and radiated to, bodies of a given temperature, is counterbalanced. If a sound or a scent wafted to it on the breeze prompts the stag to dart away from the deer-stalker, it is that there exists in its neighbourhood a relation between a certain sensible property and certain actions dangerous to the stag, while in its body there exists an adapted relation between the impression this sensible property produces, and the actions by which danger may be escaped. If inquiry has led the chemist to a law, enabling him to tell how much of any one element will combine with so much of another, it is that there has been established in him specific mental relations, which accord with specific chemical relations in the things around. Seeing, then, that in all cases we may consider the external phenomena as simply in relation, and the internal phenomena also as simply in relation; our conception of Life under its most abstract aspect will be—*The continuous adjustment of internal relations to external relations.*[18]

While it is simpler, this formula has the further advantage of being somewhat more comprehensive. To say that it includes not only those definite combinations of simultaneous and successive changes in an organism, which correspond to co-existences and sequences in the environment, but also those structural arrangements which *enable* the organism to adapt its actions to actions in the environment, is going too far; for though these structural arrangements present internal relations adjusted to external relations, yet the *continuous adjustment* of relations cannot be held to include a *fixed adjustment* already made. Life, which is made up of *dynamical* phenomena, cannot be described in terms that shall at the same time describe the apparatus manifesting it, which presents only *statical* phenomena. But while this antithesis serves to remind us that the distinction between the organism and its actions is as wide as that between Matter and Motion, it at the same time draws attention to the fact that, if the structural arrangements of the adult are not properly included in the definition, yet the developmental processes by which those arrangements were established, are included. For that process of evolution during which the organs of the embryo are fitted to their prospective functions, is the gradual or continuous adjustment of internal relations to external relations. Moreover, those structural modifications of the adult organism which, under change of climate, change of occupation, change of food, bring about some re-arrangement in the organic balance, may similarly be regarded as progressive or continuous adjustments of internal relations to external relations. So that not only does the definition, as thus expressed, comprehend all those activities, bodily and mental, which constitute our ordinary idea of Life; but it also comprehends both those processes of development by which the organism is brought into general fitness for such activities, and those after-processes of adaptation by which it is specially fitted to its special activities.

Nevertheless, so abstract a formula as this is scarcely fitted for our present purpose. Reserving it for use where specially appropriate, it will be best commonly to employ its more concrete equivalent—to consider the internal relations as "definite combinations of simultaneous and successive changes;" the external relations as "co-existences and sequences;" and the connexion between them as a "correspondence."

CHAPTER VI.

THE DEGREE OF LIFE VARIES AS THE DEGREE OF CORRESPONDENCE.

§ 31. Already it has been shown respecting each other component of the foregoing definition, that the life is high in proportion as that component is conspicuous; and it is now to be remarked, that the same thing is especially true respecting this last component—the correspondence between internal and external relations. It is manifest, *a priori*, that since changes in the physical state of the environment, as also of those mechanical actions and those variations of available food which occur in it, are liable to stop the processes going on in the organism; and since the adaptive changes in the organism have the effects of directly or indirectly counter-balancing these changes in the environment; it follows that the life of the organism will be short or long, low or high, according to the extent to which changes in the environment are met by corresponding changes in the organism. Allowing a margin for perturbations, the life will continue only while the correspondence continues; the completeness of the life will be proportionate to the completeness of the correspondence; and the life will be perfect only when the correspondence is perfect. Not to dwell in general statements, however, let us contemplate this truth under its concrete aspects.

§ 32. In life of the lowest order we find that only the most prevalent co-existences and sequences in the environment, have any simultaneous and successive changes answering to them in the organism. A plant's vital processes display adjustment solely to the continuous co-existence of certain elements and forces surrounding its roots and leaves; and vary only with the variations produced in these elements and forces by the Sun—are unaffected by the countless mechanical movements and contacts occurring around; save when accidentally arrested by these. The life of a worm is made up of actions referring to little else than the tangible properties of adjacent things. All those visible and audible changes which happen near it, and are connected with other changes that may presently destroy it, pass unrecognized—produce in it no adapted changes: its only adjustment of internal relations to external relations of this order, being seen when it escapes to the surface on feeling the vibrations produced by an approaching mole. Adjusted as are the proceedings of a bird to a far greater number of co-existences and sequences in the environment, cognizable by sight, hearing, scent, and their combinations: and numerous as are the dangers it shuns and the needs it fulfils in virtue of this extensive correspondence; it exhibits no such actions as those by which a human being counterbalances variations in temperature and supply of food, consequent on the seasons. And when we see the plant eaten, the worm trodden on, the bird dead from starvation; we see alike that the death is an arrest of such correspondence as existed, that it occurred when there was some change in the environment to which the organism made no answering change, and that thus, both in shortness and simplicity, the life was incomplete in proportion as the correspondence was incomplete. Progress towards more prolonged and higher life, evidently implies ability to respond to less general co-existences and sequences. Each step upwards must consist in adding to the previously-adjusted relations of actions or structures which the organism exhibits, some further relation parallel to a further relation in the environment. And the greater correspondence thus established, must, other things equal, show itself both in greater complexity of life, and greater length of life: a truth which will be fully perceived on remembering the enormous mortality which prevails among lowly-organized creatures, and the gradual increase of longevity and diminution of fertility which we meet with on ascending to creatures of higher and higher developments.

It must be remarked, however, that while length and complexity of life are, to a great extent, associated—while a more extended correspondence in the successive changes commonly implies increased correspondence in the simultaneous changes; yet it is not uniformly so. Between the two great divisions of life—animal and vegetal—this contrast by no means holds. A tree may live a thousand years, though the simultaneous changes going on in it answer only to the few chemical affinities in the air and the earth, and though its serial changes answer only to those of day and night, of the weather and the seasons. A tortoise, which exhibits in a given time nothing like the number of internal actions adjusted to external ones that are exhibited by a dog, yet lives far longer. The tree by its massive trunk and the tortoise by its hard carapace, are saved the necessity of responding to those many surrounding mechanical actions which organisms not thus protected must respond to or die; or rather—the tree and the tortoise display in their structures, certain simple statical relations adapted to meet countless dynamical relations external to them. But notwithstanding the qualifications suggested by such cases, it needs but to compare a microscopic fungus with an oak, an animalcule with a shark, a mouse with a man, to recognize the fact that this increasing correspondence of its changes with those of the environment which characterizes progressing life, habitually shows itself at the same time in continuity and in complication.

Even were not the connexion between length of life and complexity of life thus conspicuous, it would still be true that the life is great in proportion as the correspondence is great. For if the lengthened existence of a tree be looked upon as tantamount to a considerable amount of life; then it must be admitted that its lengthened display of correspondence is tantamount to a considerable amount of correspondence. If, otherwise, it be held that notwithstanding its much shorter existence, a dog must rank above a tortoise in degree of life because of its superior activity; then it is implied that its life is higher because its simultaneous and successive changes are more complex and more rapid—because the correspondence is greater. And since we regard as the highest life that which, like our own, shows great complexity in the correspondences, great rapidity in the succession of them, and great length in the series of them; the equivalence between degree of life and degree of correspondence is unquestionable.

§ 33. In further elucidation of this general truth, and especially in explanation of the irregularities just referred to, it must be pointed out that as the life becomes higher the environment itself becomes more complex. Though, literally, the environment means all surrounding space with the co-existences and sequences contained in it: yet, practically, it often means but a small part of this. The environment of an entozoon can scarcely be said to extend beyond the body of the animal in which the entozoon lives. That of a freshwater alga is virtually limited to the ditch inhabited by the alga. And, understanding the term in this restricted sense, we shall see that the superior organisms inhabit the more complicated environments.

Thus, contrasted with the life found on land, the lower life is that found in the sea; and it has the simpler environment. Marine creatures are affected by fewer co-existences and sequences than terrestrial ones. Being very nearly of the same specific gravity as the surrounding medium, they have to contend with less various mechanical actions. The sea-anemone fixed to a stone, and the acalephe borne along in the current, need to undergo no internal changes such as those by which the caterpillar meets the varying effects of gravitation, while creeping over and under the leaves. Again, the sea is liable to none of those extreme and rapid alterations of temperature which the air suffers. Night and day produce no appreciable modifications in it; and it is comparatively little affected by the seasons. Thus its contained fauna show no marked correspondences similar to those by which air-breathing creatures counterbalance thermal changes. Further, in respect to the supply of nutriment, the conditions are more simple. The lower tribes of animals inhabiting the water, like the plants inhabiting the air, have their food brought to them. The same current which brings oxygen to the oyster, also brings it the microscopic organisms on which it lives: the disintegrating matter and the matter to be integrated, co-exist under the simplest relation. It is otherwise with land animals. The oxygen is everywhere, but the sustenance is not everywhere: it has to be sought; and the conditions under which it is to be obtained are more or less complex. So too with that liquid by the agency of which the vital processes are carried on. To marine creatures water is ever present, and by the lowest is passively absorbed; but to most creatures living on the earth and in the air, it is made available only through those nervous changes constituting perception, and those muscular ones by which drinking is effected. Similarly, after tracing upwards from the *Amphibia* the widening extent and complexity which the environment, as practically considered, assumes—after observing further how increasing heterogeneity in the flora and fauna of the globe, itself progressively complicates the environment of each species of organism—it might finally be shown that the same general truth is displayed in the history of mankind, who, in the course of their progress, have been adding to their physical environment a social environment that has been growing ever more involved. Thus, speaking generally, it is clear that those relations in the environment to which relations in the organism must correspond, themselves increase in number and intricacy as the life assumes a higher form.

§ 34. To make yet more manifest the fact that the degree of life varies as the degree of correspondence, let me here point out, that those other distinctions successively noted when contrasting vital changes with non-vital changes, are all implied in this last distinction—their correspondence with external co-existences and sequences; and further, that the increasing fulfilment of those other distinctions which we found to accompany increasing life, is involved in the increasing fulfilment of this last distinction. We saw that living organisms are characterized by successive changes, and that as the life becomes higher, the successive changes become more numerous. Well, the environment is full of successive changes, and the greater the correspondence, the greater must be the number of successive changes in the organism. We saw that life presents simultaneous changes, and that the more elevated it is, the more marked the multiplicity of them. Well, besides countless co-existences in the environment, there are often many changes occurring in it at the same moment; and hence increased correspondence with it implies in the organism an increased display of simultaneous changes. Similarly with the heterogeneity of the changes. In the environment the relations are very varied in their kinds, and hence, as the organic actions come more and more into correspondence with them, they too must become very varied in their kinds. So again is it even with definiteness of combination. As the most important surrounding changes with which each animal has to deal, are the definitely-combined changes exhibited by other animals, whether prey or enemies, it results that definiteness of combination must be a general characteristic of the internal ones which have to correspond with them. So that throughout, the correspondence of the internal relations with the external ones is the essential thing; and all the special characteristics of the internal relations, are but the collateral results of this correspondence.

§§ 35, 36. Before closing the chapter, it will be useful to compare the definition of Life here set forth, with the definition of Evolution set forth in *First Principles*. Living bodies being bodies which display in the highest degree the structural changes constituting Evolution; and Life being made up of the functional changes accompanying these structural changes; we ought to find a certain harmony between the definitions of Evolution and of Life. Such a harmony is not wanting.

The first distinction we noted between the kind of change shown in Life, and other kinds of change, was its serial character. We saw that vital change is substantially unlike non-vital change, in being made up of *successive* changes. Now since organic bodies display so much more than inorganic bodies those continuous differentiations and integrations which constitute Evolution; and since the re-distributions of matter thus carried so far in a comparatively short period, imply concomitant re-distributions of motion; it is clear that in a given time, organic bodies must undergo changes so comparatively numerous as to render the successiveness of their changes a marked characteristic. And it will follow *a priori*, as we found it to do *a posteriori*, that the organisms exhibiting Evolution in the highest degree, exhibit the longest or the most rapid successions of changes, or both. Again, it was shown that vital change is distinguished from non-vital change by being made up of many *simultaneous* changes; and also that creatures possessing high vitality are marked off from those possessing low vitality, by the far greater number of their simultaneous changes. Here, too, there is entire congruity. In *First Principles*, § 156, we reached the conclusion that a force falling on any aggregate is divided into several forces; that when the aggregate consists of parts that are unlike, each part becomes a centre of unlike differentiations of the incident force; and that thus the multiplicity of such differentiations must increase with the multiplicity of the unlike parts. Consequently organic aggregates, which as a class are distinguished from inorganic aggregates by the greater number of their unlike parts, must be also distinguished from them by the greater number of simultaneous changes they display; and, further, that the higher organic aggregates, having more numerous unlike parts than the lower, must undergo more numerous simultaneous changes. We next found that the changes occurring in living bodies are contrasted with those occurring in other bodies, as being much more *heterogeneous*; and that the changes occurring in the superior living bodies are similarly contrasted with those occurring in inferior ones. Well, heterogeneity of function is the correlate of heterogeneity of structure; and heterogeneity of structure is the leading distinction between organic and inorganic aggregates, as well as between the more highly organized and the more lowly organized. By reaction, an incident force must be rendered multiform in proportion to the multiformity of the aggregate on which it falls; and hence those most multiform aggregates which display in the highest degree the phenomena of Evolution structurally considered, must also display in the highest degree the multiform actions which constitute Evolution functionally considered. These heterogeneous changes, exhibited simultaneously and in succession by a living organism, prove, on further inquiry, to be distinguished by their *combination* from certain non-vital changes which simulate them. Here, too, the parallelism is maintained. It was shown in *First Principles*, Chap. XIV, that an essential characteristic of Evolution is the integration of parts, which accompanies their differentiation—an integration shown both in the consolidation of each part, and in the union of all the parts into a whole. Hence, animate bodies having greater co-ordination of parts than inanimate ones must exhibit greater co-ordination of changes; and this greater co-ordination of their changes must not only distinguish organic from inorganic aggregates, but must, for the same reason, distinguish higher organisms from lower ones, as we found that it did. Once more, it was pointed out that the changes constituting Life differ from other changes in the *definiteness* of their combination, and that a distinction like in kind though less in degree, holds between the vital changes of superior creatures and those of inferior creatures. These, also, are contrasts in harmony with the contrasts disclosed by the analysis of Evolution. We saw (*First Principles*, §§ 129-137) that during Evolution there is an increase of definiteness as well as an increase of heterogeneity. We saw that the integration accompanying differentiation has necessarily the effect of increasing the distinctness with which the parts are marked off from each other, and that so, out of the incoherent and indefinite there arises the coherent and definite. But a coherent whole made up of definite parts definitely combined, must exhibit more definitely combined changes than a whole made up of parts that are neither definite in themselves nor in their combination. Hence, if living bodies display more than other bodies this structural definiteness, then definiteness of combination must be a characteristic of the changes constituting Life, and must also distinguish the vital changes of higher organisms from those of lower organisms. Finally, we discovered that all these peculiarities are subordinate to the fundamental peculiarity, that vital changes take place in correspondence with external co-existences and sequences, and that the highest Life is reached, when there is some inner relation of actions fitted to meet every outer relation of actions by which the organism can be affected. But this conception of the highest Life, is in harmony with the conception, before arrived at, of the limit of Evolution. When treating of equilibration as exhibited in organisms (*First Principles*, §§ 173, 174), it was pointed out that the tendency is towards the establishment of a balance between inner and outer changes. It was shown that "the final structural arrangements must be such as will meet all the forces acting on the aggregate, by equivalent antagonistic forces," and that "the maintenance of such a moving equilibrium" as an organism displays, "requires the habitual genesis of internal forces corresponding in number, directions, and amounts, to the external incident forces—as many inner functions, single or combined, as there are single or combined outer actions to be met." It was shown, too, that the relations among ideas are ever in progress towards a better adjustment between mental actions and those actions in the environment to which conduct must be adjusted. So that this continuous correspondence between inner and outer relations which constitutes Life, and the perfection of which is the perfection of Life, answers completely to that state of organic moving equilibrium which we saw arises in the course of Evolution and tends ever to become more complete.

CHAPTER VIA.

THE DYNAMIC ELEMENT IN LIFE.

§ 36*a*. A critical comparison of the foregoing formula with the facts proves it to be deficient in more ways than one. Let us first look at vital phenomena which are not covered by it.

Some irritant left by an insect's ovipositor, sets up on a plant the morbid growth named a gall. The processes in the gall do not correspond with any external co-existences or sequences relevant to the plant's life—show no internal relations adjusted to external relations. Yet we cannot deny that the gall is alive. So, too, is it with a cancer in or upon an animal's body. The actions going on in it have no reference, direct or indirect, to actions in the environment. Nevertheless we are obliged to say that they are vital; since it grows and after a time dies and decomposes.

A kindred lesson meets us when from pathological evidence we turn to physiological evidence. The functions of some important organs may still be carried on for a time apart from those of the body as a whole. An excised liver, kept at a fit temperature and duly supplied with blood, secretes bile. Still more striking is the independent action of the heart. If belonging to a cold-blooded animal, as a frog, the heart, when detached, continues to beat, even until its integuments have become so dry that they crackle. Now though under such conditions its pulsations, which ordinarily form an essential part of the linked processes by which the correspondence between inner and outer actions is maintained, no longer form part of such processes, we must admit that the continuance of them implies a vital activity.

Embryological changes force the same truth upon us. What are we to say of the repeated cell-fissions by which in some types a blastula, or mulberry-mass, is formed, and in other types a blastoderm? Neither these processes nor the structures immediately resulting from them, show any correspondences with co-existences and sequences in the environment; though they are first steps towards the organization which is to carry on such correspondences. Even this extremely small fulfilment of the definition is absent in the cases of rudimentary organs, and especially those rudimentary organs which after being partly formed are absorbed. No adjustment can be alleged between the inner relations which these present and any outer relations. The outer relations they refer to ceased millions of years ago. Yet unquestionably the changes which bring about the production and absorption of these futile structures are vital changes.

Take another class of exceptions. What are we to say of a laugh? No correspondence, or part of a correspondence, by which inner actions are made to balance outer actions, can be seen in it. Or again, if, while working, an artisan whistles, the making of the sounds and the co-ordination of ideas controlling them, cannot be said to exhibit adjustment between certain relations of thoughts, and certain relations of things. Such kinds of vital activities lie wholly outside of the definition given.

But perhaps the clearest and simplest proof is yielded by contrasting voluntary and involuntary muscular actions. Here is a hawk adapting its changing motions to the changing motions of a pigeon, so as eventually to strike it: the adjustment of inner relations to outer relations is manifest. Here is a boy in an epileptic fit. Between his struggles and the co-existences and sequences around him there is no correspondence whatever. Yet his movements betray vitality just as much as do the movements of the hawk. Both exhibit that principle of *activity* which constitutes the essential element in our conception of life.

§ 36*b*. Evidently, then, the preceding chapters recognize only the *form* of our conception of life and ignore the *body* of it. Partly sufficing as does the definition reached to express the one, it fails entirely to express the other. Life displays itself in ways which conform to the definition; but it also displays itself in many other ways. We are obliged to admit that the element which is common to the two groups of ways is the essential element. The essential element, then, is that special kind of energy seen alike in the usual classes of vital actions and in those unusual classes instanced above.

Otherwise presenting the contrast, we may say that due attention has been paid to the connexions among the manifestations, while no attention has been paid to that which is manifested. When it is said that life is "the definite correspondence of heterogeneous changes, both simultaneous and successive, in correspondence with external co-existences and sequences," there arises the question—Changes of what? Within the body there go on many changes, mechanical, chemical, thermal, no one of which is the kind of change in question; and if we combine in thought so far as we can these kinds of changes, in such wise that each maintains its character as mechanical, chemical, or thermal, we cannot get out of them the idea of Life. Still more clearly do we see this insufficiency when we take the more abstract definition—"the continuous adjustment of internal relations to external relations." Relations between what things? is the question then to be asked. A relation of which the terms are unspecified does not connote a thought but merely the blank form of a thought. Its value is comparable to that of a cheque on which no amount is written. If it be said that the terms cannot be specified because so many heterogeneous kinds of them have to be included, then there comes the reply that under cover of this inability to make a specification of terms that shall be adequately comprehensive, there is concealed the inability to conceive the required terms in any way.

Thus a critical testing of the definition brings us, in another way, to the conclusion reached above, that that which gives the substance to our idea of Life is a certain unspecified principle of activity. The dynamic element in life is its essential element.

§ 36*c*. Under what form are we to conceive this dynamic element? Is this principle of activity inherent in organic matter, or is it something superadded? Of these alternative suppositions let us begin with the last.

As I have remarked, in another place, the worth of an hypothesis may be judged from its genealogy; and so judged the hypothesis of an independent vital principal does not commend itself. Its history carries us back to the ghost-theory of the savage. Suggested by experiences of dreams, there arises belief in a double—a second self which wanders away during sleep and has adventures but comes back on waking; which deserts the body during abnormal insensibility of one or other kind; and which is absent for a long period at death, though even then is expected eventually to return. This indwelling other-self, which can leave the body at will, is by-and-by regarded as able to enter the bodies of fellow men or of animals; or again, by implication, as liable to have its place usurped by the intruding doubles of fellow men, living or dead, which cause fits or other ills. Along with these developments its quality changes. At first thought of as quite material it is gradually de-materialized, and in advanced times comes to be regarded as spirit or breath; as we see in ancient religious books, where "giving up the ghost" is shown by the emergence of a small floating figure from the mouth of a dying man. This indwelling second self, more and more conceived as the real self which uses the body for its purposes, is, with the advance of intelligence, still further divested of its definite characters; and, coming in mediæval days to be spoken of as "animal spirits," ends in later days in being called a vital principle.

Entirely without assignable attributes, this something occurs in thought not as an idea but as a pseud-idea (*First Principles*, Chap. II). It is assumed to be representable while really unrepresentable. We need only insist on answers to certain questions to see that it is simply a name for an alleged existence which has not been conceived and cannot be conceived.

1. Is there one kind of vital principle for all kinds of organisms, or is there a separate kind for each? To affirm the first alternative is to say that there is the same vital principle for a microbe as for a whale, for a tape-worm as for the person it inhabits, for a protococcus as for an oak; nay more—is to assert community of vital principle in the thinking man and the unthinking plant. Moreover, asserting unity of the vital principle for all organisms, is

reducing it to a force having the same unindividualized character as one of the physical forces. If, on the other hand, different kinds of organisms have different kinds of vital principles, these must be in some way distinguished from one another. How distinguished? Manifestly by attributes. Do they differ in extension? Evidently; since otherwise that which animates the vast *Sequoia* can be no larger than that which animates a yeast-plant, and to carry on the life of an elephant requires a quantity of vital principle no greater than that required for a microscopic monad. Do they differ otherwise than in amount? Certainly; since otherwise we revert to the preceding alternative, which implies that the same quality of vital principle serves for all organisms, simple and complex: the vital principle is a uniform force like heat or electricity. Hence, then, we have to suppose that every species of animal and plant has a vital principle peculiar to itself—a principle adapted to use the particular set of structures in which it is contained. But dare anyone assert this multiplication of vital principles, duplicating not only all existing plants and animals but all past ones, and amounting in the aggregate to some millions?

2. How are we to conceive that genesis of a vital principle which must go along with the genesis of an organism? Here is a pollen-grain which, through the pistil, sends its nucleus to unite with the nucleus of the ovule; or here are the nuclei of spermatozoon and ovum, which, becoming fused, initiate a new animal: in either case failure of union being followed by decomposition of the proteid materials, while union is followed by development. Whence comes that vital principle which determines the organizing process? Is it created afresh for every plant and animal? or, if not, where and how did it pre-exist? Take a simpler form of this problem. A protophyte or protozoon, having grown to a certain size, undergoes a series of complex changes ending in fission. In its undivided state it had a vital principle. What of its divided state? The parts severally swim away, each fully alive, each ready to grow and presently to subdivide, and so on and so on, until millions are soon formed. That is to say, there is a multiplication of vital principles as of the protozoa animated by them. A vital principle, then, both divides and grows. But growth implies incorporation of something. What does the vital principle incorporate? Is it some other vital principle external to it, or some materials out of which more vital principle is formed? And how, in either case, can the vital principle be conceived as other than a material something, which in its growth and multiplication behaves just as visible matter behaves?

3. Equally unanswerable is the question which arises in presence of life that has become latent. Passing over the alleged case of the mummy wheat, the validity of which is denied, there is experimental proof that seeds may, under conditions unfavourable to germination, retain for ten, twenty, and

some even for thirty years, the power to germinate when due moisture and warmth are supplied. (*Cf.* Kerner's *Nat. Hist. of Plants*, i, 51-2). Under what form has the vital principle existed during these long intervals? It is a principle of activity. In this case, then, the principle of activity becomes inactive. But how can we conceive an inactive activity? If it is a something which though inactive may be rendered active when conditions favour, we are introduced to the idea of a vital principle of which the vitality may become latent, which is absurd. What shall we say of the desiccated rotifer which for years has seemed to be nothing more than a particle of dust, but which now, when water is supplied, absorbs it, swells up, and resumes those ciliary motions by which it draws in nutriment? Was the vital principle elsewhere during these years of absolute quiescence? If so, why did it come back at the right moment? Was it all along present in the rotifer though asleep? How happened it then to awaken at the time when the supply of water enabled the tissues to resume their functions? How happened the physical agent to act not only on the material substance of the rotifer, but also on this something which is not a material substance but an immaterial source of activity? Evidently neither alternative is thinkable.

Thus, the alleged vital principle exists in the minds of those who allege it only as a verbal form, not as an idea; since it is impossible to bring together in consciousness the terms required to constitute an idea. It is not even "a figment of imagination," for that implies something imaginable, but the supposed vital principle cannot even be imagined.

§ 36*d.* When, passing to the alternative, we propose to regard life as inherent in the substances of the organisms displaying it, we meet with difficulties different in kind but scarcely less in degree. The processes which go on in living things are incomprehensible as results of any physical actions known to us.

Consider one of the simplest—that presented by an ordinary vegetal cell forming part of a leaf or other plant-structure. Its limiting membrane, originally made polyhedral by pressure of adjacent cells, is gradually moulded "into one of cylindrical, fibrous, or tabular shape, and strengthening its walls with pilasters, borders, ridges, hooks, bands, and panels of various kinds" (Kerner, i, 43): small openings into adjacent cells being either left or subsequently made. Consisting of non-nitrogenous, inactive matters, these structures are formed by the inclosed protoplast. How formed? Is it by the agency of the nucleus? But the nucleus, even had it characters conceivably adapting it to this function, is irregularly placed; and that it should work the same effects upon the cell-wall whether seated in the middle, at one end, or one side, is incomprehensible. Is the protoplasm then the active agent? But this is arranged into a network of strands and threads utterly irregular in distribution and perpetually altering their shapes and connexions. Exercise of fit directive action by the protoplasm is unimaginable.

Another instance:—Consider the reproductive changes exhibited by the *Spirogyra.* The delicate threads which, in this low type of Alga, are constituted of single elongated cells joined end to end, are here and there adjacent to one another; and from a cell of one thread and a cell of another at fit distance, grow out prominences which, meeting in the interspace and forming a channel by the dissolution of their adjoined cell-walls, empty through it the endochrome of the one cell into the other: forming by fusion of the two a zygote or reproductive body. Under what influence is this action initiated and guided? There is no conceivable directive agency in either cell by which, when conditions are fit, a papilla is so formed as to meet an opposite papilla.

Or again, contemplate the still more marvellous transformation occurring in *Hydrodictyon utriculosum.* United with others to form a cylindrical network, each sausage-shaped cell of this Alga contains, when fully developed, a lining chromatophore made of nucleated protoplasm with immersed chlorophyll-grains. This, when the cell is adult, divides into multitudinous zoospores, which presently join their ends in such ways as to form a network with meshes mostly hexagonal, minute in size, but like in arrangement to the network of which the parent cell formed a part. Eventually escaping from the mother-cell, this network grows and presently becomes as large as the parent network. Under what play of forces do these zoospores arrange themselves into this strange structure?

Kindred insoluble problems are presented by animal organisms of all grades. Of microscopic types instance the Coccospheres and Rhabdospheres found in the upper strata of sea-water. Each is a fragment of protoplasm less than one-thousandth of an inch in diameter, shielded by the elaborate protective structures it has formed. The elliptic coccoliths of the first, severally having a definite pattern, unite to form by overlapping an imbricated covering; and of the other the covering consists of numerous trumpet-mouthed processes radiating on all sides. To the question—How does this particle of granular protoplasm, without organs or definite structure, make for itself this complicated calcareous armour? there is no conceivable answer.

Like these *Protozoa,* the lowest *Metazoa* do things which are quite incomprehensible. Here is a sponge formed of classes of monads having among them no internuncial appliances by which in higher types cooperation is carried on—flagellate cells that produce the permeating currents of water, flattened cells forming protective membranes, and amœboid cells lying free in the gelatinous mesoderm. These, without apparent concert, build up not only the horny network constituting the chief mass of their habitation, but also embodied spicules, having remarkable symmetrical forms. By what combined influences the needful processes are effected, it is impossible to imagine.

If we turn to higher types of *Metazoa* in which, by the agency of a nervous system, many cooperations of parts are achieved in ways that are superficially comprehensible, we still meet with various actions of which the causation cannot be represented in thought. Lacking other calcareous matter, a hen picks up and swallows bits of broken egg-shells; and, occasionally, a cow in calf may be seen mumbling a bone she has found—evidently scraping off with her teeth some of its mass. These proceedings have reference to constitutional needs; but how are they prompted? What generates in the cow a desire to bite a substance so unlike in character to her ordinary food? If it be replied that the blood has become poor in certain calcareous salts and that hence arises the appetite for things containing them, there remains the question—How does this deficiency so act on the nervous system as to generate this vague desire and cause the movements which satisfy it? By no effort can we figure to ourselves the implied causal processes.

In brief, then, we are obliged to confess that Life in its essence cannot be conceived in physico-chemical terms. The required principle of activity, which we found cannot be represented as an independent vital principle, we now find cannot be represented as a principle inherent in living matter. If, by assuming its inherence, we think the facts are accounted for, we do but cheat ourselves with pseud-ideas.

§ 36*e*. What then are we to say—what are we to think? Simply that in this direction, as in all other directions, our explanations finally bring us face to face with the inexplicable. The Ultimate Reality behind this manifestation, as behind all other manifestations, transcends conception. It needs but to observe how even simple forms of existence are in their ultimate natures incomprehensible, to see that this most complex form of existence is in a sense doubly incomprehensible.

For the actions of that which the ignorant contemptuously call brute matter, cannot in the last resort be understood in their genesis. Were it not that familiarity blinds us, the fall of a stone would afford matter for wonder. Neither Newton nor anyone since his day has been able to conceive how the molecules of matter in the stone are affected not only by the molecules of matter in the adjacent part of the Earth but by those forming parts of its mass 8,000 miles off which severally exercise their influence without impediment from intervening molecules; and still less has there been any conceivable interpretation of the mode in which every molecule of matter in the Sun, 92 millions of miles away, has a share in controlling the movements of the Earth. What goes on in the space between a magnet and the piece of iron drawn towards it, or how on repeatedly passing a magnet along a steel needle this, by some change of molecular state as we must suppose, becomes itself a magnet and when balanced places its poles in fixed directions, we do not know. And still less can we fathom the physical process by which an ordered series of electric pulses sent through a telegraph wire may be made to excite a corresponding series of pulses in a parallel wire many miles off.

Turn to another class of cases. Consider the action of a surface of glass struck by a cathode current and which thereupon generates an order of rays able to pass through solid matters impermeable to light. Or contemplate the power possessed by uranium and other metals of emitting rays imperceptible by our eyes as light but which yet, in what appears to us absolute darkness, will, if passed through a camera, produce photographs. Even the actions of one kind of matter on another are sufficiently remarkable. Here is a mass of gold which, after the addition of 1-500th part of bismuth, has only 1-28th of the tensile strength it previously had; and here is a mass of brass, ordinarily ductile and malleable, but which, on the addition of 1-10,000th part of antimony, loses its character. More remarkable still are the influences of certain medicines. One-hundredth of a grain of nitro-glycerine is a sufficient dose. Taking an average man's weight as 150 pounds, it results that his body is appreciably affected in its state by the 115-millionth part of its weight of this nitrogenous compound.

In presence of such powers displayed by matter of simple kinds we shall see how impossible it is even to imagine those processes going on in organic matter out of which emerges the dynamic element in Life. As no separate form of proteid possesses vitality, we seem obliged to assume that the molecule of protoplasm contains many molecules of proteids, probably in various isomeric states, all capable of ready change and therefore producing great instability of the aggregate they form. As before pointed out (§ 4), a proteid-molecule includes more than 220 equivalents of several so-called elements. Each of these undecomposed substances is now recognized by chemists as almost certainly consisting of several kinds of components. Hence the implication is that a proteid-molecule contains thousands of units, of which the different classes have their respective rates of inconceivably rapid oscillation, while each unit, receiving and emitting ethereal undulations, affects others of its kind in its own and adjacent molecules: an immensely complex structure having immensely complex activities. And this complexity, material and dynamic, in the proteid-molecule we must regard as raised to a far higher degree in the unit of protoplasm. Here as elsewhere alternative impossibilities of thought present themselves. We find it impossible to think of Life as imported into the unit of protoplasm from without; and yet we find it impossible to conceive it as emerging from the cooperation of the components.

§ 36*f*. But now, having confessed that Life as a principle of activity is unknown and unknowable—that while its phenomena are accessible to thought the implied noumenon is inaccessible—that only the manifestations come within the range of our intelligence while that which is manifested lies beyond it; we may resume the conclusions reached in the preceding chapters. Our surface knowledge continues to be a knowledge valid of its kind, after recognizing the truth that it is only a surface knowledge.

For the conclusions we lately reached and the definition emerging from them, concern the *order* existing among the actions which living things exhibit; and this order remains the same whether we know or do not know the nature of that from which the actions originate. We found a distinguishing trait of Life to be that its changes display a correspondence with co-existences and sequences in the environment; and this remains a distinguishing trait, though the thing which changes remains inscrutable. The statement that the continuous adjustment of internal relations to external relations constitutes Life as cognizable by us, is not invalidated by the admission that the reality in which these relations inhere is incognizable.

Hence, then, after duly recognizing the fact that, as pointed out above, Life, even phenomenally considered, is not entirely covered by the definition, since there are various abnormal manifestations of life which it does not include, we may safely accept it as covering the normal manifestations—those manifestations which here concern us. Carrying with us the definition, therefore we may hereafter use it for guidance through all those regions of inquiry upon which we now enter.

CHAPTER VII.

THE SCOPE OF BIOLOGY.

§ 37. As ordinarily conceived, the science of Biology falls into two great divisions, the one dealing with animal life, called Zoology, and the other dealing with vegetal life, called Botany, or more properly to be called Phytology. But convenient as is this division, it is not that which arises if we follow the scientific method of including in one group all the phenomena of fundamentally the same order and putting separately in another group all the phenomena of a fundamentally different order. For animals and plants are alike in having structures; and animals and plants are alike in having functions performed by these structures; and the distinction between structures and functions transcends the difference between any one structure and any other or between any one function and any other—is, indeed, an absolute distinction, like that between Matter and Motion. Recognizing, then, the logic of the division thus indicated, we must group the parts of Biology thus:—

1. An account of the structural phenomena presented by organisms. This subdivides into:—

a. The established structural phenomena presented by individual organisms.

b. The changing structural phenomena presented by successions of organisms.

2. An account of the functional phenomena which organisms present. This, too, admits of subdivision into:—

a. The established functional phenomena of individual organisms.

b. The changing functional phenomena of successions of organisms.

3. An account of the actions of Structures on Functions and the re-actions of Functions on Structures. Like the others, this is divisible into:—

a. The actions and re-actions as exhibited in individual organisms.

b. The actions and re-actions as exhibited in successions of organisms.

4. An account of the phenomena attending the production of successions of organisms: in other words—the phenomena of Genesis.

Of course, for purposes of exploration and teaching, the division into Zoology and Botany, founded on contrasts so marked and numerous, must always be retained. But here recognizing this familiar distinction only as much as convenience obliges us to do, let us now pass on to consider, more in detail, the classification of biologic phenomena above set down in its leading outlines.

§ 38. The facts of structure shown in an individual organism, are of two chief kinds. In order of conspicuousness, though not in order of time, there come first those arrangements of parts which characterize the mature organism; an account of which, originally called Anatomy, is now called Morphology. Then come those successive modifications through which the organism passes in its progress from the germ to the developed form; an account of which is called Embryology.

The structural changes which any series of individual organisms exhibits, admit of similar classification. On the one hand, we have those inner and outer differences of shape, that arise between the adult members of successive generations descended from a common stock—differences which, though usually not marked between adjacent generations, become great in course of multitudinous generations. On the other hand, we have those developmental modifications, seen in the embryos, through which such modifications of the descended forms are reached.

Interpretation of the structures of individual organisms and successions of organisms, is aided by two subsidiary divisions of biologic inquiry, named Comparative Anatomy (properly Comparative Morphology) and Comparative Embryology. These cannot be regarded as in themselves parts of Biology; since the facts embraced under them are not substantive phenomena, but are simply incidental to substantive phenomena. All the truths of structural Biology are comprehended under the two foregoing subdivisions; and the comparison of these truths as presented in different classes of organisms, is simply a *method* of interpreting them.

Nevertheless, though Comparative Morphology and Comparative Embryology do not disclose additional concrete facts, they lead to the establishment of certain abstract facts. By them it is made manifest that underneath the superficial differences of groups and classes and types of organisms, there are hidden fundamental similarities; and that the courses of development in such groups and classes and types, though in many respects divergent, are in some essential respects, coincident. The wide truths thus disclosed, come under the heads of General Morphology and General Embryology.

By contrasting organisms there is also achieved that grouping of the like and separation of the unlike, called Classification. First by observation of external characters; second by observation of internal characters; and third by observation of the phases of development; it is ascertained what organisms are most similar in all respects; what organisms otherwise unlike are like in important traits; what organisms though apparently unallied have common primordial characters. Whence there results such an arrangement of organisms, that if certain structural attributes of any one be given, its other structural attributes may be *empirically* predicted; and which prepares the way for that interpretation of their relations and genesis, which forms an important part of *rational* Biology.

§ 39. The second main division of Biology, above described as embracing the functional phenomena of organisms, is that which is in part signified by Physiology: the remainder being distinguishable as Objective Psychology. Both of these fall into subdivisions that may best be treated separately.

That part of Physiology which is concerned with the molecular changes going on in organisms, is known as Organic Chemistry. An account of the modes in which the force generated in organisms by chemical change, is transformed into other forces, and made to work the various organs that carry on the functions of Life, comes under the head of Organic Physics. Psychology, which is mainly concerned with the adjustment of vital actions to actions in the environment (in contrast with Physiology, which is mainly concerned with vital actions apart from actions in the environment) consists of two quite distinct portions. Objective Psychology deals with those functions of the nervo-muscular apparatus by which such organisms as possess it are enabled to adjust inner to outer relations; and includes also the study of the same functions as externally manifested in conduct. Subjective Psychology deals with the sensations, perceptions, ideas, emotions, and volitions that are the direct or indirect concomitants of this visible adjustment of inner to outer relations. Consciousness under its different modes and forms, being a subject-matter radically distinct in nature from the subject-matter of Biology in general; and the method of self-analysis, by which alone the laws of dependence among changes of consciousness can be found, being a method unparalleled by anything in the rest of Biology; we are obliged to regard Subjective Psychology as a separate study. And since it would be very inconvenient wholly to dissociate Objective Psychology from Subjective Psychology, we are practically compelled to deal with the two as forming an independent science.

Obviously, the functional phenomena presented in successions of organisms, similarly divide into physiological and psychological. Under the physiological come the modifications of bodily actions that arise in the course of generations, as concomitants of structural modifications; and these may be modifications, qualitative or quantitative, in the molecular changes classed as chemical, or in the organic actions classed as physical, or in both. Under the psychological come the qualitative and quantitative modifications of instincts, feelings, conceptions, and mental processes in general, which occur in creatures having more or less intelligence, when certain of their conditions are changed. This, like the preceding department of Psychology, has in the abstract two different aspects—the objective and the subjective. Practically, however, the objective, which deals with these mental modifications as exhibited in the changing habits and abilities of successive generations of creatures, is the only one admitting of investigation; since the corresponding alterations in consciousness cannot be immediately known to any but the subjects of them. Evidently, convenience requires us to join this part of Psychology along with the other parts as components of a distinct sub-science.

Light is thrown on functions, as well as on structures, by comparing organisms of different kinds. Comparative Physiology and Comparative Psychology, are the names given to those collections of facts respecting the homologies and analogies, bodily and mental, disclosed by this kind of inquiry. These classified observations concerning likenesses and differences of functions, are helpers to interpret functions in their essential natures and relations. Hence Comparative Physiology and Comparative Psychology are names of methods rather than names of true subdivisions of Biology.

Here, however, as before, comparison of special truths, besides facilitating their interpretation, brings to light certain general truths. Contrasting functions bodily and mental as exhibited in various kinds of organisms, shows that there exists, more or less extensively, a community of processes and methods. Hence result two groups of propositions constituting General Physiology and General Psychology.

§ 40. In these divisions and subdivisions of the first two great departments of Biology, facts of Structure are considered separately from facts of Function, so far as separate treatment of them is possible. The third great department of Biology deals with them in their necessary connexions. It comprehends the determination of functions by structures, and the determination of structures by functions.

As displayed in individual organisms, the effects of structures on functions are to be studied, not only in the broad fact that the general kind of life an organism leads is necessitated by the main characters of its organization, but in the more special and less conspicuous fact, that between members of the same species, minor differences of structure lead to minor differences of power to perform certain actions, and of tendencies to perform such actions. Conversely, under the reactions of functions on structures in individual organisms, come the facts showing that functions, when fulfilled to their normal extents, maintain integrity of structure in their respective organs; and that within certain limits increases of functions are followed by such structural changes in their respective organs, as enable them to discharge better their extra functions.

Inquiry into the influence of structure on function as seen in successions of organisms, introduces us to such phenomena as Mr. Darwin's *Origin of Species* deals with. In this category come all proofs of the general truth, that when an individual is enabled by a certain structural peculiarity to perform better than others of its species some advantageous action; and when it bequeaths more or less of its structural peculiarity to descendants, among whom those which have it most markedly are best able to thrive and propagate; there arises a visibly modified type of structure, having a more or less distinct function. In the correlative class of facts (by some asserted and by others denied), which come under the category of reactions of function on structure as exhibited in successions of organisms, are to be placed all those modifications of structure which arise in races, when changes of conditions entail changes in the balance of their functions—when altered function externally necessitated, produces altered structure, and continues doing this through successive generations.

§ 41. The fourth great division of Biology, comprehending the phenomena of Genesis, may be conveniently separated into three subdivisions.

Under the first, comes a description of all the special modes whereby the multiplication of organisms is carried on; which modes range themselves under the two chief heads of sexual and asexual. An account of Sexual Multiplication includes the various processes by which germs and ova are fertilized, and by which, after fertilization, they are furnished with the materials, and maintained in the conditions, needful for their development. An account of Asexual Multiplication includes the various processes by which, from the same fertilized germ or ovum, there are produced many organisms partially or totally independent of one another.

The second of these subdivisions deals with the phenomena of Genesis in the abstract. It takes for its subject-matter such general questions as—What is the end subserved by the union of sperm-cell and germ-cell? Why cannot all multiplication be carried on after the asexual method? What are the laws of hereditary transmission? What are the causes of variation?

The third subdivision is devoted to still more abstract aspects of the subject. Recognizing the general facts of multiplication, without reference to their modes or immediate causes, it concerns itself simply with the different rates of multiplication in different kinds of organisms and different individuals of the same kind. Generalizing the numerous contrasts and variations of fertility, it seeks a rationale of them in their relations to other organic phenomena.

§ 42. Such appears to be the natural arrangement of divisions and subdivisions which Biology presents. It is, however, a classification of the parts of the science when fully developed; rather than a classification of them as they now stand. Some of the subdivisions above named have no recognized existence, and some of the others are in quite rudimentary states. It is impossible now to fill in, even in the roughest way, more than a part of the outlines here sketched.

Our course of inquiry being thus in great measure determined by the present state of knowledge, we are compelled to follow an order widely different from this ideal one. It will be necessary first to give an account of those empirical generalizations which naturalists and physiologists have established: appending to those which admit of it, such deductive interpretations as *First Principles* furnishes us with. Having done this, we shall be the better prepared for dealing with the leading truths of Biology in connexion with the doctrine of Evolution.

PART II.
THE INDUCTIONS OF BIOLOGY.

CHAPTER I.

GROWTH.

§ 43. Perhaps the widest and most familiar induction of Biology, is that organisms grow. While, however, this is a characteristic so uniformly and markedly displayed by plants and animals, as to be carelessly thought peculiar to them, it is really not so. Under appropriate conditions, increase of size takes place in inorganic aggregates, as well as in organic aggregates. Crystals grow; and often far more rapidly than living bodies. Where the requisite materials are supplied in the requisite forms, growth may be witnessed in non-crystalline masses: instance the fungous-like accumulation of carbon that takes place on the wick of an unsnuffed candle. On an immensely larger scale, we have growth in geologic formations: the slow accumulation of deposited sediment into a stratum, is not distinguishable from growth in its widest acceptation. And if we go back to the genesis of celestial bodies, assuming them to have arisen by Evolution, these, too, must have gradually passed into their concrete shapes through processes of growth. Growth is, indeed, as being an integration of matter, the primary trait of Evolution; and if Evolution of one kind or other is universal, growth is universal—universal, that is, in the sense that all aggregates display it in some way at some period.

The essential community of nature between organic growth and inorganic growth, is, however, most clearly seen on observing that they both result in the same way. The segregation of different kinds of detritus from each other, as well as from the water carrying them, and their aggregation into distinct strata, is but an instance of a universal tendency towards the union of like units and the parting of unlike units (*First Principles*, § 163). The deposit of a crystal from a solution is a differentiation of the previously mixed molecules; and an integration of one class of molecules into a solid body, and the other class into a liquid solvent. Is not the growth of an organism an essentially similar process? Around a plant there exist certain elements like the elements which form its substance; and its increase of size is effected by continually integrating these surrounding like elements with itself. Nor does the animal fundamentally differ in this respect from the plant or the crystal. Its food is a portion of the environing matter that contains some compound atoms like some of the compound atoms constituting its tissues; and either through simple imbibition or through digestion, the animal eventually integrates with itself, units like those of which it is built up, and leaves behind the unlike units. To prevent misconception, it may be well to point out that growth, as here defined, must be distinguished from certain apparent and real augmentations of bulk which simulate it. Thus, the long, white potato-shoots thrown out in the dark, are produced at the expense of the substances which the tuber contains: they illustrate not the accumulation of organic matter, but simply its re-composition and re-arrangement. Certain animal-embryos, again, during their early stages, increase considerably in size without assimilating any solids from the environment; and they do this by absorbing the surrounding water. Even in the highest organisms, as in children, there appears sometimes to occur a rapid gain in dimensions which does not truly measure the added quantity of organic matter; but is in part due to changes analogous to those just named. Alterations of this kind must not be confounded with that growth, properly so called, of which we have here to treat.

The next general fact to be noted respecting organic growth, is, that it has limits. Here there appears to be a distinction between organic and inorganic growth; but this distinction is by no means definite. Though that aggregation of inanimate matter which simple attraction produces, may go on without end; yet there appears to be an end to that more definite kind of aggregation which results from polar attraction. Different elements and compounds habitually form crystals more or less unlike in their sizes; and each seems to have a size that is not usually exceeded without a tendency arising to form new crystals rather than to increase the old. On looking at the organic kingdom as a whole, we see that the limits between which growth ranges are very wide apart. At the one extreme we have monads so minute as to be rendered but imperfectly visible by microscopes of the highest power; and at the other extreme we have trees of 400 to 500 feet high and animals of 100 feet long. It is true that though in one sense this contrast may be legitimately drawn, yet in another sense it may not; since these largest organisms arise by the combination of units which are individually like the smallest. A single plant of the genus *Protococcus*, is of the same essential structure as one of the many cells united to form the thallus of some higher Alga, or the leaf of a phænogam. Each separate shoot of a phænogam is usually the bearer of many leaves. And a tree is an assemblage of numerous united shoots. One of these great teleophytes is thus an aggregate of aggregates of aggregates of units, which severally resemble protophytes in their sizes and structures; and a like building up is traceable throughout a considerable part of the animal kingdom. Even, however, when we bear in mind this qualification, and make our comparisons between organisms of the same degree of composition, we still find the limit of growth to have a great range. The smallest branched flowering plant is extremely insignificant by the side of a forest tree; and there is an enormous difference in bulk between the least and the greatest mammal. But on comparing members of the same species, we discover the limit of growth to be much less variable. Among the *Protozoa* and *Protophyta*, each kind has a tolerably constant adult size; and among the most complex organisms the differences between those of the same kind which have reached maturity, are usually not very great. The compound plants do, indeed, sometimes present marked contrasts between stunted and well-grown individuals; but the higher animals diverge but inconsiderably from the average standards of their species.

On surveying the facts with a view of empirically generalizing the causes of these differences, we are soon made aware that by variously combining and conflicting with one another, these causes produce great irregularities of result. It becomes manifest that no one of them can be traced to its consequences, unqualified by the rest. Hence the several statements contained in the following paragraphs must be taken as subject to mutual modification.

Let us consider first the connexion between degree of growth and complexity of structure. This connexion, being involved with many others, becomes apparent only on so averaging the comparisons as to eliminate differences among the rest. Nor does it hold at all where the conditions are radically dissimilar, as between plants and animals. But bearing in mind these qualifications, we shall see that organization has a determining influence on increase of mass. Of plants the lowest, classed as Thallophytes, usually attain no considerable size. Algæ, Fungi, and the Lichens formed by association of them count among their numbers but few bulky species: the largest, such as certain Algæ found in antarctic seas, not serving greatly to raise the average; and these gigantic seaweeds possess a considerable complexity of histological organization very markedly exceeding that of their smaller allies. Though among Bryophytes and Pteridophytes there are some, as the Tree-ferns, which attain a considerable height, the majority are but of humble growth. The Monocotyledons, including at one extreme small grasses and at the other tall palms, show us an average and a maximum greater than that reached by the Pteridophytes. And the Monocotyledons are exceeded by the Dicotyledons; among which are found the monarchs of the vegetal kingdom. Passing to animals, we meet the fact that the size attained by *Vertebrata* is usually much greater than the size attained by *Invertebrata*. Of invertebrate animals the smallest, classed as *Protozoa*, are also the simplest; and the largest, belonging to the *Annulosa* and *Mollusca*, are among the most complex of their respective types. Of vertebrate animals we see that the greatest are Mammals, and that though, in past epochs, there were Reptiles of vast bulks, their bulks did not equal that of the whale: the great Dinosaurs, though as long, being nothing like as massive. Between reptiles and birds, and between land-vertebrates and water-vertebrates, the relation does not hold: the conditions of existence being in these cases widely different. But among fishes as a class, and among reptiles as a class, it is observable that, speaking generally, the larger species are framed on the higher types. The critical reader, who has mentally checked these statements in passing them, has doubtless already seen that this relation is not a dependence of organization on growth but a dependence of growth on organization. The majority of Dicotyledons are smaller than some Monocotyledons; many Monocotyledons are exceeded in size by certain Pteridophytes; and even among Thallophytes, the least developed among compound plants, there are kinds of a size which many plants of the highest order do not reach. Similarly among animals. There are plenty of Crustaceans less than *Actiniæ*; numerous reptiles are smaller than some fish; the majority of mammals are inferior in bulk to the largest reptiles; and in the contrast between a mouse and a well-grown *Medusa*, we see a creature that is elevated in type of structure exceeded in mass by one that is extremely low. Clearly then, it cannot be held that high organization is habitually accompanied by great size. The proposition here illustrated is the converse one, that great size is habitually accompanied by high organization. The conspicuous facts that the largest species of both animals and vegetals belong to the highest classes, and that throughout their various sub-classes the higher usually contain the more bulky forms, show this connexion as clearly as we can expect it to be shown, amid so many modifying causes and conditions.

The relation between growth and supply of available nutriment, is too familiar a relation to need proving. There are, however, some aspects of it that must be contemplated before its implications can be fully appreciated. Among plants, which are all constantly in contact with the gaseous, liquid, and solid matters to be incorporated with their tissues, and which, in the same locality, receive not very unlike amounts of light and heat, differences in the supplies of available nutriment have but a subordinate connexion with differences of growth. Though in a cluster of herbs springing up from the seeds let fall by a parent, the greater sizes of some than of others is doubtless due to better nutrition, consequent on accidental advantages; yet no such interpretation can be given of the contrast in size between these herbs and an adjacent tree. Other conditions here come into play: one of the most important being, an absence in the one case, and presence in the other, of an ability to secrete such a quantity of ligneous fibre as will produce a stem capable of supporting a large growth. Among animals, however, which (excepting some *Entozoa*) differ from plants in this, that instead of bathing their surfaces the matters they subsist on are dispersed, and have to be obtained, the relation between available food and growth is shown with more regularity. The *Protozoa*, living on microscopic fragments of organic matter contained in the surrounding water, are unable, during their brief lives, to accumulate any considerable quantity of nutriment.

Polyzoa, having for food these scarcely visible members of the animal kingdom, are, though large compared with their prey, small as measured by other standards; even when aggregated into groups of many individuals, which severally catch food for the common weal, they are often so inconspicuous as readily to be passed over by the unobservant. And if from this point upwards we survey the successive grades of animals, it becomes manifest that, in proportion as the size is great, the masses of nutriment are either large, or, what is practically the same thing, are so abundant and so grouped that large quantities may be readily taken in. Though, for example, the greatest of mammals, the arctic whale, feeds on such comparatively small creatures as the acalephes and molluscs floating in the seas it inhabits, its method of gulping in whole shoals of them and filtering away the accompanying water, enables it to secure great quantities of food. We may then with safety say that, other things equal, the growth of an animal depends on the abundance and sizes of the masses of nutriment which its powers enable it to appropriate. Perhaps it may be needful to add that, in interpreting this statement, the proportion of competitors must be taken into account. Clearly, not the absolute, but the relative, abundance of fit food is the point; and this relative abundance very much depends on the number of individuals competing for the food. Thus all who have had experience in fishing in Highland lochs, know that where the trout are numerous they are small, and that where they are comparatively large they are comparatively few.

What is the relation between growth and expenditure of energy? is a question which next presents itself. Though there is reason to believe such a relation exists, it is not very readily traced: involved as it is with so many other relations. Some contrasts, however, may be pointed out that appear to give evidence of it. Passing over the vegetal kingdom, throughout which the expenditure of force is too small to allow of such a relation being visible, let us seek in the animal kingdom, some case where classes otherwise allied, are contrasted in their locomotive activities. Let us compare birds on the one hand, with reptiles and mammals on the other. It is an accepted doctrine that birds are organized on a type closely allied to the reptilian type, but superior to it; and though in some respects the organization of birds is inferior to that of mammals, yet in other respects, as in the greater heterogeneity and integration of the skeleton, the more complex development of the respiratory system, and the higher temperature of the blood, it may be held that birds stand above mammals. Hence were growth dependent only on organization, we might infer that the limit of growth among birds should not be much short of that among mammals; and that the bird-type should admit of a larger growth than the reptile-type. Again, we see no manifest disadvantages under which birds labour in obtaining food, but from which reptiles and mammals are free.

On the contrary, birds are able to get at food that is fixed beyond the reach of reptiles and mammals; and can catch food that is too swift of movement to be ordinarily caught by reptiles and mammals. Nevertheless, the limit of growth in birds falls far below that reached by reptiles and mammals. With what other contrast between these classes, is this contrast connected? May we not suspect that it is connected (partially though not wholly) with the contrast between their amounts of locomotive exertion? Whereas mammals (excepting bats, which are small), are during all their movements supported by solid surfaces or dense liquids; and whereas reptiles (excepting the ancient pterodactyles, which were not very large), are similarly restricted in their spheres of movement; the majority of birds move more or less habitually through a rare medium, in which they cannot support themselves without relatively great efforts. And this general fact may be joined with the special fact, that those members of the class *Aves*, as the *Dinornis* and *Epiornis*, which approached in size to the larger *Mammalia* and *Reptilia*, were creatures incapable of flight—creatures which did not expend this excess of force in locomotion. But as implied above, and as will presently be shown, another factor of importance comes into play; so that perhaps the safest evidence that there is an antagonism between the increase of bulk and the quantity of motion evolved is that supplied by the general experience, that human beings and domestic animals, when overworked while growing, are prevented from attaining the ordinary dimensions.

One other general truth concerning degrees of growth, must be set down. It is a rule, having exceptions of no great importance, that large organisms commence their separate existences as masses of organic matter more or less considerable in size, and commonly with organizations more or less advanced; and that throughout each organic sub-kingdom, there is a certain general, though irregular, relation between the initial and the final bulks. Vegetals exhibit this relation less manifestly than animals. Yet though, among the plants that begin life as minute spores, there are some which, by the aid of an intermediate form, grow to large sizes, the immense majority of them remain small. While, conversely, the great Monocotyledons and Dicotyledons, when thrown off from their parents, have already the formed organs of young plants, to which are attached stores of highly nutritive matter. That is to say, where the young plant consists merely of a centre of development, the ultimate growth is commonly insignificant; but where the growth is to become great, there exists to start with, a developed embryo and a stock of assimilable matter. Throughout the animal kingdom this relation is tolerably manifest though by no means uniform. Save among classes that escape the ordinary requirements of animal life, small germs or eggs do not in most cases give rise to bulky creatures. Where great bulk is to be reached, the young proceeds from an egg of considerable bulk, or is born of considerable bulk ready-organized and partially active. In the class

Fishes, or in such of them as are subject to similar conditions of life, some proportion usually obtains between the sizes of the ova and the sizes of the adult individuals; though in the cases of the sturgeon and the tunny there are exceptions, probably determined by the circumstances of oviposition and those of juvenile life. Reptiles have eggs that are smaller in number, and relatively greater in mass, than those of fishes; and throughout this class, too, there is a general congruity between the bulk of the egg and the bulk of the adult creature. As a group, birds show us further limitations in the numbers of their eggs as well as farther increase in their relative sizes; and from the minute eggs of the humming-bird up to the immense ones of the *Epiornis*, holding several quarts, we see that, speaking generally, the greater the eggs the greater the birds., Finally, among mammals (omitting the marsupials) the young are born, not only of comparatively large sizes, but with advanced organizations; and throughout this sub-division of the *Vertebrata*, as throughout the others, there is a manifest connexion between the sizes at birth and the sizes at maturity. As having a kindred meaning, there must finally be noted the fact that the young of these highest animals, besides starting in life with bodies of considerable sizes, almost fully organized, are, during subsequent periods of greater or less length, supplied with nutriment—in birds by feeding and in mammals by suckling and afterwards by feeding. So that beyond the mass and organization directly bequeathed, a bird or mammal obtains a further large mass at but little cost to itself.

Were exhaustive treatment of the topic intended, it would be needful to give a paragraph to each of the incidental circumstances by which growth may be aided or restricted:—such facts as that an entozoon is limited by the size of the creature, or even the organ, in which it thrives; that an epizoon, though getting abundant nutriment without appreciable exertion, is restricted to that small bulk at which it escapes ready detection by the animal it infests; that sometimes, as in the weazel, smallness is a condition to successful pursuit of the animals preyed upon; and that in some cases, the advantage of resembling certain other creatures, and so deceiving enemies or prey, becomes an indirect cause of restricted size. But the present purpose is simply to set down those most general relations between growth and other organic traits, which induction leads us to. Having done this, let us go on to inquire whether these general relations can be deductively established.

§ 44. That there must exist a certain dependence of growth on organization, may be shown *a priori*. When we consider the phenomena of Life, either by themselves or in their relations to surrounding phenomena, we see that, other things equal, the larger the aggregate the greater is the needful complexity of structure.

In plants, even of the highest type, there is a comparatively small mutual dependence of parts: a gathered flower-bud will unfold and flourish for days if its stem be immersed in water; and a shoot cut off from its parent-tree and stuck in the ground will grow. The respective parts having vital activities that are not widely unlike, it is possible for great bulk to be reached without that structural complexity required for combining the actions of parts. Even here, however, we see that for the attainment of great bulk there requires such a degree of organization as shall co-ordinate the functions of roots and branches—we see that such a size as is reached by trees, is not possible without a vascular system enabling the remote organs to utilize each other's products. And we see that such a co-existence of large growth with comparatively low organization as occurs in some of the marine *Algæ*, occurs where the conditions of existence do not necessitate any considerable mutual dependence of parts—where the near approach of the plant to its medium in specific gravity precludes the need of a well-developed stem, and where all the materials of growth being derived from the water by each portion of the thallus, there requires no apparatus for transferring the crude food materials from part to part. Among animals which, with but few exceptions, are, by the conditions of their existence, required to absorb nutriment through one specialized part of the body, it is clear that there must be a means whereby other parts of the body, to be supported by this nutriment, must have it conveyed to them. It is clear that for an equally efficient maintenance of their nutrition, the parts of a large mass must have a more elaborate propelling and conducting apparatus; and that in proportion as these parts undergo greater waste, a yet higher development of the vascular system is necessitated. Similarly with the prerequisites to those mechanical motions which animals are required to perform. The parts of a mass cannot be made to move, and have their movements so co-ordinated as to produce locomotive and other actions, without certain structural arrangements; and, other things equal, a given amount of such activity requires more involved structural arrangements in a large mass than in a small one. There must at least be a co-ordinating apparatus presenting greater contrasts in its central and peripheral parts.

The qualified dependence of growth on organization, is equally implied when we study it in connexion with that adjustment of inner to outer relations which constitutes Life as phenomenally known to us. In plants this is less striking than in animals, because the adjustment of inner to outer relations does not involve conspicuous motions. Still, it is visible in the fact that the condition on which alone a plant can grow to a great size, is, that it shall, by the development of a massive trunk, present inner relations of forces fitted to counterbalance those outer relations of forces which tend continually, and others which tend occasionally, to overthrow it; and this formation of a core of regularly-arranged woody fibres is an advance in organization. Throughout the animal kingdom this connexion of phenomena is manifest. To obtain materials for growth; to avoid injuries which interfere with growth; and to escape those enemies which bring growth to a sudden end; implies in the organism the means of fitting its movements to meet numerous external co-existences and sequences—implies such various structural arrangements as shall make possible these variously-adapted actions. It cannot be questioned that, everything else remaining constant, a more complex animal, capable of adjusting its conduct to a greater number of surrounding contingencies, will be the better able to secure food and evade damage, and so to increase bulk. And evidently, without any qualification, we may say that a large animal, living under such complex conditions of existence as everywhere obtain, is not possible without comparatively high organization.

While, then, this relation is traversed and obscured by sundry other relations, it cannot but exist. Deductively we see that it must be modified, as inductively we saw that it is modified, by the circumstances amid which each kind of organism is placed, but that it is always a factor in determining the result.

§ 45. That growth is, *cæteris paribus*, dependent on the supply of assimilable matter, is a proposition so continually illustrated by special experience, as well as so obvious from general experience, that it would scarcely need stating, were it not requisite to notice the qualifications with which it must be taken.

The materials which each organism requires for building itself up, are not of one kind but of several kinds. As a vehicle for transferring matter through their structures, all organisms require water as well as solid constituents; and however abundant the solid constituents there can be no growth in the absence of water. Among the solids supplied, there must be a proportion ranging within certain limits. A plant round which carbonic acid, water, and ammonia exist in the right quantities, may yet be arrested in its growth by a deficiency of potassium. The total absence of lime from its food may stop the formation of a mammal's skeleton: thus dwarfing, if not eventually destroying, the mammal; and this no matter what quantities of other needful colloids and crystalloids are furnished.

Again, the truth that, other things equal, growth varies according to the supply of nutriment, has to be qualified by the condition that the supply shall not exceed the ability to appropriate it. In the vegetal kingdom, the assimilating surface being external and admitting of rapid expansion by the formation of new roots, shoots, and leaves, the effect of this limitation is not conspicuous. By artificially supplying plants with those materials which they have usually the most difficulty in obtaining, we can greatly facilitate their growth; and so can produce striking differences of size in the same species. Even here, however, the effect is confined within the limits of the ability to appropriate; since in the absence of that solar light and heat by the help of which the chief appropriation is carried on, the additional materials for growth are useless. In the animal kingdom this restriction is rigorous. The absorbent surface being, in the great majority of cases, internal; having a comparatively small area, which cannot be greatly enlarged without reconstruction of the whole body; and being in connexion with a vascular system which also must be re-constructed before any considerable increase of nutriment can be made available; it is clear that beyond a certain point, very soon reached, increase of nutriment will not cause increase of growth. On the contrary, if the quantity of food taken in is greatly beyond the digestive and absorbent power, the excess, becoming an obstacle to the regular working of the organism, may retard growth rather than advance it.

While then it is certain, *a priori*, that there cannot be growth in the absence of such substances as those of which an organism consists; and while it is equally certain that the amount of growth must primarily be governed by the supply of these substances; it is not less certain that extra supply will not produce extra growth, beyond a point very soon reached. Deduction shows to be necessary, as induction makes familiar, the truths that the value of food for purposes of growth depends not on the quantity of the various organizable materials it contains, but on the quantity of the material most needed; that given a right proportion of materials, the pre-existing structure of the organism limits their availability; and that the higher the structure, the sooner is this limit reached.

§ 46. But why should the growth of every organism be finally arrested? Though the rate of increase may, in each case, be necessarily restricted within a narrow range of variation—though the increment that is possible in a given time, cannot exceed a certain amount; yet why should the increments decrease and finally become insensible? Why should not all organisms, when supplied with sufficient materials, continue to grow as long as they live? To find an answer to this question we must revert to the nature and functions of organic matter.

In the first three chapters of Part I, it was shown that plants and animals mainly consist of substances in states of unstable equilibrium—substances which have been raised to this unstable equilibrium by the expenditure of the forces we know as solar radiations, and which give out these forces in other forms on falling into states of stable equilibrium. Leaving out the water, which serves as a vehicle for these materials and a medium for their changes; and excluding those mineral matters that play either passive or subsidiary parts; organisms are built up of compounds which are stores of force. Thus complex colloids and crystalloids which, as united together, form organized bodies, are the same colloids and crystalloids which give out, on their decomposition, the forces expended by organized bodies. Thus these nitrogenous and carbonaceous substances, being at once the materials for organic growth and the sources of organic energy, it results that as much of them as is used up for the genesis of energy is taken away from the means of growth, and as much as is economized by diminishing the genesis of energy, is available for growth. Given that limited quantity of nutritive matter which the pre-existing structure of an organism enables it to absorb; and it is a necessary corollary from the persistence of force, that the matter accumulated as growth cannot exceed that surplus which remains undecomposed after the production of the required amounts of sensible and insensible motion. This, which would be rigorously true under all conditions if exactly the same substances were used in exactly the same proportions for the production of force and for the formation of tissue, requires, however, to be taken with the qualification that some of the force-evolving substances are not constituents of tissue; and that thus there may be a genesis of force which is not at the expense of potential growth. But since organisms (or at least animal organisms, with which we are here chiefly concerned) have a certain power of selective absorption, which, partially in an individual and more completely in a race, adapts the proportions of the substances absorbed to the needs of the system; then if a certain habitual expenditure of force leads to a certain habitual absorption of force-evolving matters that are not available for growth; and if, were there less need for such matters, the ability to absorb matters available for growth would be increased to an equivalent extent; it follows that the antagonism described does, in the long run, hold even without this qualification. Hence, growth is substantially equivalent to the absorbed nutriment, minus the nutriment used up in action.

This, however, is no answer to the question—why has individual growth a limit?—why do the increments of growth bear decreasing ratios to the mass and finally come to an end? The question is involved. There are more causes than one why the excess of absorbed nutriment over expended nutriment must, other things equal, become less as the size of the animal becomes greater. In similarly-shaped bodies the masses, and therefore the weights, vary as the cubes of the dimensions; whereas the powers of bearing the stresses imposed by the weights vary as the squares of the dimensions. Suppose a creature which a year ago was one foot high, has now become two feet high, while it is unchanged in proportions and structure; what are the necessary concomitant changes? It is eight times as heavy; that is to say, it has to resist eight times the strain which gravitation puts upon certain of its parts; and when there occurs sudden arrest of motion or sudden genesis of motion, eight times the strain is put upon the muscles employed. Meanwhile the muscles and bones have severally increased their abilities to bear strains in proportion to the areas of their transverse sections, and hence have severally only four times the tenacity they had. This relative decrease in the power of bearing stress does not imply a relative decrease in the power of generating energy and moving the body; for in the case supposed the muscles have not only increased four times in their transverse sections but have become twice as long, and will therefore generate an amount of energy proportionate to their bulk. The implication is simply that each muscle has only half the power to withstand those shocks and strains which the creature's movements entail; and that consequently the creature must be either less able to bear these, or must have muscles and bones having relatively greater transverse dimensions: the result being that greater cost of nutrition is inevitably caused and therefore a correlative tendency to limit growth. This necessity will be seen still more clearly if we leave out the motor apparatus, and consider only the forces required and the means of supplying them. For since, in similar bodies, the areas vary as the squares of the dimensions, and the masses vary as the cubes; it follows that the absorbing surface has become four times as great, while the weight to be moved by the matter absorbed has become eight times as great. If then, a year ago, the absorbing surface could take up twice as much nutriment as was needed for expenditure, thus leaving one-half for growth, it is now able only just to meet expenditure, and can provide nothing for growth. However great the excess of assimilation over waste may be during the early life of an active organism, we see that because a series of numbers increasing as the cubes, overtakes a series increasing as the squares, even though starting from a much smaller number, there must be reached, if the organism lives long enough, a point at which the surplus assimilation is brought down to nothing—a point at which expenditure balances nutrition—a state of moving equilibrium. The only way in which the difficulty can be met is by gradual re-organization of the alimentary system; and, in the first place, this entails direct cost upon the organism, and, in the second place, indirect cost from the carrying of greater weight: both tending towards limitation. There are two other varying relations between degrees of growth and amounts of expended force; one of which conspires with the last, while the other conflicts with it. Consider, in the first place, the cost at which nutriment is distributed through the body and effete matters removed from it. Each increment of growth being added at the periphery of the organism, the force expended in the transfer of matter must increase in a rapid progression—a progression more rapid than that of the mass. But as the dynamic expense of distribution is small compared with the dynamic value of the materials distributed, this item in the calculation is unimportant. Now consider, in the second place, the changing proportion between production and loss of heat. In similar organisms the quantities of heat generated by similar actions going on throughout their substance, must increase as the masses, or as the cubes of the dimensions. Meanwhile, the surfaces from which loss of heat takes place, increase only as the squares of the dimensions. Though the loss of heat does not therefore increase only as the squares of the dimensions, it certainly increases at a smaller rate than the cubes. And to the extent that augmentation of mass results in a greater retention of heat, it effects an economization of force. This advantage is not, however, so important as at first appears. Organic heat is a concomitant of organic action, and is so abundantly produced during action that the loss of it is then usually of no consequence: indeed the loss is often not rapid enough to keep the supply from rising to an inconvenient excess. It is chiefly in respect of that maintenance of heat which is needful during quiescence, that large organisms have an advantage over small ones in this relatively diminished loss. Thus these two subsidiary relations between degrees of growth and amounts of expended force, being in antagonism, we may conclude that their differential result does not greatly modify the result of the chief relation.

Comparisons of these deductions with the facts appear in some cases to verify them and in other cases not to do so. Throughout the vegetal kingdom, there are no distinct limits to growth except those which death entails. Passing over a large proportion of plants which never exceed a comparatively small size, because they wholly or partially die down at the end of the year, and looking only at trees that annually send forth new shoots, even when their trunks are hollowed by decay; we may ask—How does growth happen here to be unlimited? The answer is, that plants are only accumulators: they are in no very appreciable degree expenders. As they do not undergo waste there is no reason why their growth should be arrested by the equilibration of assimilation and waste. Again, among animals there are sufficient reasons why the correspondence cannot be more than approximate. Besides the fact above noted, that there are other varying relations which complicate the chief one. We must bear in mind that the bodies compared are not truly similar: the proportions of trunk to limbs and trunk to head, vary considerably. The comparison is still more seriously vitiated by the inconstant ratio between the constituents of which the body is composed. In the flesh of adult mammalia, water forms from 68 to 71 per cent., organic substance from 24 to 28 per cent., and inorganic substance from 3 to 5 per cent.; whereas in the fœtal state, the water amounts to 87 per cent., and the solid organic constituents to only 11 per cent. Clearly this change from a state in which the force-evolving matter forms one-tenth of the whole, to a state in which it forms two and a half tenths, must greatly interfere with the parallelism between the actual and the theoretical progression. Yet another difficulty may come under notice.

The crocodile is said to grow as long as it lives; and there appears reason to think that some predaceous fishes, such as the pike, do the same. That these animals of comparatively high organization have no definite limits of growth, is, however, an exceptional fact due to the exceptional non-fulfilment of those conditions which entail limitation. What kind of life does a crocodile lead? It is a cold-blooded, or almost cold-blooded, creature; that is, it expends very little for the maintenance of heat. It is habitually inert: not usually chasing prey but lying in wait for it; and undergoes considerable exertion only during its occasional brief contests with prey. Such other exertion as is, at intervals, needful for moving from place to place, is rendered small by the small difference between the animal's specific gravity and that of water. Thus the crocodile expends in muscular action an amount of force that is insignificant compared with the force commonly expended by land-animals. Hence its habitual assimilation is diminished much less than usual by habitual waste; and beginning with an excessive disproportion between the two, it is quite possible for the one never quite to lose its advance over the other while life continues. On looking closer into such cases as this and that of the pike, which is similarly cold-blooded, similarly lies in wait, and is similarly able to obtain larger and larger kinds of prey as it increases in size; we discover a further reason for this absence of a definite limit. To overcome gravitative force the creature has not to expend a muscular power that is large at the outset, and increases as the cubes of its dimensions: its dense medium supports it. The exceptional continuance of growth observed in creatures so circumstanced, is therefore perfectly explicable.

§ 46*a.* If we go back upon the conclusions set forth in the preceding section, we find that from some of them may be drawn instructive corollaries respecting the limiting sizes of creatures inhabiting different media. More especially I refer to those varying proportions between mass and stress from which, as we have seen, there results, along with increasing size, a diminishing power of mechanical self-support: a relation illustrated in its simplest form by the contrast between a dew-drop, which can retain its spheroidal form, and the spread-out mass of water which results when many dew-drops run together. The largest bird that flies (the argument excludes birds which do not fly) is the Condor, which reaches a weight of from 30 to 40 lbs. Why does there not exist a bird of the size of an elephant? Supposing its habits to be carnivorous, it would have many advantages in obtaining prey: mammals would be at its mercy. Evidently the reason is one which has been pointed out—the reason that while the weight to be raised and kept in the air by a bird increases as the cubes of its dimensions, the ability of its bones and muscles to resist the strains which flight necessitates, increases only as the squares of the dimensions. Though, could the muscles withstand any tensile strain they were subject to, the power like the weight might increase with the cubes, yet since the texture of muscle is such that beyond a certain strain it tears, it results that there is soon reached a size at which flight becomes impossible: the structures must give way. In a preceding paragraph the limit to the size of flying creatures was ascribed to the greater physiological cost of the energy required; but it seems probable that the mechanical obstacle here pointed out has a larger share in determining the limit.

In a kindred manner there results a limitation of growth in a land-animal, which does not exist for an animal living in the water. If, after comparing the agile movements of a dog with those of a cow, the great weight of which obviously prevents agility; or if, after observing the swaying flesh of an elephant as it walks along, we consider what would happen could there be formed a land-animal equal in mass to the whale (the long Dinosaurs were not proportionately massive) it needs no argument to show that such a creature could not stand, much less move about. But in the water the strain put upon its structures by the weights of its various parts is almost if not quite taken away. Probably limitation in the quantity of food obtainable becomes now the chief, if not the sole, restraint.

And here we may note, before leaving the topic, something like a converse influence which comes into play among creatures inhabiting the water. Up to the point at which muscles tear from over-strain, larger and smaller creatures otherwise alike, remain upon a par in respect of the relative amounts of energy they can evolve. Had they to encounter no resistance from their medium, the implication would be that neither would have an advantage over the other in respect of speed. But resistance of the medium comes into play; and this, other things equal, gives to the larger creature an advantage. It has been found, experimentally, that the forces to be overcome by vessels moving through the water, built as they are with immersed hinder parts which taper as fish taper, are mainly due to what is called "skin-friction." Now in two fish unlike in size but otherwise similar skin-friction bears to the energy that can be generated, a smaller proportion in the larger than in the smaller; and the larger can therefore acquire a greater velocity. Hence the reason why large fish, such as the shark, become possible. In a habitat where there is no ambush (save in exceptional cases like that of the *Lophius* or Angler) everything depends on speed; and if, other things equal, a larger fish had no mechanical advantage over a smaller, a larger fish could not exist—could not catch the requisite amount of prey.

§ 47. Obviously this antagonism between accumulation and expenditure, must be a leading cause of the contrasts in size between allied organisms that are in many respects similarly conditioned. The life followed by each kind of animal is one involving a certain average amount of exertion for the obtainment of a given amount of nutriment—an exertion, part of which goes to the gathering or catching of food, part to the tearing and mastication of it, and part to the after-processes requisite for separating the nutritive molecules—an exertion which therefore varies according as the food is abundant or scarce, fixed or moving, according as it is mechanically easy or difficult to deal with when secured, and according as it is, or is not, readily soluble. Hence, while among animals of the same species having the same mode of life, there will be a tolerably constant ratio between accumulation and expenditure, and therefore a tolerably constant limit of growth, there is every reason to expect that different species, following different modes of life, will have unlike ratios between accumulation and expenditure, and therefore unlike limits of growth.

Though the facts as inductively established, show a general harmony with this deduction, we cannot usually trace it in any specific way; since the conflicting and conspiring factors which affect growth are so numerous.

§ 48. One of the chief causes, if not the chief cause, of the differences between the sizes of organisms, has yet to be considered. We are introduced to it by pushing the above inquiry a little further. Small animals have been shown to possess an advantage over large ones in the greater ratio which, other things equal, assimilation bears to expenditure; and we have seen that hence small animals in becoming large ones, gradually lose that surplus of assimilative power which they had, and eventually cannot assimilate more than is required to balance waste. But how come these animals while young and small to have surplus assimilative powers? Have all animals equal surpluses of assimilative powers? And if not, how far do differences between the surpluses determine differences between the limits of growth? We shall find, in the answers to these questions, the interpretation of many marked contrasts in growth that are not due to any of the causes above assigned. For example, an ox immensely exceeds a sheep in mass. Yet the two live from generation to generation in the same fields, eat the same grass, obtain these aliments with the same small expenditure of energy, and differ scarcely at all in their degrees of organization. Whence arises, then, their striking unlikeness of bulk?

We noted when studying the phenomena of growth inductively, that organisms of the larger and higher types commence their separate existences as masses of organic matter having tolerable magnitudes. Speaking generally, we saw that throughout each organic sub-kingdom the acquirement of great bulk occurs only where the incipient bulk and organization are considerable; and that they are the more considerable in proportion to the complexity of the life which the organism is to lead.

The deductive interpretation of this induction may best be commenced by an analogy. A street orange-vendor makes but a trifling profit on each transaction; and unless more than ordinarily fortunate, he is unable to realize during the day a larger amount than will meet his wants; leaving him to start on the morrow in the same condition as before. The trade of the huxter in ounces of tea and half-pounds of sugar, is one similarly entailing much labour for small returns. Beginning with a capital of a few pounds, he cannot have a shop large enough, or goods sufficiently abundant and various, to permit an extensive business. He must be content with the half-pence and pence which he makes by little sales to poor people; and if, avoiding bad debts, he is able by strict economy to accumulate anything, it can be but a trifle. A large retail trader is obliged to lay out much money in fitting up an adequate establishment; he must invest a still greater sum in stock; and he must have a further floating capital to meet the charges that fall due before his returns come in. Setting out, however, with means enough for these purposes, he is able to make many and large sales; and so to get greater and more numerous increments of profit. Similarly, to get returns in thousands merchants and manufacturers must make their investments in tens of thousands. In brief, the rate at which a man's wealth accumulates is measured by the surplus of income over expenditure; and this, save in exceptionably favourable cases, is determined by the capital with which he begins business. Now applying the analogy, we may trace in the transactions of an organism, the same three ultimate elements. There is the expenditure required for the obtainment and digestion of food; there is the gross return in the shape of nutriment assimilated or fit for assimilation; and there is the difference between this gross return of nutriment and the nutriment that was used up in the labour of securing it—a difference which may be a profit or a loss. Clearly, however, a surplus implies that the force expended is less than the force latent in the assimilated food. Clearly, too, the increment of growth is limited to the amount of this surplus of income over expenditure; so that large growth implies both that the excess of nutrition over waste shall be relatively considerable, and that the waste and nutrition shall be on extensive scales. And clearly, the ability of an organism to expend largely and assimilate largely, so as to make a large surplus, presupposes a large physiological capital in the shape of organic matter more or less developed in its structural arrangements.

Throughout the vegetal kingdom, the illustrations of this truth are not conspicuous and regular: the obvious reason being that since plants are accumulators and in so small a degree expenders, the premises of the above argument are but very partially fulfilled. The food of plants (excepting Fungi and certain parasites) being in great measure the same for all, and bathing all so that it can be absorbed without effort, their vital processes result almost entirely in profit. Once fairly rooted in a fit place, a plant may thus from the outset add a very large proportion of its entire returns to capital; and may soon be able to carry on its processes on a large scale, though it does not at first do so. When, however, plants are expenders, namely, during their germination and first stages of growth, their degrees of growth *are* determined by their amounts of vital capital. It is because the young tree commences life with a ready-formed embryo and store of food sufficient to last for some time, that it is enabled to strike root and lift its head above the surrounding herbage. Throughout the animal kingdom, however, the necessity of this relation is everywhere obvious. The small carnivore preying on small herbivores, can increase in size only by small increments: its organization unfitting it to digest larger creatures, even if it can kill them, it cannot profit by amounts of nutriment exceeding a narrow limit; and its possible increments of growth being small to set out with, and rapidly decreasing, must come to an end before any considerable size is attained. Manifestly the young lion, born of tolerable bulk, suckled until much bigger, and fed until half-grown, is enabled by the power and organization which he thus gets *gratis*, to catch and kill animals big enough to give him the supply of nutriment needed to meet his large expenditure and yet leave a large surplus for growth. Thus, then, is explained the above-named contrast between the ox and the sheep. A calf and a lamb commence their physiological transactions on widely different scales; their first increments of growth are similarly contrasted in their amounts; and the two diminishing series of such increments end at similarly-contrasted limits.

§ 49. Such are the several conditions by which the phenomena of growth are determined. Conspiring and conflicting in endless unlike ways and degrees, they in every case qualify more or less differently each other's effects. Hence it happens that we are obliged to state each generalization as true on the average, or to make the proviso—other things equal.

Understood in this qualified form, our conclusions are these. First, that growth being an integration with the organism of such environing matters as are of like natures with the matters composing the organism, its growth is dependent on the available supply of them. Second, that the available supply of assimilable matter being the same, and other conditions not dissimilar, the degree of growth varies according to the surplus of nutrition over expenditure—a generalization which is illustrated in some of the broader contrasts between different divisions of organisms. Third, that in the same organism the surplus of nutrition over expenditure differs at different stages; and that growth is unlimited or has a definite limit, according as the surplus does or does not rapidly decrease. This proposition we found exemplified by the almost unceasing growth of organisms that expend relatively little energy; and by the definitely limited growth of organisms that expend much energy. Fourth, that among organisms which are large expenders of force, the size ultimately attained is, other things equal, determined by the initial size: in proof of which conclusion we have abundant facts, as well as the *a priori* necessity that the sum-totals of analogous diminishing series, must depend upon the amounts of their initial terms. Fifth, that where the likeness of other circumstances permits a comparison, the possible extent of growth depends on the degree of organization; an inference testified to by the larger forms among the various divisions and sub-divisions of organisms.

CHAPTER II.

DEVELOPMENT.[19]

§ 50. Certain general aspects of Development may be studied apart from any examination of internal structures. These fundamental contrasts between the modes of arrangement of parts, originating, as they do, the leading external distinctions among the various forms of organization, will be best dealt with at the outset. If all organisms have arisen by Evolution, it is of course not to be expected that such several modes of development can be absolutely demarcated: we are sure to find them united by transitional modes. But premising that a classification of modes can but approximately represent the facts, we shall find our general conceptions of Development aided by one.

Development is primarily *central.* All organic forms of which the entire history is known, set out with a symmetrical arrangement of parts round a centre. In organisms of the lowest grade no other mode of arrangement is ever definitely established; and in the highest organisms central development, though subordinate to another mode of development, continues to be habitually shown in the changes of minute structure. Let us glance at these propositions in the concrete. Practically every plant and every animal in its earliest stage is a portion of protoplasm, in the great majority of cases approximately spherical but sometimes elongated, containing a rounded body consisting of specially modified protoplasm, which is called a nucleus; and the first changes that occur in the germ thus constituted, are changes that take place in this nucleus, followed by changes round the centres produced by division of this original centre. From this type of structure, the simplest organisms do not depart; or depart in no definite or conspicuous ways. Among plants, many of the simplest *Algæ* and *Fungi* permanently maintain such a central distribution; while among animals it is permanently maintained by creatures like the *Gregarina*, and in a different manner by the *Amœba*, *Actinophrys*, and their allies: the irregularities which are many and great do not destroy this general relation of parts. In larger organisms, made up chiefly of units that are analogous to these simplest organisms, the formation of units ever continues to take place round nuclei; though usually the nuclei soon cease to be centrally placed.

Central development may be distinguished into *unicentral* and *multicentral*; according as the product of the original germ develops more or less symmetrically round one centre, or develops without subordination to one centre—develops, that is, in subordination to many centres. Unicentral development, as displayed not in the formation of single cells but in the formation of aggregates, is not common. The animal kingdom shows it only in some of the small group of colonial *Radiolaria.* It is feebly represented in the vegetal kingdom by a few members of the *Volvocineæ.* On the other hand, multicentral development, or development round insubordinate centres, is variously exemplified in both divisions of the organic world. It is exemplified in two distinct ways, according as the insubordination among the centres of development is partial or total. We may most conveniently consider it under the heads hence arising.

Total insubordination among the centres of development, is shown where the units or cells, as fast as they are severally formed, part company and lead independent lives. This, in the vegetal kingdom, habitually occurs among the *Protophyta,* and in the animal kingdom, among the *Protozoa.* Partial insubordination is seen in those somewhat advanced organisms, that consist of units which, though they have not separated, have so little mutual dependence that the aggregate they form is irregular. Among plants, the Thallophytes very generally exemplify this mode of development. Lichens, spreading with flat or corrugated edges in this or that direction as the conditions determine, have no manifest co-ordination of parts. In the *Algæ* the Nostocs and various other forms similarly show us an unsymmetrical structure. Of *Fungi* we may say that creeping kinds display no further dependence of one part on another than is implied by their cohesion. And even in such better-organized plants as the *Marchantia,* the general arrangement shows no reference to a directive centre. Among animals many of the Sponges in their adult forms may be cited as devoid of that co-ordination implied by symmetry: the units composing them, though they have some subordination to local centres, have no subordination to a general centre. To distinguish that kind of development in which the whole product of a germ coheres in one mass, from that kind of development in which it does not, Professor Huxley has introduced the words "*continuous*" and "*discontinuous*;" and these seem the best fitted for the purpose. Multicentral development, then, is divisible into continuous and discontinuous.

From central development we pass insensibly to that higher kind of development for which *axial* seems the most appropriate name. A tendency towards this is vaguely manifested almost everywhere. The great majority even of *Protophyta* and *Protozoa* have different longitudinal and transverse dimensions—have an obscure if not a distinct axial structure. The originally spheroidal and polyhedral units out of which higher organisms are mainly built, usually pass into shapes that are subordinated to lines rather than to points. And in the higher organisms, considered as wholes, an arrangement of parts in relation to an axis is distinct and nearly universal. We see it in the superior orders of Thallophytes; and in all the cormophytic plants. With few exceptions the *Cœlenterata* clearly exhibit it; it is traceable, though less conspicuously, throughout the *Mollusca*; and the *Annelida*, *Arthropoda*, and *Vertebrata* uniformly show it with perfect definiteness.

This kind of development, like the first kind, is of two orders. The whole germ-product may arrange itself round a single axis, or it may arrange itself round many axes: the structure may be *uniaxial* or *multiaxial*. Each division of the organic kingdom furnishes examples of both these orders. In such *Fungi* as exhibit axial development at all, we commonly see development round a single axis. Some of the *Algæ*, as the common tangle, show us this arrangement. And of the higher plants, many Monocotyledons and small Dicotyledons are uniaxial. Of animals, the advanced are without exception in this category. There is no known vertebrate in which the whole of the germ-product is not subordinated to a single axis. In the *Arthropoda*, the like is universal; as it is also in the superior orders of *Mollusca*. Multiaxial development occurs in most of the plants we are familiar with—every branch of a shrub or tree being an independent axis. But while in the vegetal kingdom multiaxial development prevails among the highest types, in the animal kingdom it prevails only among the lowest types. It is extremely general, if not universal, among the *Cœlenterata*; it is characteristic of the *Polyzoa*; the compound Ascidians exhibit it; and it is seen, though under another form, in certain of the inferior Annelids.

Development that is axial, like development that is central, may be either continuous or discontinuous: the parts having different axes may continue united, or they may separate. Instances of each alternative are supplied by both plants and animals. Continuous multiaxial development is that which plants usually display, and need not be illustrated further than by reference to every garden. As cases of it in animals may be named all the compound *Hydrozoa* and *Actinozoa*; and such ascidian forms as the *Botryllidæ*. Of multiaxial development that is discontinuous, a familiar instance among plants exists in the common strawberry. This sends out over the neighbouring surface, long slender shoots, bearing at their extremities buds that presently strike roots and become new individuals; and these by and by lose their connexions with the original axis. Other plants there are that produce certain specialized buds called bulbils, which separating themselves and falling to the ground, grow into independent plants. Among animals the fresh-water polype very clearly shows this mode of development: the young polypes, budding out from its surface, severally arrange their parts around distinct axes, and eventually detaching themselves, lead separate lives, and produce other polypes after the same fashion. By some of the lower *Annelida*, this multiplication of axes from an original axis, is carried on after a different manner: the string of segments spontaneously divides;

and after further growth, division recurs in one or both of the halves. Moreover in the *Syllis ramosa*, there occurs lateral branching also.

Grouping together its several modes as above delineated, we see that

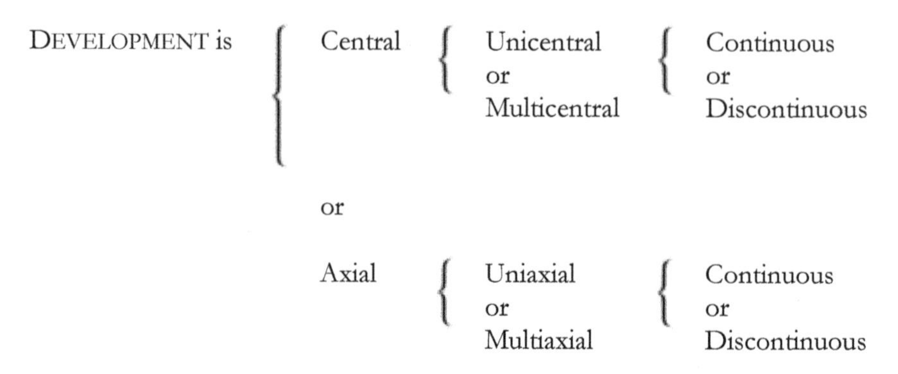

Any one well acquainted with the facts, may readily raise objections to this arrangement. He may name forms which do not obviously come under any of these heads. He may point to plants that are for a time multicentral but afterwards develop axially. And from lower types of animals he may choose many in which the continuous and discontinuous modes are both displayed. But, as already hinted, an arrangement free from such anomalies must be impossible, if the various kinds of organization have arisen by Evolution. The one above sketched out is to be regarded as a rough grouping of the facts, which helps us to a conception of them in their totality; and, so regarded, it will be of service when we come to treat of Individuality and Reproduction.

§ 51. From these most general external aspects of organic development, let us now turn to its internal and more special aspects. When treating of Evolution as a universal process of things, a rude outline of the course of structural changes in organisms was given (*First Principles*, §§ 110, 119, 132). Here it will be proper to describe these changes more fully.

The bud of any common flowering plant in its earliest stage, consists of a small hemispherical or sub-conical projection. While it increases most rapidly at the apex, this presently develops on one side of its base, a smaller projection of like general shape with itself. Here is the rudiment of a leaf, which presently spreads more or less round the base of the central hemisphere or main axis. At the same time that the central hemisphere rises higher, this lateral prominence, also increasing, gives rise to subordinate prominences or lobes. These are the rudiments of stipules, where the leaves are stipulated. Meanwhile, towards the other side of the main axis and somewhat higher up, another lateral prominence arising marks the origin of a second leaf. By the time that the first leaf has produced another pair of lobes, and the second leaf has produced its primary pair, the central hemisphere, still increasing at its apex, exhibits the rudiment of a third leaf. Similarly throughout. While the germ of each succeeding leaf thus arises, the germs of the previous leaves, in the order of their priority, are changing their rude nodulated shapes into flattened-out expansions; which slowly put on those sharp outlines they show when unfolded. Thus from that extremely indefinite figure, a rounded lump, giving off from time to time lateral lumps, which severally becoming symmetrically lobed gradually assume specific and involved forms, we pass little by little to that comparatively complex thing—a leaf-bearing shoot. Internally, a bud undergoes analogous changes; as witness this account:—"The general mass of thin-walled parenchymatous cells which occupies the apical region, and forms the *growing point* of the shoot, is covered by a single external layer of similar cells, which increase in number by the formation of new walls in one direction only, perpendicular to the surface of the shoot, and thus give rise only to the *epidermis* or single layer of cells covering the whole surface of the shoot. Meanwhile the general mass below grows as a whole, its constituent cells dividing in all directions. Of the new cells so formed, those removed by these processes of growth and division from the actual apex, begin, at a greater or less distance from it, to show signs of the differentiation which will ultimately lead to the formation of the various tissues enclosed by the epidermis of the shoot. First the pith, then the vascular bundles, and then the cortex of the shoot, begin to take on their special characters." Similarly with secondary structures, as the lateral buds whence leaves arise. In the, at first, unorganized mass of cells constituting the rudimentary leaf, there are formed vascular bundles which eventually become the veins of the leaf; and *pari passu* with these are formed the other tissues of the leaf. Nor do we fail to find an essentially parallel set of changes, when we trace the histories of the individual cells. While the tissues they compose are separating, the cells are growing step by step more unlike. Some become flat, some polyhedral, some cylindrical, some prismatic, some spindle-shaped. These develop spiral thickenings in their interiors; and those, reticulate thickenings. Here a number of cells unite together to form a tube: and there they become almost solid by the internal deposition of woody or other substance. Through such changes, too numerous and involved to be here detailed, the originally uniform cells go on diverging and rediverging until there are produced various forms that seem to have very little in common.

The arm of a man makes its first appearance in as simple a way as does the shoot of a plant. According to Bischoff, it buds-out from the side of the embryo as a little tongue-shaped projection, presenting no differences of parts; and it might serve for the rudiment of some one of the various other organs that also arise as buds. Continuing to lengthen, it presently becomes somewhat enlarged at its end; and is then described as a pedicle bearing a flattened, round-edged lump. This lump is the representative of the future hand, and the pedicle of the future arm. By and by, at the edges of this flattened lump, there appear four clefts, dividing from each other the buds of the future fingers; and the hand as a whole grows a little more distinguishable from the arm. Up to this time the pedicle has remained one continuous piece, but it now begins to show a bend at its centre, which indicates the division into arm and forearm. The distinctions thus rudely indicated gradually increase: the fingers elongate and become jointed, and the proportions of all the parts, originally very unlike those of the complete limb, slowly approximate to them. During its bud-like stage, the rudimentary arm consists only of partially-differentiated tissues. By the diverse changes these gradually undergo they are transformed into bones, muscles, blood-vessels, and nerves. The extreme softness and delicacy of these primary tissues, renders it difficult to trace the initial stages of the differentiations. In consequence of the colour of their contents, the blood-vessels are the first parts to become distinct. Afterwards the cartilaginous parts, which are the bases of the future bones, become marked out by the denser aggregation of their constituent cells, and by the production between these of a hyaline substance which unites them into a translucent mass. When first perceptible, the muscles are gelatinous, pale, yellowish, transparent, and indistinguishable from their tendons. The various other tissues of which the arm consists, beginning with very faintly-marked differences, become day by day more definite in their qualitative appearances. In like manner the units composing these tissues severally assume increasingly-specific characters. The fibres of muscle, at first made visible in the midst of their gelatinous matrix only by immersion in alcohol, grow more numerous and distinct; and by and by they begin to exhibit transverse stripes. The bone-cells put on by degrees their curious structure of branching canals. And so in their respective ways with the units of skin and the rest.

Thus in each of the organic sub-kingdoms, we see this change from an incoherent, indefinite homogeneity to a coherent, definite heterogeneity, illustrated in a quadruple way. The originally-like units called cells, become unlike in various ways, and in ways more numerous and marked as the development goes on. The several tissues which these several classes of cells form by aggregation, grow little by little distinct from each other; and little by little put on those structural complexities that arise from differentiations among their component units. In the shoot, as in the limb, the external form, originally very simple, and having much in common with simple forms in general, gradually acquires an increasing complexity, and an increasing unlikeness to other forms. Meanwhile, the remaining parts of the organism to which the shoot or limb belongs, having been severally assuming structures divergent from one another and from that of this particular shoot or limb, there has arisen a greater heterogeneity in the organism as a whole.

§ 52. One of the most remarkable inductions of embryology comes next in order. And here we find illustrated the general truth that in mental evolution as in bodily evolution the progress is from the indefinite and inexact to the definite and exact. For the first statement of this induction was but an adumbration of the correct statement.

As a result of his examinations von Baer alleged that in its earliest stage every organism has the greatest number of characters in common with all other organisms in their earliest stages; that at a stage somewhat later its structure is like the structures displayed at corresponding phases by a less extensive assemblage of organisms; that at each subsequent stage traits are acquired which successively distinguish the developing embryo from groups of embryos that it previously resembled—thus step by step diminishing the group of embryos which it still resembles; and that thus the class of similar forms is finally narrowed to the species of which it is a member. This abstract proposition will perhaps not be fully comprehended by the general reader. It will be best to re-state it in a concrete shape. Supposing the germs of all kinds of organisms to be simultaneously developing, we may say that all members of the vast multitude take their first steps in the same direction; that at the second step one-half of this vast multitude diverges from the other half, and thereafter follows a different course of development; that the immense assemblage contained in either of these divisions very soon again shows a tendency to take two or more routes of development; that each of the two or more minor assemblages thus resulting, shows for a time but small divergences among its members, but presently again divides into groups which separate ever more widely as they progress; and so on until each organism, when nearly complete, is accompanied in its further modifications only by organisms of the same species; and last of all, assumes the peculiarities which distinguish it as an individual—diverges to a slight extent to the organisms it is most like.

But, as above said, this statement is only an adumbration. The order of Nature is habitually more complex than our generalizations represent it as being—refuses to be fully expressed in simple formulæ; and we are obliged to limit them by various qualifications. It is thus here. Since von Baer's day the careful observations of numerous observers have shown his allegation to be but approximately true. Hereafter, when discussing the embryological evidence of Evolution, the causes of deviations will be discussed. For the present it suffices to recognize as unquestionable the fact that whereas the germs of organisms are extremely similar, they gradually diverge widely, in modes now regular and now irregular, until in place of a multitude of forms practically alike we finally have a multitude of forms most of which are extremely unlike. Thus, in conformity with the law of evolution, not only do the parts of each organism advance from indefinite homogeneity to definite heterogeneity, but the assemblage of all organisms does the same: a truth already indicated in *First Principles*.

§ 53. This comparison between the course of development, in any creature, and the course of development in all other creatures—this arrival at the conclusion that the course of development in each, at first the same as in all others, becomes stage by stage differentiated from the courses in all others, brings us within view of an allied conclusion. If we contemplate the successive stages passed through by any higher organism, and observe the relation between it and its environment at each of these stages; we shall see that this relation is modified in a way analogous to that in which the relation between the organism and its environment is modified, as we advance from the lowest to the highest grades. Along with the progressing differentiation of each organism from others, we find a progressing differentiation of it from its environment; like that progressing differentiation from the environment which we meet with in the ascending forms of life. Let us first glance at the way in which the ascending forms of life exhibit this progressing differentiation from the environment.

In the first place, it is illustrated in *structure.* Advance from the homogeneous to the heterogeneous, itself involves an increasing distinction from the inorganic world. Passing over the *Protozoa*, of which the simplest probably disappeared during the earliest stages of organic evolution, and limiting our comparison to the *Metazoa*, we see that low types of these, as the *Cœlenterata*, are relatively simple in their organization; and the ascent to organisms of greater and greater complexity of structure, is an ascent to organisms which are in that respect more strongly contrasted with the structureless environment. In *form*, again, we see the same truth. An ordinary characteristic of inorganic matter is its indefiniteness of form; and this is also a characteristic of the lower organisms, as compared with the higher. Speaking generally, plants are less definite than animals, both in shape and size—admit of greater modifications from variations of position and nutrition. Among animals, the simplest Rhizopods may almost be called amorphous: the form is never specific, and is constantly changing. Of the organisms resulting from the aggregation of such creatures, we see that while some, as the *Foraminifera*, assume a certain definiteness of form, in their shells at least, others, as the Sponges, are very irregular. The Zoophytes and the *Polyzoa* are compound organisms, most of which have a mode of growth not more determinate than that of plants. But among the higher animals, we find not only that the mature shape of each species is very definite, but that the individuals of each species differ little in size. A parallel increase of contrast is seen in *chemical composition.* With but few exceptions, and those only partial ones, the lowest animal and vegetal forms are inhabitants of the water; and water is almost their sole constituent. Desiccated *Protophyta* and *Protozoa* shrink into mere dust; and among the Acalephes we find but a few grains of solid matter to a pound of water. The higher aquatic plants, in common with the higher aquatic animals, possessing as they do increased tenacity of substance, also contain a greater proportion of the organic elements; further they show us a greater variety of composition in their different parts; and thus in both ways are chemically more unlike their medium. And when we pass to the superior classes of organisms—land-plants and land-animals—we see that, chemically considered, they have little in common either with the earth on which they stand or the air which surrounds them. In *specific gravity* too, we may note a like truth. The simplest forms, in common with the spores and gemmules of higher ones, are as nearly as may be of the same specific gravity as the water in which they float; and though it cannot be said that among aquatic creatures, superior specific gravity is a standard of general superiority, yet we may fairly say that the higher orders of them, when divested of the appliances by which their specific gravity is regulated, differ more from water in their relative weights than do the lowest. In terrestrial organisms, the contrast becomes marked. Trees and plants, in common with insects, reptiles, mammals, birds, are all of a specific gravity considerably less than that of the earth and immensely greater than that of the air. Yet further, we see the law fulfilled in respect of *temperature.* Plants generate but extremely small quantities of heat, which are to be detected only by delicate experiments; and practically they may be considered as having the same temperature as their environment. The temperature of aquatic animals is very little above that of the surrounding water: that of the invertebrata being mostly less than a degree above it, and that of fishes not exceeding it by more than two or three degrees; save in the case of some large red-blooded fishes, as the tunny, which exceed it in temperature by nearly ten degrees. Among insects the range is from two to ten degrees above that of the air: the excess varying according to their activity. The heat of reptiles is from four to fifteen degrees more than the heat of their medium. While mammals and birds maintain a heat which continues almost unaffected by external variations, and is often greater than that of the air by seventy, eighty, ninety, and even a hundred degrees. Once more, in greater *self-mobility* a progressive differentiation is traceable. The chief characteristic by which we distinguish dead matter is its inertness: some form of independent motion is our most familiar proof of life. Passing over the indefinite border-land between the animal and vegetal kingdoms, we may roughly class plants as organisms which, while they exhibit that kind of motion implied in growth, are not only devoid of locomotive power, but with some unimportant exceptions are devoid of the power of moving their parts in relation to each other; and thus are less differentiated from the inorganic world than animals. Though in those microscopic *Protophyta* and *Protozoa* inhabiting the water we see locomotion produced by ciliary action; yet this locomotion, while rapid relatively to the sizes of their bodies, is absolutely slow. Of the *Cœlenterata* a great part are either permanently rooted or habitually stationary; and so have scarcely any self-mobility but that implied in the relative movements of parts; while the rest, of which the common jelly-fish serves as a sample, have mostly but little ability to move themselves through the water. Among the higher aquatic *Invertebrata*,—cuttlefishes and lobsters, for instance,—there is a very considerable power of locomotion; and the aquatic *Vertebrata* are, considered as a class, much more active in their movements than the other inhabitants of the water. But it is only when we come to air-breathing creatures that we find the vital characteristics of self-mobility manifested in the highest degree. Flying insects, mammals, birds, travel with velocities far exceeding those attained by any of the lower classes of animals. Thus, on contemplating the various grades of organisms in their ascending order, we find them more and more distinguished from their inanimate media, in *structure*, in *form*, in *chemical composition*, in *specific gravity*, in *temperature*, in *self-mobility*. It is true that this generalization does not hold with complete regularity. Organisms which are in some respects the most strongly contrasted with the environing inorganic world, are in other respects less contrasted than inferior organisms. As a class, mammals are higher than birds; and yet they are of lower temperature and have smaller powers of locomotion. The stationary oyster is of higher organization than the free-swimming medusa; and the cold-blooded and less heterogeneous fish is quicker in its movements than the warm-blooded and more heterogeneous sloth. But the admission that the several aspects under which this increasing contrast shows itself, bear variable ratios to each other, does not conflict with the general truth that as we ascend in the hierarchy of organisms, we meet with not only an increasing differentiation of parts but also an increasing differentiation from the surrounding medium in sundry other physical attributes. It would seem that this trait has some necessary connexion with superior vital manifestations. One of those lowly gelatinous forms, so transparent and colourless as to be with difficulty distinguished from the water it floats in, is not more like its medium in chemical, mechanical, optical, thermal, and other properties, than it is in the passivity with which it submits to all the influences and actions brought to bear upon it; while the mammal does not more widely differ from inanimate things in these properties, than it does in the activity with which it meets surrounding changes by compensating changes in itself. And between these extremes, these two kinds of contrast vary together. So that in proportion as an organism is physically like its environment it remains a passive partaker of the changes going on in its environment; while in proportion as it is endowed with powers of counteracting such changes, it exhibits greater unlikeness to its environment.[20]

If now, from this same point of view, we consider the relation borne to its environment by any superior organism in its successive stages, we find an analogous series of contrasts. Of course in respect of degrees of *structure* the parallelism is complete. The difference, at first small, between the little-structured germ and the little-structured inorganic world, necessarily becomes greater, step by step, as the differentiations of the germ become more numerous and definite. How of *form* the like holds is equally manifest. The sphere, which is the point of departure common to all organisms, is the most generalized of figures; and one that is, under various circumstances, assumed by inorganic matter. But as it develops it loses all likeness to inorganic objects in the environment; and eventually becomes distinct even from nearly all organic objects in its environment. In *specific gravity* the alteration, though not very marked, is still in the same direction. Development being habitually accompanied by a relative decrease in the quantity of water and an increase in the quantity of constituents that are heavier than water, there results a small augmentation of relative weight. In power of maintaining a *temperature* above that of surrounding things, the differentiation from the environment that accompanies development is marked. All ova are absolutely dependent for their heat on external sources. The mammalian young one is, during its uterine life, dependent on the maternal heat; and at birth has but a partial power of making good the loss by radiation. But as it advances in development it gains an ability to maintain a constant temperature above that of surrounding things: so becoming markedly unlike them. Lastly, in *self-mobility* this increasing contrast is no less decided. Save in a few aberrant tribes, chiefly parasitic, we find the general fact to be that the locomotive power, totally absent or very small at the outset, increases with the advance towards maturity. The more highly developed the organism becomes, the stronger grows the contrast between its activity and the inertness of the objects amid which it moves.

Thus we may say that the development of an individual organism, is at the same time a differentiation of its parts from each other, and a differentiation of the consolidated whole from the environment; and that in the last as in the first respect, there is a general analogy between the progression of an individual organism and the progression from the lowest orders of organisms to the highest orders. It may be remarked that some kinship seems to exist between these generalizations and the doctrine of

Schelling, that Life is the tendency to individuation. For evidently, in becoming more distinct from one another and from their environment, organisms acquire more marked individualities. As far as I can gather from outlines of his philosophy, however, Schelling entertained this conception in a general and transcendental sense, rather than in a special and scientific one.

§ 54. Deductive interpretations of these general facts of development, in so far as they are possible, must be postponed until we arrive at the fourth and fifth divisions of this work. There are, however, one or two general aspects of these inductions which may be here conveniently dealt with deductively.

Grant that each organism is at the outset relatively homogeneous and that when complete it is relatively heterogeneous, and it necessarily follows that development is a change from the homogeneous to the heterogeneous—a change during which there must be gone through all the gradations of heterogeneity that lie between these extremes. If, again, there is at first indefiniteness and at last definiteness, the transition cannot but be from the one to the other of these through all intermediate degrees of definiteness. Further, if the parts, originally incoherent or uncombined, eventually become relatively coherent or combined, there must be a continuous increase of coherence or combination. Hence the general truth that development is a change from incoherent, indefinite homogeneity, to coherent, definite heterogeneity, becomes a self-evident one when observation has shown us the state in which organisms begin and the state in which they end.

Just in the same way that the growth of an entire organism is carried on by abstracting from the environment substances like those composing the organism; so the production of each organ within the organism is carried on by abstracting from the substances contained in the organism, those required by this particular organ. Each organ at the expense of the organism as a whole, integrates with itself certain kinds and proportions of the matters circulating around it; in the same way that the organism as a whole, integrates with itself certain kinds and proportions of matters at the expense of the environment as a whole. So that the organs are qualitatively differentiated from each other, in a way analogous to that by which the entire organism is qualitatively differentiated from things around it. Evidently this selective assimilation illustrates the general truth, set forth and illustrated in *First Principles*, that like units tend to segregate. It illustrates, moreover, the further aspect of this general truth, that the pre-existence of a mass of certain units produces a tendency for diffused units of the same kind to aggregate with this mass rather than elsewhere. It has been shown of particular salts, A and B, co-existing in a solution not sufficiently concentrated to crystallize, that if a crystal of the salt A be put into the solution, it will increase by uniting with itself the dissolved atoms of the salt A; and that similarly, though there otherwise takes place no deposition of the salt B, yet if a crystal of the salt B is placed in the solution, it will exercise a coercive force on the diffused atoms of this salt, and grow at their expense. Probably much organic assimilation occurs in the same way. Particular parts of the organism are composed of special units or have the function of secreting special units, which are ever present in them in large quantities. The fluids circulating through the body contain special units of this same order. And these diffused units are continually being deposited along with the groups of like units that already exist. How purely physical are the causes of this selective assimilation, is, indeed, shown by the fact that abnormal constituents of the blood are segregated in the same way. The chalky deposits of gout beginning at certain points, collect more and more around those points. And similarly in numerous pustular diseases. Where the component units of an organ, or some of them, do not exist as such in the circulating fluids, but are formed out of elements or compounds that exist separately in the circulating fluids, the process of differential assimilation must be of a more complex kind. Still, however, it seems not impossible that it is carried on in an analogous way. If there be an aggregate of compound atoms, each of which contains the constituents A, B, C; and if round this aggregate the constituents A and B and C are diffused in uncombined states; it may be suspected that the coercive force of these aggregated compound atoms A, B, C, may not only bring into union with themselves adjacent compound atoms A, B, C, but may cause the adjacent constituents A and B and C to unite into such compound atoms, and then aggregate with the mass.

CHAPTER IIA.

STRUCTURE.[21]

§ 54*a*. As, in the course of evolution, we rise from the smallest to the largest aggregates by a process of integration, so do we rise by a process of differentiation from the simplest to the most complex aggregates. The initial types of life are at once extremely small and almost structureless. Passing over those which swarm in the air, the water, and the soil, and are now some of them found to be causes of diseases, we may set out with those ordinarily called *Protozoa* and *Protophyta*: the lowest of which, however, are either at once plants and animals, or are now one and now the other.

That the first living things were minute portions of simple protoplasm is implied by the general theory of Evolution; but we have no evidence that such portions exist now. Even admitting that there are protoplasts (using this word to include plant and animal types) which are without nuclei, still they are not homogeneous—they are granular. Whether a nucleus is always present is a question still undecided; but in any case the types from which it is absent are extremely exceptional. Thus the most general structural traits of protoplasts are—the possession of an internal part, morphologically central though often not centrally situated, a general mass of protoplasm surrounding it, and an inclosing differentiated portion in contact with the environment. These essential elements are severally subject to various complications.

In some simple types the limiting layer or cortical substance can scarcely be said to exist as a separate element. The exoplasm, distinguished from the endoplasm by absence or paucity of granules, is continually changing places with it by the sending out of pseudopodia which are presently drawn back into the general mass: the inner and outer, being unsettled in position, are not permanently differentiated. Then we have types, exemplified by *Lithamœba*, constituted of protoplasm covered by a distinct pellicle, which in sundry groups becomes an outer shell of various structure: now jelly-like, now of cellulose, now siliceous or calcareous. While here this envelope has a single opening, there it is perforated all over—a fenestrated shell. In some cases an external layer is formed of agglutinated sand-particles; in others of imbricated plates, as in Coccospheres; and in many others radiating spicules stand out on all sides. Throughout sundry classes the exoplasm develops cilia, by the wavings of which the creatures are propelled through the water—cilia which may be either general or local. And then this cortical layer, instead of being spherical or spheroidal, may become plano-spiral, cyclical, crosier-shaped, and often many-chambered; whence there is a transition to colonies.

Meanwhile the inclosed protoplasm, at first little more than a network or foamwork containing granules and made irregular by objects drawn in as nutriment, becomes variously complicated. In some low types its continuity is broken by motionless, vacant spaces, but in higher types there are contractile vacuoles slowly pulsing, and, as we may suppose, moving the contained liquid hither and thither; while there are types having many passive vacuoles along with a few active ones. In some varieties the protruded parts, or pseudopodia, into which the protoplasm continually shapes itself, are comparatively short and club-shaped; in others they are long and fine filaments which anastomose, so forming a network running here and there into little pools of protoplasm. Then there are kinds in which the protoplasm streams up and down the protruding spicules: sometimes inside of them, sometimes outside. Always, too, there is included in the protoplasm a small body known as a centrosome.

Lastly, we have the innermost element, considered the essential element—the nucleus. According to Prof. Lankester, it is absent from *Archerina*, and there are types in which it is made visible only by the aid of special reagents. Ordinarily it is marked off from the surrounding protoplasm by a delicate membrane, just as the protoplasm itself is marked off by the exoplasm from the environment. Most commonly there is a single nucleus, but occasionally there are many, and sometimes there is a chief one with minor ones. Moreover, within the nucleus itself there have of late years been discovered remarkable structural elements which undergo complicated changes.

These brief statements indicate only the most general traits of an immense variety of structures—so immense a variety that Prof. Lankester, in distinguishing the classes, sub-classes, orders, and genera in the briefest way, occupies 37 quarto pages of small type. And to give a corresponding account of *Protophyta* would require probably something like equal space. Thus these living things, so minute that unaided vision fails to disclose them, constitute a world exhibiting varieties of structure which it requires the devotion of a life to become fully acquainted with.

§ 54*b*. If higher forms of life have arisen from lower forms by evolution, the implication is that there must once have existed, if there do not still exist, transitional forms; and there follows the comment that there *do* still exist transitional forms. Both in the plant-world and in the animal-world there are types in which we see little more than simple assemblages of *Protophyta* or of *Protozoa*—types in which the units, though coherent, are not differentiated but constitute a uniform mass. In treating of structure we are not here concerned with these unstructured types, but may pass on to those aggregates of protoplasts which show us differentiated parts—*Metaphyta* and *Metazoa*: economizing space by limiting our attention chiefly to the last.

When, half a century ago, some currency was given to the statement that all kinds of organisms, plant and animal, which our unaided eyes disclose, are severally composed of myriads of living units, some of them partially, if not completely, independent, and that thus a man is a vast nation of minute individuals of which some are relatively passive and others relatively active, the statement met, here with incredulity and there with a shudder. But what was then thought a preposterous assertion has now come to be an accepted truth.

Along with gradual establishment of this truth has gone gradual modification in the form under which it was originally asserted. If some inhabitant of another sphere were to describe one of our towns as composed exclusively of houses, saying nothing of the contained beings who had built them and lived in them, we should say that he had made a profound error in recognizing only the inanimate elements of the town and disregarding the animate elements. Early histologists made an analogous error. Plants and animals were found to consist of minute members, each of which appeared to be simply a wall inclosing a cavity—a cell. But further investigation proved that the content of the cell, presently distinguished as protoplasm, is its essential living part, and that the cell-wall, when present, is produced by it. Thus the unit of composition is a protoplast, usually enclosed, with its contained nucleus and centrosome.

§ 54*c*. As above implied, the individualities of the units are not wholly lost in the individuality of the aggregate, but continue, some of them, to be displayed in various degrees: the great majority of them losing their individualities more and more as the type of the aggregate becomes higher.

In a slightly organized Metazoon like the sponge, the subordination is but small. Only those members of the aggregate which, flattened and united together, form the outer layer and those which become metamorphosed into spicules, have entirely lost their original activities. Of the rest nearly all, lining the channels which permeate the mass, and driving onwards the contained sea-water by the motions of their whip-like appendages, substantially retain their separate lives; and beyond these there exist in the gelatinous substance lying between the inner and outer layers, which is regarded as homologous with a mesoderm, amœba-form protoplasts which move about from place to place.

Relations between the aggregate and the units which are in this case permanent, are in other cases temporary: characterizing early stages of embryonic development. For example, drawings of Echinoderm larvæ at an early stage, show us the potential independence of all the cells forming the blastosphere; for in the course of further development some of these resume the primitive amœboid state, migrate through the internal space, and presently unite to form certain parts of the growing structures. But with the progress of organization independence of this kind diminishes.

Converse facts are presented after development has been completed; for with the commencement of reproduction we everywhere see more or less resumption of individual life among the units, or some of them. It is a trait of transitional types between *Protozoa* and *Metazoa* to lead an aggregate life as a plasmodium, and then for this to break up into its members, which for a time lead individual lives as generative agents; and sundry low kinds of plants possessing small amounts of structure, have generative elements—zoospores and spermatozoids—which show us a return to unit life. Nor, indeed, are we shown this only in the lowest plants; for it has recently been found that in certain of the higher plants—even in Phænogams—spermatozoids are produced. That is to say, the units resume active lives at places where the controlling influence of the aggregate is failing; for, as we shall hereafter see, places at which generation commences answer to this description.

These different kinds of evidence jointly imply that the individual lives of the units are subordinate to the general life in proportion as this is high. Where the organism is very inferior in type the unit-life remains permanently conspicuous. In some superior types there is a display of unit-life during embryonic stages in which the co-ordinating action of the aggregate is but incipient. With the advance of development the unit-life diminishes; but still, in plants, recommences where the disintegrating process which initiates generation shows the coercive power of the organization to have become small.

Even in the highest types, however, and even when they are fully developed, unit-life does not wholly disappear: it is clearly shown in ourselves. I do not refer simply to the fact that, as throughout the animal kingdom at large and a considerable part of the vegetal kingdom, the male generative elements are units which have resumed the primitive independent life, but I refer to a much more general fact. In that part of the organism which, being fundamentally an aqueous medium, is in so far like the aqueous medium in which ordinary protozoon life is carried on, we find an essentially protozoon life. I refer of course to the blood. Whether the tendency of the red corpuscles (which are originally developed from amœba-like cells) to aggregate into *rouleaux* is to be taken as showing life in them, may be left an open question. It suffices that the white corpuscles or leucocytes, retaining the primitive amœboid character, exhibit individual activities: send out prolongations like pseudopodia, take in organic particles as food, and are independently locomotive. Though far less numerous than the red corpuscles, yet, as ten thousand are contained in a cubic millimetre of blood—a mass less than a pin's head—it results that the human body is pervaded throughout all its blood-vessels by billions of these separately living units. In the lymph, too, which also fulfils the requirements of liquidity, these amœboid units are found. Then we have the curious transitional stage in which units partially imbedded and partially free display a partial unit-life. These are the ciliated epithelium-cells, lining the air-passages and covering sundry of the mucous membranes which have more remote connexions with the environment, and covering also the lining membranes of certain main canals and chambers in the nervous system. The inner parts of these unite with their fellows to form an epithelium, and the outer parts of them, immersed either in liquid or semi-liquid (mucus), bear cilia that are in constant motion and "produce a current of fluid over the surface they cover:" thus simulating in their positions and actions the cells lining the passages ramifying through a sponge. The partially independent lives of these units is further seen in the fact that after being detached they swim about in water for a time by the aid of their cilia.

§ 54*d.* But in the *Metazoa* and *Metaphyta* at large, the associated units are, with the exceptions just indicated, completely subordinated. The unit-life is so far lost in the aggregate life that neither locomotion nor the relative motion of parts remains; and neither in shape nor composition is there resemblance to protozoa. Though in many cases the internal protoplasm continues to carry on vital processes subserving the needs of the aggregate, in others vital processes of an independent kind appear to cease.

It will naturally be supposed that after recognizing this fundamental trait common to all types of organisms above the *Protozoa* and *Protophyta*, the next step in an account of structure must be a description of their organs, variously formed and combined—if not in detail yet in their general characters. This, however, is an error. There are certain truths of structure higher in generality than any which can be alleged of organs. We shall see this if we compare organs with one another.

Here is a finger stiffened by its small bones and yet made flexible by the uniting joints. There is a femur which helps its fellow to support the weight of the body; and there again is a rib which, along with others, forms a protective box for certain of the viscera. Dissection reveals a set of muscles serving to straighten and bend the fingers, certain other muscles that move the legs, and some inconspicuous muscles which, contracting every two or three seconds, slightly raise the ribs and aid in inflating the lungs. That is to say, fingers, legs, and chest possess certain structures in common. There is in each case a dense substance capable of resisting stress and a contractile substance capable of moving the dense substance to which it is attached.

Hence, then, we have first to give an account of these and other chief elements which, variously joined together, form the different organs: we have to observe the general characters of *tissues.*

On going back to the time when the organism begins with a single cell, then becomes a spherical cluster of cells, and then exhibits differences in the modes of aggregation of these cells, the first conspicuous rise of structure (limiting ourselves to animals) is the formation of three layers. Of these the first is, at the outset and always, the superficial layer in direct contact with the environment. The second, being originally a part of the first, is also in primitive types in contact with the environment, but, being presently introverted, forms the rudiment of the food-cavity; or, otherwise arising in higher types, is in contact with the yelk or food provided by the parent. And the third, presently formed between these two, consists at the outset of cells derived from them imbedded in an intercellular substance of jelly-like consistence. Hence originate the great groups classed as epithelium-tissue, connective tissue (including osseous tissue), muscular tissue, nervous tissue. These severally contain sub-kinds, each of which is a complex of differentiated cells. Being brief, and therefore fitted for the present purposes, the sub-classification given by Prof. R. Hertwig may here be quoted;—

"The physiological character of epithelia is given in the fact that they cover the surfaces of the body, their morphological character in that they consist of closely compressed cells united only by a cementing substance.

"According to their further functional character epithelia are divided into glandular epithelia (unicellular and multicellular glands), sensory, germinal, and pavement epithelia.

"According to the structure are distinguished one-layered (cubical, cylindrical, pavement epithelia) and many-layered epithelia, ciliated and flagellated epithelia, epithelia with or without cuticle.

"The physiological character of the connective tissues rests upon the fact that they fill up spaces between other tissues in the interior of the body.

"The morphological character depends upon the presence of the intercellular substance.

"According to the quantity and the structure of the intercellular substance the connective substances are divided into (1) cellular (with little intercellular substance); (2) homogeneous; (3) fibrillar connective tissue; (4) cartilage; (5) bone.

"The physiological character of muscular tissue is contained in the increased capacity for contraction.

"The morphological character is found in the fact that the cells have secreted muscle-substance.

"According to the nature of the muscle-substance are distinguished smooth and cross-striated muscle-fibres.

"According to the character and derivation of the cells (muscle-corpuscles) the musculature is divided into epithelial (epithelial muscle-cells, primary bundles) and connective-tissue muscle cells (contractile fibre-cells).

"The physiological character of nervous tissue rests upon the transmission of sensory stimuli and voluntary impulses, and upon the co-ordination of these into unified psychic activity.

"The conduction takes place by means of nerve-fibres (non-medullated and medullated fibrils and bundles of fibrils); the co-ordination of stimuli by means of ganglion-cells (bipolar, multipolar ganglion-cells)." (*General Principles of Zoology*, pp. 117-8.)

But now concerning cells out of which, variously modified, obscured, and sometimes obliterated, tissues are formed, we have to note a fact of much significance. Along with the cell-doctrine as at first held, when attention was given to the cell itself rather than to its contents, there went the belief that each of these morphological units is structurally separate from its neighbours. But since establishment of the modern view that the essential element is the contained protoplasm, histologists have discovered that there are protoplasmic connexions between the contents of adjacent cells. Though cursorily observed at earlier dates, it was not until some twenty years ago that in plant-tissues these were clearly shown to pass through openings in the cell-walls. It is said that in some cases the openings are made, and the junctions established, by a secondary process; but the implication is that usually these living links are left between multiplying protoplasts; so that from the outset the protoplasm pervading the whole plant maintains its continuity. More recently sundry zoologists have alleged that a like continuity exists in animals. Especially has this been maintained by Mr. Adam Sedgwick. Numerous observations made on developing ova of fishes have led him to assert that in no case do the multiplying cells so-called—blastomeres and their progeny—become entirely separate. Their fission is in all cases incomplete. A like continuity has been found in the embryos of many Arthropods, and more recently in the segmenting eggs and blastulæ of Echinoderms. The *syncytium* thus formed is held by Mr. Sedgwick to be maintained in adult life, and in this belief he is in agreement with sundry others. Bridges of protoplasm have been seen between epithelium-cells, and it is maintained that cartilage-cells, connective tissue cells, the cells forming muscle-fibres, as well as nerve-cells, have protoplasmic unions. Nay, some even assert that an ovum preserves a protoplasmic connexion with the matrix in which it develops.

A corollary of great significance may here be drawn. It has been observed that within a vegetal cell the strands of protoplasm stretched in this or that direction contain moving granules, showing that the strands carry currents. It has also been observed that when the fission of a protozoon is so nearly complete that its two halves remain connected only by a thread, currents of protoplasm move through this thread, now one way now the other. The inference fairly to be drawn is that such currents pass also through the strands which unite the protoplasts forming a tissue. What must happen? So long as adjacent cells with their contents are subject to equal pressures no tendency to redistribution of the protoplasm exists, and there may then occur the action sometimes observed inside the strands within a cell: currents with their contained granules moving in opposite directions. But if the cells forming a portion of tissue are subject to greater pressure than the cells around, their contained protoplasm must be forced through the connecting threads into these surrounding cells. Every change of pressure at every point must cause movements and counter-movements of this kind. Now in the *Metazoa* at large, or at least in all exhibiting relative motions of parts, and especially in all which are capable of rapid locomotion, such changes of pressure are everywhere and always taking place. The contraction of a muscle, besides compressing its components, compresses neighbouring tissues; and every instant contractions and relaxations of muscles go on throughout the limbs and body during active exertion. Moreover, each attitude—standing, sitting, lying down, turning over—entails a different set of pressures, both of the parts on one another and on the ground; and those partial arrests of motion which result from sitting down the feet alternately when running, send jolts or waves of varying pressure through the body. The vital actions, too, have kindred effects. An inspiration alters the stress on the tissues throughout a considerable part of the trunk, and a heart-beat propels, down to the smallest arteries, waves which slightly strain the tissues at large. The component cells, thus subject to mechanical disturbances, small and great, perpetual and occasional, are ever having protoplasm forced into them and forced out of them. There are gurgitations and regurgitations which, if they do not constitute a circulation properly so called, at least imply an unceasing redistribution. And the implication is that in the course of days, weeks, months, years, each portion of protoplasm visits every part of the body.

Without here stating specifically the bearings of these inferences upon the problems of heredity, it will be manifest that certain difficulties they present are in a considerable degree diminished.

§ 54*e*. Returning from this parenthetical discussion to the subject of structure, we have to observe that besides facts presented by tissues and facts presented by organs, there are certain facts, less general than the one and more general than the other, which must now be noted. In the order of decreasing generality an account of organs should be preceded by an account of systems of organs. Some of these, as the muscular system and the osseous system, are co-extensive with tissues, but others of them are not. The nervous system, for example, contains more than one kind of tissue and is constituted of many different structures: besides afferent and efferent nerves there are the ganglia immediately controlling the viscera, and there are the spinal and cerebral masses, the last of which is divisible into numerous unlike parts. Then we have the vascular system made up of the heart, arteries, veins, and capillaries. The lymphatic system, too, with its scattered glands and ramifying channels has to be named. And then, not forgetting the respiratory system with its ancillary appliances, we have the highly heterogeneous alimentary system; including a great number of variously-constructed organs which work together. On contemplating these systems we see their common character to be that while as wholes they cooperate for the carrying on of the total life, each of them consists of cooperative parts: there is cooperation within cooperation.

There is another general aspect under which structures must be contemplated. They are divisible into the universal and the particular—those which are everywhere present and those which occupy special places. The blood which a scratch brings out shows us that the vascular system sends branches into each spot. The sensation accompanying a scratch proves that the nervous system, too, has there some of its ultimate fibrils. Unobtrusive, and yet to be found at every point, are the ducts of the lymphatic system. And in all parts exists the connective tissue—an inert tough substance which, running through interspaces, wraps up and binds together the other tissues. As is implied by this description, these structures stand in contrast with local structures. Here is a bone, there is a muscle, in this place a gland, in that a sense-organ. Each has a limited extent and a particular duty. But through every one of them ramify branches of these universal structures. Every one of them has its arteries and veins and capillaries, its nerves, its lymphatics, its connective tissue.

Recognition of this truth introduces what little has here to be said concerning organs; for of course in a work limited to principles no detailed account of these can be entered upon. This remainder truth is that, different as they may be in the rest of their structures, all organs are alike in certain of their structures. All are furnished with these appliances for nutrition, depuration and excitation: they have all to be sustained, all to be stimulated, all to be kept clean. It has finally to be remarked that the general structures which pervade all the special structures at the same time pervade one another. The universal nervous system has everywhere ramifying through it the universal vascular system which feeds it; and the universal vascular system is followed throughout all its ramifications by special nerves which control it. The lymphatics forming a drainage-system run throughout the other systems; and in each of these universal systems is present the connective tissue holding their parts in position.

§ 54*f.* So vast and varied a subject as organic structure, even though the treatment of it is limited to the enunciation of principles, cannot, of course, be dealt with in the space here assigned. Next to nothing has been said about plant-structures, and in setting forth the leading traits of animal-structures the illustrations given have been mostly taken from highly-developed creatures. In large measure adumbration rather than exposition is the descriptive word to be applied.

Nevertheless the reader may carry away certain truths which, exemplified in a few cases, are exemplified more or less fully in all cases. There is the fundamental fact that the plants and animals with which we are familiar—*Metaphyta* and *Metazoa*—are formed by the aggregation of units homologous with *Protozoa.* These units, often conspicuously showing their homology in early embryonic stages, continue some of them to show it throughout the lives of the highest type of *Metazoa*, which contain billions of units carrying on a protozoon life. Of the protoplasts not thus active the great mass, comparatively little transformed in low organisms, become more and more transformed as the ascent to high organisms goes on; so that, undergoing numerous kinds of metamorphoses, they lose all likeness to their free homologues, both in shape and composition. The cell-contained protoplasts thus variously changed are fused together into tissues in which their individualities are practically lost; but they nevertheless remain connected throughout by permeable strands of protoplasm. Arising by complication of the outer and inner layers of the embryo and growing more unlike as their units become more obscured, these tissues are formed into systems, which develop into sets of organs. Some of the resulting structures are localized and special but others are everywhere interfused.

While the first named of these facts are displayed in every *Metazoon*, and while the last named are visible only in *Metazoa* of considerably developed structures, a gradual transition is shown in intermediate kinds of *Metazoa.* Of this transition it remains to say that it is effected by the progressive development of auxiliary appliances. For example, the primitive foot-cavity is a sac with one opening only; then comes a second opening through which the waste-matter of the food is expelled. The alimentary canal between these openings is at first practically uniform; afterwards in a certain part of its wall arise numerous bile-cells; these accumulating form a hollow prominence; and this, enlarging, becomes in higher types a liver, while the hollow becomes its duct. In other gradual ways are formed other appended glands. Meanwhile the canal itself has its parts differentiated: one being limited to swallowing, another to triturating, another to adding various solvents, another to absorbing the prepared nutriment, another to ejecting the residue. Take again the visual organ. The earliest form of it is a mere pigment-speck below the surface. From this (saying nothing here of multiple eyes) we rise by successive complications to a retina formed of multitudinous sensory elements, lenses for throwing images upon it, a curtain for shutting out more or less light, muscles for moving the apparatus about, others for adjusting its focus; and, finally, added to these, either a nictitating membrane or eyelids for perpetually wiping its surface, and a set of eyelashes giving notice when a foreign body is dangerously near. This process of elaborating organs so as to meet additional requirements by additional parts, is the process pursued throughout the body at large.

Of plant-structures, concerning which so little has been said, it may here be remarked that their relative simplicity is due to the simplicity of their relations to food. The food of plants is universally distributed, while that of animals is dispersed. The immediate consequences are that in the one case motion and locomotion are superfluous, while in the other case they are necessary: the differences in the degrees of structure being consequences. Recognizing the locomotive powers of minute *Algæ* and the motions of such other *Algæ* as *Oscillatoria*, as well as those movements of leaves and fructifying organs seen in some Phænogams, we may say, generally, that plants are motionless; but that they can nevertheless carry on their lives because they are bathed by the required nutriment in the air and in the soil. Contrariwise, the nutriment animals require is distributed through space in portions: in some cases near one another and in other cases wide apart. Hence motion and locomotion are necessitated; and the implication is that animals must have organs which render them possible. In the first place there must be either limbs or such structures as those which in fish, snakes, and worms move the body along. In the second place, since action implies waste, there must be a set of channels to bring repairing materials to the moving parts. In the third place there must be an alimentary system for taking in and preparing these materials. In the fourth place there must be organs for separating and excreting waste-products. All these appliances must be more highly developed in proportion as the required activity is greater. Then there must be an apparatus for directing the motions and locomotions—a nervous system; and as fast as these become rapid and complex the nervous system must be largely developed, ending in great nervous centres—seats of intelligence by which the activities at large are regulated. Lastly, underlying all the structural contrasts between plants and animals thus originating, there is the chemical contrast; since the necessity for that highly nitrogenous matter of which animals are formed, is entailed by the necessity for rapidly evolving the energy producing motion. So that, strange as it seems, those chemical, physical, and mental characters of animals which so profoundly distinguish them from plants, are all remote results of the circumstance that their food is dispersed instead of being everywhere present.

CHAPTER III.

FUNCTION.

§ 55. Does Structure originate Function, or does Function originate Structure? is a question about which there has been disagreement. Using the word Function in its widest signification, as the totality of all vital actions, the question amounts to this—does Life produce Organization, or does Organization produce Life?

To answer this question is not easy, since we habitually find the two so associated that neither seems possible without the other; and they appear uniformly to increase and decrease together. If it be said that the arrangement of organic substances in particular forms, cannot be the ultimate cause of vital changes, which must depend on the properties of such substances; it may be replied that, in the absence of structural arrangements, the forces evolved cannot be so directed and combined as to secure that correspondence between inner and outer actions which constitutes Life. Again, to the allegation that the vital activity of every germ whence an organism arises, is obviously antecedent to the development of its structures, there is the answer that such germ is not absolutely structureless.

But in truth this question is not determinable by any evidence now accessible to us. The very simplest forms of life known (even the non-nucleated, if there are any) consist of granulated protoplasm; and granulation implies structure. Moreover since each kind of protozoon, even the lowest, has its specific mode of development and specific activity—even down to bacteria, some kinds of which, otherwise indistinguishable, are distinguishable by their different reactions on their media—we are obliged to conclude that there must be constitutional differences between the protoplasms they consist of, and this implies structural differences. It seems that structure and function must have advanced *pari passu*: some difference of function, primarily determined by some difference of relation to the environment, initiating a slight difference of structure, and this again leading to a more pronounced difference of function; and so on through continuous actions and reactions.

§ 56. Function falls into divisions of several kinds according to our point of view. Let us take these divisions in the order of their simplicity.

Under Function in its widest sense, are included both the statical and the dynamical distributions of force which an organism opposes to the forces brought to bear on it. In a tree the woody core of trunk and branches, and in an animal the skeleton, internal or external, may be regarded as passively resisting the gravity and momentum which tend habitually or occasionally to derange the requisite relations between the organism and its environment; and since they resist these forces simply by their cohesion, their functions may be classed as *statical*. Conversely, the leaves and sap-vessels in a tree, and those organs which in an animal similarly carry on nutrition and circulation, as well as those which generate and direct muscular motion, must be considered as *dynamical* in their actions. From another point of view Function is divisible into the *accumulation of energy* (latent in food); the *expenditure of energy* (latent in the tissues and certain matters absorbed by them); and the *transfer of energy* (latent in the prepared nutriment or blood) from the parts which accumulate to the parts which expend. In plants we see little beyond the first of these: expenditure being comparatively slight, and transfer required mainly to facilitate accumulation. In animals the function of *accumulation* comprehends those processes by which the materials containing latent energy are taken in, digested, and separated from other materials; the function of *transfer* comprehends those processes by which these materials, and such others as are needful to liberate the energies they contain, are conveyed throughout the organism; and the function of *expenditure* comprehends those processes by which the energy is liberated from these materials and transformed into properly co-ordinated motions. Each of these three most general divisions includes several more special divisions. The accumulation of energy may be separated into *alimentation* and *aeration*; of which the first is again separable into the various acts gone through between prehension of food and the transformation of part of it into blood. By the transfer of energy is to be understood what we call *circulation*; if the meaning of circulation be extended to embrace the duties of both the vascular system and the lymphatics. Under the head of expenditure of energy come *nervous actions* and *muscular actions*: though not absolutely co-extensive with expenditure these are almost so. Lastly, there are the subsidiary functions which do not properly fall within any of these general functions, but subserve them by removing the obstacles to their performance: those, namely, of *excretion* and *exhalation*, whereby waste products are got rid of. Again, disregarding their purposes and considering them analytically, the general physiologist may consider functions in their widest sense as the correlatives of tissues—the actions of epidermic tissue, cartilaginous tissue, elastic tissue, connective tissue, osseous tissue, muscular tissue, nervous tissue, glandular tissue. Once more, physiology in its concrete interpretations recognizes special functions as the ends of special organs—regards the teeth as having the office of mastication; the heart as an apparatus to propel blood; this gland as fitted to produce one requisite secretion and that to produce another;

each muscle as the agent of a particular motion; each nerve as the vehicle of a special sensation or a special motor impulse.

It is clear that dealing with Biology only in its larger aspects, specialities of function do not concern us; except in so far as they serve to illustrate, or to qualify, its generalities.

§ 57. The first induction to be here set down is a familiar and obvious one; the induction, namely, that complexity of function is the correlative of complexity of structure. The leading aspects of this truth must be briefly noted.

Where there are no distinctions of structure there are no distinctions of function. A Rhizopod will serve as an illustration. From the outside of this creature, which has not even a limiting membrane, there are protruded numerous processes. Originating from any point of the surface, each of these may contract again and disappear, or it may touch some fragment of nutriment which it draws with it, when contracting, into the general mass—thus serving as hand and mouth; or it may come in contact with its fellow-processes at a distance from the body and become confluent with them; or it may attach itself to an adjacent fixed object, and help by its contraction to draw the body into a new position. In brief, this speck of animated jelly is at once all stomach, all skin, all mouth, all limb, and doubtless, too, all lung. In organisms having a fixed distribution of parts there is a concomitant fixed distribution of actions. Among plants we see that when, instead of a uniform tissue like that of many *Algæ*, everywhere devoted to the same process of assimilation, there arise, as in the higher plants, root and stem and leaves, there arise correspondingly unlike processes. Still more conspicuously among animals do there result varieties of function when the originally homogeneous mass is replaced by heterogeneous organs; since, both singly and by their combinations, modified parts generate modified changes. Up to the highest organic types this dependence continues manifest; and it may be traced not only under this most general form, but also under the more special form that in animals having one set of functions developed to more than usual heterogeneity there is a correspondingly heterogeneous apparatus devoted to them. Thus among birds, which have more varied locomotive powers than mammals, the limbs are more widely differentiated; while the higher mammals, which rise to more numerous and more involved adjustments of inner to outer relations than birds, have more complex nervous systems.

§ 58. It is a generalization almost equally obvious with the last, that functions, like structures, arise by progressive differentiations. Just as an organ is first an indefinite rudiment, having nothing but some most general characteristic in common with the form it is ultimately to take; so a function begins as a kind of action that is like the kind of action it will eventually become, only in a very vague way. And in functional development, as in structural development, the leading trait thus early manifested is followed successively by traits of less and less importance. This holds equally throughout the ascending grades of organisms and throughout the stages of each organism. Let us look at cases: confining our attention to animals, in which functional development is better displayed than in plants.

The first differentiation established separates the two fundamentally-opposed functions above named—the accumulation of energy and the expenditure of energy. Passing over the *Protozoa* (among which, however, such tribes as present fixed distributions of parts show us substantially the same thing), and commencing with the lowest *Cœlenterata*, where definite tissues make their appearance, we observe that the only large functional distinction is between the endoderm, which absorbs nutriment, and the ectoderm which, by its own contractions and those of the tentacles it bears, produces motion: the contractility being however to some extent shared by the endoderm. That the functions of accumulation and expenditure are here very incompletely distinguished, may be admitted without affecting the position that this is the first specialization which begins to appear. These two most general and most radically-opposed functions become in the *Polyzoa*, much more clearly marked-off from each other: at the same time that each of them becomes partially divided into subordinate functions. The endoderm and ectoderm are no longer merely the inner and outer walls of the same simple sac into which the food is drawn: but the endoderm forms a true alimentary canal, separated from the ectoderm by a peri-visceral cavity, containing the nutritive matters absorbed from the food. That is to say, the function of accumulating force is exercised by a part distinctly divided from the part mainly occupied in expending force: the structure between them, full of absorbed nutriment, effecting in a vague way that transfer of force which, at a higher stage of evolution, becomes a third leading function. Meanwhile, the endoderm no longer discharges the accumulative function in the same way throughout its whole extent; but its different portions, œsophagus, stomach and intestine, perform different portions of this function. And instead of a contractility uniformly diffused through the ectoderm, there have arisen in the intermediate mesoderm some parts which have the office of contracting (muscles), and some parts which have the office of making them contract (nerves and ganglia). As we pass upwards, the transfer of force, hitherto effected quite incidentally, comes to have a special organ. In the ascidian, circulation is produced by a muscular tube, open at both ends, which, by a wave of contraction passing along it, sends out at one end the nutrient fluid drawn in at the other; and which, having thus propelled the fluid for a time in one direction, reverses its movement and propels it in the opposite direction. By such means does this rudimentary heart generate alternating currents in the nutriment occupying the peri-visceral cavity. How the function of transferring energy, thus vaguely indicated in these inferior forms, comes afterwards to be the definitely-separated office of a complicated apparatus made up of many parts, each of which has a particular portion of the general duty, need not be described. It is sufficiently manifest that this general function becomes more clearly marked-off from the others, at the same time that it becomes itself parted into subordinate functions.

In a developing embryo, the functions or more strictly the structures which are to perform them, arise in the same general order. A like primary distinction very early appears between the endoderm and the ectoderm—the part which has the office of accumulating energy, and the part out of which grow those organs that are the great expenders of energy. Between these two there presently arises the mesoderm in which becomes visible the rudiment of that vascular system, which has to fulfil the intermediate duty of transferring energy. Of these three general functions, that of accumulating energy is carried on from the outset: the endoderm, even while yet incompletely differentiated from the ectoderm, absorbs nutritive matters from the subjacent yelk. The transfer of energy is also to some extent effected by the rudimentary vascular system, as soon as its central cavity and attached vessels are sketched out. But the expenditure of energy (in the higher animals at least) is not appreciably displayed by those ectodermic and mesodermic structures that are afterwards to be mainly devoted to it: there is no sphere for the actions of these parts. Similarly with the chief subdivisions of these fundamental functions. The distinction first established separates the office of transforming other energy into mechanical motion, from the office of liberating the energy to be so transformed. While in the layer between endoderm and ectoderm are arising the rudiments of the muscular system, there is marked out in the ectoderm the rudiment of the nervous system. This indication of structures which are to share between them the general duty of expending energy, is soon followed by changes that foreshadow further specializations of this general duty. In the incipient nervous system there begins to arise that contrast between the cerebral mass and the spinal cord, which, in the main, answers to the division of nervous actions into directive and executive; and, at the same time, the appearance of vertebral laminæ foreshadows the separation of the osseous system, which has to resist the strains of muscular action, from the muscular system, which, in generating motion, entails these strains. Simultaneously there have been going on similar actual and potential specializations in the functions of accumulating energy and transferring energy. And throughout all subsequent phases the method is substantially the same.

This progress from general, indefinite, and simple kinds of action to special, definite, and complex kinds of action, has been aptly termed by Milne-Edwards, "the physiological division of labour." Perhaps no metaphor can more truly express the nature of this advance from vital activity in its lowest forms to vital activity in its highest forms. And probably the general reader cannot in any other way obtain so clear a conception of functional development in organisms, as he can by tracing out functional development in societies: noting how there first comes a distinction between the governing class and the governed class; how while in the governing class there slowly grow up such differences of duty as the civil, military, and ecclesiastical, there arise in the governed class fundamental industrial differences like those between agriculturists and artizans; and how there is a continual multiplication of such specialized occupations and specialized shares of each occupation.

§ 59. Fully to understand this change from homogeneity of function to heterogeneity of function, which accompanies the change from homogeneity of structure to heterogeneity of structure, it is needful to contemplate it under a converse aspect. Standing alone, the above exposition conveys an idea that is both inadequate and erroneous. The divisions and subdivisions of function, becoming definite as they become multiplied, do not lead to a more and more complete independence of functions; as they would do were the process nothing beyond that just described; but by a simultaneous process they are rendered more mutually dependent. While in one respect they are separating from each other, they are in another respect combining with each other. At the same time that they are being differentiated they are also being integrated. Some illustrations will make this plain.

In animals which display little beyond the primary differentiation of functions, the activity of that part which absorbs nutriment or accumulates energy, is not immediately bound up with the activity of that part which, in producing motion, expends energy. In the higher animals, however, the performance of the alimentary functions depends on the performance of various muscular and nervous functions. Mastication and swallowing are nervo-muscular acts; the rhythmical contractions of the stomach and the allied vermicular motions of the intestines, result from the reflex stimulation of certain muscular coats caused by food; the secretion of the several digestive fluids by their respective glands, is due to nervous excitation of them; and digestion, besides requiring these special aids, is not properly performed in the absence of a continuous discharge of energy from the great nervous centres. Again, the function of transferring nutriment or latent energy, from part to part, though at first not closely connected with the other functions, eventually becomes so. The short contractile tube which propels backwards and forwards the blood contained in the peri-visceral cavity of an ascidian, is neither structurally nor functionally much entangled with the creature's other organs. But on passing upwards through higher types, in which this simple tube is replaced by a system of branched tubes, that deliver their contents through their open ends into the tissues at distant parts; and on coming to those advanced types which have closed arterial and venous systems, ramifying minutely in every corner of every organ; we find that the vascular apparatus, while it has become structurally interwoven with the whole body, has become unable properly to fulfil its office without the help of offices that are quite separated from its own. The heart, though mainly automatic in its actions, is controlled by the nervous system, which takes a share in regulating the contractions both of the heart and the arteries. On the due discharge of the respiratory function, too, the function of circulation is directly dependent: if the aeration of the blood is impeded the vascular activity is lowered; and arrest of the one very soon causes stoppage of the other. Similarly with the duties of the nervo-muscular system. Animals of low organization, in which the differentiation and integration of the vital actions have not been carried far, will move about for a considerable time after being eviscerated, or deprived of those appliances by which energy is accumulated and transferred. But animals of high organization are instantly killed by the removal of these appliances, and even by the injury of minor parts of them: a dog's movements are suddenly brought to an end, by cutting one of the main canals along which the materials that evolve movements are conveyed. Thus while in well-developed creatures the distinction of functions is very marked, the combination of functions is very close. From instant to instant the aeration of blood implies that certain respiratory muscles are being made to contract by nervous impulses passing along certain nerves; and that the heart is duly propelling the blood to be aerated. From instant to instant digestion proceeds only on condition that there is a supply of aerated blood, and a due current of nervous energy through the digestive organs. That the heart of a mammal may act, its muscle substance must be continuously fed with an abundant supply of arterial blood.

It is not easy to find an adequate expression for this double re-distribution of functions. It is not easy to realize a transformation through which the functions thus become in one sense separated and in another sense combined, or even interfused. Here, however, as before, an analogy drawn from social organization helps us. If we observe how the increasing division of labour in societies is accompanied by a closer co-operation; and how the agencies of different social actions, while becoming in one respect more distinct, become in another respect more minutely ramified through one another; we shall understand better the increasing physiological co-operation that accompanies increasing physiological division of labour. Note, for example, that while local divisions and classes of the community have been growing unlike in their several occupations, the carrying on of their several occupations has been growing dependent on the due activity of that vast organization by which sustenance is collected and diffused. During the early stages of social development, every small group of people, and often every family, obtained separately its own necessaries; but now, for each necessary, and for each superfluity, there exists a combined body of wholesale and retail distributors, which brings its branched channels of supply within reach of all. While each citizen is pursuing a business that does not immediately aim at the satisfaction of his personal wants, his personal wants are satisfied by a general agency which brings from all places commodities for him and his fellow-citizens—an agency which could not cease its special duties for a few days, without bringing to an end his own special duties and those of most others. Consider, again, how each of these differentiated functions is everywhere pervaded by certain other differentiated functions. Merchants, manufacturers, wholesale distributors of their several species, together with lawyers, bankers, &c., all employ clerks. In clerks we have a specialized class dispersed through various other classes; and having its function fused with the different functions of these various other classes. Similarly commercial travellers, though having in one sense a separate occupation, have in another sense an occupation forming part of each of the many occupations which it aids. As it is here with the sociological division of labour, so is it with the physiological division of labour above described. Just as we see in an advanced community, that while the magisterial, the clerical, the medical, the legal, the manufacturing, and the commercial activities, have grown distinct, they have yet their agencies mingled together in every locality; so in a developed organism, we see that while the general functions of circulation, secretion, absorption, excretion, contraction, excitation, &c., have become differentiated, yet through the ramifications of the systems apportioned to them, they are closely combined with one another in every organ.

§ 60. The physiological division of labour is usually not carried so far as wholly to destroy the primary physiological community of labour. As in societies the adaptation of special classes to special duties, does not entirely disable these classes from performing one another's duties on an emergency; so in organisms, tissues and structures that have become fitted to the particular offices they have ordinarily to discharge, often remain partially able to discharge other offices. It has been pointed out by Dr. Carpenter, that "in cases where the different functions are highly specialized, the general structure retains, more or less, the primitive community of function which originally characterized it." A few instances will bring home this generalization.

The roots and leaves of plants are widely differentiated in their functions: by the roots, water and mineral substances are absorbed; while the leaves take in, and decompose, carbonic acid. Nevertheless, by many botanists it is held that some leaves, or parts of them, can absorb water; and in what are popularly called "air-plants," or at any rate in some kinds of them, the absorption of water is mainly and in some cases wholly carried on by them and by the stems. Conversely, the underground parts can partially assume the functions of leaves. The exposed tuber of a potato develops chlorophyll on its surface, and in other cases, as in that of the turnip, roots, properly so called, do the like. In trees the trunks, which have in great measure ceased to produce buds, recommence producing them if the branches are cut off; sometimes aerial branches send down roots to the earth; and under some circumstances the roots, though not in the habit of developing leaf-bearing organs, send up numerous suckers. When the excretion of bile is arrested, part goes to the skin and some to the kidneys, which presently suffer under their new task. Various examples of vicarious functions may be found among animals. The excretion of carbonic acid and absorption of oxygen are mainly performed by the lungs, in creatures which have lungs; but in such creatures there continues a certain amount of cutaneous respiration, and in soft-skinned batrachians like the frog, this cutaneous respiration is important. Again, when the kidneys are not discharging their duties a notable quantity of urea is got rid of by perspiration. Other instances are supplied by the higher functions. In man the limbs, which among lower vertebrates are almost wholly organs of locomotion, are specialized into organs of locomotion and organs of manipulation. Nevertheless, the human arms and legs do, when needful, fulfil, to some extent, each other's offices. Not only in childhood and old age are the arms used for purposes of support, but on occasions of emergency, as when mountaineering, they are used by men in full vigour. And that legs are to a considerable degree capable of performing the duties of arms, is proved by the great amount of manipulatory skill reached by them when the arms are absent. Among the perceptions, too, there are examples of partial substitution. The deaf Dr. Kitto described himself as having become excessively sensitive to vibrations propagated through the body; and as so having gained the power of perceiving, through his general sensations, those neighbouring concussions of which the ears ordinarily give notice. Blind people make hearing perform, in part, the office of vision. Instead of identifying the positions and sizes of neighbouring objects by the reflection of light from their surfaces, they do this in a rude way by the reflection of sound from their surfaces.

We see, as we might expect to see, that this power of performing more general functions, is great in proportion as the organs have been but little adapted to their special functions. Those parts of plants which show so considerable an ability to discharge each others' offices, are not widely unlike in their minute structures. And the tissues which in animals are to some extent mutually vicarious, are tissues in which the original cellular composition is still conspicuous. But we do not find evidence that the muscular, nervous, or osseous tissues are able in any degree to perform those processes which the less differentiated tissues perform. Nor have we any proof that nerve can partially fulfil the duty of muscle, or muscle that of nerve. We must say, therefore, that the ability to resume the primordial community of function, varies inversely as the established specialization of function; and that it disappears when the specialization of function becomes great.

§ 61. Something approaching to *a priori* reasons may be given for the conclusions thus reached *a posteriori*. They must be accepted for as much as they seem worth.

It may be argued that on the hypothesis of Evolution, Life necessarily comes before organization. On this hypothesis, organic matter in a state of homogeneous aggregation must precede organic matter in a state of heterogeneous aggregation. But since the passing from a structureless state to a structured state, is itself a vital process, it follows that vital activity must have existed while there was yet no structure: structure could not else arise. That function takes precedence of structure, seems also implied in the definition of Life. If Life is shown by inner actions so adjusted as to balance outer actions—if the implied energy is the *substance* of Life while the adjustment of the actions constitutes its *form*; then may we not say that the actions to be formed must come before that which forms them—that the continuous change which is the basis of function, must come before the structure which brings function into shape? Or again, since in all phases of Life up to the highest, every advance is the effecting of some better adjustment of inner to outer actions; and since the accompanying new complexity of structure is simply a means of making possible this better adjustment; it follows that the achievement of function is, throughout, that for which structure arises. Not only is this manifestly true where the modification of structure results by reaction from modification of function; but it is also true where a modification of structure otherwise produced, apparently initiates a modification of function. For it is only when such so-called spontaneous modification of structure subserves some advantageous action, that it is permanently established. If it is a structural modification that happens to facilitate the vital activities, "natural selection" retains and increases it; but if not, it disappears.

The connexion which we noted between heterogeneity of structure and heterogeneity of function—a connexion made so familiar by experience as to appear scarcely worth specifying—is clearly a necessary one. It follows from the general truth that in proportion to the heterogeneity of any aggregate, is the heterogeneity it will produce in any incident force (*First Principles*, § 156). The energy continually liberated in the organism by decomposition, is here the incident force; the functions are the variously modified forms produced in its divisions by the organs they pass through; and the more multiform the organs the more multiform must be the differentiations of the force passing through them.

It follows obviously from this, that if structure progresses from the homogeneous, indefinite, and incoherent, to the heterogeneous, definite, and coherent, so too must function. If the number of different parts in an aggregate must determine the number of differentiations produced in the energies passing through it—if the distinctness of these parts from one another, must involve distinctness in their reactions, and therefore distinctness between the divisions of the differentiated energy; there cannot but be a complete parallelism between the development of structure and the development of function. If structure advances from the simple and general to the complex and special, function must do the same.

CHAPTER IV.

WASTE AND REPAIR.

§ 62. Throughout the vegetal kingdom, the processes of Waste and Repair are comparatively insignificant in their amounts. Though all parts of plants save the leaves, or other parts which are green, give out carbonic acid; yet this carbonic acid, assuming it to indicate consumption of tissue, or rather of the protoplasm contained in the tissue, indicates but a small consumption. Of course if there is little waste there can be but little repair—that is, little of the interstitial repair which restores the integrity of parts worn by functional activity. Nor, indeed, is there displayed by plants in any considerable degree, if at all, that other species of repair which consists in the restoration of lost or injured organs. Torn leaves and the shoots that are shortened by the pruner, do not reproduce their missing parts; and though when the branch of a tree is cut off close to the trunk, the place is in course of years covered over, it is not by any reparative action in the wounded surface but by the lateral growth of the adjacent bark. Hence, without saying that Waste and Repair do not go on at all in plants, we may fitly pass them over as of no importance.

There are but slight indications of waste in those lower orders of animals which, by their comparative inactivity, show themselves least removed from vegetal life. Actiniæ kept in an aquarium, do not appreciably diminish in bulk from prolonged abstinence. Even fish, though much more active than most other aquatic creatures, appear to undergo but little loss of substance when kept unfed during considerable periods. Reptiles, too, maintaining no great temperature, and passing their lives mostly in a state of torpor, suffer but little diminution of mass by waste. When, however, we turn to those higher orders of animals which are active and hot-blooded, we see that waste is rapid: producing, when unchecked, a notable decrease in bulk and weight, ending very shortly in death. Besides finding that waste is inconsiderable in creatures which produce but little insensible and sensible motion, and that it becomes conspicuous in creatures which produce much insensible and sensible motion; we find that in the same creatures there is most waste when most motion is generated. This is clearly proved by hybernating animals. "Valentin found that the waking marmot excreted in the average 75 times more carbonic acid, and inhaled 41 times more oxygen than the same animal in the most complete state of hybernation. The stages between waking and most profound hybernation yielded intermediate figures. A waking hedgehog yielded about 20.5 times more carbonic acid, and consumed 18.4 times more oxygen than one in the state of hybernation."[22] If we take these quantities of absorbed oxygen and excreted carbonic acid, as indicating something like the relative amounts of consumed organic substance, we see that there is a striking contrast between the waste accompanying the ordinary state of activity, and the waste accompanying complete quiescence and reduced temperature. This difference is still more definitely shown by the fact, that the mean daily loss from starvation in rabbits and guinea-pigs, bears to that from hybernation, the proportion of 18.3:1. Among men and domestic animals, the relation between degree of waste and amount of expended energy, though one respecting which there is little doubt, is less distinctly demonstrable; since waste is not allowed to go on uninterfered with. We have, however, in the lingering lives of invalids who are able to take scarcely any nutriment but are kept warm and still, an illustration of the extent to which waste diminishes as the expenditure of energy declines.

Besides the connexion between the waste of the organism as a whole and the production of sensible and insensible motion by the organism as a whole, there is a traceable connexion between the waste of special parts and the activities of such special parts. Experiments have shown that "the starving pigeon daily consumes in the average 40 times more muscular substance that the marmot in the state of torpor, and only 11 times more fat, 33 times more of the tissue of the alimentary canal, 18.3 times more liver, 15 times more lung, 5 times more skin." That is to say, in the hybernating animal the parts least consumed are the almost totally quiescent motor-organs, and the part most consumed is the hydro-carbonaceous deposit serving as a store of energy; whereas in the pigeon, similarly unsupplied with food but awake and active, the greatest loss takes place in the motor-organs. The relation between special activity and special waste, is illustrated, too, in the daily experiences of all: not indeed in the amount of decrease of the active parts in bulk or weight, for this we have no means of ascertaining; but in the diminished ability of such parts to perform their functions. That legs exerted for many hours in walking and arms long strained in rowing, lose their powers—that eyes become enfeebled by reading or writing without intermission—that concentrated attention, unbroken by rest, so prostrates the brain as to incapacitate it for thinking; are familiar truths. And though we have no direct evidence to this effect, there is little danger in concluding that muscles exercised until they ache or become stiff, and nerves of sense rendered weary or obtuse by work, are organs so much wasted by action as to be partially incompetent.

Repair is everywhere and always making up for waste. Though the two processes vary in their relative rates both are constantly going on. Though during the active, waking state of an animal waste is in excess of repair, yet repair is in progress; and though during sleep repair is in excess of waste, yet some waste is necessitated by the carrying on of certain never-ceasing functions. The organs of these never-ceasing functions furnish, indeed, the most conclusive proofs of the simultaneity of repair and waste. Day and night the heart never stops beating, but only varies in the rapidity and vigour of its beats; and hence the loss of substance which its contractions from moment to moment entail, must from moment to moment be made good. Day and night the lungs dilate and collapse; and the muscles which make them do this must therefore be kept in a state of integrity by a repair which keeps pace with waste, or which alternately falls behind and gets in advance of it to a very slight extent.

On a survey of the facts we see, as we might expect to see, that the progress of repair is most rapid when activity is most reduced. Assuming that the organs which absorb and circulate nutriment are in proper order, the restoration of the body to a state of integrity, after the disintegration consequent on expenditure of energy, is proportionate to the diminution in expenditure of energy. Thus we all know that those who are in health, feel the greatest return of vigour after profound sleep—after complete cessation of motion. We know that a night during which the quiescence, bodily and mental, has been less decided, is usually not followed by that spontaneous overflow of energy which indicates a high state of efficiency throughout the organism. We know, again, that long-continued recumbency, even with wakefulness (providing the wakefulness is not the result of disorder), is followed by a certain renewal of strength; though a renewal less than that which would have followed the greater inactivity of slumber. We know, too, that when exhausted by labour, sitting brings a partial return of vigour. And we also know that after the violent exertion of running, a lapse into the less violent exertion of walking, results in a gradual disappearance of that prostration which the running produced. This series of illustrations conclusively proves that the rebuilding of the organism is ever making up for the pulling down of it caused by action; and that the effect of this rebuilding becomes more manifest, in proportion as the pulling down is less rapid. From each digested meal there is every few hours absorbed into the mass of prepared nutriment circulating through the body, a fresh supply of the needful organic compounds; and from the blood, thus occasionally re-enriched, the organs through which it passes are ever taking up materials to replace the materials used up in the discharge of functions. During activity the reintegration falls in arrear of the disintegration; until, as a consequence, there presently comes a general state of functional languor; ending, at length, in a quiescence which permits the reintegration to exceed the disintegration, and restore the parts to their state of integrity. Here, as wherever there are antagonistic actions, we see rhythmical divergences on opposite sides of the medium state—changes which equilibrate each other by their alternate excesses. (*First Principles*, §§ 85, 173.)

Illustrations are not wanting of special repair that is similarly ever in progress, and similarly has intervals during which it falls below waste and rises above it. Every one knows that a muscle, or a set of muscles, continuously strained, as by holding out a weight at arm's length, soon loses its power; and that it recovers its power more or less fully after a short rest. The several organs of the special sensations yield us like experiences. Strong tastes, powerful odours, loud sounds, temporarily unfit the nerves impressed by them for appreciating faint tastes, odours, or sounds; but these incapacities are remedied by brief intervals of repose. Vision still better illustrates this simultaneity of waste and repair. Looking at the Sun so affects the eyes that, for a short time, they cannot perceive the things around with the usual clearness. After gazing at a bright light of a particular colour, we see, on turning the eyes to adjacent objects, an image of the complementary colour; showing that the retina has, for the moment, lost the power to feel small amounts of those rays which have strongly affected it. Such inabilities disappear in a few seconds or a few minutes, according to circumstances. And here, indeed, we are introduced to a conclusive proof that special repair is ever neutralizing special waste. For the rapidity with which the eyes recover their sensitiveness, varies with the reparative power of the individual. In youth the visual apparatus is so quickly restored to its state of integrity, that many of these *photogenes*, as they are called, cannot be perceived. When sitting on the far side of a room, and gazing out of the window against a light sky, a person who is debilitated by disease or advancing years, perceives, on transferring the gaze to the adjacent wall, a momentary negative image of the window—the sash-bars appearing light and the squares dark; but a young and healthy person has no such experience. With a rich blood and vigorous circulation, the repair of the visual nerves after impressions of moderate intensity, is nearly instantaneous.

Function carried to excess may produce waste so great that repair cannot make up for it during the ordinary daily periods of rest; and there may result incapacities of the over-taxed organs, lasting for considerable periods. We know that eyes strained by long-continued minute work lose their power for months or years: perhaps suffering an injury from which they never wholly recover. Brains, too, are often so unduly worked that permanent relaxation fails to restore them to vigour. Even of the motor organs the like holds. The most frequent cause of what is called "wasting palsy," or atrophy of the muscles, is habitual excess of exertion: the proof being that the disease occurs most frequently among those engaged in laborious handicrafts, and usually attacks first the muscles which have been most worked.

There has yet to be noticed another kind of repair—that, namely, by which injured or lost parts are restored. Among the *Hydrozoa* it is common for any portion of the body to reproduce the rest; even though the rest to be so reproduced is the greater part of the whole. In the more highly-organized *Actinozoa* the half of an individual will grow into a complete individual. Some of the lower Annelids, as the *Nais*, may be cut into thirty or forty pieces and each piece will eventually become a perfect animal. As we ascend to higher forms we find this reparative power much diminished, though still considerable. The reproduction of a lost claw by a lobster or crab, is a familiar instance. Some of the inferior *Vertebrata* also, as lizards, can develop new limbs or new tails, in place of those which have been cut off; and can even do this several times over, though with decreasing completeness. The highest animals, however, thus repair themselves to but a very small extent. Mammals and birds do it only in the healing of wounds; and very often but imperfectly even in this. For in muscular and glandular organs the tissues destroyed are not properly reproduced, but are replaced by tissue of an irregular kind which serves to hold the parts together. So that the power of reproducing lost parts is greatest where the organization is lowest; and almost disappears where the organization is highest. And though we cannot say that in the intermediate stages there is a constant inverse relation between reparative power and degree of organization; yet we may say that there is some approach to such a relation.

§ 63. There is an obvious and complete harmony between the first of the above inductions and the deduction which follows immediately from first principles. We have already seen (§ 23) "that whatever amount of power an organism expends in any shape, is the correlate and equivalent of a power that was taken into it from without." Motion, sensible or insensible, generated by an organism, is insensible motion which was absorbed in producing certain chemical compounds appropriated by the organism under the form of food. As much energy as was required to raise the elements of these complex atoms to their state of unstable equilibrium, is given out in their falls to a state of stable equilibrium; and having fallen to a state of stable equilibrium they can give out no further energy, but have to be got rid of as inert and useless. It is an inevitable corollary "from the persistence of force, that each portion of mechanical or other energy which an organism exerts, implies the transformation of as much organic matter as contained this energy in a latent state;" and that this organic matter in yielding up its latent energy, loses its value for the purposes of life, and becomes waste matter needing to be excreted. The loss of these complex unstable substances must hence be proportionate to the quantity of expended force. Here, then, is the rationale of certain general facts lately indicated. Plants do not waste to any considerable degree, for the obvious reason that the sensible and insensible motions they generate are inconsiderable. Between the small waste, small activity, and low temperature of the inferior animals, the relation is similarly one admitting of *a priori* establishment. Conversely, the rapid waste of energetic, hot-blooded animals might be foreseen with equal certainty. And not less manifestly necessary is the variation in waste which, in the same organism, attends the variation in the heat and mechanical motion produced.

Between the activity of a special part and the waste of that part, a like relation may be deductively inferred; though it cannot be inferred that this relation is equally definite. Were the activity of every organ quite independent of the activities of other organs, we might expect to trace out this relation distinctly; but since increased activity in any organ or group of organs, as the muscles, necessarily entails increased activity in other organs, as in the heart, lungs, and nervous system, it is clear that special waste and general waste are too much entangled to admit of a definite relation being established between special waste and special activity. We may fairly say, however, that this relation is quite as manifest as we can reasonably anticipate.

§ 64. Deductive interpretation of the phenomena of Repair, is by no means so easy. The tendency displayed by an animal organism, as well as by each of its organs, to return to a state of integrity by the assimilation of new matter, when it has undergone the waste consequent on activity, is a tendency which is not manifestly deducible from first principles; though it appears to be in harmony with them. If in the blood there existed ready-formed units exactly like in kind to those of which each organ consists, the sorting of these units, ending in the union of each kind with already existing groups of the same kind, would be merely a good example of Segregation (*First Principles*, § 163). It would be analogous to the process by which, from a mixed solution of salts, there are, after an interval, deposited separate masses of these salts in the shape of different crystals. But as already said (§ 54), though the selective assimilation by which the repair of organs is effected, may result in part from an action of this kind, the facts cannot be thus wholly accounted for; since organs are in part made up of units which do not exist as such in the circulating fluids. We must suppose that, as suggested in § 54, groups of compound units have a certain power of moulding adjacent fit materials into units of their own form. Let us see whether there is not reason to think such a power exists.

"The poison of small-pox or of scarlatina," remarks Mr. (now Sir James) Paget, "being once added to the blood, presently affects the composition of the whole: the disease pursues its course, and, if recovery ensue, the blood will seem to have returned to its previous condition: yet it is not as it was before; for now the same poison may be added to it with impunity." ... "The change once effected, may be maintained through life. And herein seems to be a proof of the assimilative force in the blood: for there seems no other mode of explaining these cases than by admitting that the altered particles have the power of assimilating to themselves all those by which they are being replaced: in other words, all the blood that is formed after such a disease deviates from the natural composition, so far as to acquire the peculiarity engendered by the disease: it is formed according to the altered model." Now if the compound molecules of the blood, or of an organism considered in the aggregate, have the power of moulding into their own type the matters which they absorb as nutriment; and if they have the power when their type has been changed by disease, of moulding materials afterwards received into the modified type; may we not reasonably suspect that the more or less specialized molecules of each organ have, in like manner, the power of moulding the materials which the blood brings to them into similarly specialized molecules? The one conclusion seems to be a corollary from the other. Such a power cannot be claimed for the component units of the blood without being conceded to the component units of every tissue. Indeed the assertion of this power is little more than an assertion of the fact that organs composed of specialized units *are* capable of resuming their structural integrity after they have been wasted by function. For if they do this, they must do it by forming from the materials brought to them, certain specialized units like in kind to those of which they are composed; and to say that they do this, is to say that their component units have the power of moulding fit materials into other units of the same order.

§ 65. What must we say of the ability an organism has to re-complete itself when one of its parts has been cut off? Is it of the same order as the ability of an injured crystal to re-complete itself. In either case new matter is so deposited as to restore the original outline. And if in the case of the crystal we say that the whole aggregate exerts over its parts a force which constrains the newly-integrated molecules to take a certain definite form, we seem obliged, in the case of the organism, to assume an analogous force. If when the leg of a lizard has been amputated there presently buds out the germ of a new one, which, passing through phases of development like those of the original leg, eventually assumes a like shape and structure, we assert only what we see, when we assert that the entire organism, or the adjacent part of it, exercises such power over the forming limb as makes it a repetition of its predecessor. If a leg is reproduced, where there was a leg, and a tail where there was a tail, there seems no alternative but to conclude that the forces around it control the formative processes going on in each part. And on contemplating these facts in connexion with various kindred ones, there is suggested the hypothesis, that the form of each species of organism is determined by a peculiarity in the constitution of its units—that these have a special structure in which they tend to arrange themselves; just as have the simpler units of inorganic matter. Let us glance at the evidences which more especially thrust this conclusion upon us.

A fragment of a Begonia-leaf imbedded in fit soil and kept at an appropriate temperature, will develop a young Begonia; and so small is the fragment which is thus capable of originating a complete plant, that something like a hundred plants may be produced from a single leaf. The friend to whom I owe this observation, tells me that various succulent plants have like powers of multiplication. Illustrating a similar power among animals, we have the often-cited experiments of Trembley on the common polype. Each of the four pieces into which one of these creatures was cut, grew into a perfect individual. In each of these, again, bisection and tri-section were followed by like results. And so with their segments, similarly produced, until as many as fifty polypes had resulted from the original one. Bodies when cut off regenerated heads; heads regenerated bodies; and when a polype had been divided into as many pieces as was practicable, nearly every piece survived and became a complete animal. What, now, is the implication? We cannot say that in each portion of a Begonia-leaf, and in every fragment of a Hydra's body, there exists a ready-formed model of the entire organism. Even were there warrant for the doctrine that the germ of every organism contains the perfect organism in miniature, it still could not be contended that each considerable part of the perfect organism resulting from such a germ, contains another such miniature. Indeed the one hypothesis negatives the other. The implication seems, therefore, to be that the living particles composing one of these fragments, have an innate tendency to arrange themselves into the shape of the organism to which they belong. We must infer that the active units composing a plant or animal of any species have an intrinsic aptitude to aggregate into the form of that species. It seems difficult to conceive that this can be so; but we see that it *is* so. Groups of units taken from an organism (providing they are of a certain bulk and not much differentiated into special structures) *have* this power of re-arranging themselves. Manifestly, too, if we are thus to interpret the reproduction of an organism from one of its amorphous fragments, we must thus interpret the reproduction of any minor portion of an organism by the remainder. When in place of its lost claw a lobster puts forth a cellular mass which, while increasing in bulk, assumes the form and structure of the original claw, we cannot avoid ascribing this result to a play of forces like that which moulds the materials contained in a piece of Begonia-leaf into the shape of a young Begonia.

§ 66. As we shall have frequent occasion hereafter to refer to these units which possess the property of arranging themselves into the special structures of the organisms to which they belong; it will be well here to ask by what name they may be most fitly called.

On the one hand, it cannot be in those chemical compounds characterizing organic bodies that this specific property dwells. It cannot be that the molecules of albumin, or fibrin, or gelatine, or other proteid, possess this power of aggregating into these specific shapes; for in such case there would be nothing to account for the unlikenesses of different organisms. If the proclivities of proteid molecules determined the forms of the organisms built up of them or by them, the occurrence of such endlessly varied forms would be inexplicable. Hence what we may call the *chemical units* are clearly not the possessors of this property.

On the other hand, this property cannot reside in what may be roughly distinguished as the *morphological units*. The germ of every organism is a minute portion of encased protoplasm commonly called a cell. It is by multiplication of cells that all the early developmental changes are effected. The various tissues which successively arise in the unfolding organism, are primarily cellular; and in many of them the formation of cells continues to be, throughout life, the process by which repair is carried on. But though cells are so generally the ultimate visible components of organisms, that they may with some show of reason be called the morphological units; yet we cannot say that this tendency to aggregate into special forms dwells in them. In many cases a fibrous tissue arises out of a nucleated blastema, without cell-formation; and in such cases cells cannot be regarded as units possessing the structural proclivity. But the conclusive proof that the morphological units are not the building factors in an organism composed of them, is yielded by their independent homologues the so-called unicellular organisms. For each of these displays the power to assume its specific structure. Clearly, if the ability of a multicellular organism to assume its specific structure resulted from the cooperation of its component cells, then a single cell, or the independent homologue of a single cell, having no other to cooperate with, could exhibit no structural traits. Not only, however, do single-celled organisms exhibit structural traits, but these, even among the simplest, are so distinct as to originate classification into orders, genera, and species; and they are so constant as to remain the same from generation to generation.

If, then, this organic polarity (as we might figuratively call this proclivity towards a specific structural arrangement) can be possessed neither by the chemical units nor the morphological units, we must conceive it as possessed by certain intermediate units, which we may term *physiological*. There seems no alternative but to suppose that the chemical units combine into units immensely more complex than themselves, complex as they are; and that in each organism the physiological units produced by this further compounding of highly compound molecules, have a more or less distinctive character. We must conclude that in each case some difference of composition in the units, or of arrangement in their components, leading to some difference in their mutual play of forces, produces a difference in the form which the aggregate of them assumes.

The facts contained in this chapter form but a small part of the evidence which thrusts this assumption upon us. We shall hereafter find various reasons for inferring that such physiological units exist, and that to their specific properties, more or less unlike in each plant and animal, various organic phenomena are due.

CHAPTER V.

ADAPTATION.

§ 67. In plants waste and repair being scarcely appreciable, there are not likely to arise appreciable changes in the proportions of already-formed parts. The only divergences from the average structures of a species, which we may expect particular conditions to produce, are those producible by the action of these conditions on parts in course of formation; and such divergences we do find. We know that a tree which, standing alone in an exposed position, has a short and thick stem, has a tall and slender stem when it grows in a wood; and that also its branches then take a different inclination. We know that potato-sprouts which, on reaching the light, develop into foliage, will, in the absence of light, grow to a length of several feet without foliage. And every in-door plant furnishes proof that shoots and leaves, by habitually turning themselves to the light, exhibit a certain adaptation—an adaptation due, as we must suppose; to the special effects of the special conditions on the still growing parts. In animals, however, besides analogous structural changes wrought during the period of growth, by subjection to circumstances unlike the ordinary circumstances, there are structural changes similarly wrought after maturity has been reached. Organs that have arrived at their full sizes possess a certain modifiability; so that while the organism as a whole retains pretty nearly the same bulk, the proportions of its parts may be considerably varied. Their variations, here treated of under the title Adaptation, depend on specialities of individual action. In the last chapter we saw that the actions of organisms entail re-actions on them; and that specialities of action entail specialities of re-action. Here it remains to be pointed out that these special actions and re-actions do not end with temporary changes, but work permanent changes.

If, in an adult animal, the waste and repair in all parts were exactly balanced—if each organ daily gained by nutrition exactly as much as it lost daily by the discharge of its function—if excess of function were followed only by such excess of nutrition as balanced the extra waste; it is clear that there would occur no change in the relative sizes of organs. But there is no such exact balance. If the excess of function, and consequent excess of waste, is moderate, it is not simply compensated by repair but more than compensated—there is a certain increase of bulk. This is true to some degree of the organism as a whole, when the organism is framed for activity. A considerable waste giving considerable power of assimilation, is more favourable to accumulation of tissue than is quiescence with its comparatively feeble assimilation: whence results a certain adaptation of the whole organism to its requirements. But it is more especially true of the parts of an organism in relation to one another. The illustrations fall into several groups. The growth of muscles exercised to an unusual degree is a matter of common observation. In the often-cited blacksmith's arm, the dancer's legs and the jockey's crural adductors, we have marked examples of a modifiability which almost every one has to some extent experienced. It is needless to multiply proofs. The occurrence of changes in the structure of the skin, where the skin is exposed to unusual stress of function, is also familiar. That thickening of the epidermis on a labourer's palm results from continual pressure and friction, is certain. Those who have not before exerted their hands, find that such an exercise as rowing soon begins to produce a like thickening. This relation of cause and effect is still better shown by the marked indurations at the ends of a violinist's fingers. Even in mucous membrane, which ordinarily is not subject to mechanical forces of any intensity, similar modifications are possible: witness the callosity of the gums which arises in those who have lost their teeth, and have to masticate without teeth. The vascular system furnishes good instances of the increased growth that follows increased function. When, because of some permanent obstruction to the circulation, the heart has to exert a greater contractile force on the mass of blood which it propels at each pulsation, and when there results the laboured action known as palpitation, there usually occurs dilatation, or hypertrophy, or a mixture of the two: the dilatation, which is a yielding of the heart's structure under the increased strain, implying a failure to meet the emergency; but the hypertrophy, which consists in a thickening of the heart's muscular walls, being an adaptation of it to the additional effort required. Again, when an aneurism in some considerable artery has been obliterated, either artifically or by a natural inflammatory process; and when this artery has consequently ceased to be a channel for the blood; some of the adjacent arteries which anastomose with it become enlarged, so as to carry the needful quantity of blood to the parts supplied. Though we have no direct proof of analogous modifications in nervous structures, yet indirect proof is given by the greater efficiency that follows greater activity. This is manifested alike in the senses and the intellect. The palate may be cultivated into extreme sensitiveness, as in professional tea-tasters. An orchestral conductor gains, by continual practice, an unusually great ability to discriminate differences of sound. In the finger-reading of the blind we have evidence that the sense of touch may be brought by exercise to a far higher capability than is ordinary.[23] The increase of power which habitual exertion gives to mental faculties needs no illustration: every person of education has personal experience of it. Even from the osseous structures evidence may be drawn. The bones of men accustomed to great muscular action are more massive, and have more strongly marked processes for the attachment of muscles, than the bones of men who lead sedentary lives; and a like contrast holds between the bones of wild and tame animals of the same species. Adaptations of another order, in which there is a qualitative rather than a quantitative modification, arise after certain accidents to which the skeleton is liable. When the hip-joint has been dislocated, and long delay has made it impossible to restore the parts to their proper places, the head of the thigh-bone, imbedded in the surrounding muscles, becomes fixed in its new position by attachments of fibrous tissue, which afford support enough to permit a halting walk. But the most remarkable modification of this order occurs in united ends of fractured bones. "False joints" are often formed—joints which rudely simulate the hinge structure or the ball-and-socket structure, according as the muscles tend to produce a motion of flexion and extension or a motion of rotation. In the one case, according to Rokitansky, the two ends of the broken bone become smooth and covered with periosteum and fibrous tissue, and are attached by ligaments that allow a certain backward and forward motion; and in the other case the ends, similarly clothed with the appropriate membranes, become the one convex and the other concave, are inclosed in a capsule, and are even occasionally supplied with synovial fluid!

The general truth that extra function is followed by extra growth, must be supplemented by the equally general truth, that beyond a limit, usually soon reached, very little, if any, further modification can be produced. The experiences which we colligate into the one induction thrust the other upon us. After a time no training makes the pugilist or the athlete any stronger. The adult gymnast at last acquires the power to perform certain difficult feats; but certain more difficult feats no additional practice enables him to perform. Years of discipline give the singer a particular loudness and range of voice, beyond which further discipline does not give greater loudness or wider range: on the contrary, increased vocal exercise, causing a waste in excess of repair, is often followed by decrease of power. In the exaltation of the perceptions we see similar limits. The culture which raises the susceptibility of the ear to the intervals and harmonies of notes, will not turn a bad ear into a good one. Lifelong effort fails to make this artist a correct draftsman or that a fine colourist: each does better than he did at first, but each falls short of the power attained by some other artists. Nor is this truth less clearly illustrated among the more complex mental powers. A man may have a mathematical faculty, a poetical faculty, or an oratorical faculty, which special education improves to a certain extent. But unless he is unusually endowed in one of those directions, no amount of education will make him a first-rate mathematician, a first-rate poet, or a first-rate orator. Thus the general fact appears to be that while in each individual certain changes in the proportions of parts may be caused by variations of functions, the congenital structure of each individual puts a limit to the modifiability of every part. Nor is this true of individuals only: it holds, in a sense, of species. Leaving open the question whether, in indefinite times, indefinite modifications may not be produced by inheritance of functionally wrought adaptations; experience proves that within assigned times, the changes wrought in races of organisms by changes of conditions fall within narrow limits. Though by discipline, aided by selective breeding, one variety of horse has had its locomotive power increased considerably beyond the locomotive powers of other varieties; yet further increase takes place, if at all, at an inappreciable rate. The different kinds of dogs, too, in which different forms and capacities have been established, do not now show aptitudes for diverging in the same directions at considerable rates. In domestic animals generally, certain accessions of intelligence have been produced by culture; but accessions beyond these are inconspicuous. It seems that in each species of organism there is a margin for functional oscillations on all sides of a mean state, and a consequent margin for structural variations; that it is possible rapidly to push functional and structural changes towards the extreme of this margin in any direction, both in an individual and in a race; but that to push these changes further in any direction, and so to alter the organism as to bring its mean state up to the extreme of the margin in that direction, is a comparatively slow process.[24]

We also have to note that the limited increase of size produced in any organ by a limited increase of its function, is not maintained unless the increase of function is permanent. A mature man or other animal, led by circumstances into exerting particular members in unusual degrees, and acquiring extra sizes in these members, begins to lose such extra sizes on ceasing to exert the members; and eventually lapses more or less nearly into the original state. Legs strengthened by a pedestrian tour, become relatively weak again after a prolonged return to sedentary life. The acquired ability to perform feats of skill disappears in course of time, if the performance of them be given up. For comparative failure in executing a piece of music, in playing a game at chess, or in anything requiring special culture, the being out of practice is a reason which every one recognizes as valid. It is observable, too, that the rapidity and completeness with which an artificial power is lost, is proportionate to the shortness of the cultivation which evoked it. One who has for many years persevered in habits which exercise special muscles or special faculties of mind, retains the extra capacity produced, to a very considerable degree, even after a long period of desistance; but one who has persevered in such habits for but a short time has, at the end of a like period, scarcely any of the facility he had gained. Here too, as before, successions of organisms present an analogous fact. A species in which domestication continued through many generations, has organized certain peculiarities; and which afterwards, escaping domestic discipline, returns to something like its original habits; soon loses, in great measure, such peculiarities. Though it is not true, as alleged, that it resumes completely the structure it had before domestication, yet it approximates to that structure. The Dingo, or wild dog of Australia, is one of the instances given of this; and the wild horse of South America is another. Mankind, too, supplies us with instances. In the Australian bush and in the backwoods of America, the Anglo-Saxon race, in which civilization has developed the higher feelings to a considerable degree, rapidly lapses into comparative barbarism: adopting the moral code, and sometimes the habits, of savages.

§ 68. It is important to reach, if possible, some rationale of these general truths—especially of the last two. A right understanding of these laws of organic modification underlies a right understanding of the great question of species. While, as before hinted (§ 40), the action of structure on function is one of the factors in that process of differentiation by which unlike forms of plants and animals are produced, the reaction of function on structure is another factor. Hence, it is well worth while inquiring how far these inductions are deductively interpretable.

The first of them is the most difficult to deal with. Why an organ exerted somewhat beyond its wont should presently grow, and thus meet increase of demand by increase of supply, is not obvious. We know, indeed, (*First Principles*, §§ 85, 173,) that of necessity, the rhythmical changes produced by antagonistic organic actions cannot any of them be carried to an excess in one direction, without there being produced an equivalent excess in the opposite direction. It is a corollary from the persistence of force, that any deviation effected by a disturbing cause, acting on some member of a moving equilibrium, must (unless it altogether destroys the moving equilibrium) be eventually followed by a compensating deviation. Hence, that excess of repair should succeed excess of waste, is to be expected. But how happens the mean state of the organ to be changed? If daily extra waste naturally brings about daily extra repair only to an equivalent extent, the mean state of the organ should remain constant. How then comes the organ to augment in size and power?

Such answer to this question as we may hope to find, must be looked for in the effects wrought on the organism as a whole by increased function in one of its parts. For since the discharge of its function by any part is possible only on condition that those various other functions on which its own is immediately dependent are also discharged, it follows that excess in its function presupposes some excess in their functions. Additional work given to a muscle implies additional work given to the branch arteries which bring it blood, and additional work, smaller in proportion, to the arteries from which these branch arteries come. Similarly, the smaller and larger veins which take away the blood, as well as those structures which deal with effete products, must have more to do. And yet further, on the nervous centres which excite the muscle a certain extra duty must fall. But excess of waste will entail excess of repair, in these parts as well as in the muscle. The several appliances by which the nutrition and excitation of an organ are carried on, must also be influenced by this rhythm of action and reaction; and therefore, after losing more than usual by the destructive process they must gain more than usual by the constructive process. But temporarily-increased efficiency in these appliances by which blood and nervous force are brought to an organ, will cause extra assimilation in the organ, beyond that required to balance its extra expenditure. Regarding the functions as constituting a moving equilibrium, we may say that divergence of any function in the direction of increase, causes the functions with which it is bound up to diverge in the same direction; that these, again, cause the functions which they are bound up with, also to diverge in the same direction; and that these divergences of the connected functions allow the specially-affected function to be carried further in this direction than it could otherwise be—further than the perturbing force could carry it if it had a fixed basis.

It must be admitted that this is but a vague explanation. Among actions so involved as these, we can scarcely expect to do more than dimly discern a harmony with first principles. That the facts are to be interpreted in some such way, may, however, be inferred from the circumstance that an extra supply of blood continues for some time to be sent to an organ that has been unusually exercised; and that when unusual exercise is long continued a permanent increase of vascularity results.

§ 69. Answers to the questions—Why do these adaptive modifications in an individual animal soon reach a limit? and why, in the descendants of such animal, similarly conditioned, is this limit very slowly extended?—are to be found in the same direction as was the answer to the last question. And here the connexion of cause and consequence is more manifest.

Since the function of any organ is dependent on the functions of the organs which supply it with materials and stimuli; and since the functions of these subsidiary organs are dependent on the functions of organs which supply them with materials and stimuli; it follows that before any great extra power of discharging its function can be gained by a specially-exercised organ, a considerable extra power must be gained by a series of immediately-subservient organs, and some extra power by a secondary series of remotely-subservient organs. Thus there are required numerous and wide-spread modifications. Before the artery which feeds a hard-worked muscle can permanently furnish a large additional quantity of blood, it must increase in diameter; and that its increase of diameter may be of use, the main artery from which it diverges must also be so far modified as to bring this additional quantity of blood to the branch artery. Similarly with the veins; similarly with the structures which remove waste-products; similarly with the nerves. And when we ask what these subsidiary changes imply, we are forced to conclude that there must be an analogous group of more numerous changes ramifying throughout the system. The growth of the arteries primarily and secondarily implicated, cannot go to any extent without growth in the minor blood-vessels on which their nutrition depends; while their greater contractile power involves enlargement of the nerves which excite them, and some modification of that part of the spinal cord whence these nerves proceed. Thus, without tracing the like remote alterations implied by extra growth of the veins, lymphatics, glandular organs, and other agencies, it is manifest that a large amount of rebuilding must be done throughout the organism, before any organ of importance can be permanently increased in size and power to a great extent. Hence, though such extra growth in any part as does not necessitate considerable changes throughout the rest of the organism, may rapidly take place; a further growth in this part, requiring a re-modelling of numerous parts remotely and slightly affected, must take place but slowly.

We have before found our conceptions of vital processes made clearer by studying analogous social processes. In societies there is a mutual dependence of functions, essentially like that which exists in organisms; and there is also an essentially like reaction of functions on structures. From the laws of adaptive modification in societies, we may therefore hope to get a clue to the laws of adaptive modification in organisms. Let us suppose, then, that a society has arrived at a state of equilibrium analogous to that of a mature animal—a state not like our own, in which growth and structural development are rapidly going on, but a state of settled balance among the functional powers of the various classes and industrial bodies, and a consequent fixity in the relative sizes of such classes and bodies. Further, let us suppose that in a society thus balanced there occurs something which throws an unusual demand on one industry—say an unusual demand for ships (which we will assume to be built of iron) in consequence of a competing mercantile nation having been prostrated by famine or pestilence. The immediate result of this additional demand for iron ships is the employment of more workmen, and the purchase of more iron, by the ship-builders; and when, presently, the demand continuing, the ship-builders find their premises and machinery insufficient, they enlarge them. If the extra requirement persists, the high interest and high wages bring such extra capital and labour into the business as are needed for new ship-building establishments. But such extra capital and labour do not come quickly; since, in a balanced community, not increasing in population and wealth, labour and capital have to be drawn from other industries, where they are already yielding the ordinary returns. Let us now go a step further. Suppose that this iron-ship-building industry, having enlarged as much as the available capital and labour permit, is still unequal to the demand; what limits its immediate further growth? The lack of iron. By the hypothesis, the iron-producing industry, like all the other industries throughout the community, yields only as much iron as is habitually required for all the purposes to which iron is applied: ship-building being only one. If, then, extra iron is required for ship-building, the first effect is to withdraw part of the iron habitually consumed for other purposes, and to raise the price of iron. Presently, the iron-makers feel this change and their stocks dwindle. As, however, the quantity of iron required for ship-building forms but a small part of the total quantity required for all purposes, the extra demand on the iron-makers can be nothing like so great in proportion as is the extra demand on the ship-builders. Whence it follows that there will be much less tendency to an immediate enlargement of the iron-producing industry; since the extra quantity will for some time be obtained by working extra hours. Nevertheless if, as fast as more iron can be thus supplied, the ship-building industry goes on growing—if, consequently, the iron-makers experience a permanently-increased demand, and out of their greater profits get higher interest on capital, as well as pay higher wages; there will eventually be an abstraction of capital and labour from other industries to enlarge the iron-producing industry: new blast-furnaces, new rolling-mills, new cottages for workmen, will be erected. But obviously, the inertia of capital and labour to be overcome before the iron-producing industry can grow by a decrease of certain other industries, will prevent its growth from taking place until long after the increased ship-building industry has demanded it; and meanwhile, the growth of the ship-building industry must be limited by the deficiency of iron. A remoter restraint of the same nature meets us if we go a step further—a restraint which can be overcome only in a still longer time. For the manufacture of iron depends on the supply of coal. The production of coal being previously in equilibrium with the consumption; and the consumption of coal for the manufacture of iron being but a small part of the total consumption; it follows that a considerable extension of the iron manufacture, when it at length takes place, will cause but a comparatively small additional demand on the coal-owners and coal-miners—a demand which will not, for a long period, suffice to cause enlargement of the coal-trade, by drawing capital and labour from other investments and occupations. And until the permanent extra demand for coal has become great enough to draw from other investments and occupations sufficient capital and labour to sink new mines, the increasing production of iron must be restricted by the scarcity of coal, and the multiplication of ship-yards and ship-builders must be checked by the want of iron. Thus, in a community which has reached a state of moving equilibrium, though any one industry directly affected by an additional demand may rapidly undergo a small extra growth, yet a growth beyond this, requiring as it does the building-up of subservient industries, less directly and strongly affected, as well as the partial unbuilding of other industries, can take place only with comparative slowness. And a still further growth, requiring structural modifications of industries still more distantly affected, must take place still more slowly.

On returning from this analogy, we see more clearly the truth that any considerable member of an animal organism, cannot be greatly enlarged without some general reorganization. Besides a building up of the primary, secondary, and tertiary groups of the subservient parts, there must be an unbuilding of sundry non-subservient parts; or, at any rate, there must be permanently established a lower nutrition of such non-subservient parts. For it must be remembered that in a mature animal, or one which has reached a balance between assimilation and expenditure, there cannot (supposing general conditions to remain constant) be an increase in the nutrition of some organs without a decrease in the nutrition of others; and an organic establishment of the increase implies an organic establishment of the decrease—implies more or less change in the processes and structures throughout the entire system. And here, indeed, is disclosed one reason why growing animals undergo adaptations so much more readily than adult ones. For while there is surplus nutrition, it is possible for specially-exercised parts to be specially enlarged without any positive deduction from other parts. There is required only that negative deduction implied in the diminished growth of other parts.

§ 70. Pursuing the argument further, we reach an explanation of the third general truth; namely that organisms, and species of organisms, which, under new conditions, have undergone adaptive modifications, soon return to something like their original structures when restored to their original conditions. Seeing, as we have done, how excess of action and excess of nutrition in any part of an organism, must affect action and nutrition in subservient parts, and these again in other parts, until the re-action has divided and subdivided itself throughout the organism, affecting in decreasing degrees the more and more numerous parts more and more remotely implicated; we see that the consequent changes in the parts remotely implicated, constituting the great mass of the organism, must be extremely slow. Hence, if the need for the adaptive modification ceases before the great mass of the organism has been much altered in its structure by these ramified but minute reactions, we shall have a condition in which the specially-modified part is not in equilibrium with the rest. All the remotely-affected organs, as yet but little changed, will, in the absence of the perturbing cause, resume very nearly their previous actions. The parts that depend on them will consequently by and by do the same. Until at length, by a reversal of the adaptive process, the organ at first affected will be brought back almost to its original state. Reconsidering the above-drawn analogy between an organism and a society, will enable us better to recognize this necessity. If, in the case supposed, the extra demand for iron ships, after causing the erection of some additional ship-yards and the drawing of iron from other manufactures, were to cease; the old dimensions of the ship-building trade would be quickly returned to: discharged workmen would seek fresh occupations, and the new yards would be devoted to other uses. But if the increased need for ships lasted long enough, and became great enough, to cause a flow of capital and labour from other industries into the iron-manufacture, a falling off in the demand for ships, would much less rapidly entail a dwindling of the ship-building industry. For iron being now produced in greater quantity, a diminished consumption of it for ships would cause a fall in its price, and a consequent fall in the cost of ships: thus enabling the ship-builders to meet the competition which we may suppose led to a decrease in the orders they received. And since, when new blast-furnaces and rolling-mills, &c., had been built with capital drawn from other industries, its transference back into other industries would involve great loss; the owners, rather than transfer it, would accept unusually low interest, and an excess of iron would continue to be produced; resulting in an undue cheapness of ships, and a maintenance of the ship-building industry at a size beyond the need. Eventually, however, if the number of ships required still diminished, the production of iron in excess would become very unremunerative: some of the blast-furnaces would be blown out; and as much of the capital and labour as remained available would be re-distributed among other occupations. Without repeating the steps of the argument, it will be clear that were the enlargement of the ship-building industry great enough, and did it last long enough to cause an increase in the number of coal-mines, the ship-building industry would be still better able to maintain itself under adverse circumstances; but that it would, though at a more distant period, end by sinking down to the needful dimensions. Thus our conclusions are:—First, that if the extra growth caused by extra activity in a particular industry has lasted long enough only to remodel the proximately-affected industries; it will dwindle away again after a moderate period, if the need for it disappears. Second, that a long period must be required before the re-actions produced by an enlarged industry can cause a re-construction of the whole society, and before the countless re-distributions of capital and labour can again reach a state of equilibrium. And third, that only when such a new state of equilibrium is eventually reached, can the adaptive modification become a permanent one. How, in animal organisms the like argument holds, need not be pointed out. The reader will readily follow the parallel.

That organic types should be comparatively stable, might be anticipated on the hypothesis of Evolution. The structure of any organism being a product of the almost infinite series of actions and reactions to which ancestral organisms have been exposed; any unusual actions and reactions brought to bear on an individual, can have but an infinitesimal effect in permanently changing the structure of the organism as a whole. The new set of forces, compounded with all the antecedent sets of forces, can but inappreciably modify that moving equilibrium of functions which all these antecedent sets of forces have established. Though there may result a considerable perturbation of certain functions—a considerable divergence from their ordinary rhythms—yet the general centre of equilibrium cannot be sensibly changed. On the removal of the perturbing cause the previous balance will be quickly restored: the effect of the new forces being almost obliterated by the enormous aggregate of forces which the previous balance expresses.

§ 71. As thus understood, the phenomena of adaptation fall into harmony with first principles. The inference that organic types are fixed, because the deviations from them which can be produced within assignable periods are relatively small, and because, when a force producing deviation ceases, there is a return to something like the original state; proves to be an invalid inference. Without assuming fixity of species, we find good reasons for anticipating that kind and degree of stability which is observed. We find grounds for concluding, *a priori*, that an adaptive change of structure will soon reach a point beyond which further adaptation will be slow; for concluding that when the modifying cause has been but a short time in action, the modification generated will be evanescent; for concluding that a modifying cause acting even for many generations, will do but little towards permanently altering the organic equilibrium of a race; and for concluding that on the cessations of such cause, its effects will become unapparent in the course of a few generations.

CHAPTER VI.

INDIVIDUALITY.

§ 72. What is an individual? is a question which many readers will think it easy to answer. Yet it is a question that has led to much controversy among Zoologists and Botanists, and no quite satisfactory reply to it seems possible. As applied to a man, or to any one of the higher animals, which are all sharply-defined and independent, the word individual has a clear meaning: though even here, when we turn from average cases to exceptional cases—as a calf with two heads and two pairs of fore-limbs—we find ourselves in doubt whether to predicate one individuality or two. But when we extend our range of observation to the organic world at large, we find that difficulties allied to this exceptional one meets us everywhere under every variety of form.

Each uniaxial plant may perhaps fairly be regarded as a distinct individual; though there are botanists who do not make even this admission. What, however, are we to say of a multiaxial plant? It is, indeed, usual to speak of a tree with its many branches and shoots as singular; but strong reasons may be urged for considering it as plural. Every one of its axes has a more or less independent life, and when cut off and planted may grow into the likeness of its parent; or, by grafting and budding, parts of this tree may be developed upon another tree, and there manifest their specific peculiarities. Shall we regard all the growing axes thus resulting from slips and grafts and buds, as parts of one individual or as distinct individuals? If a strawberry-plant sends out runners carrying buds at their ends, which strike root and grow into independent plants that separate from the original one by decay of the runners, must we not say that they possess separate individualities; and yet if we do this, are we not at a loss to say when their separate individualities were established, unless we admit that each bud was from the beginning an individual? Commenting on such perplexities Schleiden says—"Much has been written and disputed concerning the conception of the individual, without, however, elucidating the subject, principally owing to the misconception that still exists as to the origin of the conception. Now the individual is no conception, but the mere subjective comprehension of an actual object, presented to us under some given specific conception, and on this latter it alone depends whether the object is or is not an individual. Under the specific conception of the solar system, ours is an individual: in relation to the specific conception of a planetary body, it is an aggregate of many individuals." ... "I think, however, that looking at the indubitable facts already mentioned, and the relations treated of in the course of these considerations, it will appear most advantageous and most useful, in a scientific point of view, to consider the vegetable cell as the general type of the plant (simple plant of the first order). Under this conception, *Protococcus* and other plants consisting of only one cell, and the spore and pollen-granule, will appear as individuals. Such individuals may, however, again, with a partial renunciation of their individual independence, combine under definite laws into definite forms (somewhat as the individual animals do in the globe of the *Volvox globator*[25]). These again appear empirically as individual beings, under a conception of a species (simple plants of the second order) derived from the form of the normal connexion of the elementary individuals. But we cannot stop here, since Nature herself combines these individuals, under a definite form, into larger associations, whence we draw the third conception of the plant, from a connexion, as it were, of the second power (compound plants—plants of the third order). The simple plant proceeding from the combination of the elementary individuals is then termed a bud (*gemma*), in the composition of plants of the third order."

The animal kingdom presents still greater difficulties. When, from sundry points on the body of a common polype, there bud out young polypes which, after acquiring mouths and tentacles and closing up the communications between their stomachs and the stomach of the parent, finally separate from the parent; we may with propriety regard them as distinct individuals. But when in the allied compound *Hydrozoa*, we find that these young polypes continue permanently connected with the parent; and when by this continuous budding-out there is presently produced a tree-like aggregation, having a common alimentary canal into which the digestive cavity of each polype opens; it is no longer so clear that these little sacs, furnished with mouths and tentacles, are severally to be regarded as distinct individuals. We cannot deny a certain individuality to the polypedom. And on discovering that some of the buds, instead of unfolding in the same manner as the rest, are transformed into capsules in which eggs are developed—on discovering that certain of the incipient polypes thus become wholly dependent on the aggregate for their nutrition, and discharge functions which have nothing to do with their own maintenance, we have still clearer proof that the individualities of the members are partially merged in the individuality of the group. Other organisms belonging to the same order, display still more decidedly this transition from simple individualities to a complex individuality. In the *Diphyes* there is a special modification of one or more members of the polypedom into a swimming apparatus which, by its rhythmical contractions, propels itself through the water, drawing the polypedom after it. And in the more differentiated *Physalia* various organs result from the metamorphosis of parts which are the homologues of individual polypes. In this last instance, the individuality of the aggregate is so predominant that the individualities of its members are practically lost. This combination of individualities in such way as to produce a composite individual, meets us in other forms among the ascidians. While in some of these, as in the *Clavelina* and in the *Botryllidæ*, the animals associated are but little subordinated to the community they form, in others they are so combined as to form a compound individual. The pelagic ascidian *Doliolum* is an example. "Here we find a large individual which swims by contractions of circular muscular bands, carries a train of smaller individuals attached to a long dorsal process of the test. These are arranged in three rows: those constituting the lateral row have wide mouths and no sexual organs or organs of locomotion—they subserve the nutrition of the colony, a truth which is illustrated by the fact that as soon as they are properly developed the large individual (the mother) loses her alimentary canal;" while from the median row are eventually derived the sexual zoids.

On the hypothesis of Evolution, perplexities of this nature are just such as we might anticipate. If Life in general commenced with minute and simple forms, like those out of which all organisms, however complex, now originate; and if the transitions from these primordial units to organisms made up of groups of such units, and to higher organisms made up of groups of such groups took place by degrees; it is clear that individualities of the first and simplest order would merge gradually in those of a larger and more complex order, and these again in others of an order having still greater bulk and organization. Hence it would be impossible to say where the lower individualities ceased and the higher individualities commenced.

§ 73. To meet these difficulties, it has been proposed that the whole product of a single fertilized germ shall be regarded as a single individual; whether such whole product be organized into one mass, or whether it be organized into many masses that are partially or completely separate. It is urged that whether the development of the fertilized germ be continuous or discontinuous (§ 50) is a matter of secondary importance; that the totality of living tissue to which the fertilized germ gives rise in any one case, is the equivalent of the totality to which it gives rise in any other case; and that we must recognize this equivalence, whether such totality of living tissue takes a concrete or a discrete arrangement. In pursuance of this view, a zoological individual is constituted either by any such single animal as a mammal or bird, which may properly claim the title of a *zoon*, or by any such group of animals as the numerous *Medusæ* that have been developed from the same egg, which are to be severally distinguished as *zooids*.

Admitting it to be very desirable that there should be words for expressing these relations and this equivalence, it may be objected that to apply the word individual to a number of separate living bodies, is inconvenient:

conflicting so much, as it does, with the ordinary conception which this word suggests. It seems a questionable use of language to say that the countless masses of *Anacharis Alsinastrum* (now *Eloidea canadensis*) which, within these few years, have grown up in our rivers, canals, and ponds, are all parts of one individual: and yet as this plant does not seed in England, these countless masses, having arisen by discontinuous development, must be so regarded if we accept the above definition.

It may be contended, too, that while it does violence to our established way of thinking, this mode of interpreting the facts is not without its difficulties. Something seems to be gained by restricting the application of the title individual, to organisms which, being in all respects fully developed, possess the power of producing their kind after the ordinary sexual method, and denying this title to those incomplete organisms which have not this power. But the definition does not really establish this distinction for us. On the one hand, we have cases in which, as in the working bee, the whole of the germ-product is aggregated into a single organism; and yet, though an individual according to the definition, this organism has no power of reproducing its kind. On the other hand, we have cases like that of the perfect *Aphis*, where the organism is but an infinitesimal part of the germ product, and yet has that completeness required for sexual reproduction. Further, it might be urged with some show of reason, that if the conception of individuality involves the conception of completeness, then, an organism which possesses an independent power of reproducing itself, being more complete than an organism in which this power is dependent on the aid of another organism, is more individual.

§ 74. There is, indeed, as already implied, no definition of individuality that is unobjectionable. All we can do is to make the best practicable compromise.

As applied either to an animate or an inanimate object, the word individual ordinarily connotes union among the parts of the object and separateness from other objects. This fundamental element in the conception of individuality, we cannot with propriety ignore in the biological application of the word. That which we call an individual plant or animal must, therefore, be some concrete whole and not a discrete whole. If, however, we say that each concrete living whole is to be regarded as an individual, we are still met by the question—What constitutes a concrete living whole? A young organism arising by internal or external gemmation from a parent organism, passes gradually from a state in which it is an indistinguishable part of the parent organism to a state in which it is a separate organism of like structure with the parent. At what stage does it become an individual? And if its individuality be conceded only when it completely separates from the parent, must we deny individuality to all organisms thus produced which permanently retain their connexions with their parents? Or again, what must we say of the *Hectocotylus*, which is an arm of the Cuttle-fish that undergoes a special development and then, detaching itself, lives independently for a considerable period? And what must we say of the larval nemertine worm the pilidium of which with its nervous system is left to move about awhile after the developing worm has dropped out of it?

To answer such questions we must revert to the definition of life. The distinction between individual in its biological sense, and individual in its more general sense, must consist in the manifestation of Life, properly so called. Life we have seen to be, "the definite combination of heterogeneous change, both simultaneous and successive, in correspondence with external co-existences and sequences." Hence, a biological individual is any concrete whole having a structure which enables it, when placed in appropriate conditions, to continuously adjust its internal relations to external relations, so as to maintain the equilibrium of its functions. In pursuance of this conception, we must consider as individuals all those wholly or partially independent organized masses which arise by multicentral and multiaxial development that is either continuous or discontinuous (§ 50). We must accord the title to each separate aphis, each polype of a polypedom, each bud or shoot of a lowering plant, whether it detaches itself as a bulbil or remains attached as a branch.

By thus interpreting the facts we do not, indeed, avoid all anomalies. While, among flowering plants, the power of independent growth and development is usually possessed only by shoots or axes; yet, in some cases, as in that of the Begonia-leaf awhile since mentioned, the appendage of an axis, or even a small fragment of such appendage, is capable of initiating and carrying on the functions of life; and in other cases, as shown by M. Naudin in the *Drosera intermedia*, young plants are occasionally developed from the surfaces of leaves. Nor among forms like the compound *Hydrozoa*, does the definition enable us to decide where the line is to be drawn between the individuality of the group and the individualities of the members: merging into each other, as these do, in different degrees. But, as before said, such difficulties must necessarily present themselves if organic forms have arisen by insensible gradations. We must be content with a course which commits us to the smallest number of incongruities; and this course is, to consider as an individual any organized mass which is capable of independently carrying on that continuous adjustment of inner to outer relations which constitutes Life.

CHAPTER VIA.

CELL-LIFE AND CELL-MULTIPLICATION.

§ 74*a*. The progress of science is simultaneously towards simplification and towards complication. Analysis simplifies its conceptions by resolving phenomena into their factors, and by then showing how each simple mode of action may be traced under multitudinous forms; while, at the same time, synthesis shows how each factor, by cooperation with various other factors in countless modes and degrees, produces different results innumerable in their amounts and varieties. Of course this truth holds alike of processes and of products. Observation and the grouping into classes make it clear that through multitudinous things superficially unlike there run the same cardinal traits of structure; while, along with these major unities, examination discloses innumerable minor diversities.

A concomitant truth, or the same truth under another aspect, is that Nature everywhere presents us with complexities within complexities, which go on revealing themselves as we investigate smaller and smaller objects. In a preceding chapter (§§ 54*a*, 54*b*) it was pointed out that each primitive organism, in common with each of the units out of which the higher and larger organisms are built, was found a generation ago to consist of nucleus, protoplasm, and cell-wall. This general conception of a cell remained for a time the outcome of inquiry; but with the advance of microscopy it became manifest that within these minute structures processes and products of an astonishing nature are to be seen. These we have now to contemplate.

In the passages just referred to it was said that the external layer or cell-wall is a non-essential, inanimate part produced by the animate contents. Itself a product of protoplasmic action, it takes no part in protoplasmic changes, and may therefore here be ignored.

§ 74*b*. One of the complexities within complexities was disclosed when it was found that the protoplasm itself has a complicated structure. Different observers have described it as constituted by a network or reticulum, a sponge-work, a foam-work. Of these the first may be rejected; since it implies a structure lying in one plane. If we accept the second we have to conceive the threads of protoplasm, corresponding to the fibres of the sponge, as leaving interstices filled either with liquid or solid. They cannot be filled with a continuous solid, since all motion of the protoplasm would be negatived; and that their content is not liquid seems shown by the fact that its parts move about under the form of granules or microsomes. But the conception of moving granules implies the conception of immersion in a liquid or semi-liquid substance in which they move—not a sponge-work of threads but a foam-work, consisting everywhere of septa interposed among the granules. This is the hypothesis which sundry microscopists espouse, and which seems mechanically the most feasible: the only one which consists with the "streaming" of protoplasm. Ordinarily the name protoplasm is applied to the aggregate mass—the semi-liquid, hyaline substance and the granules or microsomes it contains.

What these granules or microsomes are—whether, as some have contended, they are the essential living elements of the protoplasm, or whether, as is otherwise held, they are nutritive particles, is at present undecided. But the fact, alleged by sundry observers, that the microsomes often form rows, held together by intervening substance, seems to imply that these minute bodies are not inert. Leaving aside unsettled questions, however, one fact of significance is manifest—an immense multiplication of surfaces over which inter-action may take place. Anyone who drops into dilute sulphuric acid a small nail and then drops a pinch of iron filings, will be shown, by the rapid disappearance of the last and the long continuance of the first, how greatly the increasing of surfaces by multiplication of fragments facilitates change. The effect of subdivision in producing a large area in a small space, is shown in the lungs, where the air-cells on the sides of which the blood-vessels ramify, are less than 1/100th of an inch in diameter, while they number 700,000,000. In the composition of every tissue we see the same principle. The living part, or protoplasm, is divided into innumerable protoplasts, among which are distributed the materials and agencies producing changes. And now we find this principle carried still deeper in the structure of the protoplasm itself. Each microscopic portion of it is minutely divided in such ways that its threads or septa have multitudinous contacts with those included portions of matter which take part in its activities.

Concerning the protoplasm contained in each cell, named by some cytoplasm, it remains to say that it always includes a small body called the centrosome, which appears to have a directive function. Usually the centrosome lies outside the nucleus, but is alleged to be sometimes within it. During what is called the "resting stage," or what might more properly be called the growing stage (for clearly the occasional divisions imply that in the intervals between them there has been increase) the centrosome remains quiescent, save in the respect that it exercises some coercive influence on the protoplasm around. This results in the radially-arranged lines constituting an "aster." What is the nature of the coercion exercised by the centrosome—a body hardly distinguishable in size from the microsomes or granules of protoplasm around—is not known. It can scarcely be a repelling force; since, in a substance of liquid or semi-liquid kind, this could not produce approximately straight lines. That it is an attractive force seems more probable; and the nature of the attraction would be comprehensible did the centrosome augment in bulk with rapidity. For if integration were in progress, the drawing in of materials might well produce converging lines. But this seems scarcely a tenable interpretation; since, during the so-called "resting stage," this star-like structure exists—exists, that is, while no active growth of the centrosome is going on.

Respecting this small body we have further to note that, like the cell as a whole, it multiplies by fission, and that the bisection of it terminates the resting or growing stage and initiates those complicated processes by which two cells are produced out of one: the first step following the fission being the movement of the halves, with their respective completed asters, to the opposite sides of the nucleus.

§ 74*c*. With the hypothesis, now general, that the nucleus or kernel of a cell is its essential part, there has not unnaturally grown up the dogma that it is always present; but there is reason to think that the evidence is somewhat strained to justify this dogma.

In the first place, beyond the cases in which the nucleus, though ordinarily invisible, is said to have been rendered visible by a re-agent, there are cases, as in the already-named *Archerina*, where no re-agent makes one visible. In the second place, there is the admitted fact that some nuclei are diffused; as in *Trachelocerca* and some other Infusoria. In them the numerous scattered granules are supposed to constitute a nucleus: an interpretation obviously biassed by the desire to save the generalization. In the third place, the nucleus is frequently multiple in cells of low types; as in some families of Algæ and predominantly among Fungi. Once more, the so-called nucleus is occasionally a branching structure scarcely to be called a "kernel."

The facts as thus grouped suggest that the nucleus has arisen in conformity with the law of evolution—that the primitive protoplast, though not homogeneous in the full sense, was homogeneous in the sense of being a uniformly granular protoplasm; and that the protoplasts with diffused nuclei, together with those which are multi-nucleate, and those which have nuclei of a branching form, represent stages in that process by which the relatively homogeneous protoplast passed into the relatively heterogeneous one now almost universal.

Concerning the structure and composition of the developed nucleus, the primary fact to be named is that, like the surrounding granular cytoplasm, it is formed of two distinct elements. It has a groundwork or matrix not differing much from that of the cytoplasm, and at some periods continuous with it; and immersed in this it has a special matter named chromatin, distinguished from its matrix by becoming dyed more or less deeply when exposed to fit re-agents. During the "resting stage," or period of growth and activity which comes between periods of division, the chromatin is dispersed throughout the ground-substance, either in discrete portions or in such way as to form an irregular network or sponge-work, various in appearance. When the time for fission is approaching this dispersed chromatin begins to gather itself together: reaching its eventual concentration through several stages. By its concentration are produced the chromosomes, constant in number in each species of plant or animal. It is alleged that the substance of the chromosomes is not continuous, but consists of separate elements or granules, which have been named chromomeres; and it is also alleged that, whether in the dispersed or integrated form, each chromosome retains its individuality—that the chromomeres composing it, now spreading out into a network and now uniting into a worm-like body, form a group which never loses its identity. Be this as it may, however, the essential fact is that during the growth-period the chromatin substance is widely distributed, and concentration of it is one of the chief steps towards a division of the nucleus and presently of the cell.

During this process of mitosis or karyokinesis, the dispersed chromatin having passed through the coil-stage, reaches presently the star-stage, in which the chromosomes are arranged symmetrically about the equatorial plane of the nucleus. Meanwhile in each of them there has been a preparation for splitting longitudinally in such way that the halves when separated contain (or are assumed to contain) equal numbers of the granules or chromomeres, which some think are the ultimate morphological units of the chromosomes. A simultaneous change has occurred: there has been in course of formation a structure known as the *amphiaster*. The two centrosomes which, as before said, place themselves on opposite sides of the nucleus, become the terminal poles of a spindle-shaped arrangement of fibres, arising mainly from the groundwork of the nucleus, now continuous with the groundwork of the cytoplasm. A conception of this structure may be formed by supposing that the radiating fibres of the respective asters, meeting one another and uniting in the intermediate space, thereafter exercise a tractive force; since it is clear that, while the central fibres of the bundle will form straight lines, the outer ones, pulling against one another not in straight lines, will form curved lines, becoming more pronounced in their curvatures as the distance from the axis increases. That a tractive force is at work seems inferable from the results. For the separated halves of the split chromosomes, which now form clusters on the two sides of the equatorial plane, gradually part company, and are apparently drawn as clusters towards the opposing centrosomes. As this change progresses the original nucleus loses its individuality. The new chromosomes, halves of the previous chromosomes, concentrate to found two new nuclei; and, by something like a reversal of the stages above described, the chromatin becomes dispersed throughout the substance of each new nucleus. While this is going on the cell itself, undergoing constriction round its equator, divides into two.

Many parts of this complex process are still imperfectly understood, and various opinions concerning them are current. But the essential facts are that this peculiar substance, the chromatin, at other times existing dispersed, is, when division is approaching, gathered together and dealt with in such manner as apparently to insure equal quantities being bequeathed by the mother-cell to the two daughter-cells.

§ 74*d*. What is the physiological interpretation of these structures and changes? What function does the nucleus discharge; and, more especially, what is the function discharged by the chromatin? There have been to these questions sundry speculative answers.

The theory espoused by some, that the nucleus is the regulative organ of the cell, is met by difficulties. One of them is that, as pointed out in the chapter on "Structure," the nucleus, though morphologically central, is not central geometrically considered; and that its position, often near to some parts of the periphery and remote from others, almost of itself negatives the conclusion that its function is directive in the ordinary sense of the word. It could not well control the cytoplasm in the same ways in all directions and at different distances. A further difficulty is that the cytoplasm when deprived of its nucleus can perform for some time various of its actions, though it eventually dies without reproducing itself.

For the hypothesis that the nucleus is a vehicle for transmitting hereditary characters, the evidence seems strong. When it was shown that the head of a spermatozoon is simply a detached nucleus, and that its fusion with the nucleus of an ovum is the essential process initiating the development of a new organism, the legitimate inference appeared to be that these two nuclei convey respectively the paternal and maternal traits which are mingled in the offspring. And when there came to be discerned the karyokinesis by which the chromatin is, during cell-fission, exactly halved between the nuclei of the daughter-cells, the conclusion was drawn that the chromatin is more especially the agent of inheritance. But though, taken by themselves, the phenomena of fertilization seem to warrant this inference, the inference does not seem congruous with the phenomena of ordinary cell-multiplication—phenomena which have nothing to do with fertilization and the transmission of hereditary characters. No explanation is yielded of the fact that ordinary cell-multiplication exhibits an elaborate process for exact halving of the chromatin. Why should this substance be so carefully portioned out among the cells of tissues which are not even remotely concerned with propagation of the species? If it be said that the end achieved is the conveyance of paternal and maternal qualities in equal degrees to every tissue; then the reply is that they do not seem to be conveyed in equal degrees. In the offspring there is not a uniform diffusion of the two sets of traits throughout all parts, but an irregular mixture of traits of the one with traits of the other.

In presence of these two suggested hypotheses and these respective difficulties, may we not suspect that the action of the chromatin is one which in a way fulfils both functions? Let us consider what action may do this.

§ 74*e*. The chemical composition of chromatin is highly complex, and its complexity, apart from other traits, implies relative instability. This is further implied by the special natures of its components. Various analyses have shown that it consists of an organic acid (which has been called nucleic acid) rich in phosphorus, combined with an albuminous substance: probably a combination of various proteids. And the evidence, as summarised by Wilson, seems to show that where the proportion of phosphorized acid is high the activity of the substance is great, as in the heads of spermatozoa; while, conversely, where the quantity of phosphorus is relatively small, the substance approximates in character to the cytoplasm. Now (like sulphur, present in the albuminoid base), phosphorus is an element which, besides having several allotropic forms, has a great affinity for oxygen; and an organic compound into which it enters, beyond the instability otherwise caused, has a special instability caused by its presence. The tendency to undergo change will therefore be great when the proportion of the phosphorized component is great. Hence the statement that "the chemical differences between chromatin and cytoplasm, striking and constant as they are, are differences of degree only;" and the conclusion that the activity of the chromatin is specially associated with the phosphorus.[26]

What, now, are the implications? Molecular agitation results from decomposition of each phosphorized molecule: shocks are continually propagated around. From the chromatin, units of which are thus ever falling into stabler states, there are ever being diffused waves of molecular motion, setting up molecular changes in the cytoplasm. The chromatin stands towards the other contents of the cell in the same relation that a nerve-element stands to any element of an organism which it excites: an interpretation congruous with the fact that the chromatin is as near to as, and indeed nearer than, a nerve-ending to any minute structure stimulated by it.

Several confirmatory facts may be named. During the intervals between cell-fissions, when growth and the usual cell-activities are being carried on, the chromatin is dispersed throughout the nucleus into an irregular network: thus greatly increasing the surface of contact between its substance and the substances in which it is imbedded. As has been remarked, this wide distribution furthers metabolism—a metabolism which in this case has, as we infer, the function of generating, not special matters but special motions. Moreover, just as the wave of disturbance a nerve carries produces an effect which is determined, not by anything which is peculiar in itself, but by the peculiar nature of the organ to which it is carried—muscular, glandular or other; so here, the waves diffused from the chromatin do not determine the kinds of changes in the cytoplasm, but simply excite it: its particular activities, whether of movement, absorption, or structural excretion, being determined by its constitution. And then, further, we observe a parallelism between the metabolic changes in the two cases; for, on the one hand, "diminished staining capacity of the chromatin [implying a decreased amount of phosphorus, which gives the staining capacity] occurs during a period of intense constructive activity in the cytoplasm;" and, on the other hand, in high organisms having nervous systems, the intensity of nervous action is measured by the excretion of phosphates—by the using up of the phosphorus contained in nerve-cells.

For thus interpreting the respective functions of chromatin and cytoplasm, yet a further reason may be given. One of the earliest general steps in the evolution of the *Metazoa*, is the differentiation of parts which act from parts which make them act. The *Hydrozoa* show us this. In the hydroid stage there are no specialized contractile organs: these are but incipient: individual ectoderm cells have muscular processes. Nor is there any "special aggregation of nerve-cells." If any stimulating units exist they are scattered. But in the *Medusa*-stage nerve-matter is collected into a ring round the edge of the umbrella. That is to say, in the undeveloped form such motor action as occurs is not effected by a specialized part which excites another part; but in the developed form a differentiation of the two has taken place. All higher types exhibit this differentiation. Be it muscle or gland or other operating organ, the cause of its activity lies not in itself but in a nervous agent, local or central, with which it is connected. Hence, then, there is congruity between the above interpretation and certain general truths displayed by animal organization at large. We may infer that in a way parallel to that just indicated, cell-evolution was, under one of its aspects, a change from a stage in which the exciting substance and the substance excited were mingled with approximate uniformity, to a stage in which the exciting substance was gathered together into the nucleus and finally into the chromosomes: leaving behind the substance excited, now distinguished as cytoplasm.

§ 74*f*. Some further general aspects of the phenomena appear to be in harmony with this interpretation. Let us glance at them.

In Chapters III and IIIA of the First Part, reasons were given for concluding that in the animal organism nitrogenous substances play the part of decomposing agents to the carbo-hydrates—that the molecular disturbance set up by the collapse of a proteid molecule destroys the equilibrium of sundry adjacent carbo-hydrate molecules, and causes that evolution of energy which accompanies their fall into molecules of simpler compounds. Here, if the foregoing argument is valid, we may conclude that this highly complex phosphorized compound which chromatin contains, plays the same part to the adjacent nitrogenous compounds as these play to the carbo-hydrates. If so, we see arising a stage earlier that "general physiological method" illustrated in § 23*f*. It was there pointed out that in animal organisms the various structures are so arranged that evolution of a small amount of energy in one, sets up evolution of a larger amount of energy in another; and often this multiplied energy undergoes a second multiplication of like kind. If this view is tenable, we may now suspect that this method displayed in the structures of the *Metazoa* was initiated in the structures of the *Protozoa*, and consequently characterizes those homologues of them which compose the *Metazoa*.

When contemplated from the suggested point of view, karyokinesis appears to be not wholly incomprehensible. For if the chromatin yields the energy which initiates changes throughout the rest of the cell, we may see why there eventually arises a process for exact halving of the chromatin in a mother-cell between two daughter-cells. To make clear the reason, let us suppose the portioning out of the chromatin leaves one of the two with a sensibly smaller amount than the other. What must result? Its source of activity being relatively less, its rate of growth and its energy of action will be less. If a protozoon, the weaker progeny arising by division of it will originate an inferior stirp, unable to compete successfully with that arising from the sister-cell endowed with a larger portion of chromatin. By continual elimination of the varieties which produce unequal halving, necessarily at a disadvantage if a moiety of their members tend continually to disappear, there will be established a variety in which the halving is exact: the character of this variety being such that all its members aid the permanent multiplication of the species. If, again, the case is that of a metazoon, there will be the same eventual result. An animal or plant in which the chromatin is unequally divided among the cells, must have tissues of uncertain formation. Assume that an organ has, by survival of the fittest, been adjusted in the proportions and qualities of its parts to a given function. If the multiplying protoplasts, instead of taking equal portions of chromatin, have some of them smaller portions, the parts of the organ formed of these, developing less rapidly and having inferior energies, will throw the organ out of adjustment, and the individual will suffer in the struggle for life. That is to say, irregular division of the chromatin will introduce a deranging factor and natural selection will weed out individuals in which it occurs. Of course no interpretation is thus yielded of the special process known as karyokinesis. Probably other modes of equal division might have arisen. Here the argument implies merely that the tendency of evolution is to establish *some* mode. In verification of the view that equal division arises from the cause named, it is pointed out to me that amitosis, which is a negation of mitosis or karyokinesis, occurs in transitory tissues or diseased tissues or where degeneracy is going on.

But how does all this consist with the conclusion that the chromatin conveys hereditary traits—that it is the vehicle in which the constitutional structure, primarily of the species and secondarily of recent ancestors and parents, is represented? To this question there seems to be no definite answer. We may say only that this second function is not necessarily in conflict with the first. While the unstable units of chromatin, ever undergoing changes, diffuse energy around, they may also be units which, under the conditions furnished by fertilization, gravitate towards the organization of the species. Possibly it may be that the complex combination of proteids, common to chromatin and cytoplasm, is that part in which the constitutional characters inhere; while the phosphorized component, falling from its unstable union and decomposing, evolves the energy which, ordinarily the cause of changes, now excites the more active changes following fertilization. This suggestion harmonizes with the fact that the fertilizing substance which in animals constitutes the head of the spermatozoon, and in plants that of the spermatozoid or antherozoid, is distinguished from the other agents concerned by having the highest proportion of the phosphorized element; and it also harmonizes with the fact that the extremely active changes set up by fertilization are accompanied by decrease of this phosphorized element. Speculation aside, however, we may say that the two functions of the chromatin do not exclude one another, but that the general activity which originates from it may be but a lower phase of that special activity caused by fertilization.[27]

§ 74*g*. Here we come unawares to the remaining topic embraced under the title Cell-Life and Cell-Multiplication. We pass naturally from asexual multiplication of cells to sexual multiplication—from cell-reproduction to cell-generation. The phenomena are so numerous and so varied that a large part of them must be passed over. Conjugation among the *Protophyta* and *Protozoa*, beginning with cases in which there is a mingling of the contents of two cells in no visible respect different from one another, and developing into a great variety of processes in which they differ, must be left aside, and attention limited to the terminal process of fertilization as displayed in higher types of organisms.

Before fertilization there occurs in the ovum an incidental process of a strange kind—"strange" because it is a collateral change taking no part in subsequent changes. I refer to the production and extrusion of the "polar bodies." It is recognized that the formation of each is analogous to cell-formation in general; though process and product are both dwarfed. Apart from any ascribed meaning, the fact itself is clear. There is an abortive cell-formation. Abortiveness is seen firstly in the diminutive size of the separated body or cell, and secondly in the deficient number of its chromosomes: a corresponding deficiency being displayed in the group of chromosomes remaining in the egg—remaining, that is (on the hypothesis here to be suggested), in the sister-cell, supposing the polar body to be an aborted cell. It is currently assumed that the end to be achieved by thus extruding part of the chromosomes, is to reduce the remainder to half the number characterizing the species; so that when, to this group in the germ-cell, the sperm-cell brings a similarly-reduced group, union of the two shall bring the chromosomes to the normal number. I venture to suggest another interpretation. In doing this, however, I must forestall a conclusion contained in the next chapter; namely, the conclusion that gamogenesis begins when agamogenesis is being arrested by unfavourable conditions, and that the failing agamogenesis initiates the gamogenesis. Of numerous illustrations to be presently given I will, to make clear the conception, name only one—the formation of fructifying organs in plants at times when, and in places where, shoots are falling off in vigour and leaves in size. Here the successive foliar organs, decreasingly fitted alike in quality and dimensions for carrying on their normal lives, show us an approaching cessation of asexual multiplication, ending in the aborted individuals we call stamens; and the fact that sudden increase of nutrition while gamogenesis is being thus initiated, causes resumption of agamogenesis, shows that the gamogenesis is consequent upon the failing agamogenesis. See then the parallel. On going back from multicellular organisms to unicellular organisms (or those homologues of them which form the reproductive agents in multicellular organisms), we find the same law hold. The polar bodies are aborted cells, indicating that asexual multiplication can no longer go on, and that the conditions leading to sexual multiplication have arisen. If this be so, decrease in the chromatin becomes an initial cause of the change instead of an accompanying incident; and we need no longer assume that a quantity of precious matter is lost, not by passive incapacity, but by active expulsion. Another anomaly disappears. If from the germ-cell there takes place this extrusion of superfluous chromatin, the implication would seem to be that a parallel extrusion takes place from the sperm-cell. But this is not true. In the sperm-cell there occurs just that failure in the production of chromatin which, according to the hypothesis above sketched out, is to be expected; for, in the process of cell-multiplication, the cells which become spermatozoa are *left* with half the number of chromosomes possessed by preceding cells: there is actually that impoverishment and declining vigour here suggested as the antecedent of fertilization. It needs only to imagine the ovum and the polar body to be alike in size, to see the parallelism; and to see that obscuration of it arises from the accumulation of cytoplasm in the ovum.

A test fact remains. Sometimes the first polar body extruded undergoes fission while the second is being formed. This can have nothing to do with reducing the number of chromosomes in the ovum. Unquestionably, however, this change is included with the preceding changes in one transaction, effected by one influence. If, then, it is irrelevant to the decrease of chromosomes, so must the preceding changes be irrelevant: the hypothesis lapses. Contrariwise this fact supports the view suggested above. That extrusion of a polar body is a process of cell-fission is congruous with the fact that another fission occurs after extrusion. And that this occurs irregularly shows that the vital activities, seen in cell-growth and cell-multiplication, now succeed in producing further fission of the dwarfed cell and now fail: the energies causing asexual multiplication are exhausted and there arises the state which initiates sexual multiplication.

Maturation of the ovum having been completed, entrance of the spermatozoon, sometimes through the limiting membrane and sometimes through a micropyle or opening in it, takes place. This instantly initiates a series of complicated changes: not many seconds passing before there begins the formation of an aster around one end of the spermatozoon-head. The growth of this aster, apparently by linear rangings of the granules composing the reticulum of the germ-cell, progresses rapidly; while the whole structure hence arising moves inward. Soon there takes place the fusion of this sperm-nucleus with the germ-nucleus to form the cleavage-nucleus, which, after a pause, begins to divide and subdivide in the same manner as cells at large: so presently forming a cluster of cells out of which arise the layers originating the embyro. The details of this process do not concern us. It suffices to indicate thus briefly its general nature.

And now ending thus the account of genesis under its histological aspect, we pass to the account of genesis under its wider and more significant aspects.

CHAPTER VII.

GENESIS.

§ 75. Having, in the last chapter but one, concluded what constitutes an individual, and having, in the last chapter, contemplated the histological process which initiates a new individual, we are in a position to deal with the multiplication of individuals. For this, the title Genesis is here chosen as being the most comprehensive title—the least specialized in its meaning. By some biologists Generation has been used to signify one method of multiplication, and Reproduction to signify another method; and each of these words has been thus rendered in some degree unfit to signify multiplication in general.

Here the reader is indirectly introduced to the fact that the production of new organisms is carried on in fundamentally unlike ways. Up to quite recent times it was believed, even by naturalists, that all the various processes of multiplication observable in different kinds of organisms, have one essential character in common: it was supposed that in every species the successive generations are alike. It has now been proved, however, that in many plants and in numerous animals, the successive generations are not alike; that from one generation there proceeds another whose members differ more or less in structure from their parents; that these produce others like themselves, or like their parents, or like neither; but that eventually, the original form re-appears. Instead of there being, as in the cases most familiar to us, a constant recurrence of the same form, there is a cyclical recurrence of the same form. These two distinct processes of multiplication, may be aptly termed *homogenesis* and *heterogenesis*.[28] Under these heads let us consider them.

There are two kinds of homogenesis, the simplest of them, probably once universal but now exceptional, being that in which there is no other form of multiplication than one resulting from perpetual spontaneous fission. The rise of distinct sexes was doubtless a step in evolution, and before it took place the formation of new individuals could have arisen only by division of the old, either into two or into many. At present this process survives, so far as appears, among *Bacteria*, certain *Algæ*, and sundry *Protozoa*; though it is possible that a rarely-occurring conjugation has in these cases not yet been observed. It is a probable conclusion, however, that in the *Bacteria* at any rate, the once universal mode of multiplication still survives as an exceptional mode. But now passing over these cases, we have to note that the kind of genesis (once supposed to be the sole kind), in which the successive generations are alike, is sexual genesis, or, as it has been otherwise called—*gamogenesis*. In every species which multiplies by this kind of homogenesis, each generation consists of males and females; and from the fertilized germs they produce the next generation of similar males and females arises: the only needful qualification of this statement being that in many *Protophyta* and *Protozoa* the conjugating cells or protoplasts are not distinguishable in character. This mode of propagation has the further trait, that each fertilized germ usually gives rise to but one individual—the product of development is organized round one axis and not round several axes, Homogenesis in contrast with heterogenesis as exhibited in species which display distinct sexuality, has also the characteristic that each new individual begins as an egg detached from the maternal tissues, instead of being a portion of protoplasm continuous with them, and that its development proceeds independently. This development may be carried on either internally or externally; whence results the division into the oviparous and the viviparous. The oviparous kind is that in which the fertilized germ is extruded from the parent before it has undergone any considerable development. The viviparous kind is that in which development is considerably advanced, or almost completed, before extrusion takes place. This distinction is, however, not a sharply-defined one: there are transitions between the oviparous and the viviparous processes. In ovo-viviparous genesis there is an internal incubation; and though the young are in this case finally extruded from the parent in the shape of eggs, they do not leave the parent's body until after they have assumed something like the parental form. Looking around, we find that homogenesis is universal among the *Vertebrata*. Every vertebrate animal arises from a fertilized germ, and unites into its single individuality the whole product of this fertilized germ. In the mammals or highest *Vertebrata*, this homogenesis is in every case viviparous; in birds it is uniformly oviparous; and in reptiles and fishes it is always essentially oviparous, though there are cases of the kind above referred to, in which viviparity is simulated. Passing to the *Invertebrata*, we find oviparous homogenesis universal among the *Arachnida* (except the Scorpions, which are ovo-viviparous); universal among the higher *Crustacea*, but not among the lower; extremely general, though not universal, among Insects; and universal among the higher *Mollusca* though not among the lower. Along with extreme inferiority among animals, we find homogenesis to be the exception rather than the rule; and in the vegetal kingdom there appear to be no cases, except among the *Algæ* and a few aberrant parasites like the *Rafflesiaceæ*, in which the centre or axis which arises from a fertilized germ becomes the immediate producer of fertilized germs.

In propagation characterized by unlikeness of the successive generations, there is asexual genesis with occasionally-recurring sexual genesis; in other words—*agamogenesis* interrupted more or less frequently by *gamogenesis*. If we set out with a generation of perfect males and females, then, from their ova arise individuals which are neither males nor females, but which produce the next generation from buds. By this method of multiplication many individuals originate from a single fertilized germ. The product of development is organized round more than one centre or axis. The simplest form of heterogenesis is that seen in most uniaxial plants. If, as we find ourselves obliged to do, we regard each separate shoot or axis of growth as a distinct individual, homogenesis is seen in those which have absolutely terminal flowers; but in all other uniaxial plants, the successive individuals are not represented by the series A, A, A, A, &c., but they are represented by the series A, B, A, B, A, B, &c. For in the majority of plants which were classed as uniaxial (§ 50), and which may be conveniently so distinguished from other plants, the axis which shoots up from the seed, and substantially constitutes the plant, does not itself flower but gives lateral origin to flowering axes. Though in ordinary uniaxial plants the fructifying apparatus *appears* to be at the end of the primary, vertical axis; yet dissection shows that, morphologically considered, each fructifying axis is an offspring from the primary axis. There arises from the seed a sexless individual, from which spring by gemmation individuals having reproductive organs; and from these there result fertilized germs or seeds that give rise to sexless individuals. That is to say, gamogenesis and agamogenesis alternate: the peculiarity being that the sexual individuals arise from the sexless ones by continuous development. The *Salpæ* show us an allied form of heterogenesis in the animal kingdom. Individuals developed from fertilized ova, instead of themselves producing fertilized ova, produce, by gemmation, strings of individuals from which fertilized ova again originate. In multiaxial plants, we have a succession of generations represented by the series A, B, B, B, &c., A, B, B, B, &c. Supposing A to be a flowering axis or sexual individual, then, from any fertilized germ it casts off, there grows up a sexless individual, B; from this there bud-out other sexless individuals, B, and so on for generations more or less numerous, until at length, from some of these sexless individuals, there bud-out seed-bearing individuals of the original form A. Branched herbs, shrubs, and trees, exhibit this form of heterogenesis: the successive generations of sexless individuals thus produced being, in most cases, continuously developed, or aggregated into a compound individual, but being in some cases discontinuously developed. Among animals a kind of heterogenesis represented by the same succession of letters, occurs in such compound polypes as the *Sertularia*, and in those of the *Hydrozoa* which assume alternately the polypoid form and the form of the *Medusa*. The chief differences presented by these groups arise from the fact that the successive generations of sexless individuals produced by budding, are in some cases continuously developed, and in others discontinuously developed; and from the fact that, in some cases, the sexual individuals give off their fertilized germs while still growing on the parent-polypedom, but in other cases not until after leaving the parent-polypedom and undergoing further development. Where, as in all the foregoing kinds of agamogenesis, the new individuals bud out, not from any specialized reproductive organs but from unspecialized parts of the parent, the process has been named, by Prof. Owen, *metagenesis*. In most instances the individuals thus produced grow from the outsides of the parents—the metagenesis is external. But there is also a kind of metagenesis which we may distinguish as internal. Certain *entozoa* of the genus *Distoma* exhibit it. From the egg of a *Distoma* there results a rudely-formed creature known as a sporocyst and from this a redia. Gradually, as this divides and buds, the greater part of the inner substance is transformed into young animals called *Cercariæ* (which are the larvæ of *Distomata*); until at length it becomes little more than a living sac full of living offspring. In the *Distoma pacifica*, the brood of young animals thus arising by internal gemmation are not *Cercariæ*, but are like their parent: themselves becoming the producers of *Cercariæ*, after the same manner, at a subsequent period. So that now the succession of forms is represented by the series A, B, A, B, &c., now by the series A, B, B, A, B, B, &c., and now by A, B, B, C, A. Both cases, however, exemplify internal metagenesis in contrast with the several kinds of external metagenesis described above. That agamogenesis which is carried on in a reproductive organ—either an ovarium or the homologue of one—has been called, by Prof. Owen, *parthenogenesis*. It is the process familiarly exemplified in the *Aphides*. Here, from the fertilized eggs laid by perfect females there grow up imperfect females, in the ovaria of which are developed ova that though unfertilized, rapidly assume the organization of other imperfect females, and are born viviparously. From this second generation of imperfect females, there by-and-by arises, in the same manner, a third generation of the same kind; and so on for many generations: the series being thus symbolized by the letters A, B, B, B, B, B, &c., A. Respecting this kind of heterogenesis it should be added that, in animals as in plants, the number of generations of sexless individuals produced before the re-appearance of sexual ones, is indefinite; both in the sense that in the same species it may go on to a greater or less extent according to circumstances, and in the sense that among the generations of individuals proceeding from the same fertilized germ, a recurrence of sexual individuals takes place earlier in some of the diverging lines of multiplication than in others. In trees we see that on some branches flower-bearing axes arise while other branches are still producing only leaf-bearing axes; and in the successive generations of *Aphides* a parallel fact has been observed. Lastly has to be set down that kind of heterogenesis in which, along with gamogenesis, there occurs a form of agamogenesis exactly like it, save in the absence of fecundation. This is called true parthenogenesis—

reproduction carried on by virgin mothers which are in all respects like other mothers. Among silk-worm-moths this parthenogenesis is exceptional rather than ordinary. Usually the eggs of these insects are fertilized; but if they are not they are still laid, and some of them produce larvæ. In certain *Lepidoptera*, however, of the groups *Psychidæ* and *Tineidæ*, parthenogenesis appears to be a normal process—indeed, so far as is known, the only process; for of some species the males have never been found.

A general conception of the relations among the different modes of Genesis, thus briefly described, will be best given by the following tabular statement.

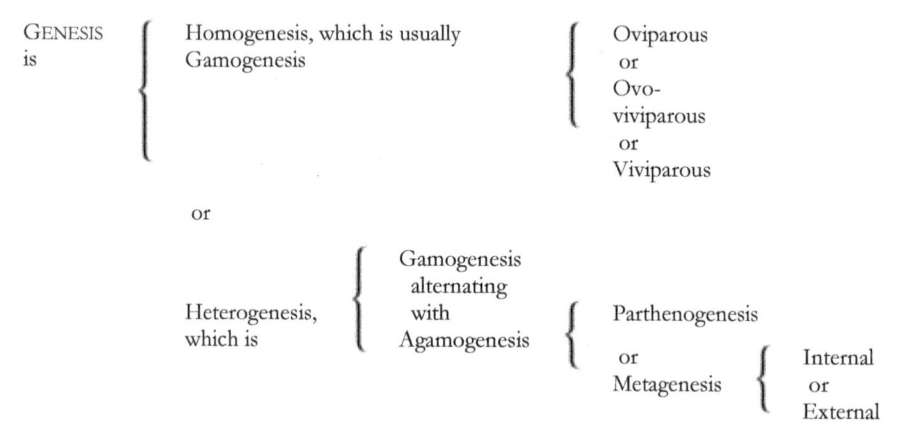

This, like all other classifications of such phenomena, presents anomalies. It may be justly objected that the processes here grouped under the head agamogenesis, are the same as those before grouped under the head of discontinuous development (§ 50): thus making development and genesis partially coincident. Doubtless it seems awkward that what are from one point of view considered as structural changes are from another point of view considered as modes of multiplication.[29] There is, however, nothing for us but a choice of imperfections. We cannot by any logical dichotomies accurately express relations which, in Nature, graduate into one another insensibly. Neither the above, nor any other scheme, can do more than give an approximate idea of the truth.

§ 76. Genesis under every form is a process of negative or positive disintegration; and is thus essentially opposed to that process of integration which is the primary process in individual evolution. Negative disintegration occurs in those cases where, as among the compound *Hydrozoa*, there is a continuous development of new individuals by budding from the bodies of older individuals; and where the older individuals are thus prevented from growing to a greater size, or reaching a higher degree of integration. Positive disintegration occurs in those forms of agamogenesis where the production of new individuals is discontinuous, as well as in all cases of gamogenesis. The degrees of disintegration are various. At the one extreme the parent organism is completely broken up, or dissolved into new individuals; and at the other extreme each new individual forms but a small deduction from the parent organism. *Protozoa* and *Protophyta* show us that form of disintegration called spontaneous fission: two or more individuals being produced by the splitting-up of the original one. The *Volvox* and the *Hydrodictyon* are plants which, having developed broods within themselves, give them exit by bursting; and among animals the one lately referred to which arises from the *Distoma* egg, entirely loses its individuality in the individualities of the numerous *Distoma*-larvæ with which it becomes filled. Speaking generally, the degree of disintegration becomes less marked as we approach the higher organic forms. Plants of superior types throw off from themselves, whether by gamogenesis or agamogenesis, parts that are relatively small; and among superior animals there is no case in which the parent individuality is habitually lost in the production of new individuals. To the last, however, there is of necessity a greater or less disintegration. The seeds and pollen-grains of a flowering plant are disintegrated portions of tissue; as are also the ova and spermatozoa of animals. And whether the fertilized germs carry away from their parents small or large quantities of nutriment, these quantities in all cases involve further negative or positive disintegrations of the parents.

Except in spore-producing plants, new individuals which result from agamogenesis usually do not separate from the parent-individuals until they have undergone considerable development, if not complete development. The agamogenetic offspring of those lowest organisms which develop centrally, do not, of course, pass beyond central structure; but the agamogenetic offspring of organisms which develop axially, commonly assume an axial structure before they become independent. The vegetal kingdom shows us this in the advanced organization of detached bulbils, and of buds that root themselves before separating. Of animals, the *Hydrozoa*, the *Trematoda*, and the *Salpæ*, present us with different kinds of agamogenesis, in all of which the new individuals are organized to a considerable extent before being cast off. This rule is not without exceptions, however. The statoblasts of the *Plumatella* (which play the part of winter eggs), developed in an unspecialized part of the body, furnish a case of metagenesis in which centres of development, instead of axes, are detached; and in the above-described parthenogenesis of moths and bees, such centres are detached from an ovarium.

When produced by gamogenesis, the new individuals become (in a morphological sense) independent of the parents while still in the shape of centres of development, rather than axes of development; and this even where the reverse is apparently the case. The fertilized germs of those inferior plants which are central, or multicentral, in their development, are of course thrown off as centres; and the same is usually the case even in those which are uniaxial or multiaxial. In the higher plants, of the two elements that go to the formation of the fertilized germ, the pollen-cell is absolutely separated from the parent-plant under the shape of a centre, and the egg-cell, though not absolutely separated from the parent, is still no longer subordinate to the organizing forces of the parent. So that when, after the egg-cell has been fertilized by matter from the pollen-tube, the development commences, it proceeds without parental control: the new individual, though remaining physically united with the old individual, becomes structurally and functionally separate: the old individual doing no more than supply materials. Throughout the animal kingdom, the new individuals produced by gamogenesis are obviously separated in the shape of centres of development wherever the reproduction is oviparous: the only conspicuous variation being in the quantity of nutritive matter bequeathed by the parent at the time of separation. And though, where the reproduction is viviparous, the process appears to be different, and in one sense is so, yet, intrinsically, it is the same. For in these cases the new individual really detaches itself from the parent while still only a centre of development; but instead of being finally cast off in this state it is re-attached, and supplied with nutriment until it assumes a more or less complete axial structure.

§ 77. As we have lately seen, the essential act in gamogenesis is the union of two cell-nuclei, produced in the great majority of cases by different parent organisms. Nearly always the containing cells, often called *gametes*, are unlike: the sperm-cell being the male product, and the germ-cell the female. But among some *Protozoa* and many of the lower *Algæ* and *Fungi*, the uniting cells show no differentiation. Sexuality is only nascent.

There are very many modes and modifications of modes in which these cells are produced; very many modes and modifications of modes by which they are brought into contact; and very many modes and modifications of modes by which the resulting fertilized germs have secured to them the fit conditions for their development. But passing over these divergent and re-divergent kinds of sexual multiplication, which it would take too much space here to specify, the one universal trait is this coalescence of a detached portion of one organism with a more or less detached portion of another.

Such simple *Algæ* as the *Desmidieæ*, which are sometimes called unicellular plants, show us a coalescence, not of detached portions of two organisms, but of two entire organisms: the entire contents of the individuals uniting to form the germ-mass. Where, as among the *Confervoideæ*, we have aggregated cells whose individualities are scarcely at all subordinate to that of the aggregate, the gamogenetic act is often effected by the union "of separate motile protoplasmic masses produced by the division of the contents of any cell of the aggregate. These free-swimming masses of protoplasm, which are quite similar to (but generally smaller than) the agamogenetic 'zoospores' of the same plants, and to the free-swimming individuals of many *Protophyta*, are apparently the primitive type of gametes (conjugating cells); but it is noteworthy that such a gamete nearly always unites with one derived from another cell or from another individual. The same fact holds with regard to the gametes of the Protophytes themselves, which are formed in the same way from the single cell of the mother individual. In the higher types of *Confervoideæ*, and in *Vaucheria*, we find these equivalent, free-swimming, gametes replaced by sexually differentiated sperm- and germ-cells, in some cases arising in different organs set apart for their production, and essentially representing those found in the higher plants. Transitional forms, intermediate between these and the cases where equivalent gametes are formed from any cell of the plant are also known."

Recent investigations concerning the conjugation of *Protozoa* have shown that there is not, as was at one time thought, a fusion of two individualities, but a fusion of parts of their nuclei. The macro-nucleus having disappeared, and the micro-nucleus having broken up into portions, each individual receives from the other one of these portions, which becomes fused with its own nuclear matter. So that even in these humble forms, where there is no differentiation of sexes, the union is not between elements that have arisen in the same individual but between those which have arisen in different individuals: the parts being in this case alike.

The marvellous phenomena initiated by the meeting of sperm-cell and germ-cell, or rather of their nuclei, naturally suggest the conception of some quite special and peculiar properties possessed by these cells. It seems obvious that this mysterious power which they display of originating a new and complex organism, distinguishes them in the broadest way from portions of organic substance in general. Nevertheless, the more we study the evidence the more are we led towards the conclusion that these cells are not fundamentally different from other cells. The first fact which points to this conclusion is the fact recently dwelt upon (§ 63), that in many plants and inferior animals, a small fragment of tissue which is but little differentiated, is capable of developing into an organism like that from which it was taken. This implies that the component units of tissues have inherent powers of arranging themselves into the forms of the organisms which originated them. And if in these component units, which we distinguished as physiological, such powers exist,—if, under fit conditions, and when not much specialized, they manifest such powers in a way as marked as that in which the contents of sperm-cells and germ-cells manifest them; then, it becomes clear that the properties of sperm-cells and germ-cells are not so peculiar as we are apt to assume. Again, the organs emitting sperm-cells and germ-cells have none of the specialities of structure which might be looked for, did sperm-cells and germ-cells need endowing with properties unlike those of all other organic agents. On the contrary, these reproductive centres proceed from tissues characterized by their low organization. In plants, for example, it is not appendages that have acquired considerable structure which produce the fructifying particles: these arise at the extremities of the axes where the degree of structure is the least. The cells out of which come the egg and the pollen-grains, are formed from undifferentiated tissue in the interior of the ovule and of the stamen. Among many inferior animals devoid of special reproductive organs, such as the *Hydra*, the ova and spermatozoa originate from the interstitial cells of the ectoderm, which lie among the bases of the functional cells—have not been differentiated for function; and in the *Medusæ*, according to Weismann, they arise in the homologous layer, save where the medusoid form remains attached, and then they arise in the endoderm and migrate to the ectoderm: lack of specialization being in all cases implied. Then in the higher animals these same generative agents appear to be merely modified epithelium-cells—cells not remarkable for their complexity of structure but rather for their simplicity. If, by way of demurrer to this view, it be asked why other epithelium-cells do not exhibit like properties; there are two replies. The first is that other epithelium-cells are usually so far changed to fit them to their special functions that they are unfitted for assuming the reproductive function. The second is that in some cases, where they are but little specialized, they *do* exhibit the like properties: not, indeed, by uniting with other cells to produce new germs but by producing new germs without such union. I learn from Dr. Hooker that the *Begonia phyllomaniaca* habitually develops young plants from the scales of its stem and leaves—nay, that many young plants are developed by a single scale. The epidermal cells composing one of these scales swell, here and there, into large globular cells; form chlorophyll in their interiors; shoot out rudimentary axes; and then, by spontaneous constrictions, cut themselves off; drop to the ground; and grow into Begonias. Moreover, in a succulent English plant, the *Malaxis paludosa*, a like process occurs: the self-detached cells being, in this case, produced by the surfaces of the leaves.[30] Thus, there is no warrant for the assumption that sperm-cells and germ-cells possess powers fundamentally unlike those of other cells. The inference to which the facts point, is, that they differ from the rest mainly in not having undergone functional adaptations. They are cells which have departed but little from the original and most general type: such specializations as some of them exhibit in the shape of locomotive appliances, being interpretable as extrinsic modifications which have reference to nothing beyond certain mechanical requirements. Sundry facts tend likewise to show that there does not exist the profound distinction we are apt to assume between the male and female reproductive elements. In the common polype sperm-cells and germ-cells are developed in the same layer of indifferent tissue; and in *Tethya*, one of the sponges, Prof. Huxley has observed that they occur mingled together in the general parenchyma. The pollen-grains and embryo-cells of plants arise in adjacent parts of the meristematic tissue of the flower-bud; and from the description of a monstrosity in the Passion-flower, recently given by Mr. Salter to the Linnæan Society, it appears both that ovules may, in their general structure, graduate into anthers, and that they may produce pollen in their interiors. Moreover, among the lower *Algæ*, which show the beginning of sexual differentiation, the smaller gametes, which we must regard as incipient sperm-cells, are sometimes able to fuse *inter se*, and give rise to a zygote which will produce a new plant. All which evidence is in perfect harmony with the foregoing conclusion; since, if sperm-cells and germ-cells have natures not essentially unlike those of unspecialized cells in general, their natures cannot be essentially unlike each other.

The next general fact to be noted is that these cells whose union constitutes the essential act of gamogenesis, are cells in which the developmental changes have come to a close—cells which are incapable of further evolution. Though they are not, as many cells are, unfitted for growth and metamorphosis by being highly specialized, yet they have lost the power of growth and metamorphosis. They have severally reached a state of equilibrium. And while the internal balance of forces prevents a continuance of constructive changes, it is readily overthrown by external destructive forces. For it almost uniformly happens that sperm-cells and germ-cells which are not brought in contact disappear. In a plant, the egg-cell, if not fertilized, is absorbed or dissipated, while the ovule aborts; and the unimpregnated ovum eventually decomposes: save, indeed, in those types in which parthenogenesis is a part of the normal cycle.

Such being the characters of these cells, and such being their fates if kept apart, we have now to observe what happens when they are united. In plants the extremity of the elongated pollen-cell applies itself to the surface of the embryo-sac, and one of its nuclei having, with some protoplasm, passed into the egg-cell, there becomes fused with the nucleus of the egg-cell. Similarly in animals, the spermatozoon passes through the limiting membrane of the ovum, and a mixture takes place between the substance of its nucleus and the substance of the nucleus of the ovum. But the important fact which it chiefly concerns us to notice, is that on the union of these reproductive elements there begins, either at once or on the return of favourable conditions, a new series of developmental changes. The state of equilibrium at which each had arrived is destroyed by their mutual influence, and the constructive changes, which had come to a close, recommence. A process of cell-multiplication is set up; and the resulting cells presently begin to aggregate into the rudiment of a new organism.

Thus, passing over the variable concomitants of gamogenesis, and confining our attention to what is constant in it, we see:—that there is habitually, if not universally, a fusion of two portions of organic substance which are either themselves distinct individuals, or are thrown off by distinct individuals; that these portions of organic substance, which are severally distinguished by their low degree of specialization, have arrived at states of structural quiescence or equilibrium; that if they are not united this equilibrium ends in dissolution; but that by the mixture of them this equilibrium is destroyed and a new evolution initiated.

§ 78. What are the conditions under which Genesis takes place? How does it happen that some organisms multiply by homogenesis and others by heterogenesis? Why is it that where agamogenesis prevails it is usually from time to time interrupted by gamogenesis? A survey of the facts discloses certain correlations which, if not universal, are too general to be without significance.

Where multiplication is carried on by heterogenesis we find, in numerous cases, that agamogenesis continues as long as the forces which result in growth are greatly in excess of the antagonist forces. Conversely, we find that the recurrence of gamogenesis takes place when the conditions are no longer so favourable to growth. In like manner where there is homogenetic multiplication, new individuals are usually not formed while the preceding individuals are still rapidly growing—that is, while the forces producing growth exceed the opposing forces to a great extent; but the formation of new individuals begins when nutrition is nearly equalled by expenditure. A few out of the many facts which seem to warrant these inductions must suffice.

The relation in plants between fructification and innutrition (or rather, between fructification and such diminished nutrition as makes growth relatively slow) was long ago asserted by a German biologist—Wolff, I am told. Since meeting with this assertion I have examined into the facts for myself. The result has been a conviction, strengthened by every inquiry, that some such relation exists. Uniaxial plants begin to produce their lateral, flowering axes, only after the main axis has developed the great mass of its leaves, and is showing its diminished nutrition by smaller leaves, or shorter internodes, or both. In multiaxial plants two, three, or more generations of leaf-bearing axes, or sexless individuals, are produced before any seed-bearing individuals show themselves. When, after this first stage of rapid growth and agamogenetic multiplication, some gamogenetic individuals arise, they do so where the nutrition is least;—not on the main axis, or on secondary axes, or even on tertiary axes, but on axes that are the most removed from the channels which supply nutriment. Again, a flowering axis is commonly less bulky than the others: either much shorter or, if long, much thinner. And further, it is an axis of which the terminal internodes are undeveloped: the foliar organs, which instead of becoming leaves become sepals, and petals, and stamens, follow each other in close succession, instead of being separated by portions of the still-growing axis. Another group of evidences meets us when we observe the variations of fruit-bearing which accompany variations of nutrition in the plant regarded as a whole. Besides finding, as above, that gamogenesis commences only when growth has been checked by extension of the remoter parts to some distance from the roots, we find that gamogenesis is induced at an earlier stage than usual by checking the nutrition. Trees are made to fruit while still quite small by cutting their roots or putting them into pots; and luxuriant branches which have had the flow of sap into them diminished, by what gardeners call "ringing," begin to produce flower-shoots instead of leaf-shoots. Moreover, it is to be remarked that trees which, by flowering early in the year, seem to show a direct relation between gamogenesis and increasing nutrition, really do the reverse; for in such trees the flower-buds are formed in the autumn. That structure which determines these buds into sexual individuals is given when the nutrition is declining. Conversely, very high nutrition in plants prevents, or arrests, gamogenesis. It is notorious that unusual richness of soil, or too large a quantity of manure, results in a continuous production of leaf-bearing or sexless shoots; and a like result happens when the cutting down of a tree, or of a large part of it, is followed by the sending out of new shoots: these, supplied with excess of sap, are luxuriant and sexless. Besides being prevented from producing sexual individuals by excessive nutrition, plants are, by excessive nutrition, made to change the sexual individuals they were about to produce, into sexless ones. This arrest of gamogenesis may be seen in various stages. The familiar instance of flowers made barren by the transformation of their stamens into petals, shows us the lowest degree of this reversed metamorphosis. Where the petals and stamens are partially changed into green leaves, the return towards the agamogenetic structure is more marked; and it is still more marked when, as occasionally happens in luxuriantly-growing plants, new flowering axes, and even leaf-bearing axes, grow out of the centres of flowers.[31] The anatomical structure of the sexual axis affords corroborative evidence: giving the impression, as it docs, of an aborted sexless axis. Besides lacking those internodes which the leaf-bearing axis commonly possesses, the flowering axis differs by the absence of rudimentary lateral axes. In a leaf-bearing shoot the axil of every leaf usually contains a small bud, which may or may not develop into a lateral shoot; but though the petals of a flower are homologous with leaves, they do not bear homologous buds at their bases. Ordinarily, too, the foliar appendages of sexual axes are much smaller than those of sexless ones—the stamens and pistils especially, which are the last formed, being extremely dwarfed; and it may be that the absence of chlorophyll from the parts of fructification is a fact of like meaning. Moreover, the formation of the seed-vessel appears to be a direct consequence of arrested nutrition. If a gloved-finger be taken to represent a growing shoot, (the finger standing for the pith of the shoot and the glove for the peripheral layers of meristem and young tissue, in which the process of growth takes place); and if it be supposed that there is a diminished supply of material for growth; then, it seems a fair inference that growth will first cease at the apex of the axis, represented by the end of the glove-finger; and supposing growth to continue in those parts of the peripheral layers of young tissue that are nearer to the supply of nutriment, their further longitudinal extension will lead to the formation of a cavity at the extremity of the shoot, like that which results in a glove-finger when the finger is partially withdrawn and the glove sticks to its end. Whence it seems, both that this introversion of the apical meristem may be considered as due to failing nutrition, and that the ovules growing from its introverted surface (which would have been its outer surface but for the defective nutrition) are extremely aborted homologues of external appendages: both they and the pollen-grains being either morphologically or literally quite terminal, and the last showing by their dehiscence the exhaustion of the organizing power.[32]

Those kinds of animals which multiply by heterogenesis, present us with a parallel relation between the recurrence of gamogenesis and the recurrence of conditions checking rapid growth: at least, this is shown where experiments have thrown light on the connexion of cause and effect; namely, among the *Aphides*. These creatures, hatched from eggs in the spring, multiply by agamogenesis, which in this case is parthenogenesis, throughout the summer. When the weather becomes cold and plants no longer afford abundant sap, perfect males and females are produced; and from gamogenesis result fertilized ova. But beyond this evidence we have much more conclusive evidence. For it has been shown, both that the rapidity of the agamogenesis is proportionate to the warmth and nutrition, and that if the temperature and supply of food be artificially maintained, the agamogenesis continues through the winter. Nay more—it not only, under these conditions, continues through one winter, but it has been known to continue for four successive years: some forty or fifty sexless generations being thus produced. And those who have investigated the matter see no reason to doubt the indefinite continuance of this agamogenetic multiplication, so long as the external requirements are duly met. Evidence of another kind, complicated by special influences, is furnished by the heterogenesis of the *Daphnia*—a small crustacean commonly known as the Water-flea, which inhabits ponds and ditches. From the nature of its habitat this little creature is exposed to very variable conditions. Besides being frozen in winter, the small bodies of water in which it lives are often unduly heated by the summer Sun, or dried up by continued drought. The circumstances favourable to the *Daphnia's* life and growth, being thus liable to interruptions which, in our climate, have a regular irregularity of recurrence; we may, in conformity with the hypothesis, expect to find both that the gamogenesis recurs along with declining physical prosperity and that its recurrence is very variable. I use the expression "declining physical prosperity" advisedly; since "declining nutrition," as measured by supply of food, does not cover all the conditions. This is shown by the experiments of Weismann (abstracted for me by Mr. Cunningham) who found that in various *Daphnideæ* which bring forth resting eggs, sexual and asexual reproduction go on simultaneously, as well as separately, in the spring and summer: these variable results being adapted to variable conditions. For not only are these creatures liable to die from lack of food, from the winter's cold, and from the drying up of their ditches, &c., as well as from the over-heating of them, but during this period of over-heating they are liable to die from that deoxygenation of the water which heat causes. Manifestly the favourable and unfavourable conditions recurring in combinations that are rarely twice alike, cannot be met by any regularly recurring form of heterogenesis; and it is interesting to see how survival of the fittest has established a mixed form. In the spring, as well as in the autumn, there is in some cases a formation of resting or winter eggs; and evidently these provide against the killing off of the whole population by summer drought. Meanwhile, by ordinary males and females there is a production of summer eggs adapted to meet the incident of drying up by drought and subsequent re-supply of water. And all along successive generations of parthenogenetic females effect a rapid multiplication as long as conditions permit. Since life and growth are impeded or arrested not by lack of food only, but by other unfavourable conditions, we may understand how change in one or more of these may set up one or other form of genesis, and how the mixture of them may cause a mixed mode of multiplication which, originally initiated by external causes, becomes by inheritance and selection a trait of the species.[33] And then in proof that external causes initiate these peculiarities, we have the fact that in certain *Daphnideæ* "which live in places where existence and parthenogenesis are possible throughout the year, the sexual period has disappeared:" there are no males.

Passing now to animals which multiply by homogenesis—animals in which the whole product of a fertilized germ aggregates round a single centre or axis instead of round many centres or axes—we see, as before, that so long as the conditions allow rapid increase in the mass of this germ-product, the formation of new individuals by gamogenesis does not take place. Only when growth is declining in relative rate, do perfect sperm-cells and germ-cells begin to appear; and the fullest activity of the reproductive function arises as growth ceases: speaking generally, at least; for though this relation is tolerably definite in the highest orders of animals which multiply by gamogenesis, it is less definite in the lower orders. This admission does not militate against the hypothesis, as it seems to do; for the indefiniteness of the relation occurs where the limit of growth is comparatively indefinite. We saw (§ 46) that among active, hot-blooded creatures, such as mammals and birds, the inevitable balancing of assimilation by expenditure establishes, for each species, an almost uniform adult size; and among creatures of these kinds (birds especially, in which this restrictive effect of expenditure is most conspicuous), the connexion between cessation of growth and commencement of reproduction is distinct. But we also saw (§ 46) that where, as in the Crocodile and the Pike, the conditions and habits of life are such that expenditure does not overtake assimilation as size increases, there is no precise limit of growth; and in creatures thus circumstanced we may naturally look for a comparatively indeterminate relation between declining growth and commencing reproduction.[34] There is, indeed, among fishes, at least one case which appears very anomalous. The male parr, or young of the male salmon, a fish of four or five inches in length, is said to produce milt. Having, at this early stage of its growth, not one-hundredth of the weight of a full-grown salmon, how does its production of milt consist with the alleged general law? The answer must be in great measure hypothetical. If the salmon is (as it appears to be in its young state) a species of fresh-water trout that has contracted the habit of annually migrating to the sea, where it finds a food on which it thrives—if the original size of this species was not much greater than that of the parr (which is nearly as large as some varieties of trout)—and if the limit of growth in the trout tribe is very indefinite, as we know it to be; then we may reasonably infer that the parr has nearly the adult form and size which this species of trout had before it acquired its migratory habit; and that this production of milt is, in such case, a concomitant of the incipient decline of growth naturally arising in the species when living under the conditions of the ancestral species. Should this be so, the immense subsequent growth of the parr into the salmon, consequent on a suddenly-increased facility in obtaining food, removes to a great distance the limit at which assimilation is balanced by expenditure; and has the effect, analogous to that produced in plants, of arresting the incipient reproductive process. A confirmation of this view may be drawn from the fact that when the parr, after its first migration to the sea, returns to fresh water, having increased in a few months from a couple of ounces to five or six pounds, it no longer shows any fitness for propagation: the grilse, or immature salmon, does not produce milt or spawn.

We conclude, then, that the products of a fertilized germ go on accumulating by simple growth, so long as the forces whence growth results are greatly in excess of the antagonist forces; but that when diminution of the one set of forces or increase of the other, causes a considerable decline in this excess and an approach towards equilibrium, fertilized germs are again produced. Whether the germ-product be organized round one axis or round the many axes that arise by agamogenesis, matters not. Whether, as in the higher animals, this approach to equilibrium results from that disproportionate increase of expenditure entailed by increase of size; or whether, as in most plants and many inferior animals, it results from absolute or relative decline of nutrition; matters not. In any case the recurrence of gamogenesis is associated with a decrease in the excess of tissue-producing power. We cannot say, indeed, that this decrease always results in gamogenesis: some organisms multiply for an indefinite period by agamogenesis only. The Weeping Willow, which has been propagated throughout Europe, does not seed in Europe; and yet, as the Weeping Willow, by its large size and the multiplication of generation upon generation of lateral axes, presents the same causes of local innutrition as other trees, we cannot ascribe the absence of sexual axes to the continued predominance of nutrition. Among animals, too, the anomalous case of the *Tineidæ*, a group of moths in which parthenogenetic multiplication goes on for generation after generation, seems to imply that gamogenesis does not necessarily result from an approximate balance of assimilation by expenditure. What we must say is that an approach towards equilibrium between the forces which cause growth and the forces which oppose growth, is the chief condition to the recurrence of gamogenesis; but that there appear to be other conditions, in the absence of which approach to equilibrium is not followed by gamogenesis.

§ 79. The above induction is an approximate answer to the question—*When* does gamogenesis recur? but not to the question which was propounded—*Why* does gamogenesis recur?—*Why* cannot multiplication be carried on in all cases, as it is in many cases, by agamogenesis? As already said, biologic science is not yet advanced enough to reply. Meanwhile, the evidence above brought together suggests a certain hypothetical answer.

Seeing, on the one hand, that gamogenesis recurs only in individuals which are approaching a state of organic equilibrium; and seeing, on the other hand, that the sperm-cells and germ-cells thrown off by such individuals are cells in which developmental changes have ended in quiescence, but in which, after their union, there arises a process of active cell-formation; we may suspect that the approach towards a state of general equilibrium in such gamogenetic individuals, is accompanied by an approach towards molecular equilibrium in them; and that the need for this union of sperm-cell and germ-cell is the need for overthrowing this equilibrium, and re-establishing active molecular change in the detached germ—a result probably effected by mixing the slightly different physiological units of slightly different individuals. The several arguments which support this view, cannot be satisfactorily set forth until after the topics of Heredity and Variation have been dealt with. Leaving it for the present, I propose hereafter to re-consider it in connexion with sundry others raised by the phenomena of Genesis.

But before ending the chapter, it may be well to note the relations between these different modes of multiplication, and the conditions of existence under which they are respectively habitual. While the explanation of the teleologist is untrue, it is often an obverse to the truth; for though, on the hypothesis of Evolution, it is clear that things are not arranged thus or thus for the securing of special ends, it is also clear that arrangements which *do* secure these special ends tend to establish themselves—are established by their fulfilment of these ends. Besides insuring a structural fitness between each kind of organism and its circumstances, the working of "natural selection" also insures a fitness between the mode and rate of multiplication of each kind of organism and its circumstances. We may, therefore, without any teleological implication, consider the fitness of homogenesis and heterogenesis to the needs of the different classes of organisms which exhibit them.

Heterogenesis prevails among organisms of which the food, though abundant compared with their expenditure, is dispersed in such a way that it cannot be appropriated in a wholesale manner. *Protophyta*, subsisting on diffused gases and decaying organic matter in a state of minute subdivision, and *Protozoa*, to which food comes in the shape of extremely small floating particles, are enabled, by their rapid agamogenetic multiplication, to obtain materials for growth better than they would do did they not thus continually divide and disperse in pursuit of it. The higher plants, having for nutriment the carbonic acid of the air and certain mineral components of the soil, show us modes of multiplication adapted to the fullest utilization of these substances. A herb with but little power of forming the woody fibre requisite to make a stem that can support wide-spreading branches, after producing a few sexless axes produces sexual ones; and maintains its race better, by the consequent early dispersion of seeds, than by a further production of sexless axes. But a tree, able to lift its successive generations of sexless axes high into the air, where each gets carbonic acid and light almost as freely as if it grew by itself, may with advantage go on budding-out sexless axes year after year; since it thereby increases its subsequent power of budding-out sexual axes. Meanwhile it may advantageously transform into seed-bearers those axes which, in consequence of their less direct access to materials absorbed by the roots, are failing in their nutrition; for it thus throws off from a point at which sustenance is deficient, a migrating group of germs that may find sustenance elsewhere. The heterogenesis displayed by animals of the Cœlenterate type has evidently a like utility. A polype, feeding on minute annelids and crustaceans which, flitting through the water, come in contact with its tentacles, and limited to that quantity of prey which chance brings within its grasp, buds out young polypes which, either as a colony or as dispersed individuals, spread their tentacles through a larger space of water than the parent alone can; and by producing them, the parent better insures the continuance of its species than it would do if it went on slowly growing until its nutrition was nearly balanced by its waste, and then multiplied by gamogenesis. Similarly with the *Aphis*. Living on sap sucked from tender shoots and leaves, and able thus to take in but a very small quantity in a given time, this creature's race is more likely to be preserved by a rapid asexual propagation of small individuals, which disperse themselves over a wide area of nutrition, than it would be did the individual growth continue so as to produce large individuals multiplying sexually. And then when autumnal cold and diminishing supply of sap put a check to growth, the recurrence of gamogenesis, or production of fertilized ova which remain dormant through the winter, is more favourable to the preservation of the race than would be a further continuance of agamogenesis. On the other hand, among the higher animals living on food which, though dispersed, is more or less aggregated into large masses, this alternation of gamic and agamic reproduction ceases to be useful. The development of the germ-product into a single organism of considerable bulk, is in many cases a condition without which these large masses of nutriment could not be appropriated; and here the formation of many individuals instead of one would be fatal. But we still see the beneficial results of the general law—the postponement of gamogenesis until the rate of growth begins to decline. For so long as the rate of growth continues rapid, there is proof that the organism gets food with facility—that expenditure does not seriously check accumulation; and that the size reached is as yet not disadvantageous: or rather, indeed, that it is advantageous. But when the rate of growth is much decreased by the increase of expenditure—when the excess of assimilative power is diminishing so fast as to indicate its approaching disappearance—it becomes needful, for the maintenance of the species, that this excess shall be turned to the production of new individuals; since, did growth continue until there was a complete balancing of assimilation and expenditure, the production of new individuals would be either impossible or fatal to the parent. And it is clear that "natural selection" will continually tend to determine the period at which gamogenesis commences, in such a way as most favours the maintenance of the race.

Here, too, may fitly be pointed out the fact that, by "natural selection," there will in every case be produced the most advantageous proportion of males and females. If the conditions of life render numerical inequality of the sexes beneficial to the species, in respect either of the number of the offspring or the character of the offspring; then, those varieties of the species which approach more than other varieties towards this beneficial degree of inequality, will be apt to supplant other varieties. And conversely, where equality in the number of males and females is beneficial, the equilibrium will be maintained by the dying out of such varieties as produce offspring among which the sexes are not balanced.

NOTE.—Such alterations of statement in this chapter as have been made necessary by the advance of biological knowledge since 1864 have not, I think, tended to invalidate its main theses, but have tended to verify them. Some explanations to be here added may remove remaining difficulties.

Certain types, which are transitional between *Protozoa* and *Metazoa*, exhibit under its simplest form the relation between self-maintenance and race-maintenance—the integration primarily effecting the one and the disintegration primarily effecting the other. Among the *Mycetozoa* a number of amœba-like individuals aggregate into what is called a plasmodium; and while, in some orders, they become fused into a mass of protoplasm through which their nuclei are dispersed, in other orders (*Sorophora*) they retain their individualities and simply form a coherent aggregate. These last, presumably the earliest in order of evolution, remain united so long as the plasmodium, having a small power of locomotion, furthers the general nutrition; but when this is impeded by drought or cold, there arise spores. Each spore contains an amœboid individual; and this, escaping when favourable conditions return, establishes by fission and by union with others like itself a new colony or plasmodium. Reduced to its lowest terms, we here see the antagonism between that growth of the coherent mass of units which accompanies its physical prosperity, and that incoherence and dispersion of the units which follows unfavourable conditions and arrest of growth, and which presently initiates new plasmodia.

This antagonism, seen in these incipient *Metazoa* which show us none of that organization characterizing the *Metazoa* in general, is everywhere in more or less disguised forms exhibited by them—must necessarily be so if growth of the individual is a process of integration while formation of new individuals is a process of disintegration. And, primarily, it is an implication that whatever furthers the one impedes the other.

But now while recognizing the truth that nutrition and innutrition (using these words to cover not supply of nutriment only but the presence of other influences favourable or unfavourable to the vital processes) primarily determine the alternations of these; we have also to recognize the truth that from the beginning survival of the fittest has been shaping the forms and effects of their antagonism. By inheritance a physiological habit which modifies the form of the antagonism in a way favourable to the species, will become established. Especially will this be the case where the lives of the individuals have become relatively definite and where special organs have been evolved for casting off reproductive centres. The resulting physiological rhythm may in such cases become so pronounced as greatly to obscure the primitive relation. Among plants we see this in the fact that those which have been transferred from one habitat to another having widely different seasons, long continue their original time of flowering, though it is inappropriate to the new circumstances—the reproductive periodicity has become organic. Similarly in each species of higher animal, development of the reproductive organs and maturation of reproductive cells take place at a settled age, whether the conditions have been favourable or unfavourable to physical prosperity. The established constitutional tendency, adapted to the needs of the species, over-rides the constitutional needs of the individual.

Even here, however, the primitive antagonism, though greatly obscured, occasionally shows itself. Instance the fact that in plants where gamogenesis is commencing a sudden access of nutrition will cause resumption of agamogenesis; and I suspect that an illustration may be found among human beings in the earlier establishment of the reproductive function among the ill-fed poor than among the well-fed rich.

One other qualification has to be added. In plants and animals which have become so definitely constituted that at an approximately fixed stage, the proclivity towards the production of new individuals becomes pronounced, it naturally happens that good nutrition aids it. Surplus nutriment being turned into the reproductive channel, the reproduction is efficient in proportion as the surplus is great. Hence the fact that in fruit trees which have reached the flowering stage, manuring has the effect that though it does not increase the quantity of blossoms it increases the quantity of fruit; and hence the fact that well-fed and easy-living races of men are prolific.

CHAPTER VIII.

HEREDITY.

§ 80. Already, in the last two chapters, the law of hereditary transmission has been tacitly assumed; as, indeed, it unavoidably is in all such discussions. Understood in its entirety, the law is that each plant or animal, if it reproduces, gives origin to others like itself: the likeness consisting, not so much in the repetition of individual traits as in the assumption of the same general structure. This truth has been rendered so familiar by daily illustration as almost to have lost its significance. That wheat produces wheat—that existing oxen have descended from ancestral oxen—that every unfolding organism eventually takes the form of the class, order, genus, and species from which it sprang; is a fact which, by force of repetition, has acquired in our minds almost the aspect of a necessity. It is in this, however, that Heredity is principally displayed: the manifestations of it commonly referred to being quite subordinate. And, as thus understood, Heredity is universal. The various instances of heterogenesis lately contemplated seem, indeed, to be at variance with this assertion. But they are not really so. Though the recurrence of like forms is, in these instances, not direct but cyclical, still, the like forms do recur; and, when taken together, the group of forms produced during one of the cycles is as much like the groups produced in preceding cycles, as the single individual arising by homogenesis is like ancestral individuals.

While, however, the general truth that organisms of a given type uniformly descend from organisms of the same type, is so well established by infinite illustrations as to have assumed the character of an axiom; it is not universally admitted that non-typical peculiarities are inherited. Many entertain a vague belief that the law of Heredity applies only to main characters of structure and not to details; or, at any rate, that though it applies to such details as constitute differences of species, it does not apply to smaller details. The circumstance that the tendency to repetition is in a slight degree qualified by the tendency to variation (which, as we shall hereafter see, is but an indirect result of the tendency to repetition), leads some to doubt whether Heredity is unlimited. A careful weighing of the evidence, however, and a due allowance for the influences by which the minuter manifestations of Heredity are obscured, may remove this scepticism.

First in order of importance comes the fact that not only are there uniformly transmitted from an organism to its offspring, those traits of structure which distinguish the class, order, genus, and species; but also those which distinguish the variety. We have numerous cases, among both plants and animals, where, by natural or artificial conditions, there have been produced divergent modifications of the same species; and abundant proof exists that the members of any one sub-species habitually transmit their distinctive peculiarities to their descendants. Agriculturists and gardeners can furnish unquestionable illustrations. Several varieties of wheat are known, of which each reproduces itself. Since the potato was introduced into England there have been formed from it a number of sub-species; some of them differing greatly in their forms, sizes, qualities, and periods of ripening. Of peas, also, the like may be said. And the case of the cabbage-tribe is often cited as showing the permanent establishment of races which have diverged widely from a common stock. Among fruits and flowers the multiplication of kinds, and the continuance of each kind with certainty by agamogenesis, and to some extent by gamogenesis, might be exemplified without end. From all sides evidence may be gathered showing a like persistence of varieties among animals. We have our distinct breeds of sheep, our distinct breeds of cattle, our distinct breeds of horses: each breed maintaining its characteristics. The many sorts of dogs which, if we accept the physiological test, we must consider as all of one species, show us in a marked manner the hereditary transmission of small differences—each sort, when kept pure, reproducing itself not only in size, form, colour, and quality of hair, but also in disposition and speciality of intelligence. Poultry, too, have their permanently-established races. And the Isle of Man sends us a tail-less kind of cat. Even in the absence of other evidence, that which ethnology furnishes would suffice. Grant them to be derived from one stock, and the varieties of man yield proof upon proof that non-specific traits of structure are bequeathed from generation to generation. Or grant only their derivation from several stocks, and we still have, between races descended from a common stock, distinctions which prove the inheritance of minor peculiarities. Besides seeing the Negroes continue to produce Negroes, copper-coloured men to produce men of a copper colour, and the fair-skinned races to perpetuate their fair skins—besides seeing that the broad-faced and flat-nosed Calmuck begets children with broad faces and flat noses, while the Jew bequeaths to his offspring the features which have so long characterized Jews; we see that those small unlikenesses which distinguish more nearly-allied varieties of men, are maintained from generation to generation. In Germany, the ordinary shape of skull is appreciably different from that common in Britain: near akin though the Germans are to the British. The average Italian face continues to be unlike the faces of northern nations. The French character is now, as it was centuries ago, contrasted in sundry respects with the characters of neighbouring peoples. Nay, even between races so closely allied as the

Scotch Celts, the Welsh Celts, and the Irish Celts, appreciable differences of form and nature have become established.

The fact that sub-species and sub-sub-species thus exemplify the general law of inheritance which shows itself in the perpetuation of ordinal, generic, and species peculiarities, is strong reason for the belief that this general lay is unlimited in its application. This has the support of still more special evidences. They are divisible into two classes. In the one come cases where congenital peculiarities, not traceable to any obvious causes, are bequeathed to descendants. In the other come cases where the peculiarities thus bequeathed are not congenital, but have resulted from changes of functions during the lives of the individuals bequeathing them. We will consider first the cases that come in the first class.

§ 81. Note at the outset the character of the chief testimony. Excluding those inductions that have been so fully verified as to rank with exact science, there are no inductions so trustworthy as those which have undergone the mercantile test. When we have thousands of men whose profit or loss depends on the truth of their inferences from perpetually-repeated observations; and when we find that their inferences, handed down from generation to generation, have generated an unshakable conviction; we may accept it without hesitation. In breeders of animals we have such a class, led by such experiences, and entertaining such a conviction—the conviction that minor peculiarities of organization are inherited as well as major peculiarities. Hence the immense prices given for successful racers, bulls of superior forms, sheep that have certain desired peculiarities. Hence the careful record of pedigrees of high-bred horses and sporting dogs. Hence the care taken to avoid intermixture with inferior stocks. As quoted by Mr. Darwin, Youatt says the principle of selection "enables the agriculturist not only to modify the character of his flock but to change it altogether." Lord Somerville, speaking of what breeders have done for sheep, says:—"It would seem that they have chalked upon a wall a form perfect in itself and then given it existence." That most skilful breeder, Sir John Sebright, used to say, with respect to pigeons, that "he would produce any given feather in three years, but it would take him six years to obtain head and beak." In all which statements the tacit assertion is, that individual traits are bequeathed from generation to generation, and may be so perpetuated and increased as to become permanent distinctions.

Of special instances there are many besides that of the often-cited Otto-breed of sheep, descended from a single short-legged lamb, and that of the six-fingered Gratio Kelleia, who transmitted his peculiarity, in different degrees, to several of his children and to some of his grandchildren. In a paper contributed to the *Edinburgh New Philosophical Journal* for July, 1863, Dr. (now Sir John) Struthers gives cases of hereditary digital variations.

Esther P——, who had six fingers on one hand, bequeathed this malformation along some lines of her descendants for two, three, and four generations. A—— S—— inherited an extra digit on each hand and each foot from his father; and C—— G——, who also had six fingers and six toes, had an aunt and a grandmother similarly formed. A collection of evidence published by Mr. Sedgwick in the *Medico-Chirurgical Review* for April and for July, 1863, in two articles on "The Influence of Sex in limiting Hereditary Transmission," includes the following cases:—Augustin Duforet, a pastry-cook of Douai, who had but two instead of three phalanges to all his fingers and toes, inherited this malformation from his grandfather and father, and had it in common with an uncle and numerous cousins. An account has been given by Dr. Lepine, of a man with only three fingers on each hand and four toes on each foot, and whose grandfather and son exhibited the like anomaly. Béchet describes Victoire Barré as a woman who, like her father and sister, had but one developed finger on each hand and but two toes on each foot, and whose monstrosity re-appeared in two daughters. And there is a case where the absence of two distal phalanges on the hands was traced for two generations. The various recorded instances in which there has been transmission from one generation to another, of webbed-fingers, of webbed-toes, of hare-lip, of congenital luxation of the thigh, of absent patellæ, of club-foot, &c., would occupy more space than can here be spared. Defects in the organs of sense are also not unfrequently inherited. Four sisters, their mother, and grandmother, are described by Duval as similarly affected by cataract. Prosper Lucas details an example of amaurosis affecting the females of a family for three generations. Duval, Graffe, Dufon, and others testify to like cases coming under their observation.[35] Deafness, too, is occasionally transmitted from parent to child. There are deaf-mutes whose imperfections have been derived from ancestors; and malformations of the external ears have also been perpetuated in offspring. Of transmitted peculiarities of the skin and its appendages, many cases have been noted. One is that of a family remarkable for enormous black eyebrows; another that of a family in which every member had a lock of hair of a lighter colour than the rest on the top of the head; and there are also instances of congenital baldness being hereditary. From one of our leading sculptors I learn that his wife has a flat mole under the foot near the little toe, and one of her sons has the same. Entire absence of teeth, absence of particular teeth, and anomalous arrangements of teeth, are recorded as traits that have descended to children. And we have evidence that soundness and unsoundness of teeth are transmissible.

The inheritance of tendencies to such diseases as gout, consumption, and insanity is universally admitted. Among the less-common diseases of which the descent has been observed, are ichthyosis, leprosy, pityriasis, sebaceous tumours, plica polonica, dipsomania, somnambulism, catalepsy, epilepsy, asthma, apoplexy, elephantiasis. General nervousness displayed by parents almost always re-appears in their children. Even a bias towards suicide appears to be sometimes hereditary.

§ 82. To prove the transmission of those structural peculiarities which have resulted from functional peculiarities, is, for several reasons, comparatively difficult. Changes produced in the sizes of parts by changes in their amounts of action, are mostly unobtrusive. A muscle which has increased in bulk is usually so obscured by natural or artificial clothing, that unless the alteration is extreme it passes without remark. Such nervous developments as are possible in the course of a single life, cannot be seen externally. Visceral modifications of a normal kind are observable but obscurely, or not at all. And if the changes of structure worked in individuals by changes in their habits are thus difficult to trace, still more difficult to trace must be the transmission of them: further hidden, as this is, by the influences of other individuals who are often otherwise modified by other habits. Moreover, such specialities of structure as are due to specialities of function, are usually entangled with specialities of structure which are, or may be, due to selection, natural or artificial. In most cases it is impossible to say that a structural peculiarity which seems to have arisen in offspring from a functional peculiarity in a parent, is wholly independent of some congenital peculiarity of structure in the parent, whence this functional peculiarity arose. We are restricted to cases with which natural or artificial selection can have had nothing to do, and such cases are difficult to find. Some, however, may be noted.

A species of plant that has been transferred from one soil or climate to another, frequently undergoes what botanists call "change of habit"—a change which, without affecting its specific characters, is yet conspicuous. In its new locality the species is distinguished by leaves that are much larger or much smaller, or differently shaped, or more fleshy; or instead of being as before comparatively smooth, it becomes hairy; or its stem becomes woody instead of being herbaceous; or its branches, no longer growing upwards, assume a drooping character. Now these "changes of habit" are clearly determined by functional changes. Occurring, as they do, in many individuals which have undergone the same transportation, they cannot be classed as "spontaneous variations." They are modifications of structure consequent on modifications of function that have been produced by modifications in the actions of external forces. And as these modifications re-appear in succeeding generations, we have, in them, examples of functionally-established variations that are hereditarily transmitted.

Evidence of analogous changes in animals is difficult to disentangle. Only among domesticated kinds have we any opportunity of tracing the results of altered habits; and here, in nearly all cases, artificial selection has obscured them. Still, there are some facts which seem to the point. Mr. Darwin, while ascribing almost wholly to "natural selection" the production of those modifications which eventuate in differences of species, nevertheless admits the effects of use and disuse. He says—"I find in the domestic duck that the bones of the wing weigh less and the bones of the leg more, in proportion to the whole skeleton, than do the same bones in the wild duck; and I presume that this change may be safely attributed to the domestic duck flying much less, and walking more, than its wild parent. The great and inherited development of the udders in cows and goats in countries where they are habitually milked, in comparison with the state of these organs in other countries, is another instance of the effect of use. Not a single domestic animal can be named which has not in some country drooping ears; and the view suggested by some authors, that the drooping is due to the disuse of the muscles of the ear, from the animals not being much alarmed by danger, seems probable." Again—"The eyes of moles and of some burrowing rodents are rudimentary in size, and in some cases are quite covered up by skin and fur. This state of the eyes is probably due to gradual reduction from disuse, but aided perhaps by natural selection." ... "It is well known that several animals belonging to the most different classes, which inhabit the caves of Styria and of Kentucky, are blind. In some of the crabs the footstalk of the eye remains, though the eye is gone; the stand for the telescope is there, though the telescope with its glasses has been lost. As it is difficult to imagine that eyes, though useless, could be in any way injurious to animals living in darkness, I attribute their loss wholly to disuse."[36] The direct inheritance of an acquired peculiarity is sometimes observable. Mr. Lewes gives a case. He "had a puppy taken from its mother at six weeks old, who, although never taught 'to beg' (an accomplishment his mother had been taught), spontaneously took to begging for everything he wanted when about seven or eight months old: he would beg for food, beg to be let out of the room, and one day was found opposite a rabbit hutch begging for rabbits." Instances are on record, too, of sporting dogs which spontaneously adopted in the field, certain modes of behaviour which their parents had learnt.

But the best examples of inherited modifications produced by modifications of function, occur in mankind. To no other cause can be ascribed the rapid metamorphoses undergone by the British races when placed in new conditions. In the United States the descendants of the immigrant Irish lose their Celtic aspect, and become Americanized. This cannot be ascribed to mixture, since the feeling with which Irish are regarded by Americans prevents any considerable amount of intermarriage. Equally marked is the case of the immigrant Germans who, though they keep very much apart, rapidly assume the prevailing type. To say that "spontaneous variation" increased by natural selection, can have produced this effect, is going too far. Peoples so numerous cannot have been supplanted in the course of two or three generations by varieties springing from them. Hence the implication is that physical and social conditions have wrought modifications of function and structure, which offspring have inherited and increased. Similarly with special cases. In the *Cyclopædia of Practical Medicine*, Vol. II., p. 419, Dr. Brown states that he "has in many instances observed in the case of individuals whose complexion and general appearance has been modified by residence in hot climates, that children born to them subsequently to such residence, have resembled them rather in their acquired than primary mien."

Some visible modifications of organs caused by changes in their functions, may be noted. That large hands are inherited by those whose ancestors led laborious lives, and that those descended from ancestors unused to manual labour commonly have small hands, are established opinions. It seems very unlikely that in the absence of any such connexion, the size of the hand should have come to be generally regarded as some index of extraction. That there exists a like relation between habitual use of the feet and largeness of the feet, we have strong evidence in the customs of the Chinese. The torturing practice of artificially arresting the growth of the feet, could never have become established among the ladies of China, had they not seen that a small foot was significant of superior rank—that is of a luxurious life—that is of a life without bodily labour. There is evidence, too, that modifications of the eyes, caused by particular uses of the eyes, are inherited. Short sight appears to be uncommon among peasants; but it is frequent among classes who use their eyes much for reading and writing, and is often congenital. Still more marked is this relation in Germany. There, the educated are notoriously studious, and judging from the numbers of young Germans who wear spectacles, there is reason to think that congenital myopia is very frequent among them.

Some of the best illustrations of functional heredity, are furnished by mental characteristics. Certain powers which mankind have gained in the course of civilization cannot, I think, be accounted for without admitting the inheritance of acquired modifications. The musical faculty is one of these. To say that "natural selection" has developed it by preserving the most musically endowed, seems an inadequate explanation. Even now that the development and prevalence of the faculty have made music an occupation by which the most musical can get sustenance and bring up families; it is very questionable whether, taking the musical career as a whole, it has any advantage over other careers in the struggle for existence and multiplication. Still more if we look back to those early stages through which the faculty must have passed before definite perception of melody was arrived at, we fail to see how those possessing the rudimentary faculty in a somewhat greater degree than the rest, would thereby be enabled the better to maintain themselves and their children. There is no explanation but that the habitual association of certain cadences of speech with certain emotions, has slowly established in the race an organized and inherited connection between such cadences and such emotions; that the combination of such cadences, more or less idealized, which constitutes melody, has all along had a meaning in the average mind, only because of the meaning which cadences had acquired in the average mind; and that by the continual hearing and practice of melody there has been gained and transmitted an increasing musical sensibility. Confirmation of this view may be drawn from individual cases. Grant that among a people endowed with musical faculty to a certain degree, spontaneous variation will occasionally produce men possessing it in a higher degree; it cannot be granted that spontaneous variation accounts for the frequent production, by such highly-endowed men, of men still more highly endowed. On the average, the children of marriages with others not similarly endowed, will be less distinguished rather than more distinguished. The most that can be expected is that this unusual amount of faculty shall re-appear in the next generation undiminished. How then shall we explain cases like those of Bach, Mozart, and Beethoven, all of them sons of men having unusual musical powers who were constantly exercising those powers, and who greatly excelled their fathers in their musical powers? What shall we say to the facts that Haydn was the son of an organist, that Hummel was born to a music master, and that Weber's father was a distinguished violinist? The occurrence of so many cases in one nation within a short period of time, cannot rationally be ascribed to the coincidence of "spontaneous variations." It can be ascribed to nothing but inherited developments of structure caused by augmentations of function.

But the clearest proof that structural alterations caused by alterations of function are inherited, occurs when the alterations are morbid. I had originally named in this place the results of M. Brown-Sequard's experiments on guinea-pigs, showing that those which had been artificially made epileptic had offspring which were epileptic; and I name them again though his inference is by many rejected. For, as exemplified a few pages back, strong evidence is often disregarded for trivial reasons by those who dislike the conclusion drawn. Just naming this evidence and its possible invalidity, let me pass to some results of experiences recently set forth by Dr. Savage, President of the Neurological Society. In an essay on "Heredity and Neurosis" published in *Brain*, Parts LXXVII, LXXVIII, 1897, he says:—"We recognise the transmission of a tendency to develop gout, and we recognise that the disease produced by the individual himself differs little from that which may have been inherited." [That is, acquired gout may be transmitted as constitutional gout.] "I have seen several patients whose history I have been able to examine carefully, in whom mental tricks have been transmitted from one generation to another." In the "musical prodigies" descending from musical parents, "there seemed to be a transmission of a greatly increased aptitude or tendency which is all one is contending for." "Though there is, in my opinion, power to transmit acquired peculiarities, yet the tendency is to transmit a predisposition." (pp. 19-21.) And an authority on nervous diseases who is second to none—Dr. Hughlings Jackson—takes the same view. The liability to consumption shown by children of consumptive parents, which no one doubts, shows us the same thing. It is admitted that consumption may be produced by conditions very unfavourable to life; and unless it is held that the disease so produced differs from the disease when inherited, the conclusion must be that here, too, there is a transmission of functionally-produced organic changes. This holds true whether the production of tubercle is due to innate defect or whether it is due to the invasion of a bacillus. For in this last case the consumptive diathesis must be regarded as a state of body more than usually liable to invasion by the bacillus, and this is the same when acquired as when transmitted.

§ 83. Two modified manifestations of Heredity remain to be noticed. The one is the re-appearance in offspring of traits not borne by the parents, but borne by the grandparents or by remoter ancestors. The other is the limitation of Heredity by sex—the restriction of transmitted peculiarities to offspring of the same sex as the parent possessing them.

Atavism, which is the name given to the recurrence of ancestral traits, is proved by many and varied facts. In the picture-galleries of old families, and on the monumental brasses in the adjacent churches, are often seen types of feature which are still, from time to time, repeated in members of these families. It is a matter of common remark that some constitutional diseases, such as gout and insanity, after missing a generation, will show themselves in the next. Dr. Struthers, in his above-quoted paper "On Variation in the Number of Fingers and Toes, and in the Phalanges in Man," gives cases of malformations common to grandparent and grandchild, but of which the parent had no trace. M. Girou (as quoted by Mr. Sedgwick) says—"One is often surprised to see lambs black, or spotted with black, born of ewes and rams with white wool, but if one takes the trouble to go back to the origin of this phenomena, it is found in the ancestors." Instances still more remarkable, in which the remoteness of the ancestors copied is very great, are given by Mr. Darwin. He points out that in crosses between varieties of the pigeon, there will sometimes re-appear the plumage of the original rock-pigeon, from which these varieties descended; and he thinks the faint zebra-like markings occasionally traceable in horses have probably a like meaning.

The other modified manifestation of heredity above referred to is the limitation of heredity by sex. In Mr. Sedgwick's essays, already named, will be found evidence implying that there exists some such tendency to limitation, which does or does not show itself distinctly according to the nature of the organic modification to be conveyed. On joining to the evidence he gives certain bodies of allied evidence we shall, I think, find the inconsistences comprehensible.

Beyond the familiar facts that in ourselves, along with the essential organs of sex there go minor structures and traits distinctive of sex, such as the beard and the voice in man, we have numerous cases in which, along with different sex-organs there go general differences, sometimes immense and often conspicuous. We have those in which (as in sundry parasites) the male is extremely small compared with the female; we have those in which the male is winged and the female wingless; we have those, as among birds, in which the plumage of males contrasts strongly with that of females; and among butterflies we have kindred instances in which the wings of the two sexes are wholly unlike—some, indeed, in which there is not simply dimorphism but polymorphism: two kinds of females both differing from the male. How shall we range these facts with the ordinary facts of inheritance? Without difficulty if heredity results from the proclivity which the component units contained in a germ-cell or a sperm-cell have to arrange themselves into a structure like that of the structure from which they were derived. For the obvious corollary is that where there is gamogenesis there will result partly concurring and partly conflicting proclivities. In the fertilized germ we have two groups of physiological units, slightly different in their structures. These slightly-different units severally multiply at the expense of the nutriment supplied to the unfolding germ—each kind moulding this nutriment into units of its own type. Throughout the process of development the two kinds of units, mainly agreeing in their proclivities and in the form which they tend to build themselves into, but having minor differences, work in unison to produce an organism of the species from which they were derived, but work in antagonism to produce copies of their respective parent-organisms. And hence ultimately results an organism in which traits of the one are mixed with traits of the other; and in which, according to the predominance of one or other group of units, one or other sex with all its concomitants is produced.

If so, it becomes comprehensible that with the predominance of either group, and the production of the same sex as that of the parent whence it was derived, there will go the repetition not only of the minor sex-traits of that parent but also of any peculiarities he or she possessed, such as monstrosities. Since the two groups are nearly balanced, and since inheritance is never an average of the two parents but a mixture of traits of the one with traits of the other, it is not difficult to see why there should be some irregularity in the transmission of these monstrosities and constitutional tendencies, though they are most frequently transmitted only to those of the same sex.[37]

§ 84. Unawares in the last paragraph there has been taken for granted the truth of that suggestion concerning Heredity ventured in § 66. Anything like a positive explanation is not to be expected in the present stage of Biology, if at all. We can look for nothing beyond a simplification of the problem; and a reduction of it to the same category with certain other problems which also admit of hypothetical solutions only. If an hypothesis which sundry widespread phenomena have already thrust upon us, can be shown to render the phenomena of Heredity more intelligible than they at present seem, we shall have reason to entertain it. The applicability of any method of interpretation to two different but allied classes of facts, is evidence of its truth.

The power which many animals display of reproducing lost parts, we saw to be inexplicable except on the assumption that the units of which any organism is built have a tendency to arrange themselves into the shape of that organism (§ 65). This power is sufficiently remarkable in cases where a lost limb or tail is replaced, but it is still more remarkable in cases where, as among some annelids, the pieces into which an individual is cut severally complete themselves by developing heads and tails, or in cases like that of the *Holothuria*, which having, when alarmed, ejected its viscera, reproduces them. Such facts compel us to admit that the components of an organism have a proclivity towards a special structure—that the adult organism when mutilated exhibits that same proclivity which is exhibited by the young organism in the course of its normal development. As before said, we may, for want of a better name, figuratively call this power organic polarity: meaning by this phrase nothing more than the observed tendency towards a special arrangement. And such facts as those presented by the fragments of a *Hydra*, and by fragments of leaves from which complete plants are produced, oblige us to recognize this proclivity as existing throughout the tissues in general—nay, in the case of the *Begonia phyllomaniaca*, obliges us to recognize this proclivity as existing in the physiological units contained in each undifferentiated cell. Quite in harmony with this conclusion, are certain implications since noticed, respecting the characters of sperm-cells and germ-cells. We saw sundry reasons for rejecting the supposition that these are highly-specialized cells and for accepting the opposite supposition, that they are cells differing from others rather in being unspecialized. And here the assumption to which we seem driven by the *ensemble* of the evidence, is, that sperm-cells and germ-cells are essentially nothing more than vehicles in which are contained small groups of the physiological units in a fit state for obeying their proclivity towards the structural arrangement of the species they belong to.

If the likeness of offspring to parents is thus determined, it becomes manifest, *à priori*, that besides the transmission of generic and specific peculiarities, there will be a transmission of those individual peculiarities which, arising without assignable causes, are classed as "spontaneous." For if the assumption of a special arrangement of parts by an organism, is due to the proclivity of its physiological units towards that arrangement; then the assumption of an arrangement of parts slightly different from that of the species, implies physiological units slightly unlike those of the species; and these slightly-unlike physiological units, communicated through the medium of sperm-cell or germ-cell, will tend, in the offspring, to build themselves into a structure similarly diverging from the average of the species.

But it is not equally manifest that, on this hypothesis, alterations of structure caused by alterations of function must be transmitted to offspring. It is not obvious that change in the form of a part, caused by changed action, involves such change in the physiological units throughout the organism that these, when groups of them are thrown off in the shape of reproductive centres, will unfold into organisms that have this part similarly changed in form. Indeed, when treating of Adaptation (§ 69), we saw that an organ modified by increase or decrease of function, can but slowly re-act on the system at large, so as to bring about those correlative changes required to produce a new equilibrium; and yet only when such new equilibrium has been established, can we expect it to be *fully* expressed in the modified physiological units of which the organism is built—only then can we count on a complete transfer of the modification to descendants. Nevertheless, that changes of structure caused by changes of action must also be transmitted, however obscurely, appears to be a deduction from first principles—or if not a specific deduction, still, a general implication. For if an organism A, has, by any peculiar habit or condition of life, been modified into the form A', it follows that all the functions of A', reproductive function included, must be in some degree different from the functions of A. An organism being a combination of rhythmically-acting parts in moving equilibrium, the action and structure of any one part cannot be altered without causing alterations of action and structure in all the rest; just as no member of the Solar System could be modified in motion or mass, without producing rearrangements throughout the whole Solar System. And if the organism A, when changed to A', must be changed in all its functions; then the offspring of A' cannot be the same as they would have been had it retained the form A. That the change in the offspring must, other things equal, be in the same direction as the change in the parent, appears implied by the fact that the change propagated throughout the parental system is a change towards a new state of equilibrium—a change tending to bring the actions of all organs, reproductive included, into harmony with these new actions. Or, bringing the question to its ultimate and simplest form, we may say that as, on the one hand, physiological units will, because of their special polarities, build themselves into an organism of a special structure; so, on the other hand, if the structure of this organism is modified by modified function, it will impress some corresponding modification on the structures and polarities of its units. The units and the aggregate must act and re-act on each other. If nothing prevents, the units will mould the aggregate into a form in equilibrium with their pre-existing polarities. If, contrariwise, the aggregate is made by incident actions to take a new form, its forces must tend to re-mould the units into harmony with this new form. And to say that the physiological units are in any degree so re-moulded as to bring their polar forces towards equilibrium with the forces of the modified aggregate, is to say that when separated in the shape of reproductive centres, these units will tend to build themselves up into an aggregate modified in the same direction.

NOTE.—A large amount of additional evidence supporting the belief that functionally produced modifications are inherited, will be found in Appendix B.

CHAPTER IX.

VARIATION.

§ 85. Equally conspicuous with the truth that every organism bears a general likeness to its parents, is the truth that no organism is exactly like either parent. Though similar to both in generic and specific traits, and usually, too, in those traits which distinguish the variety, it diverges in numerous traits of minor importance. No two plants are indistinguishable; and no two animals are without differences. Variation is co-extensive with Heredity.

The degrees of variation have a wide range. There are deviations so small as to be not easily detected; and there are deviations great enough to be called monstrosities. In plants we may pass from cases of slight alteration in the shape of a leaf, to cases where, instead of a flower with its calyx above the seed-vessel, there is produced a flower with its calyx below the seed-vessel; and while in one animal there arises a scarcely noticeable unlikeness in the length or colour of the hair, in another an organ is absent or a supernumerary organ appears. Though small variations are by far the most general, yet variations of considerable magnitude are not uncommon; and even those variations constituted by additions or suppressions of parts, are not so rare as to be excluded from the list of causes by which organic forms are changed. Cattle without horns are frequent. Of sheep there are horned breeds and breeds that have lost their horns. At one time there existed in Scotland a race of pigs with solid feet instead of cleft feet. In pigeons, according to Mr. Darwin, "the number of the caudal and sacral vertebræ vary; as does the number of the ribs, together with their relative breadth and the presence of processes."

That variations, both small and large, which arise without any specific assignable cause, tend to become hereditary, was shown in the last chapter. Indeed the evidence which proves Heredity in its smaller manifestations is the same evidence which proves Variation; since it is only when there occur variations that the inheritance of anything beyond the structural peculiarities of the species can be proved. It remains here, however, to be observed that the transmission of variations is itself variable; and that it varies both in the direction of decrease and in the direction of increase. An individual trait of one parent may be so counteracted by the influence of the other parent, that it may not appear in the offspring; or, not being so counteracted, the offspring may possess it, perhaps in an equal degree or perhaps in a less degree; or the offspring may exhibit the trait in even a still higher degree. Among illustrations of this, one must suffice. I quote it from the essay by Sir J. Struthers referred to in the last chapter.

"The great-great-grandmother, Esther P—— (who married A—— L——), had a sixth little finger on one hand. Of their eighteen children (twelve daughters and six sons), only one (Charles) is known to have had digital variety. We have the history of the descendants of three of the sons, Andrew, Charles, and James.

"(1.) Andrew L—— had two sons, Thomas and Andrew; and Thomas had two sons all without digital variety. Here we have three successive generations without the variety possessed by the great-grandmother showing itself.

"(2.) James L——, who was normal, had two sons and seven daughters, also normal. One of the daughters became Mrs. J—— (one of the informants), and had three daughters and five sons, all normal except one of the sons, James J——, now æt. 17, who had six fingers on each hand....

"In this branch of the descendants of Esther, we see it passing over two generations and reappearing in one member of the third generation, and now on both hands.

"(3.) Charles L——, the only child of Esther who had digital variety, had six fingers on each hand. He had three sons, James, Thomas, and John, all of whom were born with six fingers on each hand, while John has also a sixth toe on one foot. He had also five other sons and four daughters, all of whom were normal.

"(*a.*) Of the normal children of this, the third generation, the five sons had twelve sons and twelve daughters, and the four daughters have had four sons and four daughters, being the fourth generation, all of whom were normal. A fifth generation in this sub-group consists as yet of only two boys and two girls who are also normal.

"In this sub-branch, we see the variety of the first generation present in the second, passing over the third and fourth, and also the fifth as far as it has yet gone.

"(*b.*) James had three sons and two daughters, who are normal.

"(*c.*) Thomas had four sons and five daughters, who are normal; and has two grandsons, also normal.

"In this sub-branch of the descent, we see the variety of the first generation, showing itself in the second and third, and passing over the fourth, and (as far as it yet exists) the fifth generation.

"(*d.*) John L—— (one of the informants) had six fingers, the additional finger being attached on the outer side, as in the case of his brothers James and Thomas. All of them had the additional digits removed. John has also a sixth toe on one foot, situated on the outer side. The fifth and sixth toes have a common proximal phalange, and a common integument invests the middle and distal phalanges, each having a separate nail.

"John L—— has a son who is normal, and a daughter, Jane, who was born with six fingers on each hand and six toes on each foot. The sixth fingers were removed. The sixth toes are not wrapped with the fifth as in her father's case, but are distinct from them. The son has a son and daughter, who, like himself, are normal.

"In this, the most interesting sub-branch of the descent, we see digital increase, which appeared in the first generation on one limb, appearing in the second on two limbs, the hands; in the third on three limbs, the hands and one foot; in the fourth on all the four limbs. There is as yet no fifth generation in uninterrupted transmission of the variety. The variety does not yet occur in any member of the fifth generation of Esther's descendants, which consists, as yet, only of three boys and one girl, whose parents were normal, and of two boys and two girls, whose grandparents were normal. It is not known whether in the case of the great-great-grandmother, Esther P——, the variety was original or inherited."[38]

§ 86. Where there is great uniformity among the members of a species, the divergences of offspring from the average type are usually small; but where, among the members of a species, considerable unlikenesses have once been established, unlikenesses among the offspring are frequent and great. Wild plants growing in their natural habitats are uniform over large areas, and maintain from generation to generation like structures; but when cultivation has caused appreciable differences among the members of any species of plant, extensive and numerous deviations are apt to arise. Similarly, between wild and domesticated animals of the same species, we see the contrast that though the homogeneous wild race maintains its type with great persistence, the comparatively heterogeneous domestic race frequently produces individuals more unlike the average type than the parents are.

Though unlikeness among progenitors is one antecedent of variation, it is by no means the sole antecedent. Were it so, the young ones successively born to the same parents would be alike. If any peculiarity in a new organism were a direct resultant of the structural differences between the two organisms which produced it; then all subsequent new organisms produced by these two would show the same peculiarity. But we know that the successive offspring have different peculiarities: no two of them are ever exactly alike.

One cause of such structural variation in progeny, is functional variation in parents. Proof of this is given by the fact that, among progeny of the same parents, there is more difference between those begotten under different constitutional states than between those begotten under the same constitutional state. It is notorious that twins are more nearly alike than children borne in succession. The functional conditions of the parents being the same for twins, but not the same for their brothers and sisters (all other antecedents being constant), we have no choice but to admit that variations in the functional conditions of the parents, are the antecedents of those greater unlikenesses which their brothers and sisters exhibit.

Some other antecedent remains, however. The parents being the same, and their constitutional states the same, variation, more or less marked, still manifests itself. Plants grown from seeds out of one pod, or animals produced at one birth, are not alike. Sometimes they differ considerably. In a litter of pigs or of kittens, we rarely see uniformity of markings; and occasionally there are important structural contrasts. I have myself recently been shown a litter of Newfoundland puppies, some of which had four digits to their feet, while in others there was present, on each hind-foot, what is called the "dew-claw"—a rudimentary fifth digit.

Thus, induction points to three causes of variation, all in action together. We have heterogeneity among progenitors, which, did it act uniformly and alone in generating, by composition of forces, new deviations, would impress such new deviations to the same extent on all offspring of the same parents; which it does not. We have functional variation in the parents, which, acting either alone or in combination with the preceding cause, would entail the same structural variations on all young ones simultaneously produced; which it does not. Consequently there is some third cause of variation, yet to be found, which acts along with the structural and functional variations of ancestors and parents.

§ 87. Already, in the last section, there has been implied some relation between variation and the action of external conditions. The above-cited contrast between the uniformity of a wild species and the multiformity of the same species when cultivated or domesticated, thrusts this truth upon us. Respecting the variations of plants, Mr. Darwin remarks that "'sports' are extremely rare under nature, but far from rare under cultivation." Others who have studied the matter assert that if a species of plant which, up to a certain time, has maintained great uniformity, once has its constitution thoroughly disturbed, it will go on varying indefinitely. Though, in consequence of the remoteness of the periods at which they were domesticated, there is a lack of positive proof that our extremely variable domestic animals have become variable under the changed conditions implied by domestication, having been previously constant; yet competent judges do not doubt that this has been the case.

Now the constitutional disturbance which precedes variation, can be nothing else than an overthrowing of the pre-established equilibrium of functions. Transferring a plant from forest lands to a ploughed field or a manured garden, is altering the balance of forces to which it has been hitherto subject, by supplying it with different proportions of the assimilable matters it requires, and taking away some of the positive impediments to its growth which competing wild plants before offered. An animal taken from woods or plains, where it lived on wild food of its own procuring, and placed under restraint while artificially supplied with food not quite like what it had before, is an animal subject to new outer actions to which its inner actions must be adjusted. From the general law of equilibration we found it to follow that "the maintenance of such a moving equilibrium" as an organism displays, "requires the habitual genesis of internal forces corresponding in number, directions, and amounts, to the external incident forces—as many inner functions, single or combined, as there are single or combined outer actions to be met" (*First Principles*, § 173); and more recently (§ 27), we have seen that Life itself is "thc definite combination of heterogeneous changes, both simultaneous and successive, in correspondence with external co-existences and sequences." Necessarily, therefore, an organism exposed to a permanent change in the arrangement of outer forces must undergo a permanent change in the arrangement of inner forces. The old equilibrium has been destroyed; and a new equilibrium must be established. There must be functional perturbations, ending in a re-adjusted balance of functions.

If, then, change of conditions is the only known cause by which the original homogeneity of a species is destroyed; and if change of conditions can affect an organism only by altering its functions; it follows that alteration of functions is the only known internal cause to which the commencement of variation can be ascribed. That such minor functional changes as parents undergo from year to year are influential on the offspring, we have seen is proved by the greater unlikeness that exists between children born to the same parents at different times, than exists between twins. And here we seem forced to conclude that the larger functional variations produced by greater external changes, are the initiators of those structural variations which, when once commenced in a species, lead by their combinations and antagonisms to multiform results. Whether they are or are not the direct initiators, they must still be the indirect initiators.

§ 87*a*. In the foregoing sentence those pronounced structural variations from which may presently arise new varieties and eventually species, are ascribed to "the larger functional variations produced by greater external changes"; and this limitation is a needful one, since there is a constant cause of minor variations of a wholly different kind.

There are the variations arising from differences in the conditions to which the germ is subject, both before detachment from the parent and after. At first sight it seems that plants grown from seeds out of the same seed-vessel and animals belonging to the same litter, ought, in the absence of any differences of ancestral antecedents, to be entirely alike. But this is not so. Inevitably they are subject from the very outset to slightly different sets of agencies. The seeds in a seed-vessel do not stand in exactly the same relations to the sources of nutriment: some are nearer than others. They are somewhat differently exposed to the heat and light penetrating their envelope; and some are more impeded in their growth by neighbours than others are. Similarly with young animals belonging to the same litter. Their uterine lives are made to some extent unlike by unlike connexions with the blood-supply, by mutual interferences not all the same, and even by different relations to the disturbances caused by the mother's movements. So, too, is it after separation from the parent plant or animal. Even the biblical parable reminds us that seeds fall into places here favourable and there unfavourable in various degrees. In respect of soil, in respect of space for growth, in respect of shares of light, none of them are circumstanced in quite the same ways. With animals the like holds. In a litter of pigs some, weaker than others, do not succeed as often in getting possession of teats. And then in both cases the differences thus initiated become increasingly pronounced. Among young plants the smaller, outgrown by their better-placed neighbours, are continually more shaded and more left behind; and among the litter the weakly ones, continually thrust aside by the stronger, become relatively more weakly from deficient nutrition.

Differentiations thus arising, both before and after separation from parents, though primarily differences of growth, entail structural differences; for it is a general law of nutrition that when there is deficiency of food the non-essential organs suffer more than the essential ones, and the unlikenesses of proportion hence arising constitute unlikenesses of structure. It may be concluded, however, that variations generated in this manner usually have no permanent results. In the first place, the individuals which, primarily in growth and secondarily in smaller developments of less-important organs, are by implication inferior, are likely to be eliminated from the species. In the second place, differences of structure produced in the way shown do not express differences of constitution—are not the effects of somewhat divergent physiological units; and consequently are not likely to be repeated in posterity.

§ 88. We have still, therefore, to explain those variations which have no manifest causes of the kinds thus far considered. These are the variations termed "spontaneous." Not that those who apply to them this word, or some equivalent, mean to imply that they are uncaused. Mr. Darwin expressly guards himself against such an interpretation. He says:—"I have hitherto sometimes spoken as if the variations—so common and multiform in organic beings under domestication, and in a lesser degree in those in a state of nature—had been due to chance. This, of course, is a wholly incorrect expression, but it serves to acknowledge plainly our ignorance of the cause of each particular variation." Not only, however, do I hold, in common with Mr. Darwin, that there must be some cause for these apparently-spontaneous variations, but it seems to me that a definite cause is assignable. I think it may be shown that unlikenesses must necessarily arise even between the new individuals simultaneously produced by the same parents. Instead of the occurrence of such variations being inexplicable, the absence of them would be inexplicable.

In any series of dependent changes a small initial difference often works a marked difference in the results. The mode in which a particular breaker bursts on the beach, may determine whether the seed of some foreign plant which it bears is or is not stranded—may cause the presence or absence of this plant from the Flora of the land; and may so affect, for millions of years, in countless ways, the living creatures throughout the land. A single touch, by introducing into the body some morbid matter, may set up an immensely involved set of functional disturbances and structural alterations. The whole tenor of a life may be changed by a word of advice; or a glance may determine an action which alters thoughts, feelings, and deeds throughout a long series of years. In those still more involved combinations of changes which societies exhibit, this truth is still more conspicuous. A hair's-breadth difference in the direction of some soldier's musket at the battle of Arcola, by killing Napoleon, might have changed events throughout Europe; and though the type of social organization in each European country would have been now very much what it is, yet in countless details it would have been different.

Illustrations like these, with which pages might be filled, prepare us for the conclusion that organisms produced by the same parents at the same time, must be more or less differentiated, both by insensible initial differences and by slight differences in the conditions to which they are subject during their evolution. We need not, however, rest with assuming such initial differences: the necessity of them is demonstrable. The individual germ-cells which, in succession or simultaneously, are separated from the same parent, can never be exactly alike; nor can the sperm-cells which fertilize them. When treating of the instability of the homogeneous (*First Principles*, § 149), we saw that no two parts of any aggregate can be similarly conditioned with respect to incident forces; and that being subject to forces that are more or less unlike, they must become more or less unlike. Hence, no two ova in an ovarium or ovules in a seed-vessel—no two spermatozoa or pollen-cells, can be identical. Whether or not there arise other contrasts, there are certain to arise quantitative contrasts; since the process of nutrition cannot be absolutely alike for all. The reproductive centres must begin to differentiate from the very outset. Such being the necessities of the case, what will happen on any successive or simultaneous fertilizations? Inevitably unlikenesses between the respective parental influences must result. Quantitative differences among the sperm-cells and among the germ-cells, will insure this. Grant that the number of physiological units contained in any one reproductive cell, can rarely if ever be exactly equal to the number contained in any other, ripened at the same time or at a different time; and it follows that among the fertilized germs produced by the same parents, the physiological units derived from them respectively will bear a different numerical ratio to each other in every case. If the parents are constitutionally quite alike, the variation in the ratio between the units they severally bequeath, cannot cause unlikenesses among the offspring. But if otherwise, no two of the offspring can be alike. In every case the small initial difference in the proportions of the slightly-unlike units, will lead, during evolution, to a continual multiplication of differences. The insensible divergence at the outset will generate sensible divergences at the conclusion. Possibly some may hence infer that though, in such case, the offspring must differ somewhat from each other and from both parents, yet that in every one of them there must result a homogeneous mixture of the traits of the two parents. A little consideration shows that the reverse is inferable. If, throughout the process of development, the physiological units derived from each parent preserved the same ratio in all parts of the growing organism, each organ would show as much as every other, the influence of either parent. But no such uniform distribution is possible. It has been shown (*First Principles*, § 163), that in any aggregate of mixed units segregation must inevitably go on. Incident forces will tend ever to cause separation of the two orders of units from each other—will tend to integrate groups of the one order in one place and groups of the other order in another place. Hence there must arise not a homogeneous mean between the two parents, but a mixture of organs, some of which mainly follow the one and some the other. And this is the kind of mixture which observation shows us.

Still it may be fairly objected that however the attributes of the two parents are variously mingled in their offspring, they must in all of them fall between the extremes displayed in the parents. In no characteristic could one of the young exceed both parents, were there no cause of "spontaneous variation" but the one alleged. Evidently, then, there is a cause yet unfound.

§ 89. Thus far we have contemplated the process under its simplest aspect. While we have assumed the two parents to be somewhat unlike, we have assumed that each parent has a homogeneous constitution—is built up of physiological units which are exactly alike. But in no case can such a homogeneity exist. Each parent had parents who were more or less contrasted—each parent inherited at least two orders of physiological units not quite identical. Here then we have a further cause of variation. The sperm-cells or germ-cells which any organism produces, will differ from each other not quantitatively only but qualitatively. Of the slightly-unlike physiological units bequeathed to it, the reproductive cells it casts off cannot habitually contain the same proportions; and we may expect the proportions to vary not slightly but greatly. Just as, during the evolution of an organism, the physiological units derived from the two parents tend to segregate, and produce likeness to the male parent in this part and to the female parent in that; so, during the formation of reproductive cells, there will arise in one a predominance of the physiological units derived from the father, and in another a predominance of the physiological units derived from the mother. Thus, then, every fertilized germ, besides containing different *amounts* of the two parental influences, will contain different *kinds* of influences—this having received a marked impress from one grandparent, and that from another. Without further exposition the reader will see how this cause of complication, running back through each line of ancestry, must produce in every germ numerous minute differences among the units.

Here, then, we have a clue to the multiplied variations, and sometimes extreme variations, that arise in races which have once begun to vary. Amid countless different combinations of units derived from parents, and through them from ancestors, immediate and remote—amid the various conflicts in their slightly-different organic polarities, opposing and conspiring with one another in all ways and degrees; there will from time to time arise special proportions causing special deviations. From the general law of probabilities it may be concluded that while these involved influences, derived from many progenitors, must, on the average of cases, obscure and partially neutralize one another; there must occasionally result such combinations of them as will produce considerable divergences from average structures; and, at rare intervals, such combinations as will produce very marked divergences. There is thus a correspondence between the inferable results and the results as habitually witnessed.

§ 90. Still there remains a difficulty. It may be said that admitting functional change to be the initiator of variation—granting that the physiological units of an organism long subject to new conditions, will tend to become modified in such way as to cause change of structure in offspring; yet there will still be no cause of the supposed heterogeneity among the physiological units of different individuals. There seems validity in the objection, that as all the members of a species whose circumstances have been altered will be affected in the same manner, the results, when they begin to show themselves in descendants, will show themselves in the same manner: not multiform variations will arise, but deviations all in one direction.

The reply is simple. The members of a species thus circumstanced will *not* be similarly affected. In the absence of absolute uniformity among them, the functional changes caused in them will be more or less dissimilar. Just as men of slightly-unlike dispositions behave in quite opposite ways under the same circumstances; or just as men of slightly-unlike constitutions get diverse disorders from the same cause, and are diversely acted on by the same medicine; so, the insensibly-differentiated members of a species whose conditions have been changed, may at once begin to undergo various kinds of functional changes. As we have already seen, small initial contrasts may lead to large terminal contrasts. The intenser cold of the climate into which a species has migrated, may cause in one individual increased consumption of food to balance the greater loss of heat; while in another individual the requirement may be met by a thicker growth of fur. Or, when meeting with the new foods which a new region furnishes, accident may determine one member of the species to begin with one kind and another member with another kind; and hence may arise established habits in these respective members and their descendants. Now when the functional divergences thus set up in sundry families of a species have lasted long enough to affect their constitutions, and to modify somewhat the physiological units thrown off in their reproductive cells, the divergences produced by these in offspring will be of divers kinds. And the original homogeneity of constitution having been thus destroyed, variation may go on with increasing facility. There will result a heterogeneous mixture of modifications of structure caused by modifications of function; and of still more numerous correlated modifications, indirectly so caused. By natural selection of the most divergent forms, the unlikenesses of parents will be rendered more marked, and the limits of variation wider. Until at length the divergences of constitutions and modes of life, become great enough to lead to segregation of the varieties.

§ 91. That variations must occur, and that they must ever tend, both directly and indirectly, towards adaptive modifications, are conclusions deducible from first principles; apart from any detailed interpretations like the above. That the state of homogeneity is an unstable state we have found to be a universal truth. Each species must pass from the uniform into the more or less multiform, unless the incidence of external forces is exactly the same for all its members, which it never can be. Through the process of differentiation and integration, which of necessity brings together, or keeps together, like individuals, and separates unlike ones from them, there must nevertheless be maintained a tolerably uniform species, so long as there continues a tolerably uniform set of conditions in which it may exist. But if the conditions change, either absolutely by some disturbance of the habitat or relatively by spread of the species into other habitats, then the divergent individuals that result must be segregated by the divergent sets of conditions into distinct varieties (*First Principles*, § 166). When, instead of contemplating a species in the aggregate, we confine our attention to a single member and its descendants, we see it to be a corollary from the general law of equilibration that the moving equilibrium constituted by the vital actions in each member of this family, must remain constant so long as the external actions to which they correspond remain constant; and that if the external actions are changed, the disturbed balance of internal changes, if not overthrown, cannot cease undergoing modification until the internal changes are again in equilibrium with the external actions: corresponding structural alterations having arisen.

On passing from these derivative laws to the ultimate law, we see that Variation is necessitated by the persistence of force. The members of a species inhabiting any area cannot be subject to like sets of forces over the whole of that area. And if, in different parts of the area, different kinds or amounts or combinations of forces act on them, they cannot but become different in themselves and in their progeny. To say otherwise, is to say that differences in the forces will not produce differences in the effects; which is to deny the persistence of force.

CHAPTER X.

GENESIS, HEREDITY, AND VARIATION.

§ 92. A question raised, and hypothetically answered, in §§ 78 and 79, was there postponed until we had dealt with the topics of Heredity and Variation. Let us now resume the consideration of this question, in connexion with sundry others which the facts suggest.

After contemplating the several methods by which the multiplication of organisms is carried on—after ranging them under the two heads of Homogenesis, in which the successive generations are similarly produced, and Heterogenesis, in which they are dissimilarly produced—after observing that Homogenesis is nearly always sexual genesis, while Heterogenesis is asexual genesis with occasionally-recurring sexual genesis; we came to the questions—why is it that some organisms multiply in the one way and some in the other? and why is it that where agamogenesis prevails it is usually, from time to time, interrupted by gamogenesis? In seeking answers to these questions, we inquired whether there are common to both Homogenesis and Heterogenesis, any conditions under which alone sperm-cells and germ-cells arise and are united for the production of new organisms; and we reached the conclusion that, in all cases, they arise only when there is an approach to equilibrium between the forces which produce growth and the forces which oppose growth. This answer to the question—*when* does gamogenesis recur? still left unanswered the question—*why* does gamogenesis recur? And to this the reply suggested was, that the approach towards general equilibrium in organisms, "is accompanied by an approach towards molecular equilibrium in them; and that the need for this union of sperm-cell with germ-cell is the need for overthrowing this equilibrium, and re-establishing active molecular change in the detached germ—a result probably effected by mixing the slightly-different physiological units of slightly-different individuals." This is the hypothesis which we have now to consider. Let us first look at the evidences which certain inorganic phenomena furnish.

The molecules of any aggregate which have not a balanced arrangement, inevitably tend towards a balanced arrangement. As before mentioned (*First Principles*, § 100), amorphous wrought iron, when subject to continuous jar, begins to arrange itself into crystals—its atoms assume a condition of polar equilibrium. The particles of unannealed glass, which are so unstably arranged that slight disturbing forces make them separate into small groups, take advantage of that greater freedom of movement given by a raised temperature, to adjust themselves into a state of relative rest. During any such re-arrangement the aggregate exercises a coercive force over its units. Just as in a growing crystal the atoms successively assimilated from the solution, are made by the already crystallized atoms to take a certain form, and even to re-complete that form when it is broken; so in any mass of unstably-arranged atoms which passes into a stable arrangement, each atom conforms to the forces exercised on it by all the other atoms. This is a corollary from the general law of equilibration. We saw (*First Principles*, § 170) that every change is towards equilibrium; and that change can never cease until equilibrium is reached. Organisms, above all other aggregates, conspicuously display this progressive equilibration; because their units are of such kinds, and so conditioned, as to admit of easy re-arrangement. Those extremely active changes which go on during the early stages of evolution, imply an immense excess of the molecular forces over those antagonist forces which the aggregate exercises on the molecules. While this excess continues, it is expended in growth, development, and function: expenditure for any of these purposes being proof that part of the force constituting molecular tensions remains unbalanced. Eventually, however, this excess diminishes. Either, as in organisms which do not expend much energy, decrease of assimilation leads to its decline; or, as in organisms which expend much energy, it is counterbalanced by the rapidly-increasing reactions of the aggregate (§ 46). The cessation of growth when followed, as in some organisms, by death, implies the arrival at an equilibrium between the molecular forces and those forces which the aggregate opposes to them. When, as in other organisms, growth ends in the establishment of a moving equilibrium, there is implied such a decreased preponderance of the molecular forces, as leaves no surplus beyond that which is used up in functions. The declining functional activity characteristic of advancing life, expresses a further decline in this surplus. And when all vital movements come to an end, the implication is that the actions of the units on the aggregate and the reactions of the aggregate on the units are completely balanced. Hence, while a state of rapid growth indicates such a play of forces among the units of an aggregate as will produce active re-distribution, the diminution and arrest of growth shows that the units have fallen into such relative positions that re-distribution is no longer so facile. When, therefore, we see that gamogenesis recurs only when growth is decreasing, or has come to an end, we must say that it recurs only when the organic units are approximating to equilibrium—only when their mutual restraints prevent them from readily changing their arrangements in obedience to incident forces.

That units of like forms can be built up into a more stable aggregate than units of slightly unlike forms, is tolerably manifest *à priori*. And we have facts which prove that mixing allied but somewhat different units, *does* lead to comparative instability. Most metallic alloys exemplify this truth. Common solder, which is a mixture of lead and tin, melts at a much lower temperature than either lead or tin. The compound of lead, tin, and bismuth, called "fusible metal," becomes fluid at the temperature of boiling water; while the temperatures at which lead, tin, and bismuth become fluid are, respectively, 612°, 442°, and 497° F. Still more remarkable is the illustration furnished by potassium and sodium. These metals are very near akin in all respects—in their specific gravities, their atomic weights, their chemical affinities, and the properties of their compounds. That is to say, all the evidences unite to show that their units, though not identical, have a close resemblance. What now happens when they are mixed? Potassium alone melts at 136°, sodium alone melts at 190°, but the alloy of potassium and sodium is liquid at the ordinary temperature of the air. Observe the meaning of these facts, expressed in general terms. The maintenance of a solid form by any group of units implies among them an arrangement so stable that it is not overthrown by the incident forces. Whereas the assumption of a liquid form implies that the incident forces suffice to destroy the arrangement of the units. In the one case the thermal undulations fail to dislocate the parts; while in the other case the parts are so dislocated by the thermal undulations that they fall into total disorder—a disorder admitting of easy re-arrangement into any other order. For the liquid state is a state in which the units become so far free from mutual restraints, that incident forces can change their relative positions very readily. Thus we have reason to conclude that an aggregate of units which, though in the main similar to one another, have minor differences, must be more unstable than an aggregate of homogeneous units. The one will yield to disturbing forces which the other successfully resists.

Now though the colloidal molecules of which organisms are mainly built, are themselves highly composite; and though the physiological units compounded out of these colloidal molecules must have structures far more involved; yet it must happen with such units, as with simple units, that those which have exactly like forms will admit of arrangement into a more stable aggregate than those which have slightly-unlike forms. Among units of this order, as among units of a simpler order, imperfect similarity must entail imperfect balance in anything formed of them, and consequent diminished ability to withstand disturbing forces. Hence, given two organisms which, by diminished nutrition or increased expenditure, are being arrested in their growths—given in each an approaching equilibrium between the forces of the units and the forces of the aggregate—given, that is, such a comparatively balanced state among the units that re-arrangement of them by incident forces is no longer so easy; and it will follow that by uniting a group of units from the one organism with a group of slightly-different units from the other, the tendency towards equilibrium will be diminished, and the mixed units will be rendered more modifiable in their arrangements by the forces acting on them: they will be so far freed as to become again capable of that re-distribution which constitutes evolution.

And now let us test this hypothesis by seeing what power it gives us of interpreting established inductions.

§ 93. The majority of plants being hermaphrodites, it has, until quite recently, been supposed that the ovules of each flower are fertilized by pollen from the anthers of the same flower. Mr. Darwin, however, has shown that the arrangements are generally such as to prevent this. Either the ovules and the pollen are not ripe simultaneously, or obstacles prevent access of the one to the other. At the same time he has shown that there exist arrangements, often of a remarkable kind, which facilitate the transfer of pollen by insects from the stamens of one flower to the pistil of another. Similarly, it has been found that among the lower animals, hermaphrodism does not usually involve the production of fertile ova by the union of sperm-cells and germ-cells developed in the same individual; but that the reproductive centres of one individual are united with those of another to produce fertile ova. Either, as in *Pyrosoma*, *Perophora*, and in many higher molluscs, the ova and spermatozoa are matured at different times; or, as in annelids, they are prevented by their relative positions from coming in contact.

Remembering the fact that among the higher classes of organisms, fertilization is always effected by combining the sperm-cell of one individual with the germ-cell of another; and joining with it the above fact that among hermaphrodite organisms, the germ-cells developed in any individual are usually not fertilized by sperm-cells developed in the same individual; we see reason for thinking that the essential thing in fertilization, is the union of specially-fitted portions of *different* organisms. If fertilization depended on the peculiar properties of sperm-cell and germ-cell, as such; then, in hermaphrodite organisms, it would be a matter of indifference whether the united sperm-cells and germ-cells were those of the same individual or those of different individuals. But the circumstance that there exist in such organisms elaborate appliances for mutual fertilization, shows that unlikeness of derivation in the united reproductive centres, is the desideratum. Now this is just what the foregoing hypothesis implies. If, as was concluded, fertilization has for its object the disturbance of that approaching equilibrium existing among the physiological units separated from an adult organism; and if, as we saw reason to think, this object is effected by mixture with the slightly-different physiological units of another organism; then, we at the same time see that this object will not be effected by mixture with physiological units belonging to the same organism. Thus, the hypothesis leads us to expect such provisions as we find.

§ 94. But here a difficulty presents itself. These propositions seem to involve the conclusion that self-fertilization is impossible. It apparently follows from them, that a group of physiological units from one part of an organism ought to have no power of altering the state of approaching balance in a group from another part of it. Yet self-fertilization does occur. Though the ovules of one plant are generally fertilized by pollen from another plant of the same kind, yet they may be, some of them, fertilized by pollen of the same plant; and, indeed, there are plants in which self-fertilization is the rule: even provision being in some cases made to prevent fertilization by pollen from other individuals. And though, among hermaphrodite animals, self-fertilization is usually negatived by structural or functional arrangements, yet in certain *Entozoa* there appear to be special provisions by which the sperm-cells and the germ-cells of the same individual may be united, when not previously united with those of another individual. Nay, it has even been shown that in certain Ascidians the contents of oviduct and spermiduct of the same individual produce, when united, fertile ova whence evolve perfect individuals. Certainly, at first sight, these facts do not consist with the above supposition. Nevertheless there is something like a solution.

In the last chapter, when considering the variations caused in offspring from uniting elements representing unlike parental constitutions, it was pointed out that in an unfolding organism, composed of slightly-different physiological units derived from slightly-different parents, there cannot be maintained an even distribution of the two orders of units. We saw that the instability of the homogeneous negatives the uniform blending of them; and that, by the process of differentiation and integration, they must be more or less separated; so that in one part of the body the influence of one parent will predominate, and in another part of the body the influence of the other parent: an inference which harmonizes with daily observation. We also saw that the sperm-cells or germ-cells produced by such an organism must, in virtue of these same laws, be more or less unlike one another. It was shown that through segregation, some of the sperm-cells or germ-cells will get an excess of the physiological units derived from one side, and some of them an excess of those derived from the other side: a cause which accounts for the unlikenesses among offspring simultaneously produced. Now from this segregation of the different orders of physiological units, inherited from different parents and lines of ancestry, there arises the possibility of self-fertilization in hermaphrodite organisms. If the physiological units contained in the sperm-cells and germ-cells of the same flower, are not quite homogeneous—if in some of the ovules the physiological units derived from the one parent greatly predominate, and in some of the ovules those derived from the other parent; and if the like is true of the pollen-cells; then, some of the ovules may be nearly as much contrasted with some of the pollen-cells in the characters of their contained units, as were the ovules and pollen-cells of the parents from which the plant proceeded. Between part of the sperm-cells and part of the germ-cells, the community of nature will be such that fertilization will not result from their union; but between some of them, the differences of constitution will be such that their union will produce the requisite molecular instability. The facts, so far as they are known, seem in harmony with this deduction. Self-fertilization in flowers, when it takes place, is not so efficient as mutual fertilization. Though some of the ovules produce seeds, yet more of them than usual are abortive. From which, indeed, results the establishment of varieties that have structures favourable to mutual fertilization; since, being more prolific, these have, other things equal, greater chances in the "struggle for existence."

Further evidence is at hand supporting this interpretation. There is reason to believe that self-fertilization, which at the best is comparatively inefficient, loses all efficiency in course of time. After giving an account of the provisions for an occasional, or a frequent, or a constant crossing between flowers; and after quoting Prof. Huxley to the effect that among hermaphrodite animals, there is no case in which "the occasional influence of a distinct individual can be shown to be physically impossible;" Mr. Darwin writes—"from these several considerations and from the many special facts which I have collected, but which I am not here able to give, I am strongly inclined to suspect that, both in the vegetable and animal kingdoms, an occasional intercross with a distinct individual is a law of nature ... in none, as I suspect, can self-fertilization go on for perpetuity." This conclusion, based wholly on observed facts, is just the conclusion to which the foregoing argument points. That necessary action and the re-action between the parts of an organism and the organism as a whole—that power of an aggregate to re-mould the units, which is the correlative of the power of the units to build up into such an aggregate; implies that any differences existing among the units inherited by an organism, must gradually diminish. Being subject in common to the total forces of the organism, they will in common be modified towards congruity with these forces, and therefore towards likeness with one another. If, then, in a self-fertilizing organism and its self-fertilizing descendants, such contrasts as originally existed among the physiological units are progressively obliterated—if, consequently, there can no longer be a segregation of different physiological units in different sperm-cells and germ-cells; self-fertilization will become impossible. Step by step the fertility will diminish, and the series will finally die out.

And now observe, in confirmation of this view, that self-fertilization is limited to organisms in which an approximate equilibrium among the organic forces is not long maintained. While growth is actively going on, and the physiological units are subject to a continually-changing distribution of forces, no decided assimilation of the units can be expected: like forces acting on the unlike units will tend to segregate them, so long as continuance of evolution permits further segregation; and only when further segregation cannot go on, will the like forces tend to assimilate the units. Hence, where there is no prolonged maintenance of an approximate organic balance, self-fertilization may be possible for some generations; but it will be impossible in organisms distinguished by a sustained moving equilibrium.

§ 95. The interpretation which it affords of sundry phenomena familiar to breeders of animals, adds probability to the hypothesis. Mr. Darwin has collected a large "body of facts, showing, in accordance with the almost universal belief of breeders, that with animals and plants a cross between different varieties, or between individuals of the same variety but of another strain, gives vigour and fertility to the offspring; and on the other hand, that *close* interbreeding diminishes vigour and fertility,"—a conclusion harmonizing with the current belief respecting family-intermarriages in the human race. Have we not here a solution of these facts? Relations must, on the average of cases, be individuals whose physiological units are more nearly alike than usual. Animals of different varieties must be those whose physiological units are more unlike than usual. In the one case, the unlikeness of the units may frequently be insufficient to produce fertilization; or, if sufficient to produce fertilization, not sufficient to produce that active molecular change required for vigorous development. In the other case, both fertilization and vigorous development will be made probable.

Nor are we without a cause for the irregular manifestations of these general tendencies. The mixed physiological units composing any organism being, as we have seen, more or less segregated in the reproductive centres it throws off; there may arise various results according to the degrees of difference among the units, and the degrees in which the units are segregated. Of two cousins who have married, the common grandparents may have had either similar or dissimilar constitutions; and if their constitutions were dissimilar, the probability that their married grandchildren will have offspring will be greater than if their constitutions were similar. Or the brothers and sisters from whom these cousins descended, instead of severally inheriting the constitutions of their parents in tolerably equal degrees, may have severally inherited them in very different degrees: in which last case, intermarriages among the cousins will be less likely to prove infertile. Or the brothers and sisters from whom these cousins descended, may severally have married persons very like, or very unlike, themselves; and from this cause there may have resulted, either an undue likeness, or a due unlikeness, between the married cousins.[39] These several causes, conspiring and conflicting in endless ways and degrees, will work multiform effects. Moreover, differences of segregation will make the reproductive centres produced by the same nearly-related organisms, vary considerably in their amounts of unlikeness; and therefore, supposing their amounts of unlikeness great enough to cause fertilization, this fertilization will be effective in various degrees. Hence it may happen that among offspring of nearly-related parents, there may be some in which the want of vigour is not marked, and others in which there is decided want of vigour. So that we are alike shown why in-and-in breeding tends to diminish both fertility and vigour: and why the effect cannot be a uniform effect, but only an average effect.

§ 96. While, if the foregoing arguments are valid, gamogenesis has for its main result the initiation of a new development by the overthrow of that approximate equilibrium arrived at among the molecules of the parent-organisms, a further result appears to be subserved by it. Those inferior organisms which habitually multiply by agamogenesis, have conditions of life that are simple and uniform; while those organisms which have highly-complex and variable conditions of life, habitually multiply by gamogenesis. Now if a species has complex and variable conditions of life, its members must be severally exposed to sets of conditions that are slightly different: the aggregates of incident forces cannot be alike for all the scattered individuals. Hence, as functional deviation must ever be inducing structural deviation, each individual throughout the area occupied tends to become fitted for the particular habits which its particular conditions necessitate; and in so far, *un*fitted for the average habits proper to the species. But these undue specializations are continually checked by gamogenesis. As Mr. Darwin remarks, "intercrossing plays a very important part in nature in keeping the individuals of the same species, or of the variety, true and uniform in character:" the idiosyncratic divergences obliterate one another. Gamogenesis, then, is a means of turning to positive advantage the individual differentiations which, in its absence, would result in positive disadvantage. Were it not that individuals are ever being made unlike one another by their unlike conditions, there would not arise in them those contrasts of molecular constitution, which we have seen to be needful for producing the fertilized germs of new individuals. And were not these individual differentiations ever being mutually cancelled, they would end in a fatal narrowness of adaptation.

This truth will be most clearly seen if we reduce it to its purely abstract form, thus:—Suppose a quite homogeneous species, placed in quite homogeneous conditions; and suppose the constitutions of all its members in complete concord with their absolutely-uniform and constant conditions; what must happen? The species, individually and collectively, is in a state of perfect moving equilibrium. All disturbing forces have been eliminated. There remains no force which can, in any way, change the state of this moving equilibrium; either in the species as a whole or in its members. But we have seen (*First Principles*, § 173) that a moving equilibrium is but a transition towards complete equilibration, or death. The absence of differential or un-equilibrated forces among the members of a species, is the absence of all forces which can cause changes in the conditions of its members—is the absence of all forces which can initiate new organisms. To say, as above, that complete molecular homogeneity existing among the members of a species, must render impossible that mutual molecular disturbance which constitutes fertilization, is but another way of saying that the actions and re-actions of each organism, being in perfect balance with the actions and re-actions of the environment upon it, there remains in each organism no force by which it differs from any other—no force which any other does not meet with an equal force—no force which can set up a new evolution among the units of any other.

And so we reach the remarkable conclusion that the life of a species, like the life of an individual, is maintained by the unequal and ever-varying actions of incident forces on its different parts.[40] An individual homogeneous throughout, and having its substance everywhere continuously subject to like actions, could undergo none of those changes which life consists of; and similarly, an absolutely-uniform species, having all its members exposed to identical influences, would be deprived of that initiator of change which maintains its existence as a species. Just as, in each organism, incident forces constantly produce divergences from the mean state in various directions, which are constantly balanced by opposite divergences indirectly produced by other incident forces; and just as the combination of rhythmical functions thus maintained, constitutes the life of the organism; so, in a species, there is, through gamogenesis, a perpetual neutralization of those contrary deviations from the mean state which are caused in its different parts by different sets of incident forces; and it is similarly by the rhythmical production and compensation of these contrary deviations, that the species continues to live. The moving equilibrium in a species, like the moving equilibrium in an individual, would rapidly end in complete equilibration, or death, were not its continually-dissipated forces continually re-supplied from without. Besides owing to the external world those energies which, from moment to moment, keep up the lives of its individual members, every species owes to certain more indirect actions of the external world, those energies which enable it to perpetuate itself in successive generations.

§ 97. What evidence still remains may be conveniently woven up along with a recapitulation of the argument pursued through the last three chapters. Let us contemplate the facts in their synthetic order.

That compounding and re-compounding through which we pass from the simplest inorganic substances to the most complex organic substances, has several concomitants. Each successive stage of composition presents us with molecules that are severally larger or more integrated, that are severally more heterogeneous, that are severally more unstable, and that are more numerous in their kinds (*First Principles*, § 151). And when we come to the substances of which living bodies are formed, we find ourselves among innumerable divergent groups and sub-groups of compounds, the units of which are large, heterogeneous, and unstable, in high degrees. There is no reason to assume that this process ends with the formation of those complex colloids which constitute organic matter. A more probable assumption is that out of the complex colloidal molecules there are evolved, by a still further integration, molecules which are still more heterogeneous, and of kinds which are still more multitudinous. What must be their properties? Already the colloidal molecules are extremely unstable—capable of being variously modified in their characters by very slight incident forces; and already the complexity of their polarities prevents them from readily falling into such positions of equilibrium as results in crystallization. Now the organic molecules composed of these colloidal molecules, must be similarly characterized in far higher degrees. Far more numerous must be the minute changes that can be wrought in them by minute external forces; far more free must they remain for a long time to obey forces tending to re-distribute them; and far greater must be the number of their kinds.

Setting out with these physiological units, the existence of which various organic phenomena compel us to recognize, and the production of which the general law of Evolution thus leads us to anticipate; we get an insight into the phenomena of Genesis, Heredity, and Variation. If each organism is built of certain of these highly-plastic units peculiar to its species—units which slowly work towards an equilibrium of their complex proclivities, in producing an aggregate of the specific structure, and which are at the same time slowly modifiable by the re-actions of this aggregate—we see why the multiplication of organisms proceeds in the several ways, and with the various results, which naturalists have observed.

Heredity, as shown not only in the repetition of the specific structure but in the repetition of ancestral deviations from it, becomes a matter of course;

and it falls into unison with the fact that, in various inferior organisms, lost parts can be replaced, and that, in still lower organisms, a fragment can develop into a whole.

While an aggregate of physiological units continues to grow by the assimilation of matter which it moulds into other units of like type; and while it continues to undergo changes of structure; no equilibrium can be arrived at between the whole and its parts. Under these conditions, then, an un-differentiated portion of the aggregate—a group of physiological units not bound up into a specialized tissue—will be able to arrange itself into the structure peculiar to the species; and will so arrange itself, if freed from controlling forces and placed in fit conditions of nutrition and temperature. Hence the continuance of agamogenesis in little-differentiated organisms, so long as assimilation continues to be greatly in excess of expenditure.

But let growth be checked and development approach its completion—let the units of the aggregate be severally exposed to an almost constant distribution of forces; and they must begin to equilibrate themselves. Arranged, as they will gradually be, into comparatively stable attitudes in relation to one another, their mobility will diminish; and groups of them, partially or wholly detached, will no longer readily re-arrange themselves into the specific form. Agamogenesis will be no longer possible; or, if possible, will be no longer easy.

When we remember that the force which keeps the Earth in its orbit is the gravitation of each particle in the Earth towards every one of the group of particles existing 92,000,000 of miles off; we cannot reasonably doubt that each unit in an organism acts on all the other units, and is reacted on by them: not by gravitation only but chiefly by other energies. When, too, we learn that glass has its molecular constitution changed by light, and that substances so rigid and stable as metals have their atoms re-arranged by forces radiated in the dark from adjacent objects;[41] we are obliged to conclude that the excessively-unstable units of which organisms are built, must be sensitive in a transcendant degree to all the forces pervading the organisms composed of them—must be tending ever to re-adjust, not only their relative attitudes but their molecular structures, into equilibrium with these forces. Hence, if aggregates of the same species are differently conditioned, and re-act differently on their component units, their component units will be rendered somewhat different; and they will become the more different the more widely the re-actions of the aggregates upon them differ, and the greater the number of generations through which these different re-actions of the aggregates upon them are continued.

If, then, unlikenesses of function among individuals of the same species, produce unlikenesses between the physiological units of one individual and those of another, it becomes comprehensible that when groups of units derived from two individuals are united, the group formed will be more unstable than either of the groups was before their union. The mixed units will be less able to resist those re-distributing forces which cause evolution; and may thus have restored to them the capacity for development which they had lost.

This view harmonizes with the conclusion, which we saw reason to draw, that fertilization does not depend on any intrinsic peculiarities of sperm-cells and germ-cells, but depends on their derivation from different individuals. It explains the facts that nearly-related individuals are less likely to have offspring than others, and that their offspring, when they have them, are frequently feeble. And it gives us a key to the converse fact that the crossing of varieties results in unusual vigour.

Bearing in mind that the slightly-different orders of physiological units which an organism inherits from its parents, are subject to the same set of forces, and that when the organism is fully developed this set of forces, becoming constant, tends slowly to re-mould the two orders of units into the same form; we see how it happens that self-fertilization becomes impossible in the higher organisms, while it remains possible in the lower organisms. In long-lived creatures which have tolerably-definite limits of growth, this assimilation of the somewhat-unlike physiological units is liable to go on to an appreciable extent; whereas in organisms which do not continuously subject their component units to constant forces, there will be much less of this assimilation. And where the assimilation is not considerable, the segregation of mixed units may cause the sperm-cells and germ-cells developed in the same individual, to be sufficiently different to produce, by their union, fertile germs; and several generations of self-fertilizing descendants may succeed one another, before the two orders of units have had their unlikenesses so far diminished that they will no longer do this. The same principles explain for us the variable results of union between nearly-related organisms. According to the contrasts among the physiological units they inherit from parents and ancestors; according to the unlike proportions of the contrasted units which they severally inherit; and according to the degrees of segregation of such units in different sperm-cells and germ-cells; it may happen that two kindred individuals will produce the ordinary number of offspring or will produce none; or will at one time be fertile and at another not; or will at one time have offspring of tolerable strength and at another time feeble offspring.

To the like causes are also ascribable the phenomena of Variation. These are unobtrusive while the tolerably-uniform conditions of a species maintain tolerable uniformity among the physiological units of its members; but they become obtrusive when differences of conditions, entailing considerable functional differences, have entailed decided differences among the physiological units, and when the different physiological units, differently mingled in every individual, come to be variously segregated and variously combined.

Did space permit, it might be shown that this hypothesis is a key to many further facts—to the fact that mixed races are comparatively plastic under new conditions; to the fact that pure races show predominant influences in the offspring when crossed with mixed races; to the fact that while mixed breeds are often of larger growth, pure breeds are the more hardy—have functions less-easily thrown out of balance. But without further argument it will, I think, be admitted that the power of this hypothesis to explain so many phenomena, and to bring under a common bond phenomena which seem so little allied, is strong evidence of its truth. And such evidence gains greatly in strength on observing that this hypothesis brings the facts of Genesis, Heredity, and Variation into harmony with first principles. We see that these plastic physiological units, which we find ourselves obliged to assume, are just such more integrated, more heterogeneous, more unstable, and more multiform molecules, as would result from continuance of the steps through which organic matter is reached. We see that the differentiations of them assumed to occur in differently-conditioned aggregates, and the equilibrations of them assumed to occur in aggregates which maintain constant conditions, are but corollaries from those universal principles implied by the persistence of force. We see that the maintenance of life in the successive generations of a species, becomes a consequence of the continual incidence of new forces on the species, to replace the forces that are ever being rhythmically equilibrated in the propagation of the species. And we thus see that these apparently-exceptional phenomena displayed in the multiplication of organic beings, fall into their places as results of the general laws of Evolution. We have, therefore, weighty reasons for entertaining the hypothesis which affords us this interpretation.

CHAPTER XA.

GENESIS, HEREDITY, AND VARIATION

CONCLUDED.

§ 97*a*. Since the foregoing four chapters were written, thirty-four years ago, the topics with which they deal have been widely discussed and many views propounded. Ancient hypotheses have been abandoned, and other hypotheses, referring tacitly or avowedly to the cell-doctrine, have been set forth. Before proceeding it will be well to describe the chief among these.

Most if not all of them proceed on the assumption, shown in § 66 to be needful, that the structural characters of organisms are determined by the special natures of units which are intermediate between the chemical units and the morphological units—between the invisible molecules of proteid-substances and the visible tissue-components called cells.

Four years after the first edition of this volume was published, appeared Mr. Darwin's work, *The Variation of Animals and Plants under Domestication*; and in this he set forth his doctrine of Pangenesis. Referring to the doctrine of physiological units which the preceding chapters work out, he at first expressed a doubt whether his own was or was not the same, but finally concluded that it was different. He was right in so concluding. Throughout my argument the implication everywhere is that the physiological units are all of one kind; whereas Mr. Darwin regards his component units, or "gemmules," as being of innumerable unlike kinds. He supposes that every cell of every tissue gives off gemmules special to itself, and capable of developing into similar cells. We may here, in passing, note that this view implies a fundamental distinction between unicellular organisms and the component cells of multicellular organisms, which are otherwise homologous with them. For while in their essential structures, their essential internal changes, and their essential processes of division, the *Protozoa* and the component units of the *Metazoa* are alike, the doctrine of Pangenesis implies that though the units when separate do not give off invisible gemmules the grouped units do.

Much more recently have been enunciated the hypotheses of Prof. Weismann, differing from the foregoing hypotheses in two respects. In the first place it is assumed that the fragment of matter out of which each organism arises consists of two portions—one of them, the germ-plasm, reserved within the generative organ of the incipient individual, representing in its components the structure of the species, and gives origin to the germs of future individuals; and the other of them, similarly representative of the specific structure, giving origin to the rest of the body, or soma, but contains in its components none of those latent powers possessed by those of the germ-plasm. In the second place the germ-plasm, in common with the soma-plasm, consists of multitudinous kinds of units portioned out to originate the various organs. Of these there are groups, sub-groups, and sub-sub-groups. The largest of them, called "idants," are supposed each to contain a number of "ids"; within each id there are numerous "determinants"; and each determinant is made up of many "biophors"—the smallest elements possessing vitality. Passing over details, the essential assumption is that there exists a separate determinant for each part of the organism capable of independent variation; and Prof. Weismann infers that while there may be but one for the blood and but one for a considerable area of skin (as a stripe of the zebra) there must be a determinant for each scale on a butterfly's wing: the number on the four wings being over two hundred thousand. And then each cluster of biophors composing a determinant has to find its way to the place where there is to be formed the part it represents.

Here it is needless to specify the modifications of these hypotheses espoused by various biologists—all of them assuming that the structural traits of each species are expressed in certain units intermediate between morphological units and chemical units.

§ 97*b*. A true theory of heredity must be one which recognizes the relevant phenomena displayed by all classes of organism. We cannot assume two kinds of heredity, one for plants and another for animals. Hence a theory of heredity may be first tested by observing whether it is equally applicable to both kingdoms of living things. Genesis, heredity, and variation, as seen in plants, are simpler and more accessible than as seen in animals. Let us then note what these imply.

Already in § 77 I have illustrated the power which some plants possess of developing new individuals from mere fragments of leaves and even from detached scales. Striking as are the facts there instanced, they are scarcely more significant than some which are familiar. The formation of cauline buds, presently growing into shoots, shows us a kind of inheritance which a true theory must explain. As described by Kerner, such buds arise in Pimpernel, Toad-flax, etc., below the seed-leaves, even while yet there are no axils in which buds usually grow; and in many plants they arise from intermediate places on the stem: that is, without definite relations to pre-existing structures. How fortuitous is their origin is shown when a branch is induced to bud by keeping it wrapped round with a wet cloth. Even still better proved is the absence of any relation between cauline buds and normal germs by the frequent growth of them out of "callus"—the tissue which spreads over wounds and the cut ends of branches. It is not easy to reconcile these facts with Mr. Darwin's hypothesis of gemmules. We have to assume that where a cauline bud emerges there are present in due proportions gemmules of all the parts which will presently arise from it—leaves, stipules, bracts, petals, stamens, anthers, etc. We have to assume this though, at the time the bud originates, sundry of these organs, as the parts of flowers, do not exist on the plant or tree. And we have to assume that the gemmules of such parts are duly provided in a portion of adventitious callus, far away from the normal places of fructification. Moreover, the resulting shoot may or may not produce all the parts which the gemmules represent; and when, perhaps after years, flowers are produced on its side shoots, there must exist at each point the needful proportion of the required gemmules; though there have been no cells continually giving them off.

Still less does the hypothesis of Prof. Weismann harmonize with the evidence as plants display it. Plant-embryogeny yields no sign of separation between germ-plasm and soma-plasm; and, indeed, the absence of such separation is admitted. After instancing cases among certain of the lower animals, in which no differentiation of the two arises in the first generation resulting from a fertilized ovum, Prof. Weismann continues:—

"The same is true as regards the higher plants, in which the first shoot arising from the seed never contains germ-cells, or even cells which subsequently become differentiated into germ cells. In all these last-mentioned cases the germ-cells are not present in the first person arising by embryogeny as special cells, but are only formed in much later cell-generations from the offspring of certain cells of which this first person was composed." (*Germ-Plasm*, p. 185.)

How this admission consists with the general theory it is difficult to understand. The units of the soma-plasm are here recognized as having the same generative powers as the units of the germ-plasm. In so far as one organic kingdom and a considerable part of the other are concerned the doctrine is relinquished. Relinquishment is, indeed, necessitated even by the ordinary facts, and still more by the facts just instanced. Defence of it involves the assertion that where buds arise, normal or cauline, there exist in due proportion the various ids with their contained determinants—that these are diffused throughout the growing part of the soma; and this implies that the somatic tissue does not differ in generative power from the germ-plasm.

The hypothesis of physiological units, then, remains outstanding. For cauline buds imply that throughout the plant-tissue, where not unduly differentiated, the local physiological units have a power of arranging themselves into the structure of the species.

But this hypothesis, too, as it now stands, is inadequate. Under the form thus far given to it, it fails to explain some accompanying facts. For if the branch just instanced as producing a cauline bud be cut off and its end stuck in the ground, or if it be bent down and a portion of it covered with earth, there will grow from it rootlets and presently roots. The same portion of tissue which otherwise would have produced a shoot with all its appendages, constituting an individual, now produces only a special part of an individual.

§ 97*c*. Certain kindred facts of animal development may now be considered. Similar insufficiencies are disclosed.

The often-cited reproduction of a crab's lost claw or a lizard's tail, Mr. Darwin thought explicable by his hypothesis of diffused gemmules, representing all organs or their component cells. But though, after simple amputation, regrowth of the proximate part of the tail is conceivable as hence resulting, it is not easy to understand how the remoter part, the components of which are now absent from the organism, can arise afresh from gemmules no longer originated in due proportion. Prof. Weismann's hypothesis, again, implies that there must exist at the place of separation, a ready-provided supply of determinants, previously latent, able to reproduce the missing tail in all its details—nay, even to do this several times over: a strong supposition! The hypothesis of physiological units, as set forth in preceding chapters, appears less incompetent: reproduction of the lost part would seem to be a normal result of the proclivity towards the form of the entire organism. But now what are we to say when, instead of being cut off transversely, the tail is divided longitudinally and each half becomes a complete tail? What are we to say when, if these two tails are similarly dealt with, the halves again complete themselves; and so until as many as sixteen tails have been formed? Here the hypothesis of physiological units appears to fail utterly; for the tendency it implies is to complete the specific form, by reproducing a single tail only.

Various annulose animals display anomalies of development difficult to explain on any hypothesis. We have creatures like the fresh-water *Nais* which, though it has advanced structures, including a vascular system, branchiæ, and a nervous cord ending with cephalic ganglia, nevertheless shows us an ability like that of the *Hydra* to reproduce the whole from a small part: nearly forty pieces into which a *Nais* was cut having severally grown into complete animals. Again we have, in the order *Polychætæ*, types like *Myrianida*, in which by longitudinal budding a string of individuals, sometimes numbering even thirty, severally develop certain segments into heads, while increasing their segments in number. In yet other types there occurs not longitudinal gemmation only, but lateral gemmation: a segment will send out sideways a bud which presently becomes a complete worm. Once more, *Syllis ramosa* is a species in which the individual worms growing from lateral buds, while remaining attached to the parent, themselves give origin to buds; and so produce a branched aggregate of worms. How shall we explain the reparative and reproductive powers thus exemplified? It seems undeniable that each portion has an ability to produce, according to circumstances, the whole creature or a missing part of the creature. When we read of Sir J. Dalyell that he "cut a *Dasychone* into three pieces; the hindermost produced a head, the anterior piece developed an anus, and the middle portion formed both a head and a tail" we are not furnished with an explanation by the hypothesis of gemmules or by the hypothesis of determinants; for we cannot arbitrarily assume that wherever a missing organ has to be produced there exists the needful supply of gemmules or of determinants representing that organ. The hypothesis that physiological units have everywhere a proclivity towards the organic form of the species, appears more congruous with the facts; but even this does not cover the cases in which a new worm grows from a lateral bud. The tendency to complete the individual structure might be expected rather to restrain this breaking of the lines of complete structure.

Still less explicable in any way thus far proposed are certain remedial actions seen in animals. An example of them was furnished in § 67, where "false joints" were described—joints formed at places where the ends of a broken bone, failing to unite, remain moveable one upon the other. According to the character of the habitual motions there results a rudely formed hinge-joint or a ball-and-socket joint, either having the various constituent parts—periosteum, fibrous tissue, capsule, ligaments. Now Mr. Darwin's hypothesis, contemplating only normal structures, fails to account for this formation of an abnormal structure. Neither can we ascribe this local development to determinants: there were no appropriate ones in the germ-plasm, since no such structure was provided for. Nor does the hypothesis of physiological units, as presented in preceding chapters, yield an interpretation. These could have no other tendency than to restore the normal form of the limb, and might be expected to oppose the genesis of these new parts.

Thus we have to seek, if not another hypothesis, then some such qualification of an existing hypothesis as will harmonize it with various exceptional phenomena.

§ 97*d*. In Part II of the *Principles of Sociology*, published in 1876, will be found elaborated in detail that analogy between individual organization and social organization which was briefly sketched out in an essay on "The Social

Organism" published in 1860. In §§ 241-3 a parallel is drawn between the developments of the sustaining systems of the two; and it is pointed out how, in the one case as in the other, the components—here organic units and there citizens—have their activities and arrangements mainly settled by local conditions. One leading example is that the parts constituting the alimentary canal, while jointly fitted to the nature of the food, are severally adapted to the successive stages at which the food arrives in its progress; and that in an analogous way the industries carried on by peoples forming different parts of a society, are primarily determined by the natures of things around—agriculture, pastoral and arable, special manufactures and minings, ship-building and fishing: the respective groups falling into fit combinations and becoming partially modified to suit their work. The implication is that while the organization of a society as a whole depends on the characters of its units, in such way that by some types of men despotisms are always evolved while by other types there are evolved forms of government partially free—forms which repeat themselves in colonies—there is, on the other hand, in every case a local power of developing appropriate structures. And it might have been pointed out that similarly in types of creatures not showing much consolidation, as the *Annelida*, many of the component divisions, largely independent in their vitalities, are but little affected in their structures by the entire aggregate.

My purpose at that time being the elucidation of sociological truths, it did not concern me to carry further the biological half of this comparison. Otherwise there might have been named the case in which a supernumerary finger, beginning to bud out, completes itself as a local organ with bones, muscles, skin, nail, etc., in defiance of central control: even repeating itself when cut off. There might also have been instanced the above-named formation of a false joint with its appurtenances. For the implication in both cases is that a local group of units, determined by circumstances towards a certain structure, coerces its individual units into that structure.

Now let us contemplate the essential fact in the analogy. The men in an Australian mining-camp, as M. Pierre Leroy Beaulieu points out, fall into Anglo-Saxon usages different from those which would characterize a French mining-camp. Emigrants to a far West settlement in America quickly establish post-office, bank, hotel, newspaper, and other urban institutions. We are thus shown that along with certain traits leading to a general type of social organization, there go traits which independently produce fit local organizations. Individuals are led into occupations and official posts, often quite new to them, by the wants of those around—are now influenced and now coerced into social arrangements which, as shown perhaps by gambling saloons, by shootings at sight, and by lynchings, are scarcely at all affected by the central government. Now the physiological units in each species appear to have a similar combination of capacities. Besides their general proclivity towards the specific organization, they show us abilities to organize themselves locally; and these abilities are in some cases displayed in defiance of the general control, as in the supernumerary finger or the false joint. Apparently each physiological unit, while having in a manner the whole organism as the structure which, along with the rest, it tends to form, has also an aptitude to take part in forming any local structure, and to assume its place in that structure under the influence of adjacent physiological units.

A familiar fact supports this conclusion. Everyone has at hand, not figuratively but literally, an illustration. Let him compare the veins on the backs of his two hands, either with one another or with the veins on another person's hands, and he will see that the branchings and inosculations do not correspond: there is no fixed pattern. But on progressing inwards from the extremities, the distribution of the veins becomes settled—there is a pattern-arrangement common to all persons. These facts imply a predominating control by adjacent parts where control by the aggregate is less easy. A constant combination of forces which, towards the centre, produces a typical structure, fails to do this at the periphery where, during development, the play of forces is less settled. This peripheral vascular structure, not having become fixed because one arrangement is as good as another, is in each determined by the immediately surrounding influences.

§ 97*e*. And now let us contemplate the verifications which recent experiments have furnished—experiments made by Prof. G. Born of Breslau, confirming results earlier reached by Vulpian and adding more striking results of kindred nature. They leave no longer doubtful the large share taken by local organizing power as distinguished from central organizing power.

The independent vitality shown by separated portions of ventral skin from frog-larvæ may be named as the first illustration. With their attached yolk-cells these lived for days, and underwent such transformations as proved some structural proclivity, though of course the product was amorphous. Detached portions of tails of larvæ went on developing their component parts in much the same ways as they would have done if remaining attached. More striking still was the evidence furnished by experiments in grafting. These proved that the undifferentiated rudiment of an organ will, when cut off and joined to a non-homologous place in another individual, develop itself as it would have done if left in its original place. In brief, then, we may say that each part is in chief measure autogenous.

These strange facts presented by small aggregates of organic matter, which are the seats of extremely complex forces, will seem less incomprehensible if we observe what has taken place in a vast aggregate of inorganic matter which is the seat of very simple forces—the Solar System. Transcendently different as this is in all other respects, it is analogous in the respect that, as factors of local structures, local influences predominate over the influences of the aggregate. For while the members of the Solar System, considered as a whole, are subordinate to the totality of its forces, the arrangements in each part of it are produced almost wholly by the play of forces in that part. Though the Sun affects the motions of the Moon, and though during the evolution of the Earth-and-Moon system the Sun exercised an influence, yet the relations of our world and its satellite in respect of masses and motions were in the main locally determined. Still more clearly was it thus with Jupiter and his satellites or Saturn with his rings and satellites. Remembering that the ultimate units of matter of which the Solar System is composed are of the same kinds, and that they act on one another in conformity with the same laws, we see that, remote as the case is from the one we are considering in all other respects, it is similar in the respect that during organization the energies in each locality work effects which are almost independent of the effects worked by the general energies. In this vast aggregate, as in the minute aggregates now in question, the parts are practically autogenous.

Having thus seen that in a way we have not hitherto recognized the same general principles pervade inorganic and organic evolution, let us revert to the case of super-organic evolution from which a parallel was drawn above. As analogous to the germinal mass of units out of which a new organism is to evolve, let us take an assemblage of colonists not yet socially organized but placed in a fertile region—men derived from a society (or rather a succession of societies) of long-established type, who have in their adapted natures the proclivity towards that type. In passing from its wholly unorganized state to an organized state, what will be the first step? Clearly this assemblage, though it may have within the constitutions of its units the potentialities of a specific structure, will not develop forthwith the details of that structure. The inherited natures of its units will first show themselves by separating into large groups devoted to strongly-distinguished occupations. The great mass, dispersing over promising lands, will make preparations for farming. Another considerable portion, prompted by the general needs, will begin to form a cluster of habitations and a trading centre. Yet a third group, recognizing the demand for wood, alike for agricultural and building purposes, will betake themselves to the adjacent forests. But in no case will the primary assemblage, before these separations, settle the arrangements and actions of each group: it will leave each group to settle them for itself. So, too, after these divisions have arisen. The agricultural division will not as a whole prescribe the doings of its members. Spontaneous segregation will occur: some going to a pastoral region and some to a tract which promises good crops. Nor within each of these bodies will the organization be dictated by the whole. The pastoral group will separate itself into clusters who tend sheep on the hills and clusters who feed cattle on the plains. Meanwhile those who have gravitated towards urban occupations will some of them make bricks or quarry stone, while others fall into classes who build walls, classes who prepare fittings, classes who supply furniture. Then along with completion of the houses will go occupation of them by men who bake bread, who make clothing, who sell liquors, and so on. Thus each great group will go on organizing itself irrespective of the rest; the sub-groups within each will do the same; and so will the sub-sub-groups. Quite independently of the people on the hills and the plains and in the town, those in the forest will divide spontaneously into parties who cut down trees, parties who trim and saw them, parties who carry away the timbers; while every party forms for itself an organization of "butty" or "boss," and those who work under him. Similarly with the ultimate divisions—the separate families: the arrangements and apportionments of duties in each are internally determined. Mark the fact which here chiefly concerns us. This formation of a heterogeneous aggregate with its variously adapted parts, which while influenced by the whole are mainly self-formed, goes on among units of essentially the same natures, inherited from units who belonged to similar societies. And now, carrying this conception with us, we may dimly perceive how, in a developing embryo, there may take place the formation, first of the great divisions—the primary layers—then of the outlines of systems, then of component organs, and so on continually with the minor structures contained in major structures; and how each of these progressively smaller divisions develops its own organization, irrespective of the changes going on throughout the rest of the embryo. So that though all parts are composed of physiological units of the same nature, yet everywhere, in virtue of local conditions and the influence of its neighbours, each unit joins in forming the particular structure appropriate to the place. Thus conceiving the matter, we may in a vague way understand the strange facts of autogenous development disclosed by the above named experiments.

§ 97*f.* "But how immeasurably complex must be the physiological units which can behave thus!" will be remarked by the reader. "To be able to play all parts, alike as members of the whole and as members of this or that organ, they must have an unimaginable variety of potentialities in their natures. Each must, indeed, be almost a microcosm within a microcosm."

Doubtless this is true. Still we have a *consensus* of proofs that the component units of organisms have constitutions of extremely involved kinds. Contemplate the facts and their implications. (1) Here is some large division of the animal kingdom—say the *Vertebrata.* The component units of all its members have certain fundamental traits in common: all of them have proclivities towards formation of a vertebral column. Leaving behind the great assemblage of Fishes with its multitudinous types, each having special units of composition, we pass to the *Amphibia*, in the units of which there exist certain traits superposed upon the traits they have in common with those of Fishes. Through unknown links we ascend to incipient Mammalian types and then to developed Mammalian types, the units of which must have further superposed traits. Additional traits distinguish the units of each Mammalian order; and, again, those of every genus included in it; while others severally characterize the units of each species. Similarly with the varieties in each species, and the stirps in each variety. Now the ability of any component unit to carry within itself the traits of the sub-kingdom, class, order, genus, species, variety, and at the same time to bear the traits of immediate ancestors, can exist only in a something having multitudinous proximate elements arranged in innumerable ways. (2) Again, these units must be at once in some respects fixed and in other respects plastic. While their fundamental traits, expressing the structure of the type, must be unchangeable, their superficial traits must admit of modification without much difficulty; and the modified traits, expressing variations in the parents and immediate ancestors, though unstable, must be considered as capable of becoming stable in course of time. (3) Once more we have to think of these physiological units (or constitutional units as I would now re-name them) as having such natures that while a minute modification, representing some small change of local structure, is inoperative on the proclivities of the units throughout the rest of the system, it becomes operative in the units which fall into the locality where that change occurs.

But unimaginable as all this is, the facts may nevertheless in some way answer to it. As before remarked, progressing science reveals complexity within complexity—tissues made up of cells, cells containing nuclei and cytoplasm, cytoplasm formed of a protoplasmic matrix containing granules; and if now we conclude that the unit of protoplasm is itself an inconceivably elaborate structure, we do but recognize the complexity as going still deeper. Further, if we must assume that these component units are in every part of the body acting on one another by extremely complicated sets of forces (ethereal undulations emanating from each of the constituent molecules) determining their relative positions and actions, we are warranted by the discoveries which every day disclose more of the marvellous properties of matter. When to such examples as were given in § 36*e* we add the example yielded by recent experiments, showing that even a piece of bread, after subjection to pressure, exhibits diamagnetic properties unlike those it previously exhibited, we cannot doubt that these complex units composing living bodies are all of them seats of energies diffused around, enabling them to act and re-act so as to modify one another's states and positions. We are shown, too, that whatever be the natures of the complex forces emanating from each, it will, as a matter of course, happen that the power of each will be relatively great in its own neighbourhood and become gradually smaller in parts increasingly remote: making more comprehensible the autogenous character of each local structure.

Whatever be their supposed natures we are compelled to ascribe extreme complexity to these unknown somethings which have the power of organizing themselves into a structure of this or that species. If gemmules be alleged, then the ability of every organ and part of an organ to vary, implies that the gemmules it gives off are severally capable of receiving minute modifications of their ordinary structures: they must have many parts admitting of innumerable relations. Supposing determinants be assumed, then in addition to the complexity which each must have to express in itself the structure of the part evolved from it, it must have the further complexity implied by every superposed modification which causes a variation of that part. And, as we have just seen, the hypothesis of physiological units does not relieve us from the need for kindred suppositions.

One more assumption seems necessary if we are to imagine how changes of structure caused by changes of function can be transmitted. Reverting to § 54*d*, where an unceasing circulation of protoplasm throughout an organism was inferred, we must conceive that the complex forces of which each constitutional unit is the centre, and by which it acts on other units while it is acted on by them, tend continually to remould each unit into congruity with the structures around: superposing on it modifications answering to the modifications which have arisen in those structures. Whence is to be drawn the corollary that in course of time all the circulating units,—physiological, or constitutional if we prefer so to call them—visiting all parts of the organism, are severally made bearers of traits expressing local modifications; and that those units which are eventually gathered into sperm-cells and germ-cells also bear these superposed traits.

If against all this it be urged that such a combination of structures and forces and processes is inconceivably involved, then the reply is that so astonishing a transformation as that which an unfolding organism displays cannot possibly be effected by simple agencies.

§ 97*g*. But now let it be confessed that none of these hypotheses serves to render the phenomena really intelligible; and that probably no hypothesis which can be framed will do this. Many problems beyond those which embryology presents have to be solved; and no solution is furnished.

What are we to say of the familiar fact that certain small organs which, with the approach to maturity, become active, entail changes of structure in remote parts—that after the testes have undergone certain final developments, the hairs on the chin grow and the voice deepens? It has been contended that certain concomitant modifications in the fluids throughout the body may produce correlated sexual traits; and there is proof that in many of the lower animals the period of sexual activity is accompanied by a special bodily state—sometimes such that the flesh becomes unwholesome and even poisonous. But a change of this kind can hardly account for a structural change in the vocal organs in Man. No hypothesis of gemmules or determinants or physiological units enables us to understand how removal of the testes prevents those developments of the larynx and vocal cords which take place if they remain.

The inadequacy of our explanations we at once see in presence of a structure like a peacock's tail-feather. Mr. Darwin's hypothesis is that all parts of every organ are continually giving off gemmules, which are consequently everywhere present in their due proportions. But a completed feather is an inanimate product and, once formed, can add to the circulating fluids no gemmules representing all its parts. If we follow Prof. Weismann we are led into an astounding supposition. He admits that every variable part must have a special determinant, and that this results in the assumption of over two hundred thousand for the four wings of a butterfly. Let us ask what must happen in the case of a peacock's feather. On looking at the eye near its end, we see that the minute processes on the edge of each lateral thread must have been in some way exactly adjusted, in colour and position, so as to fall into line with the processes on adjacent threads: otherwise the symmetrical arrangement of coloured rings would be impossible. Each of these processes, then, being an independent variable, must have had its particular determinant. Now there are about 300 threads on the shaft of a large feather, and each of them bears on the average 1,600 processes, making for the whole feather 480,000 of these processes. For one feather alone there must have been 480,000 determinants, and for the whole tail many millions. And these, along with the determinants for the detailed parts of all the other feathers, and for the variable components of all organs forming the body at large, must have been contained in the microscopic head of a spermatozoon! Hardly a credible supposition. Nor is it easy to see how we are helped by the hypothesis of constitutional units. Take the feather in its budding state and ask how the group of such units, alike in structure and perpetually multiplying while the unfolding goes on, can be supposed by their mutual actions so to affect one another as eventually to produce the symmetrically-adjusted processes which constitute the terminal eye. Imagination, whatever licence may be given, utterly fails us.

At last then we are obliged to admit that the actual organizing process transcends conception. It is not enough to say that we cannot know it; we must say that we cannot even conceive it. And this is just the conclusion which might have been drawn before contemplating the facts. For if, as we saw in the chapter on "The Dynamic Element in Life," it is impossible for us to understand the nature of this element—if even the ordinary manifestations of it which a living body yields from moment to moment are at bottom incomprehensible; then, still more incomprehensible must be that astonishing manifestation of it which we have in the initiation and unfolding of a new organism.

Thus all we can do is to find some way of symbolizing the process so as to enable us most conveniently to generalize its phenomena; and the only reason for adopting the hypothesis of physiological units or constitutional units is that it best serves this purpose.

CHAPTER XI.

CLASSIFICATION.

§ 98. That orderly arrangement of objects called Classification has two purposes, which, though not absolutely distinct, are distinct in great part. It may be employed to facilitate identification, or it may be employed to organize our knowledge. If a librarian places his books in the alphabetical succession of the author's names, he places them in such way that any particular book may easily be found, but not in such way that books of a given nature stand together. When, otherwise, he makes a distribution of books according to their subjects, he neglects various superficial similarities and distinctions, and groups them according to certain primary and secondary and tertiary attributes, which severally imply many other attributes—groups them so that any one volume being inspected, the general characters of all the neighbouring volumes may be inferred. He puts together in one great division all works on History; in another all Biographical works; in another all works that treat of Science; in another Voyages and Travels; and so on. Each of his great groups he separates into sub-groups; as when he puts different kinds of Literature under the heads of Fiction, Poetry, and the Drama. In some cases he makes sub-sub-groups; as when, having divided his Scientific treatises into abstract and concrete, putting in the one Logic and Mathematics and in the other Physics, Astronomy, Geology, Chemistry, Physiology, &c.; he goes on to sub-divide his books on Physics, into those which treat of Mechanical Motion, those which treat of Heat, those which treat of Light, of Electricity, of Magnetism.

Between these two modes of classification note the essential distinctions. Arrangement according to any single conspicuous attribute is comparatively easy, and is the first that suggests itself: a child may place books in the order of their sizes, or according to the styles of their bindings. But arrangement according to combinations of attributes which, though fundamental, are not conspicuous, requires analysis; and does not suggest itself till analysis has made some progress. Even when aided by the information which the author gives on his title page, it requires considerable knowledge to classify rightly an essay on Polarization; and in the absence of a title page it requires much more knowledge. Again, classification by a single attribute, which the objects possess in different degrees, may be more or less serial, or linear. Books may be put in the order of their dates, in single file; or if they are grouped as works in one volume, works in two volumes, works in three volumes, &c., the groups may be placed in an ascending succession. But groups severally formed of things distinguished by some common attribute which implies many other attributes, do not admit of serial arrangement. You cannot rationally say either that Historical Works should come before Biographical Works, or Biographical Works before Historical Works; nor of the sub-divisions of creative Literature, into Fiction, Poetry, and the Drama, can you give a good reason why any one should take precedence of the others.

Hence this grouping of the like and separation of the unlike which constitutes Classification, can reach its complete form only by slow steps. I have shown (*Essays*, Vol. II., pp. 145-7) that, other things equal, the relations among phenomena are recognized in the order of their conspicuousness; and that, other things equal, they are recognized in the order of their simplicity. The first classifications are sure, therefore, to be groupings of objects which resemble one another in external or easily-perceived attributes, and attributes that are not of complex characters. Those likenesses among things which are due to their possession in common of simple obvious properties, may or may not coexist with further likenesses among them. When geometrical figures are classed as curvilinear and rectilinear, or when the rectilinear are divided into trilateral, quadrilateral, &c., the distinctions made connote various other distinctions with which they are necessarily bound up; but if liquids be classed according to their visible characters—if water, alcohol, sulphuret of carbon, &c., be grouped as colourless and transparent, we have things placed together which are unlike in their essential natures. Thus, where the objects classed have numerous attributes, the probabilities are that the early classifications, based on simple and manifest attributes, unite under the same head many objects that have no resemblance in the majority of their attributes. As the knowledge of objects increases, it becomes possible to make groups of which the members have more numerous properties in common; and to ascertain what property, or combination of properties, is most characteristic of each group. And the classification eventually arrived at is of such kind that the objects in each group have more attributes in common with one another than they have in common with any excluded objects; one in which the groups of such groups are integrated on the same principle; and one in which the degrees of differentiation and integration are proportioned to the degrees of intrinsic unlikeness and likeness. And this ultimate classification, while it serves to identify the things completely, serves also to express the greatest amount of knowledge concerning the things—enables us to predicate the greatest number of facts about each thing; and by so doing implies the most precise correspondence between our conceptions and the realities.

§ 99. Biological classifications illustrate well these phases through which classifications in general pass. In early attempts to arrange organisms in some systematic manner, we see at first a guidance by conspicuous and simple characters, and a tendency towards arrangement in linear order. In successively later attempts, we see more regard paid to combinations of characters which are essential but often inconspicuous, and an abandonment of a linear arrangement for an arrangement in divergent groups and re-divergent sub-groups.

In the popular mind, plants are still classed under the heads of Trees, Shrubs, and Herbs; and this serial classing according to the single attribute of magnitude, swayed the earliest observers. They would have thought it absurd to call a bamboo, thirty feet high, a kind of grass; and would have been incredulous if told that the Hart's-tongue should be placed in the same great division with the Tree-ferns. The zoological classifications current before Natural History became a science, had divisions similarly superficial and simple. Beasts, Birds, Fishes, and Creeping-things are names of groups marked off from one another by conspicuous differences of appearance and modes of life—creatures that walk and run, creatures that fly, creatures that live in the water, creatures that crawl. And these groups were thought of in the order of their importance.

The first arrangements made by naturalists were based either on single characters or on very simple combinations of characters; as that of Clusius, and afterwards the more scientific system of Cesalpino, recognizing the importance of inconspicuous structures. Describing plant-classifications, Lindley says:—"Rivinus invented, in 1690, a system depending upon the formation of the corolla; Kamel, in 1693, upon the fruit alone; Magnol, in 1720, on the calyx and corolla; and finally, Linnæus, in 1731, on variations in the stamens and pistil." In this last system, which has been for so long current as a means of identification (regarded by its author as transitional), simple external attributes are still depended on; and an arrangement, in great measure serial, is based on the degrees in which these attributes are possessed. In 1703, some thirty years before the time of Linnæus, our countryman Ray had sketched the outlines of a more advanced system. He said that—

Plants are either

Flowerless, or

Flowering; and these are

Dicotyledones, or

Monocotyledones.

Among the minor groups which he placed under these general heads, "were Fungi, Mosses, Ferns, Composites, Cichoraceæ, Umbellifers, Papilionaceous plants, Conifers, Labiates, &c., under other names, but with limits not very different from those now assigned to them." Being much in advance of his age, Ray's ideas remained dormant until the time of Jussieu; by whom they were developed into what has become known as the Natural System: a system subsequently improved by De Candolle. Passing through various modifications in the hands of successive botanists, the Natural System is now represented by the following form, which is based upon the table of contents prefixed to Vol. II. of Prof. Oliver's translation of the *Natural History of Plants*, by Prof. Kerner. His first division, Myxothallophyta (= Myxomycetes), I have ventured to omit. The territory it occupies is in dispute between zoologists and botanists, and as I have included the group in the zoological classification, agreeing that its traits are more animal than vegetal, I cannot also include it in the botanical classification.

Here, linear arrangement has disappeared: there is a breaking up into groups and sub-groups and sub-sub-groups, which do not admit of being placed in serial order, but only in divergent and re-divergent order. Were there space to exhibit the way in which the Alliances are subdivided into Orders, and these into Genera, and these into Species, the same principle of co-ordination would be still further manifested.

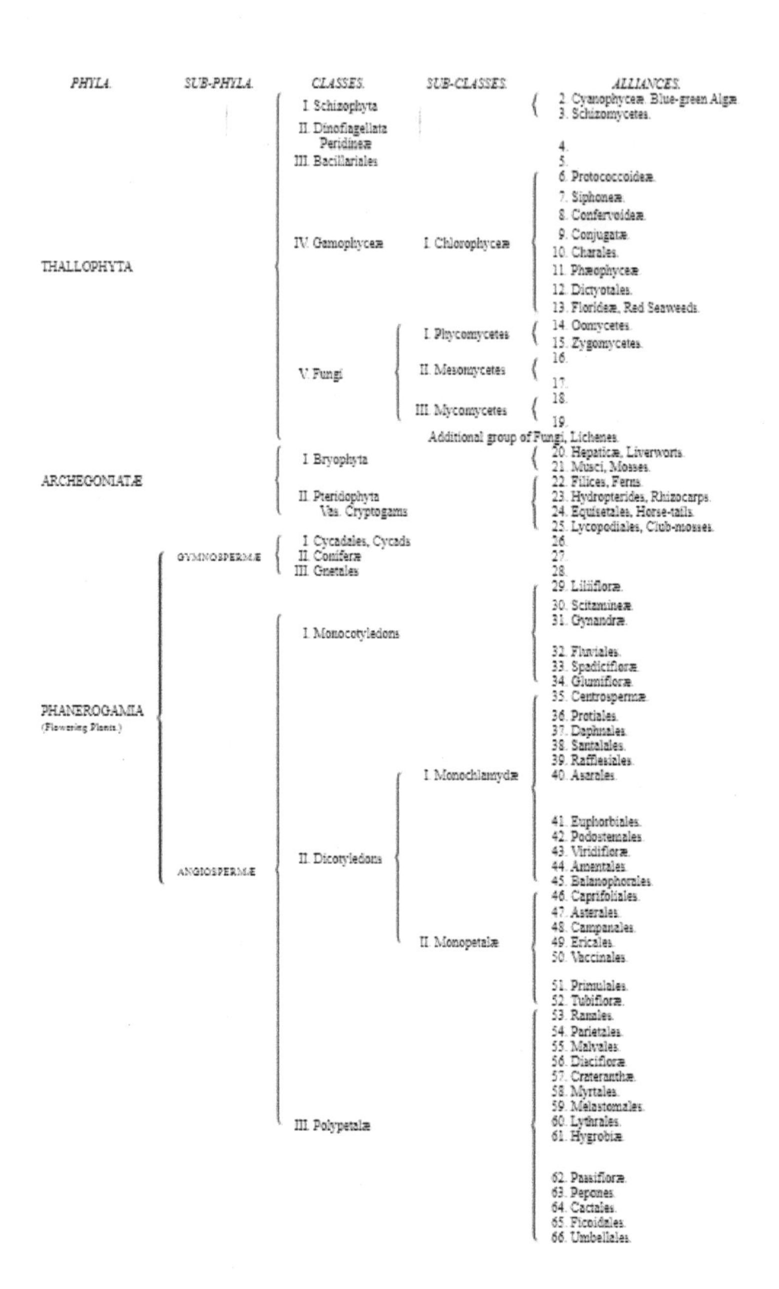

On studying the definitions of these primary, secondary, and tertiary classes, it will be found that the largest are marked off from one another by some attribute which connotes sundry other attributes; that each of the smaller classes comprehended in one of these largest classes, is marked off in a similar way from the other smaller classes bound up with it; and that so, each successively smaller class has an increased number of co-existing attributes.

§ 100. Zoological classification has had a parallel history. The first attempt which we need notice, to arrange animals in such a way as to display their affinities, is that of Linnæus. He grouped them thus:[42]—

CL. 1. MAMMALIA. *Ord.* Primates, Bruta, Feræ, Glires, Pecora, Belluæ, Cete.

CL. 2. AVES. *Ord.* Accipitres, Picæ, Anseres, Grallæ, Gallinæ, Passeres.

CL. 3. AMPHIBIA. *Ord.* Reptiles, Serpentes, Nantes.

CL. 4. PISCES. *Ord.* Apodes, Jugulares, Thoracici, Abdominales.

CL. 5. INSECTA. *Ord.* Coleoptera, Hemiptera, Lepidoptera, Neuroptera, Diptera, Aptera.

CL. 6. VERMES. *Ord.* Intestina, Mollusca, Testacea, Lithophyta, Zoophyta.

This arrangement of classes is obviously based on apparent gradations of rank; and the placing of the orders similarly betrays an endeavour to make successions, beginning with the most superior forms and ending with the most inferior forms. While the general and vague idea of perfection determines the leading character of the classification, its detailed groupings are determined by the most conspicuous external attributes. Not only Linnæus but his opponents, who proposed other systems, were "under the impression that animals were to be arranged together into classes, orders, genera, and species, according to their more or less close external resemblance." This conception survived until the time of Cuvier. "Naturalists," says Agassiz, "were bent upon establishing one continual uniform series to embrace all animals, between the links of which it was supposed there were no unequal intervals. The watchword of their school was: *Natura non facit saltum.* They called their system *la chaine des êtres.*"

The classification of Cuvier, based on internal organization instead of external appearance, was a great advance. He asserted that there are four principal forms, or four general plans, on which animals are constructed; and, in pursuance of this assertion, he drew out the following scheme.

First Branch. ANIMALIA VERTEBRATA.

Cl. 1. Mammalia.

Cl. 2. Birds.

Cl. 3. Reptilia.

Cl. 4. Fishes.

Second Branch. ANIMALIA MOLLUSCA.

Cl. 1. Cephalapoda.

Cl. 2. Pteropoda.

Cl. 3. Gasteropoda.

Cl. 4. Acephala.

Cl. 5. Brachiopoda.

Cl. 6. Cirrhopoda.

Third Branch. ANIMALIA ARTICULATA.

Cl. 1. Annelides.

Cl. 2. Crustacea.

Cl. 3. Arachnides.

Cl. 4. Insects.

Fourth Branch. ANIMALIA RADIATA.

Cl. 1. Echinoderms.

Cl. 2. Intestinal Worms.

Cl. 3. Acalephæ.

Cl. 4. Polypi.

Cl. 5. Infusoria.

But though Cuvier emancipated himself from the conception of a serial progression throughout the Animal Kingdom, sundry of his contemporaries and successors remained fettered by the old error. Less regardful of the differently-combined sets of attributes distinguishing the different sub-kingdoms, and swayed by the belief in a progressive development which was erroneously supposed to imply a linear arrangement of animals, they persisted in thrusting organic forms into a quite unnatural order. The following classification of Lamarck illustrates this.

INVERTEBRATA.

I. APATHETIC ANIMALS. Cl. 1. Infusoria Cl. 2. Polypi. Cl. 3. Radiaria. Cl. 4. Tunicata. Cl. 5. Vermes.	Do not feel, and move only by their excited irritability. No brain, no elongated medullary mass; no senses; forms varied; rarely articulations.
II. SENSITIVE ANIMALS. Cl. 7. Arachnids. Cl. 8. Crustacea. Cl. 9. Annelids. Cl. 10. Cirripeds. Cl. 11. Conchifera. Cl. 12. Mollusks.	Feel, but obtain from their sensations only perceptions of objects, a sort of simple ideas, which they are unable to combine to obtain complex ones. No vertebral column; a brain and mostly an elongated medullary mass; some distinct senses; muscles attached under the skin; form symmetrical, the parts being in pairs.

VERTEBRATA.

III. INTELLIGENT ANIMALS. Cl. 13. Fishes. Cl. 14. Reptiles. Cl. 15. Birds. Cl. 16. Mammalia.	Feel; acquire preservable ideas; perform with them operations by which they obtain others; are intelligent in different degrees. A vertebral column; a brain and a spinal marrow; distinct senses; the muscles attached to the internal skeleton; form symmetrical, the parts being in pairs.

Passing over sundry classifications in which the serial arrangement dictated by the notion of ascending complexity, is variously modified by the recognition of conspicuous anatomical facts, we come to classifications which recognize another order of facts—those of development. The embryological inquiries of Von Baer led him to arrange animals as follows:—

III. Peripheric Type. (RADIATA.) *Evolutio radiata.* The development proceeds from a centre, producing identical parts in a radiating order.

III. Massive Type. (MOLLUSCA.) *Evolutio contorta.* The development produces identical parts curved around a conical or other space.

III. Longitudinal Type. (ARTICULATA.) *Evolutio gemina.* The development produces identical parts arising on both sides of an axis, and closing up along a line opposite the axis.

IV. Doubly Symmetrical Type. (VERTEBRATA.) *Evolutio bigemina.* The development produces identical parts arising on both sides of an axis, growing upwards and downwards, and shutting up along two lines, so that the inner layer of the germ is inclosed below, and the upper layer above. The embryos of these animals have a dorsal cord, dorsal plates, and ventral plates, a nervous tube and branchial fissures.

Recognizing these fundamental differences in the modes of development, as answering to fundamental divisions in the animal kingdom, Von Baer shows (among the *Vertebrata* at least) how the minor differences which arise at successively later embryonic stages, correspond with the minor divisions.

Like the modern classification of plants, the modern classification of animals shows us the assumed linear order completely broken up. In his lectures at the Royal Institution, in 1857, Prof. Huxley expressed the relations existing among the several great groups of the animal kingdom, by placing them at the ends of four or five radii, diverging from a centre. The diagram I cannot obtain; but in the published reports of his lectures at the School of Mines the groups were arranged as on the following page. What remnant there may seem to be of linear succession in some of the sub-groups contained in it, is merely an accident of typographical convenience. Each of them is to be regarded simply as a cluster. And if Prof. Huxley had further developed the arrangement, by dispersing the sub-groups and sub-sub-groups on the same principle, there would result an arrangement perhaps not much unlike that shown on the page succeeding this.

VERTEBRATA

(*Abranchiata*)
Mammalia
Aves
Reptilia
(*Branchiata*)
Amphibia
Pisces.

MOLLUSCA			ANNULOSA	
Cephalopoda	Heteropoda	}	*Articulata.*	
	Gasteropoda-dioecia		Insecta	Arachnida
			Myriapoda	Crustacea

{ Pulmonata Gasteropoda- *Annuloida.*
Pteropoda monœcia

Lamellibranchiata

Annellata	Scoleidæ
Echinodermata	Trematoda
Rotifera	Tæniadæ
	Turbellaria
	Nematoidea

CŒLENTERATA

Hydrozoa Actinozoa.

PROTOZOA

Infusoria	Spongiadæ	Gregarinidæ
Noctilucidæ	Foraminifera	*Thallassicollidæ*

In the woodcut, the dots represent orders, the names of which it is impracticable to insert. If it be supposed that when magnified, each of these dots resolves itself into a cluster of clusters, representing genera and species, an approximate idea will be formed of the relations among the successively-subordinate groups constituting the animal kingdom. Besides the subordination of groups and their general distribution, some other facts are indicated. By the distances of the great divisions from the general centre, are rudely symbolized their respective degrees of divergence from the form of simple, undifferentiated organic matter; which we may regard as their common source. Within each group, the remoteness from the local centre represents, in a rough way, the degree of departure from the general plan of the group. And the distribution of the sub-groups within each group, is in most cases such that those which come nearest to neighbouring groups, are those which show the nearest resemblances to them—in their analogies though not in their homologies. No such scheme, however, can give a correct conception. Even supposing the above diagram expressed the relations of animals to one another as truly as they can be expressed on a plane surface (which of course it does not), it would still be inadequate. Such relations cannot be represented in space of two dimensions, but only in space of three dimensions.

§ 100*a*. Two motives have prompted me to include in its original form the foregoing sketch: the one being that in conformity with the course previously pursued, of giving the successive forms of classifications, it seems desirable to give this form which was approved thirty-odd years ago; and the other being that the explanatory comments remain now as applicable as they were then. Replacement of the diagram by one expressing the relations of classes as they are now conceived, is by no means an easy task; for the conceptions formed of them are unsettled. Concerning the present attitude of zoologists, Prof. MacBride writes:—

"They all recognize a certain number of phyla. Each phylum includes a group of animals about whose relation to each other no one entertains a doubt. Each zoologist, however, has his own idea as to the relationship which the various phyla bear to each other.

"The phyla recognized at present are:—

(1) Protozoa.

(2) Porifera (Sponges).

(3) Cœlenterata.

(4) Echinodermata.

(5) Platyhelminthes { Cestodes.
Trematodes.
Turbellaria.

(6) Nemertea.

(7) Nematoda.

(8) Acanthocephala (Echinorhyncus).

(9) Chætognatha (Sagitta).

(10) Rotifera.

(11) Annelida (Includes Leeches and Gephyrea, Chætifera).

(12) Gephyrea, Achæta.

(13) Arthropods { Tracheata (Peripatus, Myriapods, Insects).
Arachnids.
Crustacea.
Pycnogonida.

(14) Mollusca.

(15) Polyzoa (Including Phoronis).

(16) Brachiopoda.

(17) Chordata (Includes Balanoglossus and Tunicates. Some continental zoologists do not admit Balanoglossus)."

[This last phylum of course includes the *Vertebrata.*]

Though under present conditions, as above implied, it would be absurd to attempt a definite scheme of relationships, yet it has seemed to me that the adumbration of a scheme, presenting in a vague way such relationships as are generally agreed upon and leaving others indeterminate, may be ventured; and that a general impression hence resulting may be useful. On the adjacent page I have tried to make a tentative arrangement of this kind.

At the bottom of the table I have placed together, under the name "Compound *Protozoa,*" those kinds of aggregated *Protozoa* which show no differentiations among the members of groups, and are thus distinguished from *Metazoa*; and I have further marked the distinction by their position, which implies that from them no evolution of higher types has taken place. Respecting the naming of the sub-kingdoms, phyla, classes, orders, &c., I have not maintained entire consistency. The relative values of groups cannot be typographically expressed in a small space with a limited variety of letters. The sizes of the letters mark the classificatory ranks, and by the thickness I have rudely indicated their zoological importance. In fixing the order of subordination of groups I have been aided by the table of contents prefixed to Mr. Adam Sedgwick's *Student's Text Book of Zoology* and have also made use of Prof. Ray Lankester's classifications of several sub-kingdoms.

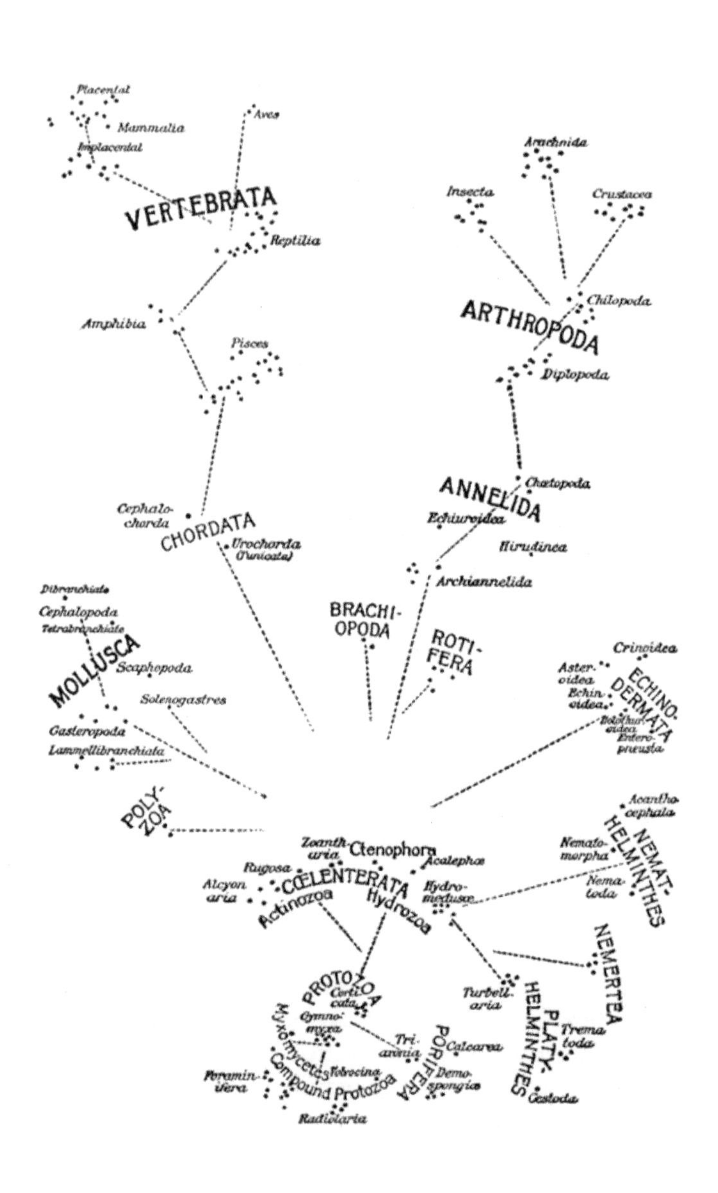

Let me again emphasize the fact that the relationships of these diverging and re-diverging groups cannot be expressed on a flat surface. If we imagine a laurel-bush to be squashed flat by a horizontal plane descending upon it, we shall see that sundry of the upper branches and twigs which were previously close together will become remote, and that the relative positions of parts can remain partially true only with the minor branches. The reader must therefore expect to find some of the zoological divisions which in the order of nature are near one another, shown in the table as quite distant.

§ 101. While the classifications of botanists and zoologists have become more and more natural in their arrangements, there has grown up a certain artificiality in their abstract nomenclature. When aggregating the smallest groups into larger groups and these into groups still larger, they have adopted certain general terms expressive of the successively more comprehensive divisions; and the habitual use of these terms, needful for purposes of convenience, has led to the tacit assumption that they answer to actualities in Nature. It has been taken for granted that species, genera, orders, and classes, are assemblages of definite values—that every genus is the equivalent of every other genus in respect of its degree of distinctness; and that orders are separated by lines of demarcation which are as broad in one place as another. Though this conviction is not a formulated one, the disputes continually occurring among naturalists on the questions, whether such and such organisms are specifically or generically distinct, and whether this or that peculiarity is or is not of ordinal importance, imply that the conviction is entertained even where not avowed. Yet that differences of opinion like these arise and remain unsettled, except when they end in the establishment of sub-species, sub-genera, sub-orders, and sub-classes, sufficiently shows that the conviction is ill-based. And this is equally shown by the impossibility of obtaining any definition of the degree of difference which warrants each further elevation in the hierarchy of classes.

It is, indeed, a wholly gratuitous assumption that organisms admit of being placed in groups of equivalent values; and that these may be united into larger groups which are also of equivalent values; and so on. There is no *à priori* reason for expecting this; and there is no *à posteriori* evidence implying it, save that which begs the question—that which asserts one distinction to be generic and another to be ordinal, because it is assumed that such distinctions must be either generic or ordinal. The endeavour to thrust plants and animals into these definite partitions is of the same nature as the endeavour to thrust them into linear series. Not that it does violence to the facts in anything like the same degree; but still, it does violence to the facts. Doubtless the making of divisions and sub-divisions, is extremely useful; or rather, it is necessary. Doubtless, too, in reducing the facts to something like order they must be partially distorted. So long as the distorted form is not mistaken for the actual form, no harm results. But it is needful for us to remember that while our successively subordinate groups have a certain general correspondence with the realities, they tacitly ascribe to the realities a regularity which does not exist.

§ 102. A general truth of much significance is exhibited in these classifications. On observing the natures of the attributes which are common to the members of any group of the first, second, third, or fourth rank, we see that groups of the widest generality are based on characters of the greatest importance, physiologically considered; and that the characters of the successively-subordinate groups, are characters of successively-subordinate importance. The structural peculiarity in which all members of one sub-kingdom differ from all members of another sub-kingdom, is a peculiarity that affects the vital actions more profoundly than does the structural peculiarity which distinguishes all members of one class from all members of another class. Let us look at a few cases.

We saw (§ 56), that the broadest division among the functions is the division into "the *accumulation of energy* (latent in food); the *expenditure of energy* (latent in the tissues and certain matters absorbed by them); and the *transfer of energy* (latent in the prepared nutriment or blood) from the parts which accumulate to the parts which expend." Now in the lowest animals, united under the general name *Protozoa*, there is either no separation of the parts performing these functions or very indistinct separation: in the *Rhizopoda*, all parts are alike accumulators of energy, expenders of energy and transferers of energy; and though in the higher members of the group, the *Infusoria*, there are some specializations corresponding to these functions, yet there are no distinct tissues appropriated to them. Similarly when we pass from simple types to compound types—from *Protozoa* to *Metazoa*. The animals known as *Cœlenterata* are characterized in common by the possession of a part which accumulates energy more or less marked off from the part which does not accumulate energy, but only expends it; and the *Hydrozoa* and *Actinozoa*, which are sub-divisions of the *Cœlenterata*, are contrasted in this, that in the second these parts are much more differentiated from one another, as well as more complicated. Besides a completer differentiation of the organs respectively devoted to the accumulation of energy and the expenditure of energy, animals next above the *Cœlenterata* possess rude appliances for the transfer of energy: the peri-visceral sac, or closed cavity between the intestine and the walls of the body, serves as a reservoir of absorbed nutriment, from which the surrounding tissues take up the materials they need. And then out of this sac originates a more efficient appliance for the transfer of energy: the more highly-organized animals, belonging to whichever sub-kingdom, all of them possess definitely-constructed channels for distributing the matters containing energy. In all of them, too, the function of expenditure is divided between a directive apparatus and an executive apparatus—a nervous system and a muscular system. But these higher sub-kingdoms are clearly separated from one another by differences in the relative positions of their component sets of organs. The habitual attitudes of annulose and molluscous creatures, is such that the neural centres are below the alimentary canal and the hæmal centres above. And while by these traits the annulose and molluscous types are separated from the vertebrate, they are separated from each other by this, that in the one the body is "composed of successive segments, usually provided with limbs," but in the other, the body is not segmented, "and no true articulated limbs are ever developed."

The sub-kingdoms being thus distinguished from one another, by the presence or absence of specialized parts devoted to fundamental functions, or else by differences in the distributions of such parts, we find, on descending to the classes, that these are distinguished from one another, either by modifications in the structures of fundamental parts, or by the presence or absence of subsidiary parts, or by both. Fishes and *Amphibia* are unlike higher vertebrates in possessing branchiæ, either throughout life or early in life. And every higher vertebrate, besides having lungs, is characterized by having, during development, an amnion and an allantois. Mammals, again, are marked off from Birds and Reptiles by the presence of mammæ, as well as by the form of the occipital condyles. Among Mammals, the next division is based on the presence or absence of a placenta. And divisions of the *Placentalia* are mainly determined by the characters of the organs of external action.

Thus, without multiplying illustrations and without descending to genera and species, we see that, speaking generally, the successively smaller groups are distinguished from one another by traits of successively less importance, physiologically considered. The attributes possessed in common by the largest assemblages of organisms, are few in number but all-essential in kind. Each secondary assemblage, included in one of the primary assemblages, is characterized by further common attributes that influence the functions less profoundly. And so on with each lower grade.

§ 103. What interpretation is to be put on these truths of classification? We find that organic forms admit of an arrangement everywhere indicating the fact, that along with certain attributes, certain other attributes, which are not directly connected with them, always exist. How are we to account for this fact? And how are we to account for the fact that the attributes possessed in common by the largest assemblages of forms, are the most vitally-important attributes?

No one can believe that combinations of this kind have arisen fortuitously. Even supposing fortuitous combinations of attributes might produce organisms that would work, we should still be without a clue to this special mode of combination. The chances would be infinity to one against organisms which possessed in common certain fundamental attributes, having also in common numerous non-essential attributes.

Nor, again, can any one allege that such combinations are necessary, in the sense that all other combinations are impracticable. There is not, in the nature of things, a reason why creatures covered with feathers should always have beaks: jaws carrying teeth would, in many cases, have served them equally well or better. The most general characteristic of an entire sub-kingdom, equal in extent to the *Vertebrata*, might have been the possession of nictitating membranes; while the internal organizations throughout this sub-kingdom might have been on many different plans.

If, as an alternative, this peculiar subordination of traits which organic forms display be ascribed to design, other difficulties suggest themselves. To suppose that a certain plan of organization was fixed on by a Creator for each vast and varied group, the members of which were to have many different modes of life, and that he bound himself to adhere rigidly to this plan, even in the most aberrant forms of the group where some other plan would have been more appropriate, is to ascribe a very strange motive. When we discover that the possession of seven cervical vertebræ is a general characteristic of mammals, whether the neck be immensely long as in the giraffe, or quite rudimentary as in the whale, shall we say that though, for the whale's neck, one vertebra would have been equally good, and though, for the giraffe's neck, a dozen would probably have been better than seven, yet seven was the number adhered to in both cases, because seven was fixed upon for the mammalian type? And then, when it turns out that this possession of seven cervical vertebræ is not an absolutely-universal characteristic of mammals (there is one which has eight), shall we conclude that while, in a host of cases, there was a needless adherence to a plan for the sake of consistency, there was yet, in some cases, an inconsistent abandonment of the plan? I think we may properly refuse to draw any such conclusion.

What, then, is the meaning of these peculiar relations of organic forms? The answer to this question must be postponed. Having here contemplated the problem as presented in these wide inductions which naturalists have reached; and having seen what proposed solutions of it are inadmissible; we shall see, in the next division of this work, what is the only possible solution.

CHAPTER XII.

DISTRIBUTION.

§ 104. There is a distribution of organisms in Space, and there is a distribution of organisms in Time. Looking first at their distribution in Space, we observe in it two different classes of facts. On the one hand, the plants and animals of each species have their habitats limited by external conditions: they are necessarily restricted to spaces in which their vital actions can be performed. On the other hand, the existence of certain conditions does not determine the presence of organisms that are fit for them. There are many spaces perfectly adapted for life of a high order in which only life of a much lower order is found.

While, in the inevitable restriction of organisms to environments with which their natures correspond we find a *negative* cause of distribution, there remains to be found that *positive* cause whence results the presence of organisms in some places appropriate to them and their absence from other places equally appropriate or more appropriate. Let us consider the phenomena as thus classed.

§ 105. Facts which illustrate the limiting influence of surrounding conditions are abundant, and familiar to all readers. It will be needful, however, here to cite a few typical ones of each order.

The confinement of different kinds of plants and different kinds of animals, to the media for which they are severally adapted, is the broadest fact of distribution. We have extensive groups of plants that are respectively sub-aerial and sub-aqueous; and of the sub-aqueous some are exclusively marine, while others exist only in rivers and lakes. Among animals we similarly find some classes confined to the air and others to the water; and of the water-breathers some are restricted to salt water and others to fresh water. Less conspicuous is the fact that within each of these contrasted media there are further widespread limitations. In the sea, certain organisms exist only between certain depths, and others only between other depths—the limpet and the mussel within the littoral zone, and numerous kinds at the bottom of the ocean; and on the land, there are Floras and Faunas peculiar to low regions and others peculiar to high regions. Next we have the familiar geographical limitations made by climate. There are temperatures which restrict each kind of organism between certain isothermal lines, and hygrometric states which prevent the spread of each kind of organism beyond areas having a certain humidity or a certain dryness. Besides such general limitations we find much more special limitations. Some minute vegetal forms occur only in snow. Hot springs have their peculiar *Infusoria.* The habitats of certain Fungi are mines or other dark places. And there are creatures unknown beyond the water contained in particular caves. After these limits to distribution imposed by physical conditions, come limits imposed by the presence or absence of other organisms. Obviously, graminivorous animals are confined within tracts which produce plants fit for them to feed on. The great carnivores cannot exist out of regions where there are creatures large enough and numerous enough to serve for prey. The needs of the sloth limit it to certain forest-covered spaces; and there can be no insectivorous bats where there are no night-flying insects. To these dependences of the relatively-superior organisms on the relatively-inferior organisms which they consume, must be added certain reciprocal dependences of the inferior on the superior. Mr. Darwin's inquiries have shown how generally the fertilization of plants is due to the agency of insects, and how certain plants, being fertilizable only by insects of certain structures, are limited to regions inhabited by insects of such structures. Conversely, the spread of organisms is often bounded by the presence of particular organisms beyond the bounds—either competing organisms or organisms directly inimical. A plant fit for some territory adjacent to its own, fails to overrun it because the territory is pre-occupied by some plant which is its superior, either in fertility or power of resisting destructive agencies; or else fails because there lives in the territory some mammal which browses on its foliage or bird which devours nearly all its seeds. Similarly, an area in which animals of a particular species might thrive, is not colonized by them because they are not fleet enough to escape some beast of prey inhabiting this area, or because the area is infested by some insect which destroys them, as the tsetse destroys the cattle in parts of Africa. Yet another more special series of limitations accompanies parasitism. There are parasitic plants that flourish only on trees of some few species, and others that have particular animals for their habitats—as the fungus which is fatal to the silk-worm, or that which so strangely grows out of a New Zealand caterpillar. Of animal-parasites various kinds lead lives involving specialities of distribution. We have kinds which use other creatures for purposes of locomotion, as the *Chelonobia* uses the turtle, and as a certain *Actinia* uses the shell inhabited by a hermit-crab. We have the parasitism in which one creature habitually accompanies another to share its prey, like the annelid which takes up its abode in a hermit-crab's shell, and snatches from the hermit-crab the morsels of food it is eating. We have again the commoner parasitism of the *Epizoa*—animals which attach themselves to the surfaces of other animals, and feed on their juices or on their secretions. And once more, we have the equally common parasitism of the *Entozoa*—creatures which live within other creatures. Besides being restricted to the bodies of the organisms it infests, each species has usually still narrower limits of distribution; in some cases the infested organisms furnish fit habitats for the parasites only in certain regions, and in other cases only when in certain constitutional states. There are more indirect modes in which the distributions of organisms affect one another. Plants of some kinds are eaten by animals only in the absence of kinds that are preferred to them; and hence the prosperity of such plants partly depends on the presence of the preferred plants. Mr. Bates has shown that some South American butterflies thrive in regions where insectivorous birds would destroy them, did they not closely resemble butterflies of another genus which are disliked by those birds. And Mr. Darwin gives cases of dependence still more remote and involved.

Such are the chief negative causes of distribution—the inorganic and organic agencies that set bounds to the spaces which organisms of each species inhabit. Fully to understand their actions we must contemplate them as working not separately but in concert. We have to regard the physical influences, varying from year to year, as now producing an extension or restriction of the habitat in this direction and now in that, and as producing secondary extensions and restrictions by their effects on other kinds of organisms. We have to regard the distribution of each species as affected not only by causes which favour multiplication of prey or of enemies within its own area, but also by causes which produce such results in neighbouring areas. We have to conceive the forces by which the limit is maintained, as including all meteorologic influences, united with the influences, direct or remote, of numerous co-existing species.

One general truth, indicated by sundry of the above illustrations, calls for special notice—the truth that all kinds of organisms intrude on one another's spheres of existence. Of the ways in which they do this the commonest is invasion of territory. That tendency which we see in the human races, to overrun and occupy one another's lands, as well as the lands inhabited by inferior creatures, is a tendency exhibited by all classes of organisms in various ways. Among them, as among mankind, there are permanent conquests, temporary occupations, and occasional raids. Every spring an inroad is made into the area which our own birds occupy, by birds from the South; and every winter the fieldfares of the North come to share the hips and haws of our hedges, and thus entail on our native birds some mortality. Besides these regularly-recurring incursions there are irregular ones; as of locusts into countries not usually visited by them, or of certain rodents which from time to time swarm into areas adjacent to their own. Every now and then an incursion ends in permanent settlement—perhaps in conquest over indigenous species. Within these few years an American water-weed has taken possession of our ponds and rivers, and to some extent supplanted native water-weeds. Of animals may be named a small kind of red ant, having habits allied to those of tropical ants, which has of late overrun many houses in London. The rat, which must have taken to infesting ships within these few centuries, furnishes a good illustration of the readiness of animals to occupy new places that are available. And the way in which vessels visiting India are cleared of the European cockroach by the kindred *Blatta orientalis*, shows us how these successful invasions last only until there come more powerful invaders. Animals encroach on one another's spheres of existence in further ways than by trespassing on one another's areas: they adopt one another's modes of life. There are cases in which this usurpation of habits is slight and temporary; and there are cases where it is marked and permanent. Grey crows often join gulls in picking up food between tide-marks; and gulls may occasionally be seen many miles inland, feeding in ploughed fields and on moors. Mr. Darwin has watched a fly-catcher catching fish. He says that the greater titmouse sometimes adopts the practices of the shrike, and sometimes of the nuthatch, and that some South American woodpeckers are frugivorous while others chase insects on the wing. Of habitual intrusions on the occupations of other creatures, one case is furnished by the sea-eagle, which, besides hunting the surface of the land for prey, like the rest of the hawk-tribe, often swoops down upon fish. And Mr. Darwin names a species of petrel that has taken to diving, and has a considerably modified organization. The last cases introduce a still more remarkable class of facts of kindred meaning. This intrusion of organisms on one another's modes of life goes to the extent of intruding on one another's media. The great mass of flowering plants are terrestrial, and (aside from other needs) are required to be so by their process of fructification. But there are some which live in the water, and protrude their flowers above the surface. Nay, there is a still more striking instance. At the sea-side may be found an alga a hundred yards inland, and a phænogam rooted in salt water. Among animals these interchanges of media are numerous. Nearly all coleopterous insects are terrestrial; but the water-beetle, which like the rest of its order is an air-breather, has aquatic habits. Water appears to be an extremely unfit medium for a fly; and yet Mr. [now Sir John] Lubbock has discovered more than one species of fly living beneath the surface of the water and coming up occasionally for air. Birds, as a class, are specially fitted for an aerial existence; but certain tribes of them have taken to an aquatic existence—swimming on the surface of the water and making continual incursions beneath it, and some kinds have wholly lost the power of flight. Among mammals, too, which have limbs and lungs implying an organization for terrestrial life, may be named kinds living more or less in the water and are more or less adapted to it. We have water-rats and otters which unite the two kinds of life, and show but little modification; hippopotami passing the greater part of their time in the water, and somewhat more fitted to it; seals living almost exclusively in the sea, and having the mammalian form greatly obscured; whales wholly confined to the sea, and having so little the aspect of mammals as to be mistaken for fish. Conversely, sundry inhabitants of the water make excursions on the land. Eels migrate at night from one pool to another. There are fish with specially-modified gills and fin-rays serving as stilts, which, when the rivers they inhabit are partially dried-up, travel in search of better quarters. And while some kinds of crabs do not make land-excursions beyond high-water mark, other kinds pursue lives almost wholly terrestrial.

Guided by these two classes of facts, we must regard the bounds to each species' sphere of existence as determined by the balancing of two antagonist sets of forces. The tendency which every species has to intrude on other areas, other modes of life, and other media, is restrained by the direct and indirect resistance of conditions, organic and inorganic. And these expansive and repressive energies, varying continually in their respective intensities, rhythmically equilibrate each other—maintain a limit that perpetually oscillates from side to side of a certain mean.

§ 106. As implied at the outset, the character of a region, when unfavourable to any species, sufficiently accounts for the absence of this species; and thus its absence is not inconsistent with the hypothesis that each species was originally placed in the regions most favourable to it. But the absence of a species from regions that *are* favourable to it cannot be thus accounted for. Were plants and animals localized wholly with reference to the fitness of their constitutions to surrounding conditions, we might expect Floras to be similar, and Faunas to be similar, where the conditions are similar; and we might expect dissimilarities among Floras and among Faunas, proportionate to the dissimilarities of their conditions. But we do not find such anticipations verified.

Mr. Darwin says that "in the Southern hemisphere, if we compare large tracts of land in Australia, South Africa, and western South America, between latitudes 25° and 35°, we shall find parts extremely similar in all their conditions, yet it would not be possible to point out three faunas and floras more utterly dissimilar. Or again we may compare the productions of South America south of lat. 35° with those north of 25°, which consequently inhabit a considerably different climate, and they will be found incomparably more closely related to each other, than they are to the productions of Australia or Africa under nearly the same climate." Still more striking are the contrasts which Mr. Darwin points out between adjacent areas that are totally cut off from each other. "No two marine faunas are more distinct, with hardly a fish, shell, or crab in common, than those of the eastern and western shores of South and Central America; yet these great faunas are separated only by the narrow, but impassable, isthmus of Panama." On opposite sides of high mountain-chains, also, there are marked differences in the organic forms—differences not so marked as where the barriers are absolutely impassable, but much more marked than are necessitated by unlikenesses of physical conditions.

Not less suggestive is the converse fact that wide geographical areas which offer decided geologic and meteorologic contrasts, are peopled by nearly-allied groups of organisms, if there are no barriers to migration. "The naturalist in travelling, for instance, from north to south never fails to be struck by the manner in which successive groups of beings, specifically distinct, yet clearly related, replace each other. He hears from closely allied, yet distinct kinds of birds, notes nearly similar, and sees their nests similarly constructed, but not quite alike, with eggs coloured in nearly the same manner. The plains near the Straits of Magellan are inhabited by one species of Rhea (American Ostrich), and northward the plains of La Plata by another species of the same genus; and not by a true ostrich or emu, like those found in Africa and Australia under the same latitude. On these same plains of La Plata, we see the agouti and bizcacha, animals having nearly the same habits as our hares and rabbits and belonging to the same order of Rodents, but they plainly display an American type of structure. We ascend the lofty peaks of the Cordillera and we find an alpine species of bizcacha; we look to the waters, and we do not find the beaver or musk-rat, but the coypu and capybara, rodents of the American type. Innumerable other instances could be given. If we look to the islands off the American shore, however much they may differ in geological structure, the inhabitants, though they may be all peculiar species, are essentially American."

What is the generalization implied by these two groups of facts? On the one hand, we have similarly-conditioned, and sometimes nearly-adjacent, areas, occupied by quite different Faunas. On the one hand, we have areas remote from one another in latitude, and contrasted in soil as well as climate, occupied by closely-allied Faunas. Clearly then, as like organisms are not universally, or even generally, found in like habitats, nor very unlike organisms in very unlike habitats, there is no manifest pre-determined adaptation of the organisms to the habitats. The organisms do no occur in such and such places solely because they are either specially fit for those places, or more fit for them than all other organisms.

The induction under which these facts come, and which unites them with various other facts, is a totally-different one. When we see that the similar areas peopled by dissimilar forms, are those between which there are impassable barriers; while the dissimilar areas peopled by similar forms, are those between which there are no such barriers; we are at once reminded of the general truth exemplified in the last section—the truth that each species of organism tends ever to expand its sphere of existence—to intrude on other areas, other modes of life, other media. And we are shown that through these perpetually-recurring attempts to thrust itself into every accessible habitat, each species spreads until it reaches limits which are for the time insurmountable.

§ 107. We pass now to the distribution of organic forms in Time. Geological inquiry has established the truth that during a Past of immeasurable duration, plants and animals have existed on the Earth. In all countries their buried remains are found in greater or less abundance. From comparatively small areas multitudinous different types have been exhumed. Every exploration of new areas, and every closer inspection of areas already explored, brings more types to light. And beyond question, an exhaustive examination of all exposed strata, and of all strata now covered by the sea, would disclose types immensely out-numbering those at present known. Further, geologists agree that even had we before us every kind of fossil which exists, we should still have nothing like a complete index to the past inhabitants of our globe. Many sedimentary deposits have been so altered by the heat of adjacent molten matter, as greatly to obscure the organic remains contained in them. The extensive formations once called "transition," and now re-named "metamorphic," are acknowledged to be formations of sedimentary origin, from which all traces of such fossils as they probably included have been obliterated by igneous action. And the accepted conclusion is that igneous rock has everywhere resulted from the melting-up of beds of detritus originally deposited by water. How long the reactions of the Earth's molten nucleus on its cooling crust, have been thus destroying the records of Life, it is impossible to say; but there are strong reasons for believing that the records which remain bear but a small ratio to the records which have been destroyed. Thus we have but extremely imperfect data for conclusions respecting the distribution of organic forms in Time. Some few generalizations, however, may be regarded as established.

One is that the plants and animals now existing mostly differ from the plants and animals which have existed. Though there are species common to our present Fauna and to past Faunas, yet the *facies* of our present Fauna differs, more or less, from the *facies* of each past Fauna. On carrying out the comparison, we find that past Faunas differ from one another, and that the differences between them are proportionate to their degrees of remoteness from one another in Time, as measured by their relative positions in the sedimentary series. So that if we take the assemblage of organic forms living now, and compare it with the successive assemblages of organic forms which have lived in successive geologic epochs, we find that the farther we go back into the past, the greater does the unlikeness become. The number of species and genera common to the compared assemblages, becomes smaller and smaller; and the assemblages differ more and more in their general characters. Though a species of brachiopod now extant is almost identical with a species found in Silurian strata, though between the Silurian Fauna and our own there are sundry common genera of molluscs, yet it is undeniable that there is a proportion between lapse of time and divergence of organic forms.

This divergence is comparatively slow and continuous where there is continuity in the geological formations, but is sudden, and comparatively wide, wherever there occurs a great break in the succession of strata. The contrasts which thus arise, gradually or all at once, in formations that are continuous or discontinuous, are of two kinds. Faunas of different eras are distinguished partly by the absence from the one of type's present in the other, and partly by the unlikenesses between the types common to both. Such contrasts between Faunas as are due to the appearance or disappearance of types, are of secondary significance: they possibly, or probably, do not imply anything more than migrations or extinctions. The most significant contrasts are those between successive groups of organisms of the same type. And among such, as above said, the differences are, speaking generally, small and continuous where a series of conformable strata gives proof of continued existence of the type in the locality; while they are comparatively large and abrupt where the adjacent formations are shown to have been separated by long intervals.

Another general fact, referred to by Mr. Darwin as one which palæontology has made tolerably certain, is that forms and groups of forms which have once disappeared from the Earth, do not reappear. Passing over the few species which have continued throughout the whole period geologically recorded, it may be said that each species after arising, spreading for an era, and continuing abundant for an era, eventually declines and becomes extinct; and that similarly, each genus during a longer period increases in the number of its species, and during a longer period dwindles and at last dies out. After making its exit neither species nor genus ever re-enters. The like is true even of those larger groups called orders. Four types of reptiles which were once abundant have not been found in modern formations, and do not at present exist. Though nothing less than an exhaustive examination of all strata, can prove conclusively that a type of organization when once lost is never reproduced, yet so many facts point to this inference that its truth can scarcely be doubted.

To frame a conception of the total amount and general direction of the change in organic forms during the time measured by our sedimentary series, is at present impossible—the data are insufficient. The immense contrast between the few and low forms of the earliest-known Fauna, and the many and high forms of our existing Fauna, has been commonly supposed to prove, not only great change but great progress. Nevertheless, this appearance of progress may be, and probably is, mainly illusive. Wider knowledge has shown that remains of comparatively well-organized creatures really existed in strata long supposed to be devoid of them, and that where they are absent, the nature of the strata often explains their absence, without assuming that they did not exist when these strata were formed. It is a tenable hypothesis that the successively-higher types fossilized in our successively-later deposits, indicate nothing more than successive migrations from pre-existing continents to continents that were step by step emerging from the ocean—migrations which necessarily began with the inferior orders of organisms, and included the successively-superior orders as the new lands became more accessible to them and better fitted for them.[43]

While the evidence usually supposed to prove progression is thus untrustworthy, there is trustworthy evidence that there has been, in many cases, little or no progression. Though the orders which have existed from palæozoic and mesozoic times down to the present day, are almost universally changed, yet a comparison of ancient and modern members of these orders shows that the total amount of change is not relatively great, and that it is not manifestly towards a higher organization. Though nearly all the living forms which have prototypes in early formations differ from these prototypes specially, and in most cases generically, yet ordinal peculiarities are, in numerous cases, maintained from the earliest times geologically recorded, down to our own time; and we have no visible evidence of superiority in the existing genera of these orders. In his lecture "On the Persistent Types of Animal Life," Prof. Huxley enumerated many cases. On the authority of Dr. Hooker he stated "that there are Carboniferous plants which appear to be generically identical with some now living: that the cone of the Oolitic *Araucaria* is hardly distinguishable from that of an existing species; that a true *Pinus* appears in the Purbecks and a *Juglans* in the chalk." Among animals he named palæozoic and mesozoic corals which are very like certain extant corals; genera of Silurian molluscs that answer to existing genera; insects and arachnids in the coal-formations that are not more than generically distinct from some of our own insects and arachnids. He instanced "the Devonian and Carboniferous *Pleuracanthus*, which differs no more from existing sharks than these do from one another;" early mesozoic reptiles "identical in the essential characters of their organization with those now living;" and Triassic mammals which did not differ "nearly so much from some of those which now live, as these differ from one another." Continuing the argument in his "Anniversary Address to the Geological Society" in 1862, Prof. Huxley gave many cases in which the changes that have taken place, are not changes towards a more specialized or higher organization—asking "in what sense are the Liassic Chelonia inferior to those which now exist? How are the Cretaceous Ichthyosauria, Plesiosauria, or Pterosauria less embryonic or more differentiated species than those of the Lias?" While, however, contending that in most instances "positive evidence fails to demonstrate any sort of progressive modification towards a less embryonic or less generalized type in a great many groups of animals of long-continued geological existence," Prof. Huxley added that there are other groups, "co-existing with them under the same conditions, in which more or less distinct indications of such a process seem to be traceable." And in illustration of this, he named that better development of the vertebræ which characterizes some of the more modern fishes and reptiles, when compared with ancient fishes and reptiles of the same orders; and the "regularity and evenness of the dentition of the *Anoplotherium* as contrasting with that of existing Artiodactyles."[44]

The facts thus summed up do not show that higher forms have not arisen in the course of geologic time, any more than the facts commonly cited prove that higher forms have arisen; nor are they regarded by Professor Huxley as showing this. Were those which have survived from palæozoic and mesozoic days down to our own day, the only types; and did the modifications, rarely of more than generic value, which these types have undergone, give no better evidences of increased complexity than are actually given by them; then it would be inferable that there has been no appreciable advance. But there now exist, and have existed during the more recent geologic epochs, various types which are not known to have existed in earlier epochs—some of them widely unlike these persistent types and some of them nearly allied to these persistent types. As yet, we know nothing about the origins of these new types. But it is possible that causes like those which have produced generic differences in the persistent types, have, in some or many cases, produced modifications great enough to constitute ordinal differences. If structural contrasts not exceeding certain moderate limits are held to mark only generic distinctions; and if organisms displaying larger contrasts are regarded as ordinally or typically distinct; it is obvious that the persistence of a given type through a long geologic period without apparently undergoing deviations of more than generic value, by no means disproves the occurrence of far greater deviations in other cases; since the forms resulting from such far greater deviations, being regarded as typically distinct forms, will not be taken as evidence of great change in an original type. That which Prof. Huxley's argument proves, and that only which he considers it to prove, is that organisms have no innate tendencies to assume higher forms; and that "any admissible hypothesis of progressive modification, must be compatible with persistence without progression through indefinite periods."

One very significant fact must be added concerning the relation between distribution in Time and distribution in Space. I quote it from Mr. Darwin:—"Mr. Clift many years ago showed that the fossil mammals from the Australian caves were closely allied to the living marsupials of that continent. In South America a similar relationship is manifest, even to an uneducated eye, in the gigantic pieces of armour like those of the armadillo, found in several parts of La Plata; and Professor Owen has shown in the most striking manner that most of the fossil mammals, buried there in such numbers, are related to the South American types. This relationship is even more clearly seen in the wonderland collection of fossil bones made by MM. Lund and Clausen in the caves of Brazil. I was so much impressed with these facts that I strongly insisted, in 1839 and 1845, on this 'law of the succession of types,'—on 'this wonderful relationship in the same continent between the dead and the living.' Professor Owen has subsequently extended the same generalization to the Mammals of the Old World. We see the same law in this author's restorations of the extinct and gigantic birds of New Zealand. We see it also in the birds of the caves of Brazil. Mr. Woodward has shown that the same law holds good with sea-shells, but from the wide distribution of most genera of molluscs, it is not well displayed by them. Other cases could be added, as the relation between the extinct and living landshells of Madeira, and between the extinct and living brackish-water shells of the Aralo-Caspian Sea."

The general results, then, are these. Our knowledge of distribution in Time, being derived wholly from the evidence afforded by fossils, is limited to that geologic time of which some records remain—cannot extend to those remoter times the records of which have been obliterated. From these remaining records, which probably form but a small fraction of the whole, the general facts deducible are these:—That such organic types as have lived through successive epochs, have almost universally undergone modifications of specific and generic values—modifications which have commonly been great in proportion as the period has been long. That besides the types which have persisted from ancient eras down to our own era, other types have from time to time made their appearance in the ascending series of strata—types of which some are lower and some higher than the types previously recorded; but whence these new types came, and whether any of them arose by divergence from the previously-recorded types, the evidence does not yet enable us to say. That in the course of long geologic epochs nearly all species, most genera, and a few orders, have become extinct; and that a species, genus, or order, which has once disappeared from the Earth never reappears. And, lastly, that the Fauna now occupying each separate area of the Earth's surface is very nearly allied to the Fauna which existed on that area during recent geologic times.

§ 108. Omitting sundry minor generalizations, the exposition of which would involve too much detail, what is to be said of these major generalizations?

The distribution in Space cannot be said to imply that organisms have been designed for their particular habitats and placed in them; since, besides the habitat in which each kind of organism is found there are commonly other habitats, as good or better for it, from which it is absent—habitats to which it is so much better fitted than organisms now occupying them, that it extrudes these organisms when allowed the opportunity. Neither can we suppose that the purpose has been to establish varieties of Floras and Faunas; since, if so, why are the Floras and Faunas but little divergent in widely-sundered areas between which migration is possible, while they are markedly divergent in adjacent areas between which migration is impossible?

Passing to distributions in Time, there arise the questions—why during nearly the whole of that vast period geologically recorded have there existed none of those highest organic forms which have now overrun the Earth?—how is it that we find no traces of a creature endowed with large capacities for knowledge and happiness? The answer that the Earth was not, in remote times, a fit habitation for such a creature, besides being unwarranted by the evidence, suggests the equally awkward question—why during untold millions of years did the Earth remain fit only for inferior creatures? What, again, is the meaning of extinction of types? To conclude that the saurian type was replaced by other types at the beginning of the tertiary period, because it was not adapted to the conditions which then arose, is to conclude that it could not be modified into fitness for the conditions; and this conclusion is at variance with the hypothesis that creative skill is shown in the multiform adaptations of one type to many ends.

What interpretations may rationally be put on these and other general facts of distribution in Space and Time, will be seen in the next division of this work.

PART III.
THE EVOLUTION OF LIFE.

CHAPTER I.

PRELIMINARY.

§ 109. In the foregoing Part, we have contemplated the most important of the generalizations to which biologists have been led by observation of organisms; as well as some others which contemplation of the facts has suggested to me. These Inductions of Biology have also been severally glanced at on their deductive sides; for the purpose of noting the harmony existing between them and those primordial truths set forth in *First Principles*. Having thus studied the leading phenomena of life separately, we are prepared for studying them as an aggregate, with the view of arriving at the most general interpretation of them.

There is an *ensemble* of vital phenomena presented by each organism in the course of its growth, development, and decay; and there is an *ensemble* of vital phenomena presented by the organic world as a whole. Neither of these can be properly dealt with apart from the other. But the last of them may be separately treated more conveniently than the first. What interpretation we put on the facts of structure and function in each living body, depends entirely on our conception of the mode in which living bodies in general have originated. To form some conclusion respecting this mode—a provisional if not a permanent conclusion—must therefore be our first step.

We have to choose between two hypotheses—the hypothesis of Special Creation and the hypothesis of Evolution. Either the multitudinous kinds of organisms which now exist, and the far more multitudinous kinds which have existed during past geologic eras, have been from time to time separately made; or they have arisen by insensible steps, through actions such as we see habitually going on. Both hypotheses imply a Cause. The last, certainly as much as the first, recognizes this Cause as inscrutable. The point at issue is, how this inscrutable Cause has worked in the production of living forms. This point, if it is to be decided at all, is to be decided only by examination of evidence. Let us inquire which of these antagonist hypotheses is most congruous with established facts.

CHAPTER II.

GENERAL ASPECTS OF THE SPECIAL-CREATION-HYPOTHESIS.[45]

§ 110. Early ideas are not usually true ideas. Undeveloped intellect, be it that of an individual or that of the race, forms conclusions which require to be revised and re-revised, before they reach a tolerable correspondence with realities. Were it otherwise there would be no discovery, no increase of intelligence. What we call the progress of knowledge, is the bringing of Thoughts into harmony with Things; and it implies that the first Thoughts are either wholly out of harmony with Things, or in very incomplete harmony with them.

If illustrations be needed the history of every science furnishes them. The primitive notions of mankind as to the structure of the heavens were wrong; and the notions which replaced them were successively less wrong. The original belief respecting the form of the Earth was wrong; and this wrong belief survived through the first civilizations. The earliest ideas that have come down to us concerning the natures of the elements were wrong; and only in quite recent times has the composition of matter in its various forms been better understood. The interpretations of mechanical facts, of meteorological facts, of physiological facts, were at first wrong. In all these cases men set out with beliefs which, if not absolutely false, contained but small amounts of truth disguised by immense amounts of error.

Hence the hypothesis that living beings resulted from special creations, being a primitive hypothesis, is probably an untrue hypothesis. It would be strange if, while early men failed to reach the truth in so many cases where it is comparatively conspicuous, they reached it in a case where it is comparatively hidden.

§ 111. Besides the improbability given to the belief in special creations, by its association with mistaken beliefs in general, a further improbability is given to it by its association with a special class of mistaken beliefs. It belongs to a family of beliefs which have one after another been destroyed by advancing knowledge; and is, indeed, almost the only member of the family surviving among educated people.

We all know that the savage thinks of each striking phenomenon, or group of phenomena, as caused by some separate personal agent; that out of this conception there grows up a polytheistic conception, in which these minor personalities are variously generalized into deities presiding over different divisions of nature; and that these are eventually further generalized. This progressive consolidation of causal agencies may be traced in the creeds of all races, and is far from complete in the creed of the most advanced races. The unlettered rustics who till our fields, do not let the consciousness of a supreme power wholly absorb the aboriginal conceptions of good and evil spirits, and of charms or secret potencies dwelling in particular objects. The earliest mode of thinking changes only as fast as the constant relations among phenomena are established. Scarcely less familiar is the truth, that while accumulating knowledge makes these conceptions of personal causal agents gradually more vague, as it merges them into general causes, it also destroys the habit of thinking of them as working after the methods of personal agents. We do not now, like Kepler, assume guiding spirits to keep the planets in their orbits. It is no longer the universal belief that the sea was once for all mechanically parted from the dry land; or that the mountains were placed where we see them by a sudden creative act. All but a narrow class have ceased to suppose sunshine and storm to be sent in some arbitrary succession. The majority of educated people have given up thinking of epidemics of punishments inflicted by an angry deity. Nor do even the common people regard a madman as one possessed by a demon. That is to say, we everywhere see fading away the anthropomorphic conception of Cause. In one case after another, is abandoned the ascription of phenomena to a will analogous to the human will, working by methods analogous to human methods.

If, then, of this once-numerous family of beliefs the immense majority have become extinct, we may not unreasonably expect that the few remaining members of the family will become extinct. One of these is the belief we are here considering—the belief that each species of organism was specially created. Many who in all else have abandoned the aboriginal theory of things, still hold this remnant of the aboriginal theory. Ask any well-informed man whether he accepts the cosmogony of the Indians, or the Greeks, or the Hebrews, and he will regard the question as next to an insult. Yet one element common to these cosmogonies he very likely retains: not bearing in mind its origin. For whence did he get the doctrine of special creations? Catechise him, and he is forced to confess that it was put into his mind in childhood, as one portion of a story which, as a whole, he has long since rejected. Why this fragment is likely to be right while all the rest is wrong, he is unable to say. May we not then expect that the relinquishment of all other parts of this story, will by and by be followed by the relinquishment of this remaining part of it?

§ 112. The belief which we find thus questionable, both as being a primitive belief and as being a belief belonging to an almost-extinct family, is a belief not countenanced by a single fact. No one ever saw a special creation; no one ever found proof of an indirect kind that a special creation had taken place. It is significant, as Dr. Hooker remarks, that naturalists who suppose new species to be miraculously originated, habitually suppose the origination to occur in some region remote from human observation. Wherever the order of organic nature is exposed to the view of zoologists and botanists, it expels this conception; and the conception survives only in connexion with imagined places, where the order of organic nature is unknown.

Besides being absolutely without evidence to give it external support, this hypothesis of special creations cannot support itself internally—cannot be framed into a coherent thought. It is one of those illegitimate symbolic conceptions which are mistaken for legitimate symbolic conceptions (*First Principles*, § 9), because they remain untested. Immediately an attempt is made to elaborate the idea into anything like a definite shape, it proves to be a pseud-idea, admitting of no definite shape. Is it supposed that a new organism, when specially created, is created out of nothing? If so, there is a supposed creation of matter; and the creation of matter is inconceivable—implies the establishment of a relation in thought between nothing and something—a relation of which one term is absent—an impossible relation. Is it supposed that the matter of which the new organism consists is not created for the occasion, but is taken out of its pre-existing forms and arranged into a new form? If so, we are met by the question—how is the re-arrangement effected? Of the myriad atoms going to the composition of the new organism, all of them previously dispersed through the neighbouring air and earth, does each, suddenly disengaging itself from its combinations, rush to meet the rest, unite with them into the appropriate chemical compounds, and then fall with certain others into its appointed place in the aggregate of complex tissues and organs? Surely thus to assume a myriad supernatural impulses, differing in their directions and amounts, given to as many different atoms, is a multiplication of mysteries rather than the solution of a mystery. For every one of these impulses, not being the result of a force locally existing in some other form, implies the creation of force; and the creation of force is just as inconceivable as the creation of matter. It is thus with all attempted ways of representing the process. The old Hebrew idea that God takes clay and moulds a new creature, as a potter moulds a vessel, is probably too grossly anthropomorphic to be accepted by any modern defender of the special-creation doctrine. But having abandoned this crude belief, what belief is he prepared to substitute? If a new organism is not thus produced, then in what way is one produced? or rather—in what way does he conceive a new organism to be produced? We will not ask for the ascertained mode, but will be content with a mode which can be consistently imagined. No such mode, however, is assignable. Those who entertain the proposition that each kind of organism results from a divine interposition, do so because they refrain from translating words into thoughts. They do not really believe, but rather *believe they believe.* For belief, properly so called, implies a mental representation of the thing believed, and no such mental representation is here possible.

§ 113. If we imagine mankind to be contemplated by some being as short-lived as an ephemeron, but possessing intelligence like our own—if we imagine such a being studying men and women, during his few hours of life, and speculating as to the mode in which they came into existence; it is manifest that, reasoning in the usual way, he would suppose each man and woman to have been separately created. No appreciable changes of structure occurring in any of them during the time over which his observations extended, this being would probably infer that no changes of structure were taking place, or had taken place; and that from the outset each man and woman had possessed all the characters then visible—had been originally formed with them. The application is obvious. A human life is ephemeral compared with the life of a species; and even the period over which the records of all human lives extend, is ephemeral compared with the life of a species. There is thus a parallel contrast between the immensely-long series of changes which have occurred during the life of a species, and that small portion of the series open to our view. And there is no reason to suppose that the first conclusion drawn by mankind from this small part of the series visible to them, is any nearer the truth than would be the conclusion of the supposed ephemeral being respecting men and women.

This analogy, suggesting as it does how the hypothesis of special creations is merely a formula for our ignorance, raises the question—What reason have we to assume special creations of species but not of individuals; unless it be that in the case of individuals we directly know the process to be otherwise, but in the case of species do not directly know it to be otherwise? Have we any ground for concluding that species were specially created, except the ground that we have no immediate knowledge of their origin? And does our ignorance of the manner in which they arose warrant us in asserting that they arose by special creation?

Another question is suggested by this analogy. Those who, in the absence of immediate evidence of the way in which species arose, assert that they arose not in a natural way allied to that in which individuals arise, but in a supernatural way, think that by this supposition they honour the Unknown Cause of things; and they oppose any antagonist doctrine as amounting to an exclusion of divine power from the world. But if divine power is demonstrated by the separate creation of each species, would it not have been still better demonstrated by the separate creation of each individual? Why should there exist this process of natural genesis? Why should not omnipotence have been proved by the supernatural production of plants and animals everywhere throughout the world from hour to hour? Is it replied that the Creator was able to make individuals arise from one another in a natural succession, but not to make species thus arise? This is to assign a limit to power instead of magnifying it. Either it was possible or not possible to create species and individuals after the same general method. To say that it was not possible is suicidal in those who use this argument; and if it was possible, it is required to say what end is served by the special creation of species which would not have been better served by the special creation of individuals. Again, what is to be thought of the fact that the immense majority of these supposed special creations took place before mankind existed? Those who think that divine power is demonstrated by special creations, have to answer the question—to whom demonstrated? Tacitly or avowedly, they regard the demonstrations as being for the benefit of mankind. But if so, to what purpose were the millions of these demonstrations which took place on the Earth when there were no intelligent beings to contemplate them? Did the Unknowable thus demonstrate his power to himself? Few will have the hardihood to say that any such demonstration was needful. There is no choice but to regard them, either as superfluous exercises of power, which is a derogatory supposition, or as exercises of power that were necessary because species could not be otherwise produced, which is also a derogatory supposition.

§ 113*a*. Other implications concerning the divine character must be recognized by those who contend that each species arose by divine fiat. It is hardly supposable that Infinite Power is exercised in trivial actions effecting trivial changes. Yet the organic world in its hundreds of thousands of species shows in each sub-division multitudinous forms which, though unlike enough to be classed as specifically distinct, diverge from one another only in small details which have no significance in relation to the life led. Sometimes the number of specific distinctions is so great that did they result from human agency we should call them whimsical.

For example, in Lake Baikal are found 115 species of an amphipod, *Gammarus*; and the multiplicity becomes startling on learning that this number exceeds the number of all other species of the genus: various as are the conditions to which, throughout the rest of the world, the genus is subject. Still stranger seems the superfluous exercise of power on examining the carpet of living forms at the bottom of the ocean. Not dwelling on the immense variety of creatures unlike in type which live miles below the surface in absolute darkness, it will suffice to instance the *Polyzoa* alone: low types of animals so small that a thousand of them would not cover a square inch, and on which, nevertheless, there has been, according to the view we are considering, an exercise of creative skill such that by small variations of structure more than 350 species have been produced!

Kindred illustrations are furnished by the fauna of caverns. Are we to suppose that numerous blind creatures—crustaceans, myriapods, spiders, insects, fishes—were specially made sightless to fit them for the Mammoth Cave? Or what shall we say of the *Proteus*, a low amphibian with rudimentary eyes, which inhabits certain caves in Carniola, Carinthia and Dalmatia and is not found elsewhere. Must we conclude that God went out of his way to devise an animal for these places?

More puzzling still is a problem presented to the special-creationist by a batrachian inhabiting Central Australia. In a region once peopled by numerous animals but now made unfit by continuous droughts, there exists a frog which, when the pools are drying up, fills itself with water and burrowing in the mud hibernates until the next rains; which may come in a year or may be delayed for two years. What is to be thought of this creature? Were its structure and the accompanying instinct divinely planned to fit it to this particular habitat?

Many such questions might be asked which, if answered as the current theory necessitates, imply a divine nature hardly like that otherwise assumed.

§ 114. Those who espouse the aboriginal hypothesis entangle themselves in yet other theological difficulties. This assumption that each kind of organism was specially designed, carries with it the implication that the designer intended everything which results from the design. There is no escape from the admission that if organisms were severally constructed with a view to their respective ends, then the character of the constructor is indicated both by the ends themselves, and the perfection or imperfection with which the organisms are fitted to them. Observe the consequences.

Without dwelling on the question recently raised, why during untold millions of years there existed on the Earth no beings endowed with capacities for wide thought and high feeling, we may content ourselves with asking why, at present, the Earth is largely peopled by creatures which inflict on one another so much suffering? Omitting the human race, whose defects and miseries the current theology professes to account for, and limiting ourselves to the lower creation, what must we think of the countless different pain-inflicting appliances and instincts with which animals are endowed? Not only now, and not only ever since men have lived, has the Earth been a scene of warfare among all sentient creatures; but palæontology shows us that from the earliest eras geologically recorded, there has been going on this universal carnage. Fossil structures, in common with the structures of existing animals, show us elaborate weapons for destroying other animals. We have unmistakable proof that throughout all past time, there has been a ceaseless devouring of the weak by the strong. How is this to be explained? How happens it that animals were so designed as to render this bloodshed necessary? How happens it that in almost every species the number of individuals annually born is such that the majority die by starvation or by violence before arriving at maturity? Whoever contends that each kind of animal was specially designed, must assert either that there was a deliberate intention on the part of the Creator to produce these results, or that there was an inability to prevent them. Which alternative does he prefer?—to cast an imputation on the divine character or to assert a limitation of the divine power? It is useless for him to plead that the destruction of the less powerful by the more powerful, is a means of preventing the miseries of decrepitude and incapacity, and therefore works beneficently. For even were the chief mortality among the aged instead of among the young, there would still arise the unanswerable question—why were not animals constructed in such ways as to avoid these evils? why were not their rates of multiplication, their degrees of intelligence, and their propensities, so adjusted that these sufferings might be escaped? And if decline of vigour was a necessary accompaniment of age, why was it not provided that the organic actions should end in sudden death, whenever they fell below the level required for pleasurable existence? Will any one who contends that organisms were specially designed, assert that they could not have been so designed as to prevent suffering? And if he admits that they could have been made so as to prevent suffering, will he assert that the Creator preferred making them in such ways as to inflict suffering?

Even as thus presented the difficulty is sufficiently great; but it appears immensely greater when we examine the facts more closely. So long as we contemplate only the preying of the superior on the inferior, some good appears to be extracted from the evil—a certain amount of life of a higher order, is supported by sacrificing a great deal of life of a lower order. So long, too, as we leave out all mortality but that which, by carrying off the least perfect members of each species, leaves the most perfect members to survive and multiply; we see some compensating benefit reached through the suffering inflicted. But what shall we say on finding innumerable cases in which the suffering inflicted brings no compensating benefit? What shall we say when we see the inferior destroying the superior? What shall we say on finding elaborate appliances for furthering the multiplication of organisms incapable of feeling, at the expense of misery to organisms capable of happiness?

Of the animal kingdom as a whole, more than half the species are parasites. "The number of these parasites," says Prof. Owen, "may be conceived when it is stated that almost every known animal has its peculiar species, and generally more than one, sometimes as many as, or even more kinds than, infest the human body." This parasitism begins among the most minute creatures and pervades the entire animal kingdom from the lowest to the highest. Even *Protozoa*, made visible to us only by the microscope, are infested, as is *Paramœcium* by broods of *Sphærophrya*; while in large and complex animals parasites are everywhere present in great variety. More than this is true. There are parasites upon parasites—an arrangement such that those which are torturing the creatures they inhabit are themselves tortured by indwelling creatures still smaller: looking like an ingenious accumulation of pains upon pains.

But passing over the evils thus inflicted on animals of inferior dignity, let us limit ourselves to the case of Man. The *Bothriocephalus latus* and the *Tænia solium*, are two kinds of tape-worm, which flourish in the human intestines; producing great constitutional disturbances, sometimes ending in insanity; and from the germs of the *Tænia*, when carried into other parts of the body, arise certain partially-developed forms known as *Cysticerci*, *Echinococci*, and *Cœnuri*, which cause disorganization more or less extensive in the brain, the lungs, the liver, the heart, the eye, &c., often ending fatally after long-continued suffering. Five other parasites, belonging to a different class, are found in the viscera of man—the *Trichocephalus*, the *Oxyuris*, the *Strongylus* (two species), the *Ancylostomum* and the *Ascaris*; which, beyond that defect of nutrition which they necessarily cause, sometimes induce certain irritations that lead to complete demoralization. Of another class of *entozoa*, belonging to the subdivision *Trematoda*, there are five kinds found in different organs of the human body—the liver and gall-duct, the portal vein, the intestine, the bladder, the eye. Then we have the *Trichina spiralis*, which passes through one phase of its existence imbedded in the muscles and through another phase of its existence in the intestine; and which, by the induced disease *Trichinosis*, has lately committed such ravages in Germany as to cause a panic. To these we must add the Guinea-worm, which in some part of Africa and India makes men miserable by burrowing in their legs; and the more terrible African parasite the *Bilharzia*, which affects 30 per cent. of the natives on the east coast with bleeding of the bladder. From *entozoa*, let us pass to *epizoa*. There are two kinds of *Acari*, one of them inhabiting the follicles of the skin and the other producing the itch. There are creatures that bury themselves beneath the skin and lay their eggs there; and there are three species of lice which infest the surface of the body. Nor is this all. Besides animal parasites there are sundry vegetal parasites, which grow and multiply at our cost. The *Sarcina ventriculi* inhabits the stomach, and produces gastric disturbance. The *Leptothrix buccalis* is extremely general in the mouth, and may have something to do with the decay of teeth. And besides these there are microscopic fungi which produce ringworm, porrigo, pityriasis, thrush, &c. Thus the human body is the habitat of parasites, internal and external, animal and vegetal, numbering, if all are set down, between two and three dozen species; sundry of which are peculiar to Man, and many of which produce great suffering and not unfrequently death. What interpretation is to be put on these facts by those who espouse the hypothesis of special creations? According to this hypothesis, all these parasites were designed for their respective modes of life. They were endowed with constitutions fitting them to live by absorbing nutriment from the human body; they were furnished with appliances, often of a formidable kind, enabling them to root themselves in and upon the human body; and they were made prolific in an almost incredible degree, that their germs might have a sufficient number of chances of finding their way into the human body. In short, elaborate contrivances were combined to insure the continuance of their respective races; and to make it impossible for the successive generations of men to avoid being preyed on by them. What shall we say to this arrangement? Shall we say that "the head and crown of things," was provided as a habitat for these parasites? Shall we say that these degraded creatures, incapable of thought or enjoyment, were created that they might cause human misery? One or other of these alternatives must be chosen by those who contend that every kind of organism was separately devised by the Creator. Which do they prefer? With the conception of two antagonist powers, which severally work good and evil in the world, the facts are congruous enough. But with the conception of a supreme beneficence, this gratuitous infliction of pain is absolutely incompatible.

§ 115. See then the results of our examination. The belief in special creations of organisms arose among men during the era of profoundest darkness; and it belongs to a family of beliefs which have nearly all died out as enlightenment has increased. It is without a solitary established fact on which to stand; and when the attempt is made to put it into definite shape in the mind, it turns out to be only a pseud-idea. This mere verbal hypothesis, which men idly accept as a real or thinkable hypothesis, is of the same nature as would be one, based on a day's observation of human life, that each man and woman was specially created—an hypothesis not suggested by evidence but by lack of evidence—an hypothesis which formulates ignorance into a semblance of knowledge. Further, we see that this hypothesis, failing to satisfy men's intellectual need of an interpretation, fails also to satisfy their moral sentiment. It is quite inconsistent with those conceptions of the divine nature which they profess to entertain. If infinite power was to be demonstrated, then, either by the special creation of every individual, or by the production of species by some method of natural genesis, it would be better demonstrated than by the use of two methods, as assumed by the hypothesis. And if infinite goodness was to be demonstrated, then, not only do the provisions of organic structure, if they are specially devised, fail to demonstrate it, but there is an enormous mass of them which imply malevolence rather than benevolence.

Thus the hypothesis of special creations turns out to be worthless by its derivation; worthless in its intrinsic incoherence; worthless as absolutely without evidence; worthless as not supplying an intellectual need; worthless as not satisfying a moral want. We must therefore consider it as counting for nothing, in opposition to any other hypothesis respecting the origin of organic beings.

CHAPTER III.

GENERAL ASPECTS OF THE EVOLUTION-HYPOTHESIS.

§ 116. Just as the supposition that races of organisms have been specially created, is discredited by its origin; so, conversely, the supposition that races of organisms have been evolved, is credited by its origin. Instead of being a conception suggested and accepted when mankind were profoundly ignorant, it is a conception born in times of comparative enlightenment. Moreover, the belief that plants and animals have arisen in pursuance of uniform laws, instead of through breaches of uniform laws, is a belief which has come into existence in the most-instructed class, living in these better-instructed times. Not among those who have disregarded the order of Nature, has this idea made its appearance; but among those who have familiarized themselves with the order of Nature. Thus the derivation of this modern hypothesis is as favourable as that of the ancient hypothesis is unfavourable.

§ 117. A kindred antithesis exists between the two families of beliefs, to which the beliefs we are comparing severally belong. While the one family has been dying out the other family has been multiplying. As fast as men have ceased to regard different classes of phenomena as caused by special personal agents, acting irregularly; so fast have they come to regard these different classes of phenomena as caused by a general agency acting uniformly—the two changes being correlatives. And as, on the one hand, the hypothesis that each species resulted from a supernatural act, having lost nearly all its kindred hypotheses, may be expected soon to die; so, on the other hand, the hypothesis that each species resulted from the action of natural causes, being one of an increasing family of hypotheses, may be expected to survive.

Still greater will the probability of its survival and establishment appear, when we observe that it is one of a particular genus of hypotheses which has been rapidly extending. The interpretation of phenomena as results of Evolution, has been independently showing itself in various fields of inquiry, quite remote from one another. The supposition that the Solar System has been evolved out of diffused matter, is a supposition wholly astronomical in its origin and application. Geologists, without being led thereto by astronomical considerations, have been step by step advancing towards the conviction that the Earth has reached its present varied structure by modification upon modification. The inquiries of biologists have proved the falsity of the once general belief, that the germ of each organism is a minute repetition of the mature organism, differing from it only in bulk; and they have shown, contrariwise, that every organism advances from simplicity to complexity through insensible changes. Among philosophical politicians, there has been spreading the perception that the progress of society is an evolution: the truth that "constitutions are not made but grow," is seen to be a part of the more general truth that societies are not made but grow. It is now universally admitted by philologists that languages, instead of being artificially or supernaturally formed, have been developed. And the histories of religion, of science, of the fine arts, of the industrial arts, show that these have passed through stages as unobtrusive as those through which the mind of a child passes on its way to maturity. If, then, the recognition of evolution as the law of many diverse orders of phenomena, has been spreading; may we not say that there thence arises the probability that evolution will presently be recognized as the law of the phenomena we are considering? Each further advance of knowledge confirms the belief in the unity of Nature; and the discovery that evolution has gone on, or is going on, in so many departments of Nature, becomes a reason for believing that there is no department of Nature in which it does not go on.

§ 118. The hypotheses of Special Creation and Evolution, are no less contrasted in respect of their legitimacy as hypotheses. While, as we have seen, the one belongs to that order of symbolic conceptions which are proved to be illusive by the impossibility of realizing them in thought; the other is one of those symbolic conceptions which are more or less fully realizable in thought. The production of all organic forms by the accumulation of modifications and of divergences by the continual addition of differences to differences, is mentally representable in outline, if not in detail. Various orders of our experiences enable us to conceive the process. Let us look at one of the simplest.

There is no apparent similarity between a straight line and a circle. The one is a curve; the other is defined as without curvature. The one encloses a space; the other will not enclose a space though produced for ever. The one is finite; the other may be infinite. Yet, opposite as the two are in their characters, they may be connected together by a series of lines no one of which differs from the adjacent ones in any appreciable degree. Thus, if a cone be cut by a plane at right angles to its axis we get a circle. If, instead of being perfectly at right angles, the plane subtends with the axis an angle of 89° 59', we have an ellipse which no human eye, even when aided by an accurate pair of compasses, can distinguish from a circle. Decreasing the angle minute by minute, this closed curve becomes perceptibly eccentric, then manifestly so, and by and by acquires so immensely elongated a form so as to bear no recognizable resemblance to a circle. By continuing this process the ellipse changes insensibly into a parabola. On still further diminishing the angle, the parabola becomes an hyperbola. And finally, if the cone be made gradually more obtuse, the hyperbola passes into a straight line as the angle of the cone approaches 180°. Here then we have five different species of line—circle, ellipse, parabola, hyperbola, and straight line—each having its peculiar properties and its separate equation, and the first and last of which are quite opposite in nature, connected together as members of one series, all producible by a single process of insensible modification.

But the experiences which most clearly illustrate the process of general evolution, are our experiences of special evolution, repeated in every plant and animal. Each organism exhibits, within a short time, a series of changes which, when supposed to occupy a period indefinitely great, and to go on in various ways instead of one way, give us a tolerably clear conception of organic evolution at large. In an individual development, we see brought into a comparatively infinitesimal time, a series of metamorphoses equally great with each of those which the hypothesis of evolution assumes to have taken place during immeasurable geologic epochs. A tree differs from a seed in every respect—in bulk, in structure, in colour, in form, in chemical composition. Yet is the one changed in the course of a few years into the other: changed so gradually, that at no moment can it be said—Now the seed ceases to be and the tree exists. What can be more widely contrasted than a newly-born child and the small, semi-transparent, gelatinous spherule constituting the human ovum? The infant is so complex in structure that a cyclopædia is needed to describe its constituent parts. The germinal vesicle is so simple that it may be defined in a line. Nevertheless, nine months suffice to develop the one out of the other; and that, too, by a series of modifications so small, that were the embryo examined at successive minutes, even a microscope would not disclose any sensible changes. Aided by such facts, the conception of general evolution may be rendered as definite a conception as any of our complex conceptions can be rendered. If, instead of the successive minutes of a child's fœtal life, we take the lives of successive generations of creatures—if we regard the successive generations as differing from one another no more than the fœtus differs in successive minutes; our imaginations must indeed be feeble if we fail to realize in thought, the evolution of the most complex organism out of the simplest. If a single cell, under appropriate conditions, becomes a man in the space of a few years; there can surely be no difficulty in understanding how, under appropriate conditions, a cell may, in the course of untold millions of years, give origin to the human race.

Doubtless many minds are so unfurnished with those experiences of Nature out of which this conception is built, that they find difficulty in forming it. Looking at things rather in their statical than in their dynamical aspects, they never realize the fact that, by small increments of modification, any amount of modification may in time be generated. The surprise they feel on finding one whom they last saw as a boy, grown into a man, becomes incredulity when the degree of change is greater. To such, the hypothesis that by any series of changes a protozoon can give origin to a mammal, seems grotesque—as grotesque as Galileo's assertion of the Earth's movement seemed to his persecutors; or as grotesque as the assertion of the Earth's sphericity seems now to the New Zealanders. But those who accept a literally-unthinkable proposition as quite satisfactory, may not unnaturally be expected to make a converse mistake.

§ 119. The hypothesis of evolution is contrasted with the hypothesis of special creations, in a further respect. It is not simply legitimate instead of illegitimate, because representable in thought instead of unrepresentable; but it has the support of some evidence, instead of being absolutely unsupported by evidence. Though the facts at present assignable in *direct* proof that by progressive modifications, races of organisms which are apparently distinct from antecedent races have descended from them, are not sufficient; yet there are numerous facts of the order required. Beyond all question unlikenesses of structure gradually arise among the members of successive generations. We find that there is going on a modifying process of the kind alleged as the source of specific differences: a process which, though slow, does, in time, produce conspicuous changes—a process which, to all appearance, would produce in millions of years, any amount of change.

In the chapters on "Heredity" and "Variation," contained in the preceding Part, many such facts were given, and more might be added. Although little attention has been paid to the matter until recent times, the evidence already collected shows that there take place in successive generations, alterations of structure quite as marked as those which, in successive short intervals, arise in a developing embryo—nay, often much more marked; since, besides differences due to changes in the relative sizes or parts, there sometimes arise differences due to additions and suppressions of parts. The structural modification proved to have taken place since organisms have been observed, is not less than the hypothesis demands—bears as great a ratio to this brief period, as the total amount of structural change seen in the evolution of a complex organism out of a simple germ, bears to that vast period during which living forms have existed on the Earth.

We have, indeed, much the same kind and quantity of direct evidence that all organic beings have arisen through the actions of natural causes, which we have that all the structural complexities of the Earth's crust have arisen through the actions of natural causes. Between the known modifications undergone by organisms, and the totality of modifications displayed in their structures, there is no greater disproportion than between the observed geological changes, and the totality of geological changes supposed to have been similarly caused. Here and there are sedimentary deposits now slowly taking place. At this place a shore has been greatly encroached on by the sea during recorded times; and at another place an estuary has become shallower within some generations. In one region an upheaval is going on at the rate of a few feet in a century; while in another region occasional earthquakes cause slight variations of level. Appreciable amounts of denudation by water are visible in some localities; and in other localities glaciers are detected in the act of grinding down the rocky surfaces over which they glide. But these changes are infinitesimal compared with the aggregate of changes to which the Earth's crust testifies, even in its still extant systems of strata. If, then, the small changes now being wrought on the Earth's crust by natural agencies, yield warrant for concluding that by such agencies acting through vast epochs, all the structural complexities of the Earth's crust have been produced; do not the small known modifications produced in races of organisms by natural agencies, yield warrant for concluding that by natural agencies have been produced all those structural complexities which we see in them?

The hypothesis of Evolution then, has direct support from facts which, though small in amount, are of the kind required; and the ratio which these facts bear to the generalization based on them, seems as great as is the ratio between facts and generalization which, in another case, produces conviction.

§ 120. Let us put ourselves for a moment in the position of those who, from their experiences of human modes of action, draw differences respecting the mode of action of that Ultimate Power manifested to us through phenomena. We shall find the supposition that each kind of organism was separately designed and put together, to be much less consistent with their professed conception of this Ultimate Power, than is the supposition that all kinds of organisms have resulted from one unbroken process. Irregularity of method is a mark of weakness. Uniformity of method is a mark of strength. Continual interposition to alter a pre-arranged set of actions, implies defective arrangement in those actions. The maintenance of those actions, and the working out by them of the highest results, implies completeness of arrangement. If human workmen, whose machines as at first constructed require perpetual adjustment, show their increasing skill by making their machines self-adjusting; then, those who figure to themselves the production of the world and its inhabitants by a "Great Artificer," must admit that the achievement of this end by a persistent process, adapted to all contingencies, implies greater skill than its achievement by the process of meeting the contingencies as they severally arise.

So, too, it is with the contrast under its moral aspect. We saw that to the hypothesis of special creations, a difficulty is presented by the absence of high forms of life during immeasurable epochs of the Earth's existence. But to the hypothesis of evolution, absence of them is no such obstacle. Suppose evolution, and this question is necessarily excluded. Suppose special creations, and this question can have no satisfactory answer. Still more marked is the contrast between the two hypotheses, in presence of that vast amount of suffering entailed on all orders of sentient beings by their imperfect adaptations to their conditions of life, and the further vast amount of suffering entailed on them by enemies and by parasites. We saw that if organisms were severally designed for their respective places in Nature, the inevitable conclusion is that these innumerable kinds of inferior organisms which prey on superior organisms, were intended to inflict all the pain and mortality which results. But the hypothesis of evolution involves us in no such dilemma. Slowly, but surely, evolution brings about an increasing amount of happiness. In all forms of organization there is a progressive adaptation, and a survival of the most adapted. If, in the uniform working out of the process, there are evolved organisms of low types which prey on those of higher types, the evils inflicted form but a deduction from the average benefits. The universal multiplication of the most adapted must cause the spread of those superior organisms which, in one way or other, escape the invasions of the inferior; and so tends to produce a type less liable to the invasions of the inferior. Thus the evils accompanying evolution are ever being self-eliminated. Though there may arise the question—Why could they not have been avoided? there does not arise the question—Why were they deliberately inflicted? Whatever may be thought of them, it is clear that they do not imply gratuitous malevolence.

§ 121. In all respects, then, the hypothesis of evolution contrasts favourably with the hypothesis of special creation. It has arisen in comparatively-instructed times and in the most cultivated class. It is one of those beliefs in the uniform concurrence of phenomena, which are gradually supplanting beliefs in their irregular and arbitrary concurrence; and it belongs to a genus of these beliefs which has of late been rapidly spreading. It is a definitely-conceivable hypothesis; being simply an extension to the organic world at large, of a conception framed from our experiences of individual organisms; just as the hypothesis of universal gravitation was an extension of the conception which our experiences of terrestrial gravitation had produced. This definitely-conceivable hypothesis, besides the support of numerous analogies, has the support of direct evidence. We have proof that there is going on a process of the kind alleged; and though the results of this process, as actually witnessed, are minute in comparison with the totality of results ascribed to it, yet they bear to such totality a ratio as great as that by which an analogous hypothesis is justified. Lastly, that sentiment which the doctrine of special creations is thought necessary to satisfy, is much better satisfied by the doctrine of evolution; since this doctrine raises no contradictory implications respecting the Unknown Cause, such as are raised by the antagonist doctrine.

And now, having observed how, under its most general aspects, the hypothesis of organic evolution commends itself to us by its derivation, by its coherence, by its analogies, by its direct evidence, by its implications; let us go on to consider the several orders of facts which yield indirect support to it. We will begin by noting the harmonies between it and sundry of the inductions set forth in Part II.

CHAPTER IV.

THE ARGUMENTS FROM CLASSIFICATION.

§ 122. In § 103, we saw that the relations which exist among the species, genera, orders, and classes of organisms, are not interpretable as results of any such causes as have usually been assigned. We will here consider whether they are interpretable as the results of evolution. Let us first contemplate some familiar facts.

The Norwegians, Swedes, Danes, Germans, Dutch, and Anglo-Saxons, form together a group of Scandinavian races, which are but slightly divergent in their characters. Welsh, Irish, and Highlanders, though they have differences, have not such differences as hide a decided community of nature: they are classed together as Celts. Between the Scandinavian race as a whole and the Celtic race as a whole, there is a distinction greater than that between the sub-divisions which make up the one or the other. Similarly, the several peoples inhabiting Southern Europe are more nearly allied to one another, than the aggregate they form is allied to the aggregates of Northern peoples. If, again, we compare these European varieties of Man, taken as a group, with that group of Eastern varieties which had a common origin with it, we see a stronger contrast than between the groups of European varieties themselves. And once more, ethnologists find differences of still higher importance between the Aryan stock as a whole and the Mongolian stock as a whole, or the Negro stock as a whole. Though these contrasts are partially obscured by intermixtures, they are not so much obscured as to hide the truths that the most-nearly-allied varieties of Man are those which diverged from one another at comparatively-recent periods; that each group of nearly-allied varieties is more strongly contrasted with other such groups that had a common origin with it at a remoter period; and so on until we come to the largest groups, which are the most strongly contrasted, and of whose divergence no trace is extant.

The relations existing among the classes and sub-classes of languages, have been briefly referred to by Mr. Darwin in illustration of his argument. We know that languages have arisen by evolution. Let us then see what grouping of them evolution has produced. On comparing the dialects of adjacent counties in England, we find that their differences are so small as scarcely to distinguish them. Between the dialects of the Northern counties taken together, and those of the Southern counties taken together, the contrast is stronger. These clusters of dialects, together with those of

Scotland and Ireland, are nevertheless so similar that we regard them as one language. The several languages of Scandinavian Europe, including English, are much more unlike one another than are the several dialects which each of them includes; in correspondence with the fact that they diverged from one another at earlier periods than did their respective dialects. The Scandinavian languages have nevertheless a certain community of character, distinguishing them as a group from the languages of Southern Europe; between which there are general and special affinities that similarly unite them into a group formed of sub-groups containing sub-sub-groups. And this wider divergence between the order of languages spoken in Northern Europe and the order of languages spoken in Southern Europe, answers to the longer time that has elapsed since their differentiation commenced. Further, these two orders of modern European languages, as well as Latin and Greek and certain extinct and spoken languages of the East, are shown to have traits in common which unite them into one great class known as Aryan languages; radically distinguished from the classes of languages spoken by the other main divisions of the human race.

§ 123. Now this kind of subordination of groups which we see arises in the course of continuous descent, multiplication, and divergence, is just the kind of subordination of groups which plants and animals exhibit: it is just the kind of subordination which has thrust itself on the attention of naturalists in spite of pre-conceptions.

The original idea was that of arrangement in linear order. We saw that even after a considerable acquaintance with the structures of organisms had been acquired, naturalists continued their efforts to reconcile the facts with the notion of a uni-serial succession. The accumulation of evidence necessitated the breaking up of the imagined chain into groups and sub-groups. Gradually there arose the conviction that these groups do not admit of being placed in a line. And the conception finally arrived at, is that of certain great sub-kingdoms, very widely divergent, each made up of classes much less divergent, severally containing orders still less divergent; and so on with genera and species.

Hence this "grand fact in natural history of the subordination of group under group, which from its familiarity does not always sufficiently strike us," is perfectly in harmony with the hypothesis of evolution. The extreme significance of this kind of relation among organic forms is dwelt on by Mr. Darwin, who shows how an ordinary genealogical tree represents, on a small scale, a system of grouping analogous to that which exists among organisms in general, and which is explained on the supposition of a genealogical tree by which all organisms are affiliated. If, wherever we can trace direct descent, multiplication, and divergence, this formation of groups within groups takes place; there results a strong presumption that the groups within groups which constitute the animal and vegetal kingdoms, have arisen by direct descent, multiplication, and divergence—that is, by evolution.

§ 124. Strong confirmation of this inference is yielded by the fact, that the more marked differences which divide groups are, in both cases, distinguished from the less marked differences which divide sub-groups, by this, that they are not simply greater in *degree*, but they are more radical in *kind*. Objects, as the stars, may present themselves in small clusters, which are again more or less aggravated into clusters of clusters, in such manner that the individuals of each simple cluster are much closer together than are the simple clusters gathered into a compound cluster: in which case, the trait that unites groups of groups differs from the trait that unites groups, not in *nature* but only in *amount*. But this is not so either with the groups and sub-groups which we know have resulted from evolution, or with those which we here infer have resulted from evolution. In both cases the highest or most general classes, are marked off from one another by fundamental differences that have no common measure with the differences that mark off small classes. Observe the parallelism.

We saw that each sub-kingdom of animals is distinguished from other sub-kingdoms, by some unlikeness in its main plan of organization; such as the presence or absence of a peri-visceral cavity. Contrariwise, the members of the smallest groups are united together, and separated from the members of other small groups, by modifications which do not affect the relations of essential parts. That this is just the kind of arrangement which results from evolution, the case of languages will show.

On comparing the dialects spoken in different parts of England, we find scarcely any difference but those of pronunciation: the structures of the sentences are almost uniform. Between English and the allied modern languages there are divergences of structure: there are some unlikenesses of idiom; some unlikenesses in the ways of modifying the meanings of verbs; and considerable unlikenesses in the uses of genders. But these unlikenesses are not sufficient to hide a general community of organization. A greater contrast of structure exists between these modern languages of Western Europe, and the classic languages. Differentiation into abstract and concrete elements, which is shown by the substitution of auxiliary words for inflections, has produced a higher specialization, distinguishing these languages as a group from the older languages. Nevertheless, both the ancient and modern languages of Europe, together with some Eastern languages derived from the same original, have, under all their differences of organization, a fundamental likeness; since in all of them words are formed by such a coalescence and integration of roots as destroys the independent meanings of the roots. These Aryan languages, and others which have the *amalgamate* character, are united by it into a class distinguished from the *aptotic* and *agglutinate* languages; in which the roots are either not united at all, or so incompletely united that one of them still retains its independent meaning. And philologists find that these radical traits which severally determine the grammatical forms, or modes of combining ideas, characterize the primary divisions among languages.

So that among languages, where we know that evolution has been going on, the greatest groups are marked off from one another by the strongest structural contrasts; and as the like holds among groups of organisms, there results a further reason for inferring that these have been evolved.

§ 125. There is yet another parallelism of like meaning. We saw (§ 101) that the successively-subordinate groups—classes, orders, genera, and species—into which zoologists and botanists segregate animals and plants, have not, in reality, those definite values conventionally given to them. There are well-marked species, and species so imperfectly marked that some systematists regard them as varieties. Between genera strong contrasts exist in many cases, and in other cases contrasts so much less decided as to leave it doubtful whether they imply generic distinctions. So, too, is it with orders and classes: in some of which there have been introduced sub-divisions, having no equivalents in others. Even of the sub-kingdoms the same truth holds. The contrast between the *Cœlenterata* and the *Mollusca*, is far less than that between the *Cœlenterata* and the *Vertebrata*.

Now just this same indefiniteness of value, or incompleteness of equivalence, is observable in those simple and compound and re-compound groups which we see arising by evolution. In every case the endeavour to arrange the divergent products of evolution, is met by a difficulty like that which would meet the endeavour to classify the branches of a tree, into branches of the first, second, third, fourth, &c., orders—the difficulty, namely, that branches of intermediate degrees of composition exist. The illustration furnished by languages will serve us once more. Some dialects of English are but little contrasted; others are strongly contrasted. The alliances of the several Scandinavian tongues with one another are different in degree. Dutch is much less distinct from German than Swedish is; while between Danish and Swedish there is so close a kinship that they might almost be regarded as widely-divergent dialects. Similarly on comparing the larger divisions, we see that the various languages of the Aryan stock have deviated from their original to very unlike distances. The general conclusion is manifest. While the kinds of human speech fall into groups, and sub-groups, and sub-sub-groups; yet the groups are not equal to one another in value, nor have the sub-groups equal values, nor the sub-sub-groups.

If, then, when classified, organisms fall into assemblages such that those of the same grade are but indefinitely equivalent; and if, where evolution is known to have taken place, there have arisen assemblages between which the equivalence is similarly indefinite; there is additional reason for inferring that organisms are products of evolution.

§ 126. A fact of much significance remains. If groups of organic forms have arisen by divergence and re-divergence; and if, while the groups have been developing from simple groups into compound groups, each group and sub-group has been giving origin to more complex forms of its own type; then it is inferable that there once existed greater structural likenesses between the members of allied groups than exists now. This, speaking generally, proves to be so.

Between the sub-kingdoms the gaps are extremely wide; but such distant kinships as may be discerned, bear out anticipation. Thus in the formation of the germinal layers there is a general agreement among them; and there is a further agreement among sundry of them in the formation of a gastrula. This simplest and earliest likeness, significant of primitive kinship, is in most cases soon obscured by divergent modes of development; but sundry sub-kingdoms continue to show relationships by the likenesses of their larval forms; as we see in the trochophores of the *Polyzoa*, *Annelida*, and *Mollusca*—sub-kingdoms the members of which by their later structural changes are rendered widely unlike.

More decided approximations exist between the lower members of classes. In tracing down the *Crustacea* and the *Arachnida* from their more complex to their simpler forms, zoologists meet with difficulties: respecting some of these simpler forms, it becomes a question which class they belong to. The *Lepidosiren*, about which there have been disputes whether it is a fish or an amphibian, is inferior, in the organization of its skeleton, to the great majority of both fishes and amphibia. Widely as they differ from them, the lower mammals have some characters in common with birds, which the higher mammals do not possess.

Now since this kind of relationship of groups is not accounted for by any other hypothesis, while the hypothesis of evolution gives us a clue to it; we must include it among the supports of this hypothesis which the facts of classification furnish.

§ 127. What shall we say of these leading truths when taken together? That naturalists have been gradually compelled to arrange organisms in groups within groups, and that this is the arrangement which we see arises by descent, alike in individual families and among races of men, is a striking circumstance. That while the smallest groups are the most nearly related, there exist between the great sub-kingdoms, structural contrasts of the profoundest kind, cannot but impress us as remarkable, when we see that where it is known to take place evolution actually produces these feebly-distinguished small groups, and these strongly-distinguished great groups. The impression made by these two parallelisms, which add meaning to each other, is deepened by the third parallelism, which enforces the meaning of both—the parallelism, namely, that as, between the species, genera, orders, classes, &c., which naturalists have formed, there are transitional types; so between the groups, sub-groups, and sub-sub-groups, which we know to have been evolved, types of intermediate values exist. And these three correspondences between the known results of evolution and the results here ascribed to evolution, have further weight given to them by the fact, that the kinship of groups through their lowest members is just the kinship which the hypothesis of evolution implies.

Even in the absence of these specific agreements, the broad fact of unity amid multiformity, which organisms so strikingly display, is strongly suggestive of evolution. Freeing ourselves from pre-conceptions, we shall see good reason to think with Mr. Darwin, "that propinquity of descent—the only known cause of the similarity of organic beings—is the bond, hidden as it is by various degrees of modification, which is partly revealed to us by our classifications." When we consider that this only known cause of similarity, joined with the only known cause of divergence (the influence of conditions), gives us a key to these likenesses obscured by unlikenesses; we shall see that were there none of those remarkable harmonies above pointed out, the truths of classification would still yield strong support to our conclusion.

CHAPTER V.

THE ARGUMENTS FROM EMBRYOLOGY.

§ 127*a*. Already I have emphasized the truth that Nature is always more complex than we suppose (§ 74*a*)—that there are complexities within complexities. Here we find illustrated this truth under another aspect. When seeking to formulate the arguments from Embryology, we are shown that the facts as presented in Nature are not to be expressed in the simple generalizations we at first make.

While we recognize this truth we must also recognize the truth that only by enunciation and acceptance of imperfect generalizations can we progress to perfect ones. The order of Evolution is conformed to by ideas as by other things. The advance is, and must be, from the indefinite to the definite. It is impossible to express the totality of any natural phenomenon in a single proposition. To the primary statement expressing that which is most dominant have to be added secondary statements qualifying it. We see this even in so simple a case as the flight of a projectile. The young artillery officer is first taught that a cannon-shot describes a curve treated as a parabola, though literally part of an extremely eccentric ellipse not distinguishable from a parabola. Presently he learns that atmospheric resistance, causing a continual decrease of velocity, entails a deviation from that theoretical path which is calculated on the supposition that the velocity is uniform; and this incorrectness he has to allow for. Then, further, there comes the lateral deviation due to wind, which may be appreciable if the wind is strong and the range great. To introduce him all at once to the correct conception thus finally reached would be impossible: it has to be reached through successive qualifications. And that which holds even in this simple case necessarily holds more conspicuously in complex cases.

The title of the chapter suggests a metaphor, which is, indeed, something more than a metaphor. There is an embryology of conceptions. That this statement is not wholly a figure of speech, we shall see on considering that cerebral organization is a part of organization at large; and that the evolving nervous plexus which is the correlative of an evolving conception, must conform to the general law of change conformed to in the evolution of the whole nervous structure as well as in the evolution of the whole bodily structure. As the body has at first a rude form, very remotely suggesting that which is presently developed by the superposing of modifications on modifications; so the brain as a whole and its contained ideas together make up an inner world answering with extreme indefiniteness to that outer world to which it is brought by successive approximations into tolerable correspondence; and so any nervous plexus and its associated hypothesis, which refer to some external group of phenomena under investigation, have to reach their final developments by successive corrections.

This being the course of discovery must also be the course of exposition. In pursuance of this course we may therefore fitly contemplate that early *formula* of embryological development which we owe to von Baer.

§ 128. Already in § 52, where the generalization of von Baer respecting the relations of embryos was set forth, there was given the warning, above repeated with greater distinctness, that it is only an adumbration.

In the words of his translator, he "found that in its earliest stage, every organism has the greatest number of characters in common with all other organisms in their earliest stages; that at a stage somewhat later, its structure is like the structures displayed at corresponding phases by a less extensive multitude of organisms; that at each subsequent stage, traits are acquired which successively distinguished the developing embryo from groups of embryos that it previously resembled—thus step by step diminishing the class of embryos which it still resembles; and that thus the class of similar forms is finally narrowed to the species of which it is a member."

Assuming for a moment that this generalization is true as it stands, or rather, assuming that the qualifications needed are not such as destroy its correspondence with the average facts, we shall see that it has profound significance. For if we follow out in thought the implications—if we conceive the germs of all kinds of organisms simultaneously developing, and imagine that after taking their first step together, at the second step one half of the vast multitude diverges from the other half; if, at the next step, we mentally watch the parts of each great assemblage beginning to take two or more routes of development; if we represent to ourselves such bifurcations going on, stage after stage, in all the branches; we shall see that there must result an aggregate analogous, in its arrangement of parts, to a tree. If this vast genealogical tree be contemplated as a whole, made up of trunk, main branches, secondary branches, and so on as far as the terminal twigs; it will be perceived that all the various kinds of organisms represented by these terminal twigs, forming the periphery of the tree, will stand related to one another in small groups, which are united into groups of groups, and so on. The embryological tree, expressing the developmental relations of organisms, will be similar to the tree which symbolizes their classificatory relations. That subordination of classes, orders, genera, and species, to which naturalists have been gradually led, is just that subordination which results from the divergence and re-divergence of embryos, as they all unfold. On the hypothesis of evolution this parallelism has a meaning—indicates that primordial kinship of all organisms, and that progressive differentiation of them, which the hypothesis alleges. But on any other hypothesis the parallelism is meaningless; or rather, it raises a difficulty; since it implies either an effect without a cause or a design without a purpose.

§ 129. This conception of a tree, symbolizing the relationships of types and a species derived from the same root, has a concomitant conception. The implication is that each organism, setting out from the simple nucleated cell, must in the course of its development follow the line of the trunk, some main branch, some sub-branch, some sub-sub-branch, &c., of this embryological tree; and so on till it reaches that ultimate twig representing the species of which it is a member. It must in a general way go through the particular line of forms which preceded it in all past times: there must be what has been aptly called a "recapitulation" of the successive ancestral structures. This, at least, is the conclusion necessitated by the generalization we are considering under its original crude form.

Von Baer lived in the days when the Development Hypothesis was mentioned only to be ridiculed, and he joined in the ridicule. What he conceived to be the meaning of these groupings of organisms and these relations among their embryological histories, is not obvious. The only alternative to the hypothesis of Evolution is the hypothesis of Special Creation; and as he did not accept the one it is inferable that he accepted the other. But if he did this he must in the first place have found no answer to the inquiry why organisms specially created should have the embryological kinships he described. And in the second place, after discovering that his alleged law was traversed by many and various nonconformities, he would have been without any explanation of these. Observe the positions which were open to him and the reasons which show them to be untenable.

If it be said that the conditions of the case necessitated the derivation of all organisms from simple germs, and therefore necessitated a morphological unity in their primitive states; there arises the obvious answer, that the morphological unity thus implied, is not the only morphological unity to be accounted for. Were this the only unity, the various kinds of organisms, setting out from a common primordial form, should all begin from the first to diverge individually, as so many radii from a centre; which they do not. If, otherwise, it be said that organisms were framed upon certain types, and that those of the same type continue developing together in the same direction, until it is time for them to begin putting on their specialities of structure; then the answer is, that when they do finally diverge they ought severally to develop in direct lines towards their final forms. No reason can be assigned why, having parted company, some should progress towards their final forms by irregular or circuitous routes. On the hypothesis of design such deviations are inexplicable.

The hypothesis of evolution, however, while it pre-supposes those kinships among embryos in their early forms which are found to exist, also leads us to expect nonconformities in their courses of development. If, as any rational theory of evolution implies, the progressive differentiations of types from one another during past times, have resulted from the direct and indirect effects of external conditions—if races of organisms have become different, either by immediate adaptations to unlike habits of life, or by the mediate adaptations resulting from preservation of the individuals most fitted for such habits of life, or by both; and if most embryonic changes are significant of changes that were undergone by ancestral races; then these irregularities must be anticipated. For the successive changes in modes of life pursued by successive ancestral races, can have had no regularity of sequence. In some cases they must have been more numerous than in others; in some cases they must have been greater in degree than in others; in some cases they must have been to simpler modes, in some cases to more complex modes, and in some cases to modes neither higher nor lower. Of two cognate races which diverged in the remote past, the one may have had descendants that have remained tolerably constant in their habits, while the other may have had descendants that have passed through widely-aberrant modes of life; and yet some of these last may have eventually taken to modes of life like those of the other races derived from the same stock. And if the metamorphoses of embryos indicate, in a general way, the changes of structure undergone by ancestors; then, the later embryologic changes of such two allied races will be somewhat different, though they may end in very similar forms. An illustration will make this clear. Mr. Darwin says: "Petrels are the most aërial and oceanic of birds, but in the quiet sounds of Tierra del Fuego, the *Puffinuria berardi*, in its general habits, in its astonishing power of diving, its manner of swimming, and of flying when unwillingly it takes flight, would be mistaken by any one for an auk or grebe; nevertheless, it is essentially a petrel, but with many parts of its organization profoundly modified." Now if we suppose these grebe-like habits to be continued through a long epoch, the petrel-form to be still more obscured, and the approximation to the grebe-form still closer; it is manifest that while the chicks of the grebe and the *Puffinuria* will, during their early stages of development, display that likeness involved by their common derivation from some early type of bird, the chick of the *Puffinuria* will eventually begin to show deviations, representative of the ancestral petrel-structure, and will afterwards begin to lose these distinctions and assume the grebe-structure.

Hence, remembering the perpetual intrusions of organisms on one another's modes of life, often widely different; and remembering that these intrusions have been going on from the beginning; we shall be prepared to find that the general law of embryonic parallelism is qualified by irregularities which are mostly small, in many cases considerable, and occasionally great. The hypothesis of evolution accounts for these: it does more—it implies the necessity of them.

§ 130. The substitutions of organs and the suppressions of organs, are among those secondary embryological phenomena which harmonize with the belief in evolution but cannot be reconciled with any other belief. Some embryos, during early stages of development, possess organs that afterwards dwindle away, as there arise other organs to discharge the same functions. And in other embryos organs make their appearance, grow to certain points, have no functions to discharge, and disappear by absorption.

We have a remarkable instance of substitution in the temporary appliances for respiration, which some embryos exhibit. During the first phase of its development, the mammalian embryo possesses a system of blood-vessels distributed over what is called the *area vasculosa*—a system of vessels homologous with one which, among fishes, serves for aërating the blood until the permanent respiratory organs come into play. Now since this system of blood-vessels, not being in proximity to an oxygenated medium, cannot be serviceable to the mammalian embryo during development of the lungs, as it is serviceable in the embryo-fish during development of the gills, this needless formation of it is unaccountable as a result of design. But it is quite congruous with the supposition that the mammalian type arose out of lower vertebrate types. For in such case the mammalian embryo, passing through states representing in a general way those which its remote ancestors had in common with the lower *Vertebrata*, develops this system of vessels in like manner with them. An instance more significant still is furnished by certain *Amphibia*. One of the facts early made familiar to the natural-history student is that the tadpole breathes by external branchiæ, and that these, needful during its aquatic life, dwindle away as fast as it develops the lungs fitting it for terrestrial life. But in one of the higher *Amphibia*, the viviparous Salamander, these transformations ordinarily undergone during the free life of the larva, are undergone by the embryo in the egg. The branchiæ are developed though there is no use for them: lungs being substituted as breathing appliances before the creature is born.

Even more striking than the substitutions of organs are the suppressions of organs. Mr. Darwin names some cases as "extremely curious; for instance, the presence of teeth in fœtal whales, which when grown up have not a tooth in their heads;... It has even been stated on good authority that rudiments of teeth can be detected in the beaks of certain embryonic birds." Irreconcilable with any teleological theory, these facts do not even harmonize with the theory of fixed types which are maintained by the development of all the typical parts, even where not wanted; seeing that the disappearance of these incipient organs during fœtal life spoils the typical resemblance. But while to other hypotheses these facts are stumbling-blocks, they yield strong support to the hypothesis of evolution.

Allied to these cases, are the cases of what has been called retrograde development. Many parasitic creatures and creatures which, after leading active lives for a time, become fixed, lose, in their adult states, the limbs and senses they had when young. It may be alleged, however, that these creatures could not secure the habitats needful for them, without possessing, during their larval stages, eyes and swimming appendages which eventually become useless; that though, by losing these, their organization retrogresses in one direction, it progresses in another direction; and that, therefore, they do not exhibit the needless development of a higher type on the way to a lower type. Nevertheless there are instances of a descent in organization, following an apparently-superfluous ascent. Mr. Darwin says that in some genera of cirripedes, "the larvæ become developed either into hermaphrodites having the ordinary structure, or into what I have called complemental males, and in the latter, the development has assuredly been retrograde; for the male is a mere sack, which lives for a short time, and is destitute of mouth, stomach, or other organ of importance, excepting for reproduction."

§ 130*a*. But now let us contemplate more closely the energies at work in the unfolding embryo, or rather the energies which the facts appear to imply.

Whatever natures we ascribe to the hypothetical units proper to each kind of organism, we must conclude that from the beginning of embryonic development, they have a proclivity towards the structure of that organism. Because of their phylogenetic origin, they must tend towards the form of the primitive type; but the superposed modifications, conflicting with their initial tendency, must cause a swerving towards each successively higher type. To take an illustration:—If in the germ-plasm out of which will come a vertebrate animal there is a proclivity towards the primitive piscine form, there must, if the germ-plasm is derived from a mammal, be also from the outset a proclivity towards the mammalian form. While the initial type tends continually to establish itself the terminal type tends also to establish itself. The intermediate structures must be influenced by their conflict, as well as by the conflict of each with the proclivities towards the amphibian and reptilian types. This complication of tendencies is increased by the intervention of several other factors.

There is the factor of economy. An embryo in which the transformations have absorbed the smallest amount of energy and wasted the smallest amount of matter, will have an advantage over embryos the transformations of which have cost more in energy and matter: the young animal will set out with a greater surplus of vitality, and will be more likely than others to live and propagate. Again, in the embryos of its descendants, inheriting the tendency to economical transformation, those which evolve at the least cost will thrive more than the rest and be more likely to have posterity. Thus will result a continual shortening of the processes. We can see alike that this must take place and that it does take place. If the whole series of phylogenetic changes had to be repeated—if the embryo mammal had to become a complete fish, and then a complete amphibian, and then a complete reptile, there would be an immense amount of superfluous building up and pulling down, entailing great waste of time and of materials. Evidently these abridgments which economy entails, necessitate that unfolding embryos bear but rude resemblances to lower types ancestrally passed through—vaguely represent their dominant traits only.

From this principle of economy arise several derivative principles, which may be best dealt with separately.

§ 130*b*. In some cases the substitution of an abridged for an unabridged course of evolution causes the entire disappearance of certain intermediate forms. Structural arrangements once passed through during the unfolding are dropped out of the series.

In the evolution of these embryos with which there is not laid up a large amount of food-yolk there occurs at the outset a striking omission of this kind. When, by successive fissions, the fertilized cell has given rise to a cluster of cells constituting a hollow sphere, known as a *blastula*, the next change under its original form is the introversion of one side, so as to produce two layers in place of one. An idea of the change may be obtained by taking an india-rubber ball (having a hole through which the air may escape) and thrusting in one side until its anterior surface touches the interior surface of the other side. If the cup-shaped structure resulting be supposed to have its wide opening gradually narrowed, until it becomes the mouth of an internal chamber, it will represent what is known as a *gastrula*—a double layer of cells, of which the outer is called epiblast and the inner hypoblast (answering to ectoderm and endoderm) inclosing a cavity known as the *archenteron*, or primitive digestive sac. But now in place of this original mode of forming the *gastrula*, there occurs a mode known as delamination. Throughout its whole extent the single layer splits so as to become a double layer—one sphere of cells inclosing the other; and after this direct formation of the double layer there is a direct formation of an opening through it into the internal cavity. There is thus a shortening of the primitive process: a number of changes are left out.

Often a kindred passing over of stages at later periods of development may be observed. In certain of the *Mollusca*, as the *Patella chiton*, the egg gives origin to a free-swimming larva known as a trochosphere, from which presently comes the ordinary molluscous organization. In the highest division of the Molluscs, however, the Cephalopods, no trochosphere is formed. The nutritive matter laid up in the egg is used in building up the young animal without any indication of an ancestral larva.

§ 130*c*. Among principles derived from the principle of economy is the principle of pre-adaptation—a name which we may appropriately coin to indicate an adaptation made in advance of the time at which it could have arisen in the course of phylogenetic history.

How pre-adaptation may result from economy will be shown by an illustration which human methods of construction furnish. Let us assume that building houses of a certain type has become an established habit, and that, as a part of each house, there is a staircase of given size. And suppose that in consequence of changed conditions—say the walling in of the town, limiting the internal space and increasing ground-rents—it becomes the policy to build houses of many stories, let out in flats to different tenants. For the increased passing up and down, a staircase wider at its lower part will be required. If now the builder, when putting up the ground floor, follows the old dimensions, then after all the stories are built, the lower part of the staircase, if it is to yield equal facilities for passage, must be reconstructed. Instead of a staircase adapted to those few stories which the original type of house had, economy will dictate a pre-adaptation of the staircase to the additional stories.

On carrying this idea with us, we shall see that if from some type of organism there is evolved a type in which enlargement of a certain part is needed to meet increased functions, the greater size of this part will begin to show itself during early stages of unfolding. That unbuilding and rebuilding which would be needful were it laid down of its original size, will be made needless if from the beginning it is laid down of a larger size. Hence, in successive generations, the greater prosperity and multiplication of individuals in which this part is at the outset somewhat larger than usual, must eventually establish a marked excess in its development at an early stage. The facts agree with this inference.

Referring to the contrasts between embryos, Mr. Adam Sedgwick says that "a species is distinct and distinguishable from its allies from the very earliest stages." Whereas, according to the law of von Baer, "animals so closely allied as the fowl and duck would be indistinguishable in the early stages of development," "yet I can distinguish a fowl and a duck embryo on the second day by the inspection of a single transverse section through the trunk." This experience harmonizes with the statement of the late Prof. Agassiz, that in some cases traits characterizing the species appear at an earlier period than traits characterizing the genus.

Similar in their implications are the facts recently published by Dr. E. Mehnert, concerning the feet of pentadactyle vertebrates. A leading example is furnished by the foot in the struthious birds. Out of the original five digits the two which eventually become large while the others disappear, soon give sign of their future predominance: their early sizes being in excess of those required for the usual functional requirements in birds, and preparing the way for their special requirements in the struthious birds. Dr. Mehnert shows that a like lesson is given by the relative developments of legs and wings in these birds. Ordinarily in vertebrates the fore limbs grow more rapidly than the hind limbs; but in the ostrich, in which the hind limbs or legs have to become so large while the wings are but little wanted, the leg development goes in advance of the wing-development in early embryonic stages: there is a pre-adaptation.

Much more striking are examples furnished by creatures whose modes of existence require that they shall have enormous fertility—require that the generative system shall be very large. Ordinarily the organs devoted to maintenance of the race develop later than the organs devoted to maintenance of the individual. But this order is inverted in certain *Entozoa.* To these creatures, imbedded in nutritive matters, self-maintenance cost nothing, and the structures devoted to it are relatively of less importance than the structures devoted to race-maintenance, which, to make up for the small chance any one germ has of getting into a fit habitat, have to produce immense numbers of germs. Here the rudiments of the generative systems are the first to become visible—here, in virtue of the principle of pre-adaptation, a structure belonging to the terminal form asserts itself so early in the developmental process as almost to obliterate the structure of the initial form.

It may be that in some cases where the growth of certain organs goes in advance of the normal order, the element of time comes into play—the greater time required for construction. To elucidate this let us revert to our simile. Suppose that the staircase above instanced, or at any rate its lower part, is required to be of marble with balusters finely carved. If this piece of work is not promptly commenced and pushed on fast, it will not be completed when the rest of the house is ready: workmen and tools will still block it up at a time when it should be available. Similarly among the parts of an unfolding embryo, those in which there is a great deal of constructive work must early take such shape as will allow of this. Now of all the tissues the nervous tissue is that which takes longest to repair when injured; and it seems a not improbable inference that it is a tissue which is slower in its histological development than others. If this be so, we may see why, in the embryos of the higher vertebrates, the central nervous system quickly grows large in comparison to the other systems—why by pre-adaptation the brain of a chick develops in advance of other organs so much more than the brain of a fish.

§ 130*d*. Yet another complication has to be noted. From the principle of economy, it seems inferable that decrease and disappearance of organs which were useful in ancestral types but have ceased to be useful, should take place uniformly; but they do not. In the words of Mr. Adam Sedgwick, "some ancestral organs persist in the embryo in a functionless rudimentary (vestigial) condition and at the same time without any reference to adult structures, while other ancestral organs have disappeared without leaving a trace."[46] This anomaly is rendered more striking when joined with the fact that some of the structures which remain conspicuous are relatively ancient, while some which have been obliterated are relatively modern—*e. g.*, "gill slits [which date back to the fish-ancestor], have been retained in embryology, whereas other organs which have much more recently disappeared, *e. g.* teeth of birds, fore-limbs of snakes [dating back to the reptile ancestor], have been entirely lost."[47] Mr. Sedgwick ascribes these anomalies to the difference between larval development and embryonic development, and expresses his general belief thus:—

"The conclusion here reached is that, whereas larval development must retain traces (it may be very faint) of ancestral stages of structure because they are built out of ancestral stages, embryonic development need not necessarily do so, and very often does not; that embryonic development in so far as it is a record at all, is a record of structural features of previous larval stages. Characters which disappear during free life disappear also in the embryo, but characters which though lost by the adult are retained in the larva may ultimately be absorbed into the embryonic phase and leave their traces in embryonic development."[48]

To set forth the evidence justifying this view would encumber too much the general argument. Towards elucidation of such irregularities let me name two factors which should I think be taken into account.

Abridgment of embryonic stages cannot go on uniformly with all disused organs. Where an organ is of such size that progressive diminution of it will appreciably profit the young animal, by leaving it a larger surplus of unused material, we may expect progressive diminution to occur. Contrariwise, if the organ is relatively so small that each decrease will not, by sensibly increasing the reserve of nutriment, give the young animal an advantage over others, decrease must not be looked for: there may be a survival of it even though of very ancient origin.

Again, the reduction of a superfluous part can take place only on condition that the economy resulting from each descending variation of it, is of greater importance than are the effects of variations simultaneously occurring in other parts. If by increase or decrease of any other parts of the embryo, survival of the animal is furthered in a greater degree than by decrease of this superfluous part, then such decrease is unlikely; since it is illegitimate to count upon the repeated concurrence of favourable variations in two or more parts which are independent. So that if changes of an advantageous kind are going on elsewhere in the embryo a useless part may remain long undiminished.

Yet another cause operates, and perhaps cooperates. Embryonic survival of an organ which has become functionless, may readily happen if, during subsequent stages of development, parts of it are utilized as parts of other organs. In the words of Mr. J. T. Cunningham:—

"It seems to be a general fact that a structure which in metamorphosis disappears completely may easily be omitted altogether in embryonic development, while one which is modified into something else continues to pass more or less through its original larval condition." (*Science Progress*, July, 1897, p. 488.)

One more factor of considerable importance should be taken into account. A disused organ which entails evil because construction of it involves needless cost, may entail further evil by being in the way. This, it seems to me, is the reason why the fore-limbs of snakes have disappeared from their embryos. When the long-bodied lizard out of which the ophidian type evolved, crept through stiff herbage, and moved its head from side to side to find openings, there resulted alternate bends of its body, which were the beginnings of lateral undulations; and we may easily see that in proportion as it thus progressed by insinuating itself through interstices, the fore-limbs, less and less used for walking, would be more and more in the way; and the lengthening of the body, increasing the undulatory motion and decreasing the use of the fore-limbs, would eventually make them absolute impediments. Hence besides the benefit in economy of construction gained by embryos in which the fore-limbs were in early stages a little less developed than usual, they would gain an advantage by having, when mature, smaller fore-limbs than usual, leading to greater facility of locomotion. There would be a double set of influences causing, through selection, a comparatively rapid decrease of these appendages. And we may I think see also, on contemplating the kind of movement, that the fore-limbs would be more in the way than the hind limbs, which would consequently dwindle with such smaller rapidity as to make continuance of the rudiments of them comprehensible.

§ 131-132. So that while the embryonic law enunciated by von Baer is in harmony with the hypothesis of evolution, and is, indeed, a law which this hypothesis implies, the nonconformities to the law are also interpretable by this hypothesis.

Parallelism between the courses of development in species allied by remote ancestry, is liable to be variously modified in correspondence with the later ancestral forms passed through after divergence of such species. The substitution of a direct for an indirect process of formation, which we have reason to believe will show itself, must obscure the embryonic history. And the principle of economy which leads to this substitution produces effects that are very irregular and uncertain in consequence of the endlessly varied conditions. Thus several causes conspire to produce deviations from the general law.

Let it be remarked, finally, that the ability to trace out embryologic kinships and the inability to do this, occur just where, according to the hypothesis of Evolution, they should occur. We saw in § 100*a* that zoologists are agreed in grouping animals into some 17 phyla—*Mollusca*, *Arthropoda*, *Echinodermata*, &c.—each of which includes a number of classes severally sub-divided into orders, genera, species. All the members of each phylum are so related embryologically, that the existence of a common ancestor of them in the remote past is considered certain. But when it comes to the relations among the archaic ancestors, opinion is unsettled. Whether, for instance, the primitive *Chordata*, out of which the *Vertebrata* emerged, have molluscan affinities or annelidan affinities, is still a matter in dispute. With regard to the origins of various other types no settled conclusions are held. Now it is clear that on tracing down each branch of the great genealogical tree, kinships would be much more manifest among the recently-differentiated forms than among those forms which diverged from one another in the earliest stages of organic life, and had separated widely before any of the types we now know had come into existence.

CHAPTER VI.

THE ARGUMENTS FROM MORPHOLOGY.

§ 133. Leaving out of consideration those parallelisms among their modes of development which characterize organisms belonging to each group, that community of plan which exists among them when mature is extremely remarkable and extremely suggestive. As before shown (§ 103), neither the supposition that these combinations of attributes which unite classes are fortuitous, nor the supposition that no other combinations were practicable, nor the supposition of adherence to pre-determined typical plans, suffices to explain the facts. An instance will best prepare the reader for seeing the true meaning of these fundamental likenesses.

Under the immensely-varied forms of insects, greatly elongated like the dragon-fly or contracted in shape like the lady-bird, winged like the butterfly or wingless like the flea, we find this character in common—there are primarily seventeen segments.[49] These segments may be distinctly marked or they may be so fused as to make it difficult to find the divisions between them, but they always exist. What now can be the meaning of this community of structure throughout the hundred thousand kinds of insects filling the air, burrowing in the earth, swimming in the water? Why under the down-covered body of a moth and under the hard wing-cases of a beetle, should there be discovered the same number of divisions? Why should there be no more somites in the Stick-insect, or other Phasmid a foot long, than there are in a small creature like the louse? Why should the inert *Aphis* and the swift-flying Emperor-butterfly be constructed on the same fundamental plan? It cannot be by chance that there exist equal numbers of segments in all these multitudes of species. There is no reason to think it was *necessary*, in the sense that no other number would have made a possible organism. And to say that it is the result of *design*—to say that the Creator followed this pattern throughout, merely for the purpose of maintaining the pattern—is to assign an absurd motive. No rational interpretation of these and countless like morphological facts, can be given except by the hypothesis of evolution; and from the hypothesis of evolution they are corollaries. If organic forms have arisen from common stocks by perpetual divergences and re-divergences—if they have continued to inherit, more or less clearly, the characters of ancestral races; then there will naturally result these communities of fundamental structure among creatures which have severally become modified in multitudinous ways and degrees, in adaptation to their respective modes of life. To this let it be added that while the belief in an intentional adhesion to a pre-determined pattern throughout a whole group, is negatived by the occurrence of occasional deviations from the pattern; such deviations are reconcilable with the belief in evolution. As pointed out in the last chapter, ancestral traits will be obscured more or less according as the superposed modifications of structure, have or have not been furthered by the conditions of life and development to which the type has been subjected.

§ 134. Besides these wide-embracing and often deeply-hidden homologies, which hold together different animals, there are the scarcely-less significant homologies between different organs of the same animal. These, like the others, are obstacles to the supernatural interpretations and supports of the natural interpretation.

One of the most familiar and instructive examples is furnished by the vertebral column. Snakes, which move sinuously through and over plants and stones, obviously need a segmentation of the bony axis from end to end; and inasmuch as flexibility is required throughout the whole length of the body, there is advantage in the comparative uniformity of this segmentation. The movements would be impeded if, instead of a chain of vertebræ varying but little in their lengths, there existed in the middle of the series some long bony mass that would not bend. But in the higher *Vertebrata*, the mechanical actions and reactions demand that while some parts of the vertebral column shall be flexible, other parts shall be inflexible. Inflexibility is specially requisite in that part of it called the sacrum; which, in mammals and birds, forms a fulcrum exposed to the greatest strains the skeleton has to bear. Now in both mammals and birds, this rigid portion of the vertebral column is not made of one long segment or vertebra, but of several segments fused together. In man there are five of these confluent sacral vertebræ; and in the ostrich tribe they number from seventeen to twenty. Why is this? Why, if the skeleton of each species was separately contrived, was this bony mass made by soldering together a number of vertebræ like those forming the rest of the column, instead of being made out of one single piece? And why, if typical uniformity was to be maintained, does the number of sacral vertebræ vary within the same order of birds? Why, too, should the development of the sacrum be by the round-about process of first forming its separate constituent vertebræ, and then destroying their separateness? In the embryo of a mammal or bird, the central element of the vertebral column is, at the outset, continuous. The segments that are to become vertebræ, arise gradually in the adjacent mesoderm, and enwrap this originally-homogeneous axis or notochord. Equally in those parts of the spine which are to remain flexible, and in those parts which are to grow rigid, these segments are formed; and that part of the spine which is to compose the sacrum, having acquired this segmental structure, loses it again by coalescence of the segments. To what end is this construction and re-construction? If, originally, the spine in vertebrate animals consisted from head to tail of separate moveable segments, as it does still in fishes and some reptiles—if, in the evolution of the higher *Vertebrata*, certain of these moveable segments were rendered less moveable with respect to one another, by the mechanical conditions they were exposed to, and at length became relatively immovable; it is comprehensible why the sacrum formed out of them, should continue ever after to show its originally-segmented structure. But on any other hypothesis this segmented structure is inexplicable. "We see the same law in comparing the wonderfully complex jaws and legs in crustaceans," says Mr. Darwin: referring to the fact that those numerous lateral appendages which, in the lower crustaceans, most of them serve as legs, and have like shapes, are, in the higher crustaceans, some of them represented by enormously-developed claws, and others by variously-modified foot-jaws. "It is familiar to almost every one," he continues, "that in a flower the relative position of the sepals, petals, stamens, and pistils, as well as their intimate structure, are intelligible on the view that they consist of metamorphosed leaves arranged in a spire. In monstrous plants we often get direct evidence of the possibility of one organ being transformed into another; and we can actually see in embryonic crustaceans and in many other animals, and in flowers, that organs, which when mature become extremely different, are at an early stage of growth exactly alike." ... "Why should one crustacean, which has an extremely complex mouth formed of many parts consequently always have fewer legs; or conversely, those with many legs have simpler mouths? Why should the sepals, petals, stamens, and pistils in any individual flower, though fitted for such widely-different purposes, be all constructed on the same pattern?"

To these and countless similar questions, the theory of evolution furnishes the only rational answer. In the course of that change from homogeneity to heterogeneity of structure displayed in evolution under every form, it will necessarily happen that from organisms made up of numerous like parts, there will arise organisms made up of parts more and more unlike: which unlike parts will nevertheless continue to bear traces of their primitive likeness.

§ 135. One more striking morphological fact, near akin to some of the facts dwelt on in the last chapter, must be here set down—the frequent occurrence, in adult animals and plants, of rudimentary and useless organs, which are homologous with organs that are developed and useful in allied animals and plants. In the last chapter we saw that during the development of embryos, there often arise organs which disappear on being replaced by other organs discharging the same functions in better ways; and that in some cases, organs develop to certain points and are then re-absorbed without performing any functions. Very generally, however, the partially-developed organs are retained throughout life.

The osteology of the higher *Vertebrata* supplies abundant examples. Vertebral processes which, in one tribe, are fully formed and ossified from independent centres, are, in other tribes, mere tubercles not having independent centres of ossification. While in the tail of this animal the vertebræ are severally composed of centrum and appendages, in the tail of that animal they are simple osseous masses without any appendages; and in another animal they have lost their individualities by coalescence with neighbouring vertebræ into a rudimentary tail. From the structures of the limbs analogous facts are cited by comparative anatomists. The undeveloped state of certain metacarpal bones, characterizes whole groups of mammals. In one case we find the normal number of digits; and, in another case, a smaller number with an atrophied digit to make out the complement. Here is a digit with its full number of phalanges; and there a digit of which one phalange has been arrested in its growth. Still more remarkable are the instances of entire limbs being rudimentary; as in certain snakes, which have hind legs hidden beneath the integument. So, too, is it with dermal appendages. Some of the smooth-skinned amphibia have scales buried in the skin. The seal, which is a mammal considerably modified in adaptation to an aquatic life, and which uses its feet mainly as paddles, has toes that still bear external nails; but the manatee, which is a much more transformed mammal, has nailless paddles which, when the skin is removed, are said, by Humboldt, to display rudimentary nails at the ends of the imbedded digits. Nearly all birds are covered with developed feathers, severally composed of a shaft bearing fibres, each of which, again, bears a fringe of down. But in some birds, as in the ostrich, various stages of arrested development of the feathers may be traced: between the unusually-elaborated feathers of the tail, and those about the beak which are reduced to simple hairs, there are transitions. Nor is this the extreme case. In the *Apteryx* we see the whole of the feathers reduced to a hair-like form. Again, the hair which commonly covers the body in mammals is, over the greater part of the human body almost rudimentary, and is in some parts reduced to mere down—down which nevertheless proves itself to be homologous with the hair of mammals in general, by occasionally developing into the original form. Numerous cases of aborted organs are given by Mr. Darwin, of which a few may be here added. "Nothing can be plainer," he remarks, "than that wings are formed for flight, yet in how many insects do we see wings so reduced in size as to be utterly incapable of flight, and not rarely lying under wing-cases, firmly soldered together?" ... "In plants with separated sexes, the male flowers often have a rudiment of a pistil; and Kölreuter found that by crossing such male plants with an hermaphrodite species, the rudiment of the pistil in the hybrid offspring was much increased in size; and this shows that the rudiment and the perfect pistil are essentially alike in nature." And then, to complete the proof that these undeveloped parts are marks of descent from races in which they were developed, there are not a few direct experiences of this relation. "We have plenty of cases of rudimentary organs in our domestic productions—as the stump of a tail in tailless breeds—the vestige of an ear in earless breeds—the re-appearance of minute dangling horns in hornless breeds of cattle." (*Origin of Species*, 1859, pp. 451, 454.)

Here, as before, the teleological doctrine fails utterly; for these rudimentary organs are useless, and occasionally even detrimental; as is the *appendix vermiformis*, in Man—a part of the cæcum which is of no value for the purpose of absorption but which, by detaining small foreign bodies, often causes severe inflammation and death. The doctrine of typical plans is equally out of court; for while, in some members of a group, rudimentary organs completing the general type are traceable, in other members of the same group such organs are unrepresented. There remains only the doctrine of evolution; and to this, these rudimentary organs offer no difficulties. On the contrary, they are among its most striking evidences.

§ 136. The general truths of morphology thus coincide in their implications. Unity of type, maintained under extreme dissimilarities of form and mode of life, is explicable as resulting from descent with modification; but is otherwise inexplicable. The likenesses disguised by unlikenesses, which the comparative anatomist discovers between various organs in the same organism, are worse than meaningless if it be supposed that organisms were severally framed as we now see them; but they fit in quite harmoniously with the belief that each kind of organism is a product of accumulated modifications upon modifications. And the presence, in all kinds of animals and plants, of functionally-useless parts corresponding to parts that are functionally-useful in allied animals and plants, while it is totally incongruous with the belief in a construction of each organism by miraculous interposition, is just what we are led to expect by the belief that organisms have arisen by progression.

CHAPTER VII.

THE ARGUMENTS FROM DISTRIBUTION.

§ 137. In §§ 105 and 106, we contemplated the phenomena of distribution in Space. The general conclusions reached, in great part based on the evidence brought together by Mr. Darwin, were that, "on the one hand, we have similarly-conditioned, and sometimes nearly-adjacent, areas, occupied by quite different Faunas. On the other hand, we have areas remote from each other in latitude, and contrasted in soil as well as climate, which are occupied by closely-allied Faunas." Whence it was inferred that "as like organisms are not universally, or even generally, found in like habitats; nor very unlike organisms, in very unlike habitats; there is no manifest pre-determined adaptation of the organisms to the habitats." In other words, the facts of distribution in Space do not conform to the hypothesis of design. At the same time we saw that "the similar areas peopled by dissimilar forms, are those between which there are impassable barriers; while the dissimilar areas peopled by similar forms, are those between which there are no such barriers;" and these generalizations appeared to harmonize with the abundantly-illustrated truth, "that each species of organism tends ever to expand its sphere of existence—to intrude on other areas, other modes of life, other media."

By way of showing still more clearly the effects of competition among races of organisms, let me here add some recently-published instances of the usurpations of areas, and changes of distribution hence resulting. In the *Natural History Review* for January, 1864, Dr. Hooker quotes as follows from some New Zealand naturalists:—"You would be surprised at the rapid spread of European and other foreign plants in this country. All along the sides of the main lines of road through the plains, a *Polygonum* (*aviculare*), called 'Cow Grass,' grows most luxuriantly, the roots sometimes two feet in depth, and the plants spreading over an area from four to five feet in diameter. The dock (*Rumex obtusifolius* or *R. crispus*) is to be found in every river bed, extending into the valleys of the mountain rivers, until these become mere torrents. The sow-thistle is spread all over the country, growing luxuriantly nearly up to 6000 feet. The water-cress increases in our still rivers to such an extent, as to threaten to choke them altogether ... I have measured stems twelve feet long and three-quarters of an inch in diameter. In some of the mountain districts, where the soil is loose, the white clover is completely displacing the native grasses, forming a close sward.... In fact, the young native vegetation appears to shrink from competition with these more vigorous intruders." "The native (Maori) saying is 'as the white man's rat has driven away the native rat, so the European fly drives away our own, and the clover kills our fern, so will the Maoris disappear before the white man himself.'"

Given this universal tendency of the superior to overrun the habitats of the inferior,[50] let us consider what, on the hypothesis of evolution, will be the effects on the geographical relationships of species.

§ 138. A race of organisms cannot expand its sphere of existence without subjecting itself to new external conditions. Those of its members which spread over adjacent areas, inevitably come in contact with circumstances partially different from their previous circumstances; and such of them as adopt the habits of other organisms, necessarily experience re-actions more or less contrasted with the re-actions before experienced. Now if changes of organic structure are caused, directly or indirectly, by changes in the incidence of forces; there must result unlikenesses of structure between the divisions of a race which colonizes new habitats. Hence, in the absence of obstacles to migration, we may anticipate manifest kinships between the animals and plants of one area, and those of areas adjoining it. This inference corresponds with an induction before set down (§ 106). In addition to illustrations of it already quoted from Mr. Darwin, his pages furnish others. One is that species which inhabit islands are allied to species which inhabit neighbouring main lands; and another is that the faunas of clustered islands show marked similarities. "Thus the several islands of the Galapagos Archipelago are tenanted," says Mr. Darwin, "in a quite marvellous manner, by very closely related species; so that the inhabitants of each separate island, though mostly distinct, are related in an incomparably closer degree to each other than to the inhabitants of any other part of the world." Mr. Wallace has traced "variation as specially influenced by locality" among the *Papilionidæ* inhabiting the East Indian Archipelago: showing how "the species and varieties of Celebes possess a striking character in the form of the anterior wings, different from that of the allied species and varieties of all the surrounding islands;" and how "tailed species in India and the western islands lose their tails as they spread eastward through the archipelago." During his travels on the Upper Amazons, Mr. Bates found that "the greater part of the species of *Ithomiæ* changed from one locality to another, not further removed than 100 to 200 miles;" that "many of these local species have the appearance of being geographical varieties;" and that in some species "most of the local varieties are connected with their parent form by individuals exhibiting all the shades of variation."

Further general relationships are to be inferred. If races of organisms, ever being thrust by pressure of population into new habitats, undergo modifications of structure as they diverge more and more widely in Space, it follows that, speaking generally, the widest divergences in Space will indicate the longest periods during which the descendants from a common stock have been subject to modifying conditions; and hence that, among organisms of the same group, the smaller contrasts of structure will be limited to the smaller areas. This we find: "varieties being," as Dr. Hooker says in his *Flora of Tasmania*, "more restricted in locality than species, and these again than genera." Again, if races of organisms spread, and as they spread are altered by changing incident forces; it follows that where the incident forces vary greatly within given areas, the alterations will be more numerous than in equal areas which are less-variously conditioned. This, too, proves to be the fact. Dr. Hooker points out that the relatively uniform regions have the fewest species; while in the most multiform regions the species are the most numerous.

§ 139. Let us consider next, how the hypothesis of evolution corresponds with the facts of distribution, not over different areas but through different media. If all forms of organisms have descended from some primordial form, it follows that since this primordial form must have inhabited some one medium out of the several media now inhabited, the peopling of other media by its descendants implies migration from one medium to others—implies adaptations to media quite unlike the original medium. To speak specifically—water being the medium in which the lowest living forms exist, the implication is that the earth and the air have been colonized from the water. Great difficulties appear to stand in the way of this assumption. Ridiculing those who alleged the uniserial development of organic forms, who, indeed, laid themselves open to ridicule by their many untenable propositions, Von Baer writes—"A fish, swimming towards the shore desires to take a walk, but finds his fins useless. They diminish in breadth for want of use, and at the same time elongate. This goes on with children and grandchildren for a few millions of years, and at last who can be astonished that the fins become feet? It is still more natural that the fish in the meadow, finding no water, should gape after air, thereby, in a like period of time developing lungs; the only difficulty being that in the meanwhile, a few generations must manage without breathing at all." Though, as thus presented, the belief in a transition looks laughable; and though such derivation of terrestrial vertebrates by direct modification of piscine vertebrates, is untenable; yet we must not conclude that no migrations of the kind alleged can have taken place. The adage that "truth is stranger than fiction," applies quite as much to Nature in general as to human life. Besides the fact that certain fish actually do "take a walk" without any obvious reason; and besides the fact that sundry kinds of fish ramble about on land when prompted by the drying-up of the waters they inhabit; there is the still more astounding fact that one kind of fish climbs trees. Few things seem more manifestly impossible, than that a water-breathing creature without efficient limbs, should ascend eight or ten feet up the trunk of a palm; and yet the *Anabas scandens* does as much. To previous testimonies on this point Capt. Mitchell has recently added others. Such remarkable cases of temporary changes of media, will prepare us for conceiving how, under special conditions, permanent changes of media may have taken place; and for considering how the doctrine of evolution is elucidated by them.

Inhabitants of the sea, of rivers, and of lakes, are many of them left from time to time partially or completely without water; and those which show the power to change their media temporarily or permanently, are in very many cases of the kinds most liable to be thus deserted by their medium. Let us consider what the sea-shore shows us. Twice a day the rise and the fall of the tide covers and uncovers plants and animals, fixed and moving; and through the alternation of spring and neap tides, it results that the exposure of the organisms living low down on the beach, varies both in frequency and duration: while some of them are left dry only once a fortnight for a very short time, others, a little higher up, are left dry during two or three hours at several ebb tides every fortnight. Then by small gradations we come to such as, living at the top of the beach, are bathed by salt-water only at long intervals; and still higher to some which are but occasionally splashed in stormy weather. What, now, do we find among the organisms thus subject to various regular and irregular alterations of media? Besides many plants and many fixed animals, we find moving animals of numerous kinds; some of which are confined to the lower zones of this littoral region, but others of which wander over the whole of it. Omitting the humbler types, it will suffice to observe that each of the two great sub-kingdoms, *Mollusca* and *Arthropoda*, supplies examples of creatures having a wide excursiveness within this region. We have gasteropods which, when the tide is down, habitually creep snail-like over sand and sea-weed, even up as far as high-water mark. We have several kinds of crustaceans, of which the crab is the most conspicuous, running about on the wet beach, and sometimes rambling beyond the reach of the water. And then note the striking fact that each of the forms thus habituated to changes of media, is allied to forms which are mainly or wholly terrestrial. On the West Coast of Ireland marine gasteropods are found on the rocks three hundred feet above the sea, where they are only at long intervals wetted by the spray; and though between gasteropods of this class and land-gasteropods the differences are considerable, yet the land-gasteropods are more closely allied to them than to any other *Mollusca.* Similarly, the two highest orders of crustaceans have their species which live occasionally, or almost entirely, out of the water: there is a kind of lobster in the Mauritius which climbs trees; and there is the land-crab of the West Indies, which deserts the sea when it reaches maturity and re-visits it only to spawn. Seeing, thus, how there are many kinds of marine creatures whose habitats expose them to frequent changes of media; how some of the higher kinds so circumstanced, show a considerable adaptation to both media; and how these amphibious kinds are allied to kinds that are mainly or wholly terrestrial; we shall see that the migrations from one medium to another, which evolution pre-supposes, are by no means impracticable. With such evidence before us, the assumption that the distribution of the *Vertebrata* through media so different as air and water, may have been gradually effected in some analogous manner, would not be altogether unwarranted even had we no clue to the process. We shall find, however, a tolerably distinct clue. Though rivers, and lakes, and pools, have no sensible tidal variations, they have their rises and falls, regular and irregular, moderate and extreme. Especially in tropical climates, we see them annually full for a certain number of months, and then dwindling away and drying up. The drying up may reach various degrees and last for various periods. It may go to the extent only of producing a liquid mud, or it may reduce the mud to a hardened, fissured solid. It may last for a few days or for months. That is to say, aquatic forms which are in one place annually subject to a slight want of water for a short time, are elsewhere subject to greater wants for longer times: we have gradations of transition, analogous to those which the tides furnish. Now it is well known that creatures inhabiting such waters have, in various degrees, powers of meeting these contingencies. The contained fish either bury themselves in the mud when the dry season comes, or ramble in search of other waters. This is proved by evidence from India, Guiana, Siam, Ceylon; and some of these fish, as the *Anabas scandens*, are known to survive for days out of the water. But the facts of greatest significance are furnished by an allied class of *Vertebrata*, almost peculiar to habitats of this kind. The *Amphibia* are not, like fish, usually found in waters that are never partially or wholly dried up; but they nearly all inhabit waters which, at certain seasons, evaporate, in great measure or completely—waters in which most kinds of fish cannot exist. And what are the leading structural traits of these *Amphibia*? They have two respiratory systems—pulmonic and branchial—variously developed in different orders; and they have two or four limbs, also variously developed. Further, the class *Amphibia* consists of two groups, in one of which this duality of the respiratory system is permanent, and the development of the limbs always incomplete; and in the other of which the branchiæ disappear as the lungs and limbs become fully developed. The lowest group, the *Perennibranchiata*, have internal organs for aerating the blood which approach in various degrees to lungs, until "in the *Siren*, the pulmonic respiration is more extensive and important than the branchial;" and to these creatures, having a habitat partially aërial and partially aquatic, there are at the same time supplied, in the shallow water covering soft mud, the mechanical conditions which render swimming difficult and rudimentary limbs useful. In the higher group, the *Caducibranchiata*, we find still more suggestive transformations. Having at first a structure resembling that which is permanent in the perennibranchiate amphibian, the larva of the caducibranchiate amphibian pursues for a time a similar life; but, eventually, while the branchial appendages dwindle the lungs grow: the respiration of air, originally supplementary to the respiration of water, predominates over it more and more, till it replaces it entirely; and an additional pair of legs is produced. This having been done, the creature either becomes, like the *Triton*, one which quits the water only occasionally; or, like the Frog, one which pursues a life mainly terrestrial, and returns to the water now and then. Finally, if we ask under what conditions this metamorphosis of a water-breather into an air-breather completes itself, the answer is—it completes itself at the time when the shallow pools inhabited by the larvæ are being dried up, or in danger of being dried up, by the summer's sun.[51]

See, then, how significant are the facts when thus brought together. There are particular habitats in which animals are subject to changes of media. In such habitats exist animals having, in various degrees, the power to live in both media, consequent on various phases of transitional organization. Near akin to these animals there are some that, after passing their early lives in the water, acquire more completely the structures fitting them to live on land, to which they then migrate. Lastly, we have closely-allied creatures, like the Surinam toad and the terrestrial salamander, which, though they belong by their structures to the class *Amphibia*, are not amphibious in their habits—creatures the larvæ of which do not pass their early lives in the water, and yet go through these same metamorphoses! Must we then think, like Von Baer, that the distribution of kindred organisms through different media presents an insurmountable difficulty? On the contrary, with facts like these before us, the evolution-hypothesis supplies possible interpretations of many phenomena that are else unaccountable. After seeing the ways in which such changes of media are in some cases gradually imposed by physical conditions, and in other cases voluntarily commenced and slowly increased in the search after food; we shall begin to understand how, in the course of evolution, there have arisen strange obscurations of one type by the externals of another type. When we see land-birds occasionally feeding by the water-side, and then learn that one of them, the water-ouzel, an "anomalous member of the strictly terrestrial thrush family, wholly subsists by diving—grasping the stones with its feet and using its wings under water"—we are enabled to comprehend how, under pressure of population, aquatic habits may be acquired by creatures organized for aërial life; and how there may eventually arise an ornithic type in which the traits of the bird are very much disguised. On finding among mammals some that, in search of prey or shelter, have taken to the water in various degrees, we shall cease to be perplexed on discovering the mammalian structure hidden under a fish-like form, as it is in the *Cetacea* and the *Sirenia*: especially on finding that in the sea-lion and the seals there are transitional forms. Grant that there has ever been going on that re-distribution of organisms which we see still resulting from their intrusions on one another's areas, media, and modes of life; and we have an explanation of those multitudinous cases in which homologies of structure are complicated with analogies. And while it accounts for the occurrence in one medium of organic types fundamentally organized for another medium, the doctrine of evolution accounts also for the accompanying unfitnesses. Either the seal has descended from some mammal which little by little became aquatic in its habits, in which case the structure of its hind limbs has a meaning; or else it was specially framed for its present habitat, in which case the structure of its hind limbs is incomprehensible.

§ 140. The facts respecting distribution in Time, which have more than any others been cited both in proof and in disproof of evolution, are too fragmentary to be conclusive either way. Were the geological record complete, or did it, as both Uniformitarians and Progressionists have commonly assumed, give us traces of the earliest organic forms; the evidence hence derived, for or against, would have had more weight than any other evidence. As it is, all we can do is to see whether such fragmentary evidence as remains, is congruous with the hypothesis.

Palæontology has shown that there is a "general relation between lapse of time and divergence of organic forms" (§ 107); and that "this divergence is comparatively slow and continuous where there is continuity in the geological formations, but is sudden and comparatively wide wherever there occurs a great break in the succession of strata." Now this is obviously what we should expect. The hypothesis implies structural changes that are not sudden but gradual. Hence, where conformable strata indicate a continuous record, we may anticipate successions of forms only slightly different from one another; while we may rationally look for marked contrasts between the groups of forms fossilized in adjacent strata, where there is evidence of a great blank in the record.

The permanent disappearances of species, of genera, and of orders, which we saw to be a fact tolerably-well established, is also a fact for which the belief in evolution prepares us. If later organic forms have in all cases descended from earlier organic forms, and have diverged during their descent, both from their prototypes and from one another; then it follows that such of them as become extinct at any epoch, will never re-appear at a subsequent epoch; since there can never again arise a concurrence and succession of conditions such as those under which each type was evolved.

Though comparisons of ancient and modern organic forms, prove that many types have persisted through enormous periods of time, without undergoing great changes; it was shown that such comparisons do not disprove the occurrence in other organic forms, of changes great enough to produce what are called different types. The result of inductive inquiry we saw to be, that while a few modern higher types yield signs of having been developed from ancient lower types; and that while there are many modern types which *may* have been thus developed, though we are without evidence that they have been so; yet that "any admissible hypothesis of progressive modification must be compatible with persistence without progression through indefinite periods." Now these results are quite congruous with the hypothesis of evolution. As rationally interpreted, evolution must in all cases be understood to result, directly or indirectly, from the incidence of forces. If there are no changes of conditions entailing organic changes, organic changes are not to be expected. Only in organisms which fall under conditions leading to additional modifications answering to additional needs, will there be that increased heterogeneity which characterizes higher forms. Hence, though the facts of palæontology cannot be held conclusive proof of evolution, yet they are congruous with it; and some of them yield it strong support.

§ 141. One general truth respecting distribution in Time, is profoundly significant. If, instead of contemplating the relations among past forms of life taken by themselves, we contemplate the relations between them and the forms now existing, we find a connexion which is in harmony with the belief in evolution but irreconcilable with any other belief.

Note, first, how full of meaning is the close kinship existing between the aggregate of organisms now living, and the aggregate of organisms which lived in the most recent geologic times. In the last-formed strata, nearly all the imbedded remains are those of species which still flourish. Strata a little older contain a few fossils of species now extinct, though, usually, species greatly resembling extant ones. Of the remains found in strata of still earlier date, the extinct species form a larger percentage; and the differences between them and the allied species now living are more marked. That is to say, the gradual change of organic types in Time, which we before saw is indicated by the geological record, is equally indicated by the relation between existing organic types and organic types of the epochs preceding our own. The evidence completely accords with the belief in a descent of present life from past life. Doubtless such a kinship is not incongruous with the doctrine of special creations. It may be argued that the introduction, from time to time, of new species better fitted to the somewhat changed conditions of the Earth's surface, would result in an apparent alliance between our living Flora and Fauna, and the Floras and Faunas that lately lived. No one can deny it. But on passing from the most general aspect of the alliance to its more special aspects, we shall find this interpretation completely negatived.

For besides a close kinship between the aggregate of surviving forms and the aggregate of forms which have died out in recent geologic times; there is a peculiar connexion of like nature between present and past forms in each great geographical region. The instructive fact, before cited from Mr. Darwin, is the "wonderful relationship in the same continent between the dead and the living." This relationship is not explained by the supposition that new species have been at intervals supernaturally placed in each habitat, as the habitat became modified; since, as we saw, species are by no means uniformly found in the habitats to which they are best adapted. It cannot be said that the marsupials imbedded in recent Australian strata, having become extinct because of unfitness to some new external condition, the existing marsupials were then specially created to fit the modified environment; since sundry animals found elsewhere are so much more in harmony with these new Australian conditions that, when taken to Australia, they rapidly extrude the marsupials. While, therefore, the similarity between the existing Australian Fauna and the Fauna which immediately preceded it over the same area, is just that which the belief in evolution leads us to expect; it is a similarity which cannot be otherwise accounted for. And so is it with parallel relations in New England, in South America, and in Europe.

§ 142. Given, then, that pressure which species exercise on one another, in consequence of the universal overfilling of their respective habitats—given the resulting tendency to thrust themselves into one another's areas, and media, and modes of life, along such lines of least resistance as from time to time are found—given besides the changes in modes of life, hence arising, those other changes which physical alterations of habitats necessitate—given the structural modifications directly or indirectly produced in organisms by modified conditions; and the facts of distribution in Space and Time are accounted for. That divergence and re-divergence of organic forms, which we saw to be shadowed forth by the truths of classification and the truths of embryology, we see to be also shadowed forth by the truths of distribution. If that aptitude to multiply, to spread, to separate, and to differentiate, which the human races have in all times shown, be a tendency common to races in general, as we have ample reason to assume; then there will result those kinds of spacial relations and chronological relations among the species, and genera, and orders, peopling the Earth's surface, which we find exist. The remarkable identities of type discovered between organisms inhabiting one medium, and strangely modified organisms inhabiting another medium, are at the same time rendered comprehensible. And the appearances and disappearances of species which the geological record shows us, as well as the connexions between successive groups of species from early eras down to our own, cease to be inexplicable.

CHAPTER VIII.

HOW IS ORGANIC EVOLUTION CAUSED?

§ 143. Already it has been necessary to speak of the causes of organic evolution in general terms; and now we are prepared for considering them specifically. The task before us is to affiliate the leading facts of organic evolution, on those same first principles conformed to by evolution at large.

Before attempting this, however, it will be instructive to glance at the causes of organic evolution which have been from time to time alleged.

§ 144. The theory that plants and animals of all kinds were gradually evolved, seems to have been at first accompanied only by the vaguest conception of cause—or rather, by no conception of cause properly so called, but only by the blank form of a conception. One of the earliest who in modern times (1735) contended that organisms are indefinitely modifiable, and that through their modifications they have become adapted to various modes of existence, was De Maillet. But though De Maillet supposed all living beings to have arisen by a natural, continuous process, he does not appear to have had any definite idea of that which determines this process. In 1794, in his *Zoonomia*, Dr. Erasmus Darwin gave reasons (sundry of them valid ones) for believing that organized beings of every kind, have descended from one, or a few, primordial germs; and along with some observable causes of modification, which he points out as aiding the developmental process, he apparently ascribes it, in part, to a tendency given to such germ or germs when created. He suggests the possibility "that all warm-blooded animals have arisen from one living filament, which THE GREAT FIRST CAUSE endued with animality, with the power of acquiring new parts, attended with new propensities, directed by irritations, sensations, volitions, and associations; and thus possessing the faculty of continuing to improve by its own inherent activity." In this passage we see the idea to be, that evolution is pre-determined by some intrinsic proclivity. "It is curious," says Mr. Charles Darwin, "how largely my grandfather, Dr. Erasmus Darwin, anticipated the erroneous grounds of opinion, and the views of Lamarck." One of the anticipations was this ascription of development to some inherent tendency. To the "plan général de la nature, et sa marche uniforme dans ses opérations," Lamarck attributes "la progression évidente qui existe dans la composition de l'organisation des animaux;" and "la *gradation* régulière qu'ils devroient offrir dans la composition de leur organisation," he thinks is rendered irregular by secondary causes. Essentially the same in kind, though somewhat different in form, is the conception put forth in the *Vestiges of Creation*; the author of which contends "that the several series of animated beings, from the simplest and oldest up to the highest and most recent, are, under the providence of God, the results, *first*, of an impulse which has been imparted to the forms of life, advancing them, in definite times, by generation, through grades of organization terminating in the highest dicotyledons and vertebrata;" and that the progression resulting from these impulses, is modified by certain other causes. The broad contrasts between lower and higher forms of life, are regarded by him as implying an innate aptitude to give birth to forms of more perfect structures. The last to re-enunciate this doctrine has been Prof. Owen; who asserts "the axiom of the continuous operation of creative power, or of the ordained becoming of living things." Though these words do not suggest a very definite idea, yet they indicate the belief that organic progress is a result of some in-dwelling tendency to develop, supernaturally impressed on living matter at the outset—some ever-acting constructive force which, independently of other forces, moulds organisms into higher and higher forms.

In whatever way it is formulated, or by whatever language it is obscured, this ascription of organic evolution to some aptitude naturally possessed by organisms, or miraculously imposed on them, is unphilosophical. It is one of those explanations which explain nothing—a shaping of ignorance into the semblance of knowledge. The cause assigned is not a true cause—not a cause assimilable to known causes—not a cause that can be anywhere shown to produce analogous effects. It is a cause unrepresentable in thought: one of those illegitimate symbolic conceptions which cannot by any mental process be elaborated into a real conception. In brief, this assumption of a persistent formative power inherent in organisms, and making them unfold into higher types, is an assumption no more tenable than the assumption of special creations: of which, indeed, it is but a modification; differing only by the fusion of separate unknown processes into a continuous unknown process.

§ 145. Besides this intrinsic tendency to progress which Dr. Darwin ascribes to animals, he says they have a capacity for being modified by processes which their own desires initiate. He speaks of powers as "excited into action by the necessities of the creatures which possess them, and on which their existence depends;" and more specifically he says that "from their first rudiment or primordium, to the termination of their lives, all animals undergo perpetual transformations; which are in part produced by their own exertions, in consequence of their desires and aversions, of their pleasures and their pains, or of irritations, or of associations; and many of these acquired forms or properties are transmitted to their posterity." While it embodies a belief for which much may be said, this passage involves the assumption that desires and aversions, existing before experiences of the actions to which they are related, were the originators of the actions, and therefore of the structural modifications caused by them. In his *Philosophie Zoologique*, Lamarck much more specifically asserts "le *sentiment intérieur*," to be in all creatures that have developed nervous systems, an independent cause of those changes of form which are due to the exercise of organs: distinguishing it from that simple *irritability* possessed by inferior animals, which cannot produce what we call a desire or emotion; and holding that these last, along with all "qui manquent de système nerveux, ne vivent qu'à l'aide des excitations qu'ils reçoivent de l'extérieur." Afterwards he says—"je reconnus que la nature, obligée d'abord d'emprunter des milieux environnants la *puissance excitatrice* des mouvements vitaux et des actions des animaux imparfaits, sut, en composant de plus en plus l'organisation animale, transporter cette puissance dans l'intérieur même de ces êtres, et qu'à la fin, elle parvint à mettre cette même puissance à la disposition de l'individu." And still more definitely he contends that if one considers "la *progression* qui se montre dans la composition de l'organisation," ... "alors on eût pu apercevoir comment les *besoins*, d'abord réduits à nullité, et dont le nombre ensuite s'est accru graduellement, ont amené le penchant aux actions propres à y satisfaire: comment les actions devenues habituelles et énergiques, ont occasionné le développement des organes qui les exécutent."

Now though this conception of Lamarck is more precisely stated, and worked out with much greater elaboration and wider knowledge of the facts, it is essentially the same as that of Dr. Darwin; and along with the truth it contains, contains also the same error more distinctly pronounced. Merely noting that desires or wants, acting directly only on the nervo-muscular system, can have no immediate influence on very many organs, as the viscera, or such external appendages as hair and feathers; and observing, further, that even some parts which belong to the apparatus of external action, such as the bones of the skull, cannot be made to grow by increase of function called forth by desire; it will suffice to point out that the difficulty is not solved, but simply slurred over, when needs or wants are introduced as independent causes of evolution. True though it is, as Dr. Darwin and Lamarck contend, that desires, by leading to increased actions of motor organs, may induce further developments of such organs; and true, as it probably is, that the modifications hence arising are transmissible to offspring; yet there remains the unanswered question—Whence do these desires originate? The transference of the exciting power from the exterior to the interior, as described by Lamarck, begs the question. How comes there a wish to perform an action not before performed? Until some beneficial result has been felt from going through certain movements, what can suggest the execution of such movements? Every desire consists primarily of a mental representation of that which is desired, and secondarily excites a mental representation of the actions by which it is attained; and any such mental representations of the end and the means, imply antecedent experience of the end and antecedent use of the means. To assume that in the course of evolution there from time to time arise new kinds of actions dictated by new desires, is simply to remove the difficulty a step back.

§ 146. Changes of external conditions are named, by Dr. Darwin, as causes of modifications in organisms. Assigning as evidence of original kinship, that marked similarity of type which exists among animals, he regards their deviations from one another, as caused by differences in their modes of life: such deviations being directly adaptive. After enumerating various appliances for procuring food, he says they all "seem to have been gradually produced during many generations by the perpetual endeavour of the creatures to supply the want of food, and to have been delivered to their posterity with constant improvement of them for the purposes required." And the creatures possessing these various appliances are considered as having been rendered unlike by seeking for food in unlike ways. As illustrating the alterations wrought by changed circumstances, he names the acquired characters of domestic animals. Lamarck has elaborated the same view in detail: using for the purpose, with great ingenuity, his extensive knowledge of the animal kingdom. From a passage in the *Avertissement* it would at first sight seem that he looks upon direct adaptation to new conditions as the chief cause of evolution. He says—"Je regardai comme certain que le *mouvement des fluides* dans l'intérieur des animaux, mouvement qui c'est progressivement accéléré avec la composition plus grande de l'organisation; et que *l'influence des circonstances* nouvelles, à mesure que les animaux s'y exposèrent en se répandant dans tous les lieux habitables, furent les deux causes générales qui ont amené les différents animaux à l'état où nous les voyons actuellement." But elsewhere the view he expresses appears decidedly different from this. He asserts that "dans sa marche, la nature a commencé, et recommence encore tous les jours, par former les corps organisés les plus simples;" and that "les premières ébauches de l'animal et du végétal étant formées dans les lieux et les circonstances convenables, les facultés d'une vie commençante et d'un mouvement organique établi, ont nécessairement développé peu à peu les organes, et qu'avec le temps elles les ont diversifies ainsi que les parties." And then, further on, he puts in italics this proposition:—"*La progression dans la composition de l'organisation subit, çà et là, dans la série générale des animaux, des anomalies opérées par l'influence des circonstances d'habitation, et par celle des habitudes contractées.*" These, and sundry other passages, joined with his general scheme of classification, make it clear that Lamarck conceived adaptive modification to be, not the cause of progression, but the cause of irregularities in progression. The inherent tendency which organisms have to develop into more perfect forms, would, according to him, result in a uniform series of forms; but varieties in their conditions work divergences of structure, which break up the series into groups: groups which he nevertheless places in uni-serial order, and regards as still substantially composing an ascending succession.

§ 147. These speculations, crude as they may be considered, show much sagacity in their respective authors, and have done good service. Without embodying the truth in definite shapes, they contain adumbrations of it. Not directly, but by successive approximations, do mankind reach correct conclusions; and those who first think in the right direction, loose as may be their reasonings, and wide of the mark as their inferences may be, yield indispensable aid by framing provisional conceptions and giving a bent to inquiry.

Contrasted with the dogmas of his age, the idea of De Maillet was a great advance. Before it can be ascertained how organized beings have been gradually evolved, there must be reached the conviction that they *have* been gradually evolved; and this conviction he reached. His wild notions about the way in which natural causes acted in the production of plants and animals, must not make us forget the merit of his intuition that animals and plants *were* produced by natural causes. In Dr. Darwin's brief exposition, the belief in a progressive genesis of organisms is joined with an interpretation having considerable definiteness and coherence. In the space of ten pages he not only indicates several of the leading classes of facts which support the hypothesis of development, but he does something towards suggesting the process of development. His reasonings show an unconscious mingling of the belief in a supernaturally-impressed tendency to develop, with the belief in a development arising from the changing incidence of conditions. Probably had he pursued the inquiry further, this last belief would have grown at the expense of the first. Lamarck, in elaborating this general conception, has given greater precision both to its truth and to its error. Asserting the same imaginary factors and the same real factors, he has traced out their supposed actions in detail; and has, in consequence, committed himself to a greater number of untenable positions. But while, in trying to reconcile the facts with a theory which is only an adumbration of the truth, he laid himself open to the criticisms of his contemporaries; he proved himself profounder than his contemporaries by seeing that natural genesis, however caused, has been going on. If they were wise in not indorsing a theory which fails to account for a great part of the facts; they were unwise in ignoring that degree of congruity with the facts, which shows the theory to contain some fundamental verity.

Leaving out, however, the imaginary factors of evolution which these speculations allege, and looking only at the one actual factor which Dr. Darwin and Lamarck assign as accounting for some of the phenomena; it is manifest, from our present stand-point, that this, so far as it is a cause of evolution, is a proximate cause and not an ultimate cause. To say that functionally-produced adaptation to conditions originates either evolution in general, or the irregularities of evolution, is to raise the further question—why is there a functionally-produced adaptation to conditions?—why do use and disuse generate appropriate changes of structure? Neither this nor any other interpretation of biologic evolution which rests simply on the basis of biologic induction, is an ultimate interpretation. The biologic induction must itself be interpreted. Only when the process of evolution of organisms is affiliated on the process of evolution in general, can it be truly said to be explained. The thing required is to show that its various results are corollaries from first principles. We have to reconcile the facts with the universal laws of the re-distribution of matter and motion.

CHAPTER IX.

EXTERNAL FACTORS.

§ 148. When illustrating the rhythm of motion (*First Principles*, § 83) it was pointed out that besides the daily and annual alternations in the quantities of light and heat which any portion of the Earth's surface receives from the Sun, there are alternations which require immensely-greater periods to complete. Reference was made to the fact that "every planet, during a certain long period, presents more of its northern than of its southern hemisphere to the Sun at the time of its nearest approach to him; and then again, during a like period, presents more of its southern hemisphere than of its northern—a recurring coincidence which, though it causes in some planets no sensible alterations of climate, involves, in the case of the Earth, an epoch of 21,000 years during which each hemisphere goes through a cycle of temperate seasons, and seasons that are extreme in their heat and cold." Further, we saw that there is a variation of this variation. The slow rhythm of temperate and intemperate climates, which takes 21,000 years to complete itself, undergoes exaggeration and mitigation during epochs that are far longer. The Earth's orbit slowly alters in form: now approximating to a circle, and now becoming more eccentric. During the period in which the Earth's orbit has least eccentricity, the temperate and intemperate climates which repeat their cycle in 21,000 years, are severally less temperate and less intemperate, than when, some one or two millions of years later, the Earth's orbit has reached its extreme of eccentricity.

Thus, besides those daily variations in the quantities of light and heat received by organisms, and responded to by variations in their functions; and besides the annual variations in the quantities of light and heat which organisms receive, and similarly respond to by variations in their functions; there are variations that severally complete themselves in 21,000 years and in some millions of years—variations to which there must also be responses in the changed functions of organisms. The whole vegetal and animal kingdoms, are subject to quadruply-compounded rhythms in the incidence of the forces on which life primarily depends—rhythms so involved in their slow working round that at no time during one of these vast epochs, can the incidence of these various forces be exactly the same as at any other time. To the direct effects so produced on organisms, have to be added much more important indirect effects. Changes of distribution must result. Certain redistributions are occasioned even by the annual variations in the quantities of the solar rays received by each part of the Earth's surface. The migrations of birds thus caused are familiar. So, too, are the migrations of certain fishes: in some cases from one part of the sea to another; in some cases from salt water to fresh water; and in some cases from fresh water to salt water. Now just as the yearly changes in the amounts of light and heat falling on each locality, yearly extend and restrict the habitats of many organisms which are able to move about with some rapidity; so must the alterations of temperate and intemperate climates produce extensions and restrictions of habitats. These, though slow, must be universal—must affect the habitats of stationary organisms as well as those of locomotive ones. For if, during an astronomic era, there is going on at any limit to a plant's habitat, a diminution of the winter's cold or summer's heat, which had before stopped its spread at that limit; then, though the individual plants are fixed, yet the species will move: the seeds of plants living at the limit, will produce individuals which survive beyond the limit. The gradual spread so effected, having gone on for some ten thousand years, the opposite change of climate will begin to cause retreat. The tide of each species will, during one half of a long epoch, slowly flow into new regions, and then will slowly ebb away from them. Further, this rise and fall in the tide of each species will, during far longer intervals, undergo increasing rises and falls and then decreasing rises and falls. There will be an alteration of spring tides and neap tides, answering to the changing eccentricity of the Earth's orbit.

These astronomical rhythms, therefore, entail on organisms unceasing changes in the incidence of forces in two ways. They directly subject them to variations of solar influences, in such a manner that each generation is somewhat differently affected in its functions; and they indirectly bring about complicated alterations in the environing agencies, by carrying each species into the presence of new physical conditions, new soil and surface.

§ 149. The power of geological actions to modify everywhere the circumstances in which plants and animals are placed, is conspicuous. In each locality denudation slowly uncovers different deposits, and slowly changes the exposed areas of deposits already uncovered. Simultaneously, the alluvial beds in course of formation, are qualitatively affected by these progressive changes in the natures and proportions of the strata denuded. The inclinations of surfaces and their directions with respect to the Sun, are at the same time modified; and the organisms existing on them are thus having their thermal conditions continually altered, as well as their drainage. Igneous action, too, complicates these gradual modifications. A flat region cannot be step by step thrust up into a protuberance without unlike climatic changes being produced in its several parts, by their exposures to different aspects. Extrusions of trap, wherever they take place, revolutionize the localities; both over the areas covered and over the areas on to which their detritus is carried. And where volcanoes are formed, the ashes they occasionally send out modify the character of the soil throughout large surrounding tracts.

In like manner alterations in the Earth's crust cause the ocean to be ever subjecting the organisms it contains to new combinations of conditions. Here the water is being deepened by subsidence, and there shallowed by upheaval. While the falling upon it of sediment brought down by neighbouring large rivers, is raising the sea-bottom in one place, in another the habitual rush of the tide is carrying away the sediment deposited in past times. The mineral character of the submerged surface on which sea-weeds grow and molluscs crawl, is everywhere occasionally changed; now by the bringing away from an adjacent shore some previously untouched strata; and now by the accumulation of organic remains, such as the shells of pteropods or of foraminifera. A further series of alterations in the circumstances of marine organisms, is entailed by changes in the movements of the water. Each modification in the outlines of neighbouring shores makes the tidal streams vary their directions or velocities or both. And the local temperature is from time to time raised or lowered, because some far-distant change of form in the Earth's crust has wrought a divergence in those circulating currents of warm and cold water which pervade the ocean.

These geologically-caused changes in the physical characters of each environment, occur in ever-new combinations, and with ever-increasing complexity. As already shown (*First Principles*, § 158), it follows from the law of the multiplication of effects, that during long periods each tract of the Earth's surface increases in heterogeneity of both form and substance. So that plants and animals of all kinds are, in the course of generations, subjected by alterations in the crust of the Earth, to sets of incident forces differing from previous sets, both by changes in the proportions of the factors and, occasionally, by the addition of new factors.

§ 150. Variations in the astronomical conditions joined with variations in the geological conditions, bring about variations in the meteorological conditions. Those slow alternations of elevation and subsidence which take place over immense areas, here producing a continent where once there was a fathomless ocean, and there causing wide seas to spread where in a long past epoch there stood snow-capped mountains, gradually work great atmospheric changes. While the highest parts of an emerging surface of the Earth's crust exist as a cluster of islands, the plants and animals which in course of time migrate to them have climates that are peculiar to small tracts of land surrounded by large tracts of water. As, by successive upheavals, greater areas are exposed, there begin to arise sensible contrasts between the states of their peripheral parts and their central parts. The breezes which daily moderate the extremes of temperature near the shores, cease to affect the interiors; and the interiors, less qualified too in their heat and cold by such ocean-currents as approach the coast, acquire more decidedly the characters due to their latitudes. Along with the further elevations which unite the members of the archipelago into a continent, there come new meteorologic changes, as well as exacerbations of the old. The winds, which were comparatively uniform in their directions and periods when only islands existed, grow involved in their distribution, and widely-different in different parts of the continent. The quantities of rain which they discharge and of moisture which they absorb, vary everywhere according to the proximity to the sea and to surfaces of land having special characters.

Other complications result from variations of height above the sea: elevation producing a decrease of heat and consequently an increase in the precipitation of water—a precipitation which takes the shape of snow where the elevation is very great, and of rain where it is not so great. The gatherings of clouds and descents of showers around mountain tops, are familiar to every tourist. Inquiries in the neighbouring valleys prove that within distances of a mile or two the recurring storms differ in their frequency and violence. Nay, even a few yards off, the meteorological conditions vary in such regions: as witness the way in which the condensing vapour keeps eddying round on one side of some high crag, while the other side is clear; or the way in which the snowline runs irregularly to different heights, in all the hollows and ravines of each mountain side.

As climatic variations thus geologically produced, are compounded with those which result from slow astronomical changes; and as no correspondence exists between the geologic and the astronomic rhythms; it results that the same plexus of actions never recurs. Hence the incident forces to which the organisms of every locality are exposed by atmospheric agencies, are ever passing into unparalleled combinations; and these are on the average ever becoming more complex.

§ 151. Besides changes in the incidence of inorganic forces, there are equally continuous, and still more involved, changes in the incidence of forces which organisms exercise on one another. As before pointed out (§ 105), the plants and animals inhabiting each locality are held together in so entangled a web of relations, that any considerable modification which one species undergoes, acts indirectly on many other species, and eventually changes, in some degree, the circumstances of nearly all the rest. If an increase of heat, or modification of soil, or decrease of humidity, causes a particular kind of plant either to thrive or to dwindle, an unfavourable or favourable effect is wrought on all such competing kinds of plants as are not immediately influenced in the same way. The animals which eat the seeds or browse on the leaves, either of the plant primarily affected or those of its competitors, are severally altered in their states of nutrition and in their numbers; and this change presently tells on various predatory animals and parasites. And since each of these secondary and tertiary changes becomes itself a centre of others, the increase or decrease of each species produces waves of influence which spread and reverberate and re-reverberate throughout the whole Flora and Fauna of the locality.

More marked and multiplied still, are the ultimate effects of those causes which make possible the colonization of neighbouring areas. Each intruding plant or animal, besides the new inorganic conditions to which it is subject, is subject to organic conditions different from those to which it has been accustomed. It has to compete with some organisms unlike those of its preceding habitat. It must preserve itself from enemies not before encountered. Or it may meet with a species over which it has some advantage greater than any it had over the species it was previously in contact with. Even where migration does not bring it face to face with new competitors or new enemies or new prey, it inevitably experiences new proportions among these. Further, an expanding species is almost certain to invade more than one adjacent region. Spreading both north and south, or east and west, it will come among the plants and animals, here of a level district and there of a hilly one—here of an inland tract and there of a tract bordered by the sea. And while different groups of its members will thus expose themselves to the actions and reactions of different Floras and Faunas, these different Floras and Faunas will simultaneously have their organic conditions changed by the intruders.

This process becomes gradually more active and more complicated. Though, in particular cases, a plant or animal may fall into simpler relations with the living things around than those it was before placed in, yet it is manifest that, on the average, the organic environments of organisms have been advancing in heterogeneity. As the number of species with which each species is directly or indirectly implicated, multiplies, each species is oftener subject to changes in the organic actions which influence it. These more frequent changes severally grow more involved. And the corresponding reactions affect larger Floras and Faunas, in ways increasingly complex and varied.

§ 152. When the astronomic, geologic, meteorologic, and organic agencies which are at work on each species of plant and animal are contemplated as becoming severally more complicated in themselves, and as co-operating in ways that are always partially new; it will be seen that throughout all time there has been an exposure of organisms to endless successions of modifying causes which gradually acquire an intricacy scarcely conceivable. Every kind of plant and animal may be regarded as for ever passing into a new environment—as perpetually having its relations to external circumstances altered, either by their changes with respect to it when it remains stationary, or by its changes with respect to them when it migrates, or by both.

Yet a further cause of progressive alteration and complication in the incident forces, exists. All other things continuing the same, every additional faculty by which an organism is brought into relation with external objects, as well as every improvement in such faculty, becomes a means of subjecting the organism to a greater number and variety of external stimuli, and to new combinations of external stimuli. So that each advance in complexity of organization, itself becomes an added source of complexity in the incidence of external forces.

Once more, every increase in the locomotive powers of animals, increases both the multiplicity and the multiformity of the actions of things upon them, and of their reactions upon things. Doubling a creature's activity quadruples the area that comes within the range of its excursions; thus augmenting in number and heterogeneity, the external agencies which act on it during any given interval.

By compounding the actions of these several orders of factors, there is produced a geometric progression of changes, increasing with immense rapidity. And there goes on an equally rapid increase in the frequency with which the combinations of the actions are altered, and the intricacies of their co-operations enhanced.

CHAPTER X.

INTERNAL FACTORS.

§ 153. We saw at the outset (§§ 10-16), that organic matter is built up of molecules so unstable, that the slightest variation in their conditions destroys their equilibrium, and causes them either to assume altered structures or to decompose. But a substance which is beyond all others changeable by the actions and reactions of the forces liberated from instant to instant within its own mass, must be a substance which is beyond all others changeable by the forces acting on it from without. If their composition fits organic aggregates for undergoing with special facility and rapidity those re-distributions of matter and motion whence result individual organization and life; then their composition must make them similarly apt to undergo those permanent re-distributions of matter and motion which are expressed by changes of structure, in correspondence with permanent re-distributions of matter and motion in their environments.

In *First Principles*, when considering the phenomena of Evolution at large, the leading characters and causes of those changes which constitute organic evolution were briefly traced. Under each of the derivative laws of force to which the passage from an incoherent, indefinite homogeneity to a coherent, definite heterogeneity, conforms, were given illustrations drawn from the metamorphoses of living bodies. Here it will be needful to contemplate the several resulting processes as going on at once, in both individuals and species.

§ 154. Our postulate being that organic evolution in general commenced with homogeneous organic matter, we have first to remember that the state of homogeneity is an unstable state (*First Principles*, § 149). In any aggregate "the relations of outside and inside, and of comparative nearness to neighbouring sources of influence, imply the reception of influences that are unlike in quantity, or quality, or both; and it follows that unlike changes will be produced in the parts thus dissimilarly acted upon." Further, "if any given whole, instead of being absolutely uniform throughout, consists of parts distinguishable from one another—if each of these parts, while somewhat unlike other parts, is uniform within itself; then, each of them being in unstable equilibrium, it follows that while the changes set up within it must render it multiform, they must at the same time render the whole more multiform than before;" and hence, "whether that state with which we commence be or be not one of perfect homogeneity, the process must equally be towards a relative heterogeneity." This loss of homogeneity which the special instability of organic aggregates fits them to display more promptly and variously than any other aggregates, must be shown in more numerous ways in proportion as the incident forces are more numerous. Every differentiation of structure being a result of some difference in the relations of the parts to the agencies acting on them, it follows that the more multiplied and more unlike the agencies, the more varied must be the differentiations wrought. Hence the change from a state of homogeneity to a state of heterogeneity, will be marked in proportion as the environing actions to which the organism is supposes it is only are complex. This transition from a uniform to a multiform state, must continue through successive individuals. Given a series of organisms, each of which is developed from a portion of a preceding organism, and the question is whether, after exposure of the series for a million years to changed incident forces, one of its members will be the same as though the incident forces had only just changed. To say that it will, is implicitly to deny the persistence of force. In relation to any cause of divergence, the whole series of such organisms may be considered as fused together into a continuously-existing organism; and when so considered, it becomes manifest that a continuously-acting cause will go on working a continuously-increasing effect, until some counteracting cause prevents any further effect.

But now if any primordial organic aggregate must, in itself and through its descendants, gravitate from uniformity to multiformity, in obedience to the more or less multiform forces acting on it; what must happen if these multiform forces are themselves undergoing slow variations and complications? Clearly the process, ever-advancing towards a temporary limit but ever having its limit removed, must go on unceasingly. On those structural changes wrought in the once homogeneous aggregate by an original set of incident forces, will be superposed further changes wrought by a modified set of incident forces; and so on throughout all time. Omitting for the present those circumstances which check and qualify its consequences, the instability of the homogeneous must be recognized as an ever-acting cause of organic evolution, as of all other evolution.

While it follows that every organism, considered as an individual and as one of a series, tends thus to pass into a more heterogeneous state; it also follows that every species, considered as an aggregate of individuals, tends to do the like. Throughout the area it inhabits, the conditions can never be absolutely uniform: its members must, in different parts of the area, be exposed to different sets of incident forces. Still more decided must this difference of exposure be when its members spread into other habitats. Those expansive and repressive energies which set to each species a limit that perpetually oscillates from side to side of a certain mean, are, as we lately saw, frequently changed by new combinations of the external factors—astronomic, geologic, meteorologic, and organic. Hence there from time to time arise lines of diminished resistance, along which the species flows into new localities. Such portions of the species as thus migrate, are subject to circumstances unlike its previous average circumstances. And from multiformity of the circumstances, must come multiformity of the species.

Thus the law of the instability of the homogeneous has here a three-fold corollary. As interpreted in connexion with the ever-progressing, ever-complicating changes in external factors, it involves the conclusion that there is a prevailing tendency towards greater heterogeneity in all kinds of organisms, considered both individually and in successive generations; as well as in each assemblage of organisms constituting a species; and, by consequence, in each genus, order, and class.

§ 155. When considering the causes of evolution in general, we further saw (*First Principles*, § 156), that the multiplication of effects aids continually to increase that heterogeneity into which homogeneity inevitably lapses. It was pointed out that since "the several parts of an aggregate are differently modified by any incident force;" and since "by the reactions of the differently modified parts the incident force itself must be divided into differently modified parts;" it follows that "each differentiated division of the aggregate thus becomes a centre from which a differentiated division of the original force is again diffused. And since unlike forces must produce unlike results, each of these differentiated forces must produce, throughout the aggregate, a further series of differentiations." To this it was added that, in proportion as the heterogeneity increases, the complications arising from this multiplication of effects grow more marked; because the more strongly contrasted the parts of an aggregate become, the more different must be their reactions on incident forces, and the more unlike must be the secondary effects which these initiate; and because every increase in the number of unlike parts adds to the number of such differentiated incident forces, and such secondary effects.

How this multiplication of effects conspires, with the instability of the homogeneous, to work an increasing multiformity of structure in an organism, was shown at the time; and the foregoing pages contain further incidental illustrations. In § 69 it was pointed out that a change in one function must produce ever-complicating perturbations in other functions; and that, eventually, all parts of the organism must be modified in their states. Suppose that the head of a bison becomes much heavier, what must be the indirect results? The muscles of the neck are put to greater exertions; and its vertebræ have to bear additional tensions and pressures, caused both by the increased weight of the head, and by the stronger contractions of the muscles that support and move it. These muscles also affect their special attachments: several of the dorsal spines suffer augmented strains; and the vertebræ to which they are fixed are more severely taxed. Further, this heavier head and the more massive neck it necessitates, require a stronger fulcrum: the whole thoracic arch, and the fore-limbs which support it, are subject to greater continuous stress and more violent occasional shocks. And the required strengthening of the fore-quarters cannot take place without the centre of gravity being changed, and the hind limbs being differently reacted upon during locomotion. Any one who compares the outline of the bison with that of its congener, the ox, will see how profoundly a heavier head affects the entire osseous and muscular systems. Besides this multiplication of mechanical effects, there is a multiplication of physiological effects. The vascular apparatus is modified throughout its whole structure by each considerable modification in the proportions of the body. Increase in the size of any organ implies a quantitative, and often a qualitative, reaction on the blood; and thus alters the nutrition of all other organs. Such physiological correlations are exemplified in the many differences which accompany difference of sex. That the minor sexual peculiarities are brought about by the physiological actions and reactions, is shown both by the fact that they are commonly but faintly marked until the fundamentally distinctive organs are developed, and that when the development of these is prevented, the minor sexual peculiarities do not arise. No further proof is, I think, needed, that in any individual organism or its descendants, a new external action must, besides the primary internal change which it works, work many secondary changes, as well as tertiary changes still more multiplied. That tendency towards greater heterogeneity which is given to an organism by disturbing its environment, is helped by the tendency which every modification has to produce other modifications—modifications which must become more numerous in proportion as the organism becomes more complex. Lastly, among the indirect and involved manifestations of this tendency, we must not omit the innumerable small irregularities of structure which result from the crossing of dissimilarly-modified individuals. It was shown (§§ 89, 90) that what are called "spontaneous variations," are interpretable as results of miscellaneously compounding the changes wrought in different lines of ancestors by different conditions of life. These still more complex and multitudinous effects so produced, are further illustrations of the multiplication of effects.

Equally in the aggregate of individuals constituting a species, does multiplication of effects become the continual cause of increasing multiformity. The lapse of a species into divergent varieties, initiates fresh combinations of forces tending to work further divergences. The new varieties compete with the parent species in new ways; and so add new elements to its circumstances. They modify somewhat the conditions of other species existing in their habitat, or in the habitat they have invaded; and the modifications wrought in such other species become additional sources of influence. The Flora and Fauna of every region are united by their entangled relations into a whole, of which no part can be affected without affecting the rest. Hence, each differentiation in a local assemblage of species, becomes the cause of further differentiations.

§ 156. One of the universal principles to which we saw that the re-distribution of matter and motion conforms, is that in any aggregate made up of mixed units, incident forces produce segregation—separate unlike units and bring together like units; and it was shown that the increasing integration and definiteness which characterizes each part of an evolving organic aggregate, as of every other aggregate, results from this (*First Principles*, § 166). It remains here to say that while the actions and reactions between organisms and their changing environments, add to the heterogeneity of organic structures, they also give to the heterogeneity this growing distinctness. At first sight the reverse might be inferred. It might be argued that any new set of effects wrought in an organism by some new set of external forces, must tend more or less to obliterate the effects previously wrought—must produce confusion or indefiniteness. A little consideration, however, will dissipate this impression.

Doubtless the condition under which alone increasing definiteness of structure can be acquired by any part of an organism, either in an individual or in successive generations, is that such part shall be exposed to some set of tolerably-constant forces; and doubtless, continual change of circumstances interferes with this. But the interference can never be considerable. For the pre-existing structure of an organism prevents it from living under any new conditions except such as are congruous with the fundamental characters of its organization—such as subject its essential organs to actions substantially the same as before. Great changes must kill it. Hence, it can continuously expose itself and its descendants, only to those moderate changes which do not destroy the general harmony between the aggregate of incident forces and the aggregate of its functions. That is, it must remain under influences calculated to make greater the definiteness of the chief differentiations already produced. If, for example, we set out with an animal in which a rudimentary vertebral column with its attached muscular system has been established; it is clear that the mechanical arrangements have become thereby so far determined, that subsequent modifications are extremely likely, if not certain, to be consistent with the production of movement by the actions of muscles on a flexible central axis. Hence, there will continue a general similarity in the play of forces to which the flexible central axis is subject; and so, notwithstanding the metamorphoses which the vertebrate type undergoes, there will be a maintenance of conditions favourable to increasing definiteness and integration of the vertebral column. Moreover, this maintenance of such conditions becomes secure in proportion as organization advances. Each further complexity of structure, implying some further complexity in the relations between an organism and its environment, must tend to specialize the actions and reactions between it and its environment—must tend to increase the stringency with which it is restrained within such environments as admit of those special actions and reactions for which its structure fits it; that is, must further guarantee the continuance of those actions and reactions to which its essential organs respond, and therefore the continuance of the segregating process.

How in each species, considered as an aggregate of individuals, there must arise stronger and stronger contrasts among those divergent varieties which result from the instability of the homogeneous and the multiplication of effects, need only be briefly indicated. It has already been shown (*First Principles*, § 166), that in conformity to the universal law that mixed units are segregated by like incident forces, there are produced increasingly-definite distinctions among varieties, wherever there occur definitely-distinguished sets of conditions to which the varieties are respectively subject.

§ 157. Probably in the minds of some, the reading of this chapter has been accompanied by a running commentary, to the effect that the argument proves too much. The apparent implication is, that the passage from an indefinite, incoherent homogeneity to a definite, coherent heterogeneity in organic aggregates, must have been going on universally; whereas we find that in many cases there has been persistence without progression. This apparent implication, however, is not a real one.

For though every environment on the Earth's surface undergoes changes; and though usually the organisms which each environment contains, cannot escape certain resulting new influences; yet occasionally such new influences are escaped, by the survival of species in the unchanged parts of their habitats, or by their spread into neighbouring habitats which the change has rendered like their original habitats, or by both. Any alteration in the temperature of a climate or its degree of humidity, is unlikely to affect simultaneously the whole area occupied by a species; and further, it can scarcely fail to happen that the addition or subtraction of heat or moisture, will give to a part of some adjacent area, a climate like that to which the species has been habituated. If, again, the circumstances of a species are modified by the intrusion of some foreign kind of plant or animal, it follows that since the intruders will probably not spread throughout its whole habitat, the species will, in one or more localities, remain unaffected by them. Especially among marine creatures, must there frequently occur cases in which modifying causes are continually eluded. Comparatively uniform as are the physical conditions to which the sea exposes its inhabitants, it becomes possible for such of them as live on widely-diffused food, to be widely distributed; and wide distribution generally prevents the members of a species from being all subject to the same cause. Our commonest cirriped, for instance, subsisting on minute creatures everywhere dispersed through the water; needing only to have some firm surface on which to build up its shell; and in scarcely any danger from surrounding animals; is able to exist on shores so widely remote from one another, that nearly every change in the incident forces must fall within narrower areas than that which the species occupies. Nearly always, therefore, a portion of the species will survive unmodified. Its easily-transported germs will take possession of such new habitats as have been rendered fitter by the change that has unfitted some parts of its original habitat. Hence, on successive occasions, while some parts of the species are slightly transformed, another part may continually escape transformation by migrating hither and thither, where the simple conditions needed for its existence recur in nearly the same combinations as before. And it will so become possible for it to survive, with insignificant structural changes, throughout long geologic periods.

§ 158. The results to which we find ourselves led, are these.

In subordination to the different amounts and kinds of forces to which its different parts are exposed, every individual organic aggregate, like all other aggregates, tends to pass from its original indistinct simplicity towards a more distinct complexity. Unless we deny the persistence of force, we must admit that the lapse of an organism's structure from an indefinitely homogeneous to a definitely heterogeneous state, must be cumulative in successive generations, if the forces causing it continue to act. And for the like reasons, the increasing assemblage of individuals arising from a common stock, is also liable to lose its original uniformity; and, in successive generations, to grow more pronounced in its multiformity.

These changes, which would go to but a comparatively small extent were organisms exposed to constant external conditions, are kept up by the continual changes in external conditions, produced by astronomic, geologic, meteorologic, and organic agencies: the average result being, that on previous complications wrought by previous incident forces, new complications are continually superposed by new incident forces. And hence simultaneously arises increasing heterogeneity in the structures of individuals, in the structures of species, and in the structures of the Earth's Flora and Fauna.

But while, in very many or in most cases, the ever-changing incidence of forces is ever adding to the complexity of organisms, and to the complexity of the organic world as a whole; it does this only where its action cannot be eluded. And since, by migration, it is possible for a species to keep itself under conditions that are tolerably constant, there must be a proportion of cases in which greater heterogeneity of structure is not to be expected.

To show, however, that there must arise a certain average tendency to the production of greater heterogeneity is not sufficient. Aggregates might be rendered more heterogeneous by changing incident forces, without having given to them that kind of heterogeneity required for carrying on life. Hence it remains now to inquire how the production and maintenance of this kind of heterogeneity is insured.

CHAPTER XI.

DIRECT EQUILIBRATION.

§ 159. Every change is towards a balance of forces; and of necessity can never cease until a balance of forces is reached. When treating of equilibration under its general aspects (*First Principles*, Part II., Chap. xxii.), we saw that every aggregate having compound movements tends continually towards a moving equilibrium; since any unequilibrated force to which such an aggregate is subject, if not of a kind to overthrow it altogether, must continue modifying its state until an equilibrium is brought about. And we saw that the structure simultaneously reached must be "one presenting an arrangement of forces that counterbalance all the forces to which the aggregate is subject;" since, "so long as there remains a residual force in any direction—be it excess of a force exercised by an aggregate on its environment, or of a force exercised by its environment on the aggregate, equilibrium does not exist; and therefore the re-distribution of matter must continue."

It is essential that this truth should here be fully comprehended; and to the end of insuring clear comprehension of it, some re-illustration is desirable. The case of the Solar System will best serve our purpose. An assemblage of bodies, each of which has its simple and compound motions that severally alternate between two extremes, and the whole of which has its involved perturbations, that now increase and now decrease, is here presented to us. Suppose a new factor were brought to bear on this moving equilibrium—say by the arrival of some wandering mass, or by an additional momentum given to one of the existing masses—what would be the result? If the strange body or the extra energy were very large, it might so derange the entire system as to cause its collapse. But what if the incident energy, falling on the system from without, proved insufficient to overthrow it? There would then arise a set of perturbations which would, in the course of an enormous period, slowly work round into a modified moving equilibrium. The effects primarily impressed on the adjacent masses, and in a smaller degree on the remoter masses, would presently become complicated with the secondary effects impressed by the disturbed masses on one another; and these again with tertiary effects. Waves of perturbation would continue to be propagated throughout the entire system; until, around a new centre of gravity, there had been established a set of planetary motions different from the preceding ones. The new energy must gradually be used up in overcoming the energies resisting the divergence it generates; which antagonizing energies, when no longer opposed, set up a counter-action, ending in a compensating divergence in the opposite direction, followed by a re-compensating divergence, and so on. Now though instead of being, like the Solar System, in a state of *independent* moving equilibrium, an organism is in a state of *dependent* moving equilibrium (*First Principles*, § 170); yet this does not prevent the manifestation of the same law. Every animal daily obtains from without, a supply of energy to replace the energy it expends; but this continual giving to its parts a new momentum, to make up for the momentum continually lost, does not interfere with the carrying on of actions and reactions like those just described. Here, as before, we have a definitely-arranged aggregate of parts, called organs, having their definitely-established actions and reactions, called functions. These rhythmical actions or functions, and the various compound rhythms resulting from their combinations, are so adjusted as to balance the actions to which the organism is subject: there is a constant or periodic genesis of energies which, in their kinds, amounts, and directions, suffice to antagonize the energies the organism has constantly or periodically to bear. If, then, there exists this moving equilibrium among a set of internal actions, exposed to a set of external actions, what must result if any of the external actions are changed? Of course there is no longer an equilibrium. Some energy which the organism habitually generates, is too great or too small to balance some incident energy; and there arises a residual energy exerted by the environment on the organism, or by the organism on the environment. This residual or unbalanced energy, of necessity expends itself in producing some change of state in the organism. Acting directly on some organ and modifying its function, it indirectly modifies dependent functions and remotely influences all the functions. As we have already seen (§§ 68, 69), if this new energy is permanent, its effects must be gradually diffused throughout the entire system; until it has come to be equilibrated in producing those structural rearrangements whence result a counter-balancing energy.

The bearing of this general truth on the question we are now dealing with is obvious. Those modifications upon modifications, which the unceasing mutations of their environments have been all along generating in organisms, have been in each case modifications involved by the establishment of a new balance with the new combination of actions. In every species throughout all geologic time, there has been perpetually going on a rectification of the equilibrium, which has been perpetually disturbed by the alteration of its circumstances; and every further heterogeneity has been the addition of a structural change entailed by a new equilibration, to the structural changes entailed by previous equilibrations. There can be no other ultimate interpretation of the matter, since change can have no other goal.

This equilibration between the functions of an organism and the actions in its environment, may be either direct or indirect. The new incident force may either immediately call forth some counteracting force, and its concomitant structural change; or it may be eventually balanced by some otherwise-produced change of function and structure. These two processes of equilibration are quite distinct, and must be separately dealt with. We will devote this chapter to the first of them.

§ 160. Direct equilibration is that process currently known as *adaptation*. We have already seen (Part II., Chap, v.), that individual organisms become modified when placed in new conditions of life—so modified as to re-adjust the powers to the requirements; and though there is great difficulty in disentangling the evidence, we found reason for thinking (§ 82) that structural changes thus caused by functional changes are inherited. In the last chapter, it was argued that if, instead of the succession of individuals constituting a species, there were a continuously-existing individual, any functional and structural divergence produced by a new incident action, would increase until the new incident action was counterpoised; and that the replacing of a continuously-existing individual by a succession of individuals, each formed out of the modified substance of its predecessor, will not prevent the like effect from being produced. Here we further find that this limit towards which any such organic change advances, in the species as in the individual, is a new moving equilibrium adjusted to the new arrangement of external forces.

But now what are the conditions under which alone, direct equilibration can occur? Are all the modifications that serve to re-fit organisms to their environments, directly adaptive modifications? And if otherwise, which are the directly adaptive and which are not? How are we to distinguish between them?

There can be no direct equilibration with an external agency which, if it acts at all, acts fatally; since the organism to be adapted disappears. Conversely, some inaccessible benefit which a small modification in the organism would make accessible, cannot by its action tend to produce this modification: the modification and the benefit do not stand in dynamic relation. The only new incident forces which can work the changes of function and structure required to bring any animal or plant into equilibrium with them, are such incident forces as operate on this animal or plant, either continuously or frequently. They must be capable of appreciably changing that set of complex rhythmical actions and reactions constituting the life of the organism; and yet must not usually produce perturbations that are fatal. Let us see what are the limits to direct equilibration hence arising.

§ 161. In plants, organs engaged in nutrition, and exposed to variations in the amounts and proportions of matters and forces utilized in nutrition, may be expected to undergo corresponding variations. We find evidence that they do this. The "changes of habit" which are common in plants, when taken to places unlike in climate or soil to those before inhabited by them, are changes of parts in which the modified external actions directly produce modified internal actions. The characters of the stem and shoots as woody or succulent, erect or procumbent; of the leaves in respect of their sizes, thicknesses, and textures; of the roots in their degrees of development and modes of growth; are obviously in immediate relation to the characters of the environment. A permanent difference in the quantity of light or heat affects, day after day, the processes going on in the leaves. Habitual rain or drought alters all the assimilative actions, and appreciably influences the organs that carry them on. Some particular substance, by its presence in the soil, gives new qualities to some of the tissues; causing greater rigidity or flexibility, and so affecting the general aspect. Here then we have changes towards modified sets of functions and structures, in equilibrium with modified sets of external forces.

But now let us turn to other classes of organs possessed by plants—organs which are not at once affected in their actions by variations of incident forces. Take first the organs of defence. Many plants are shielded against animals that would else devour them, by formidable thorns; and others, like the nettle, by stinging hairs. These must be counted among the appliances by which equilibrium is maintained between the actions in the organism and the actions in its environment; seeing that were these defences absent, the destruction by herbivorous animals would be so much increased, that the number of young plants annually produced would not suffice, as it now does, to balance the mortality, and the species would disappear. But these defensive appliances, though they aid in maintaining the balance between inner and outer actions, cannot have been directly called forth by the outer actions which they serve to neutralize; for these outer actions do not continuously affect the functions of the plant even in a general way, still less in the special way required. Suppose a species of nettle bare of poison-hairs, to be habitually eaten by some mammal intruding on its habitat. The actions of this mammal would have no direct tendency to develop poison-hairs in the plant; since the individuals devoured could not bequeath changes of structure, even were the actions of a kind to produce fit ones; and since the individuals which perpetuated themselves would be those on which the new incident force had not fallen. Organs of another class, similarly circumstanced, are those of reproduction. Like the organs of defence these are not, during the life of the individual plant, variably exercised by variable external actions; and therefore do not fulfil those conditions under which structural changes may be directly caused by changes in the environment. The generative apparatus contained in every flower acts only once during its existence; and even then, the parts subserve their ends in a passive rather than an active way. Functionally-produced modifications are therefore out of the question. If a plant's anthers are so placed that the insect which most commonly frequents its flowers, must come in contact with the pollen, and fertilize with it other flowers of the same species; and if this insect, dwindling away or disappearing from the locality, leaves behind no insects having such shapes and habits as cause them to do the same thing efficiently, but only some which do it inefficiently; it is clear that this change of its conditions has no immediate tendency to work in the plant any such structural change as shall bring about a new balance with its conditions. For the anthers, which, even when they discharge their functions, do it simply by standing in the way of the insect, are, under the supposed circumstances, left untouched by the insect; and this remaining untouched cannot have the effect of so modifying the stamens as to bring the anthers into a position to be touched by some other insect. Only those individuals whose parts of fructification so far differed from the average form that some other insect could serve them as pollen-carrier, would have good chances of perpetuating themselves. And on their progeny, inheriting the deviation, there would act no external force directly tending to make the deviation greater; since the new circumstances to which re-adaptation is required, are such as do not in the least alter the equilibrium of functions constituting the life of the individual plant.

§ 162. Among animals, adaptation by direct equilibration is similarly traceable wherever, during the life of the individual, an external change generates some constant or repeated change of function. This is conspicuously the case with such parts of an animal as are immediately exposed to diffused influences, like those of climate, and with such parts of an animal as are occupied in its mechanical actions on the environment. Of the one class of cases, the darkening of the skin which follows exposure to one or other extreme of temperature, may be taken as an instance; and with the other class of cases we are made familiar by the increase and decrease which use and disuse cause in the organs of motion. It is needless here to exemplify these: they were treated of in the Second Part of this work.

But in animals, as in plants, there are many indispensable offices fulfilled by parts between which and the external conditions they respond to, there is no such action and reaction as can directly produce an equilibrium. This is especially manifest with dermal appendages. Some ground exists for the conclusion that the greater or less development of hairs, is in part immediately due to increase or decrease of demand on the passive function, as forming a non-conducting coat; but be this as it may, it is impossible that there can exist any such cause for those immense developments of hairs which we see in the quills of the porcupine, or those complex developments of them known as feathers. Such an enamelled armour as is worn by *Lepidosteus*, is inexplicable as a direct result of any functionally-worked change. For purposes of defence, such an armour is as needful, or more needful, for hosts of other fishes; and did it result from any direct reaction of the organism against any offensive actions it was subject to, there seems no reason why other fishes should not have developed similar protective coverings. Of sundry reproductive appliances the like may be said. The secretion of an egg-shell round the substance of an egg, in the oviduct of a bird, is quite inexplicable as a consequence of some functionally-wrought modification of structure, immediately caused by some modification of external conditions. The end fulfilled by the egg-shell, is that of protecting the contained mass against certain slight pressures and collisions, to which it is liable during incubation. How, by any process of direct equilibration, could it come to have the required thickness? or, indeed, how could it come to exist at all? Suppose this protective envelope to be too weak, so that some of the eggs a bird lays are broken or cracked. In the first place, the breakages or crackings are actions which cannot react on the maternal organism in such ways as to cause the secretion of thicker shells for the future: to suppose that they can, is to suppose that the bird understands the cause of the evil, and that the secretion of thicker shells can be effected by its will. In the second place, such developing chicks as are contained in the shells which crack or break, are almost certain to die; and cannot, therefore, acquire appropriately-modified constitutions: even supposing any relation could exist between the impression received and the change required. Meanwhile, such eggs as escape breakage are not influenced at all by the requirement; and hence, on the birds developed from them, there cannot have acted any force tending to work the needful adjustment of functions. In no way, therefore, can a direct equilibration between constitution and conditions be here produced. Even in organs that can be modified by certain incident actions into correspondence with such incident actions, there are some re-adjustments which cannot be effected by direct balancing. It is thus with the bones. The majority of the bones have to resist muscular strains; and variations in the muscular strains call forth, by reaction, variations in the strengths of the bones. Here there is direct equilibration. But though the greater massiveness acquired by bones subject to greater strains, may be ascribed to counter-acting forces evoked by forces brought into action; it is impossible that the acquirement of greater lengths by bones can be thus accounted for. It has been supposed that the elongation of the metatarsals in wading birds, has resulted from direct adaptation to conditions of life. To justify this supposition, however, it must be shown that the mechanical actions and reactions in the legs of a wading bird, differ from those in the legs of other birds; and that the differential actions are equilibrated by the extra lengths. There is not the slightest evidence of this. The metatarsals of a bird have to bear no appreciable strains but those due to the superincumbent weight. Standing in the water does not appreciably alter such strains; and even if it did, an increase in the lengths of these bones would not fit them any better to meet the altered strains.

§ 163. The conclusion at which we arrive is, then, that there go on in all organisms, certain changes of function and structure that are directly consequent on changes in the incident forces—inner changes by which the outer changes are balanced, and the equilibrium restored. Such re-equilibrations, which are often conspicuously exhibited in individuals, we have reason to believe continue in successive generations; until they are completed by the arrival at structures fitted to the modified conditions. But, at the same time, we see that the modified conditions to which organisms may be adapted by direct equilibration, are conditions of certain classes only. That a new external action may be met by a new internal action, it is needful that it shall either continuously or frequently be borne by the individuals of the species, without killing or seriously injuring them; and shall act in such way as to affect their functions. And we find that many of the environing agencies—evil or good—to which organisms have to be adjusted, are not of these kinds: being agencies which either do not immediately affect the functions at all, or else affect them in ways that prove fatal.

Hence there must be at work some other process which equilibrates the actions of organisms with the actions they are exposed to. Plants and animals that continue to exist, are necessarily plants and animals whose powers balance the powers acting on them; and as their environments change, the changes which plants and animals undergo must necessarily be changes towards re-establishment of the balance. Besides direct equilibration, there must therefore be an indirect equilibration. How this goes on we have now to inquire.

CHAPTER XII.

INDIRECT EQUILIBRATION.

§ 164. Besides those perturbations produced in any organism by special disturbing forces, there are ever going on many others—the reverberating effects of disturbing forces previously experienced by the individual, or by ancestors; and the multiplied deviations of function so caused imply multiplied deviations of structure. In § 155 there was re-illustrated the truth, set forth at length when treating of Adaptation (§ 69), that an organism in a state of moving equilibrium, cannot have extra function thrown on any organ, and extra growth produced in such organ, without correlative changes being entailed throughout all other functions, and eventually throughout all other organs. And when treating of Variation (§ 90), we saw that individuals which have been made, by their different circumstances, to deviate functionally and structurally from the average type in different directions, will bequeath to their joint offspring, compound perturbations of function and compound deviations of structure, endlessly varied in their kinds and amounts.

Now if the individuals of a species are thus necessarily made unlike in countless ways and degrees—if in one individual the amount of energy in a particular direction is greater than in any other individual, or if here a peculiar combination gives a resulting action which is not found elsewhere; then, among all the individuals, some will be less liable than others to have their equilibria overthrown by a particular incident force previously unexperienced. Unless the change in the environment is so violent as to be universally fatal to the species, it must affect more or less differently the slightly-different moving equilibria which the members of the species present. Inevitably some will be more stable than others when exposed to this new or altered factor. That is to say, those individuals whose functions are most out of equilibrium with the modified aggregate of external forces, will be those to die; and those will survive whose functions happen to be most nearly in equilibrium with the modified aggregate of external forces.

But this survival of the fittest[52] implies multiplication of the fittest. Out of the fittest thus multiplied there will, as before, be an overthrowing of the moving equilibrium wherever it presents the least opposing force to the new incident force. And by the continual destruction of the individuals least capable of maintaining their equilibria in presence of this new incident force, there must eventually be reached an altered type completely in equilibrium with the altered conditions.

§ 165. This survival of the fittest, which I have here sought to express in mechanical terms, is that which Mr. Darwin has called "natural selection, or the preservation of favoured races in the struggle for life." That there goes on a process of this kind throughout the organic world, Mr. Darwin's great work on the *Origin of Species* has shown to the satisfaction of nearly all naturalists. Indeed, when once enunciated, the truth of his hypothesis is so obvious as scarcely to need proof. Though evidence may be required to show that natural selection accounts for everything ascribed to it, yet no evidence is required to show that natural selection has always been going on, is going on now, and must ever continue to go on. Recognizing this as an *à priori* certainty, let us contemplate it under its two distinct aspects.

That organisms which live, thereby prove themselves fit for living, in so far as they have been tried, while organisms which die, thereby prove themselves in some respects unfitted for living, are facts no less manifest than is the fact that this self-purification of a species must tend ever to insure adaptation between it and its environment. This adaptation may be either so *maintained* or so *produced.* Doubtless many who have looked at Nature with philosophic eyes, have observed that death of the worst and multiplication of the best, tends towards maintenance of a constitution in harmony with surrounding circumstances. That the average vigour of any race would be diminished did the diseased and feeble habitually survive and propagate; and that the destruction of such, through failure to fulfil some of the conditions to life, leaves behind those which are able to fulfil the conditions to life, and thus keeps up the average fitness to the conditions of life; are almost self-evident truths. But to recognize "Natural Selection" as a means of preserving an already-established balance between the powers of a species and the forces to which it is subject, is to recognize only its simplest and most general mode of action. It is the more special mode of action with which we are here concerned. This more special mode of action, Mr. Darwin has been the first to recognize as an all-important factor, though, besides his co-discoverer Mr. A. R. Wallace, some others have perceived that such a factor is at work. To him we owe due appreciation of the fact that natural selection is capable of *producing* fitness between organisms and their circumstances. He has worked up an enormous mass of evidence showing that this "preservation of favoured races in the struggle for life," is an ever-acting cause of divergence among organic forms. He has traced out the involved results of the process with marvellous subtlety. He has shown how hosts of otherwise inexplicable facts, are accounted for by it. In brief, he has proved that the cause he alleges is a true cause; that it is a cause which we see habitually in action; and that the results to be inferred from it are in harmony with the phenomena which the Organic Creation presents, both as a whole and in its details. Let us glance at a few of the more important interpretations which the hypothesis furnishes.

A soil possessing some ingredient in unusual quantity, may supply to a plant an excess of the matter required for certain of its tissues; and may cause all the parts formed of such tissues to be abnormally developed. Suppose that among these are the hairs clothing its surfaces, including those which grow on its seeds. Thus furnished with somewhat longer fibres, its seeds, when shed, are carried a little further by the wind before they fall to the ground. The plants growing from them, being rather more widely dispersed than those produced by other individuals of the same species, will be less liable to smother one another; and a greater number may therefore reach maturity and fructify. Supposing the next generation subject to the same peculiarity of nutrition, some of the seeds borne by its members will not simply inherit this increased development of hairs, but will carry it further; and these, still more advantaged in the same way as before, will, on the average, have still more numerous chances of continuing the race. Thus, by the survival, generation after generation, of those possessing these longer hairs, and the inheritance of successive increments of growth in the hairs, there may result a seed deviating greatly from the original. Other individuals of the same species, subject to the different physical conditions of other localities, may develop somewhat thicker or harder coatings to their seeds: so rendering their seeds less digestible by the birds which devour them. Such thicker-coated seeds, by escaping undigested more frequently than thinner-coated ones, will have additional chances of growing and leaving offspring; and this process, acting in a cumulative manner season after season, will produce a seed diverging in another direction from the ancestral type. Again, elsewhere, some modification in the physiologic actions of the plant may lead to an unusual secretion of an essential oil in the seeds; rendering them unpalatable to creatures which would otherwise feed on them: so giving an advantage to the variety in its rate of multiplication. This incidental peculiarity, proving a preservative, will, as before, be increased by natural selection until it constitutes another divergence. Now in such cases, we see that plants may become better adapted, or re-adapted, to the aggregate of surrounding agencies, not through any *direct* action of such agencies on them, but through their *indirect* action—through the destruction by them of the individuals least congruous with them, and the survival of those most congruous with them. All these slight variations of function and structure, arising among the members of a species, serve as so many experiments; the great majority of which fail, but a few of which succeed. Just as each plant bears a multitude of seeds, out of which some two or three happen to fulfil all the conditions required for reaching maturity and continuing the race; so each species is ever producing numerous slightly-modified forms, deviating in all directions from the average, out of which most fit the surrounding conditions no better than their parents, or not so well, but some few of which fit the conditions better; and, doing so, are enabled the better to preserve themselves, and to produce offspring similarly capable of preserving themselves. Among animals the like process results in the like development of various structures which cannot have been affected by the performance of functions—their functions being purely passive. The thick shell of a mollusk cannot have arisen from direct reactions of the organism against the external actions to which it is exposed; but it is quite explicable as an effect of the survival, generation after generation, of individuals whose thicker coverings protected them against enemies. Similarly with such dermal structure as that of the tortoise. Though we have evidence that the skin, where it is continually exposed to pressure and friction, may thicken, and so re-establish the equilibrium by opposing a greater inner force to a greater outer force; yet we have no evidence that a coat of armour like that of the tortoise can be so produced. Nor, indeed, are the conditions under which alone its production in such a manner could be accounted for, fulfilled; since the surface of the tortoise is not exposed to greater pressure and friction than the surfaces of other creatures. This massive carapace, and the strangely-adapted osseous frame-work which supports it, are inexplicable as results of evolution, unless through the process of natural selection. So, too, is it with the formation of odoriferous glands in some mammals, or the growth of such excrescences as those of the camel. Thus, in short, is it with all those organs of animals which do not play active parts.

Besides giving us explanations of structural characters that are otherwise unaccountable, Mr. Darwin shows how natural selection explains peculiar relations between individuals in certain species. Such facts as the dimorphism of the primrose and other flowers, he proves to be in harmony with his hypothesis, though stumbling-blocks to all other hypotheses. The various differences which accompany difference of sex, sometimes slight, sometimes very great, are similarly accounted for. As before suggested (§ 79), natural selection appears capable of producing and maintaining the right proportion of the sexes in each species; and it requires but to contemplate the bearings of the argument, to see that the formation of different sexes may itself have been determined in the same way.

To convey here an adequate idea of Mr. Darwin's doctrine, throughout the immense range of its applications, is of course impossible. The few illustrations just given, are intended simply to remind the reader what Mr. Darwin's hypothesis is, and what are the else insoluble problems which it solves for us.

§ 166. But now, though it seems to me that we are thus supplied with a key to phenomena which are multitudinous and varied beyond all conception; it also seems to me that there is a moiety of the phenomena which this key will not unlock. Mr. Darwin himself recognizes use and disuse of parts, as causes of modifications in organisms; and does this, indeed, to a greater extent than do some who accept his general conclusion. But I conceive that he does not recognize them to a sufficient extent. While he shows that the inheritance of changes of structure caused by changes of function, is utterly insufficient to explain a great mass—probably the greater mass—of morphological phenomena; I think he leaves unconsidered a mass of morphological phenomena which are explicable as results of functionally-produced modifications, and are not explicable as results of natural selection.

By induction, as well as by inference from the hypothesis of natural selection, we know that there exists a balance among the powers of organs which habitually act together—such proportions among them that no one has any considerable excess of efficiency. We see, for example, that throughout the vascular system there is maintained an equilibrium of the component parts: in some cases, under continued excess of exertion, the heart gives way, and we have enlargement; in other cases the large arteries give way, and we have aneurisms; in other cases the minute blood-vessels give way—now bursting, now becoming chronically congested. That is to say, in the average constitution, no superfluous strength is possessed by any of the appliances for circulating the blood. Take, again, a set of motor organs. Great strain here causes the fibres of a muscle to tear. There the muscle does not yield but the tendon snaps. Elsewhere neither muscle nor tendon is damaged, but the bone breaks. Joining with these instances the general fact that, under the same adverse conditions, different individuals show their slight differences of constitution by going wrong some in one way and some in another; and that even in the same individual, similar adverse conditions will now affect one viscus and now another; it becomes manifest that though there cannot be maintained an accurate balance among the powers of the organs composing an organism, yet their excesses and deficiencies of power are extremely slight. That they must be extremely slight, is, as before said, a deduction from the hypothesis of natural selection. Mr. Darwin himself argues "that natural selection is continually trying to economise in every part of the organization. If under changed conditions of life a structure before useful becomes less useful, any diminution, however slight, in its development, will be seized on by natural selection, for it will profit the individual not to have its nutriment wasted in building up an useless structure." In other words, if any muscle has more fibres than are required, or if a bone is stronger than needful, no advantage results but rather a disadvantage—a disadvantage which will decrease the chances of survival. Hence it follows that among any organs which habitually act in concert, an increase of one can be of no service unless there is a concomitant increase of the rest. The co-operative parts must vary together; otherwise variation will be detrimental. A stronger muscle must have a stronger bone to resist its contractions; must have stronger correlated muscles and ligaments to secure the neighbouring articulations; must have larger blood-vessels to bring it supplies; must have a more massive nerve to transmit stimulus, and some extra development of a nervous centre to supply the extra stimulus. The question arises, then,—do variations of the appropriate kinds occur simultaneously in all these co-operative parts? Have we any reason to think that the parts spontaneously increase or decrease together? The assumption that they do seems to me untenable; and its untenability will, I think, become conspicuous if we take a case, and observe how extremely numerous and involved are the variations which must be supposed to occur together. In illustration of another point, we have already considered the modifications required to accompany increased weight of the head (§ 155). Instead of the bison, the moose deer, or the extinct Irish elk, will here best serve our purpose. In this last species the male has enormously-developed horns, used for purposes of offence and defence. These horns, weighing upwards of a hundred-weight, are carried at great mechanical disadvantage: supported as they are, along with the massive skull which bears them, at the extremity of the outstretched neck. Further, that these heavy horns may be of use in fighting, the supporting bones and muscles must be strong enough, not simply to carry them, but to put them in motion with the rapidity needed for giving blows. Let us, then, ask how, by natural selection, this complex apparatus of bones and muscles can have been developed, *pari passu* with the horns? If we suppose the horns to have been originally of like size with those borne by other kinds of deer; and if we suppose that in some individual they became larger by spontaneous variation; what would be the concomitant changes required to render their greater size useful? Other things equal, the blow given by a larger horn would be a blow given by a heavier mass moving at a smaller velocity: the momentum would be the same as before; and the area of contact with the body struck being somewhat increased, while the velocity was decreased, the injury done would be less. That horns may become better weapons, the whole apparatus concerned in moving them must be so strengthened as to impress more force on them, and to bear the more violent reactions of the blows given. The bones of the skull on which the horns are seated must be thickened; otherwise they will break. The vertebræ of the neck must be further developed; and unless the ligaments which hold together these vertebræ, and the muscles which move them, are also enlarged, nothing will be gained. Again the upper dorsal vertebræ and their spines must be strengthened, that they may withstand the stronger contractions of the neck-muscles; and like changes must be made on the scapular arch. Still more must there be required a simultaneous development of the bones and muscles of the fore-legs; since these extra growths in the horns, in the skull, in the neck, in the shoulders, add to the burden they have to bear; and without they are strengthened the creature will not only suffer from loss of speed but will fail in fight. Hence, to make larger horns of use, additional sizes must be acquired by numerous bones, muscles, and ligaments, as well as by the blood-vessels and nerves on which their actions depend. On calling to mind how the spraining of a single small muscle in the foot incapacitates for walking, or how permanent weakness in a knee-ligament will diminish the power of the leg, it will be seen that unless all these many changes are simultaneously made, they may as well be none of them made—or rather, they would better be none of them made; since the enlargements of some parts, by putting greater strains on connected parts, would render them relatively weaker if they remained unenlarged. Can we with any propriety assume that these many enlargements duly proportioned will be simultaneously effected by spontaneous variations? I think not. It would be a strong supposition that the vertebræ and muscles of the neck suddenly became bigger at the same time as the horns. It would be a still stronger supposition that the upper dorsal vertebræ not only at the same time became more massive, but appropriately altered their proportions, by the development of their immense neural spines. And it would be an assumption still more straining our powers of belief, that along with heavier horns there should spontaneously take place the required strengthenings in the bones, muscles, arteries, and nerves of the scapular and the fore-legs.

Besides the multiplicity of directly-coöperative organs, the multiplicity of organs which do not coöperate, save in the degree implied by their combination in the same organism, seems to me a further hindrance to the development of special structures by natural selection alone. Where the life is simple, or where circumstances render some one function supremely important, survival of the fittest may readily bring about the appropriate structural change, without aid from the transmission of functionally-caused modifications. But in proportion as the life grows complex—in proportion as a healthy existence cannot be secured by a large endowment of some one power, but demands many powers; in the same proportion do there arise obstacles to the increase of any particular power by "the preservation of favoured races in the struggle for life." As fast as the faculties are multiplied, so fast does it become possible for the several members of a species to have various kinds of superiorities over one another. While one saves its life by higher speed, another does the like by clearer vision, another by keener scent, another by quicker hearing, another by greater strength, another by unusual power of enduring cold or hunger, another by special sagacity, another by special timidity, another by special courage; and others by other bodily and mental attributes. Conditions being alike, each of these life-saving attributes is likely to be transmitted to posterity. But we may not assume that it will be increased in subsequent generations by natural selection. Increase of it can result only if individuals possessing average endowments of it are more frequently killed off than individuals highly endowed with it; and this can happen only when the attribute is one of greater importance, for the time being, than most of the other attributes. If those members of the species which have but ordinary shares of it, nevertheless survive by virtue of other superiorities which they severally possess; then it is not easy to see how this particular attribute can be developed by natural selection in subsequent generations. The probability seems rather to be that, by gamogenesis, this extra endowment will, on the average, be diminished in posterity—just serving in the long run to make up for the deficient endowments of those whose special powers lie in other directions; and so to keep up the normal structure of the species. As fast as the number of bodily and mental faculties increases, and as fast as maintenance of life comes to depend less on the amount of any one and more on the combined actions of all; so fast does the production of specialities of character by natural selection alone, become difficult. Particularly does this seem to be so with a species so multitudinous in its powers as mankind; and above all does it seem to be so with such of the human powers as have but minor shares in aiding the struggle for life—the æsthetic faculties, for example.

It by no means follows, however, that in cases of this kind, and cases of the preceding kind, natural selection plays no part. Wherever it is not the chief agent in working organic changes, it is still, very generally, a secondary agent. The survival of the fittest must nearly always further the production of modifications which produce fitness, whether they be incidental modifications, or modifications caused by direct adaptation. Evidently, those individuals whose constitutions have facilitated the production in them of any structural change consequent on any functional change demanded by some new external condition, will be the individuals most likely to live and to leave descendants. There must be a natural selection of functionally-acquired peculiarities, as well as of spontaneously-acquired peculiarities; and hence such structural changes in a species as result from changes of habit necessitated by changed circumstances, natural selection will render more rapid than they would otherwise be.

There are, however, some modifications in the sizes and forms of parts, which cannot have been aided by natural selection; but which must have resulted wholly from the inheritance of functionally-caused alterations. The dwindling of organs of which the undue sizes entail no appreciable evils, furnishes the best evidence of this. Take, for an example, that diminution of the jaws and teeth which characterizes the civilized races, as contrasted with the savage races.[53] How can the civilized races have been benefited in the struggle for life, by the slight decrease in these comparatively-small bones? No functional superiority possessed by a small jaw over a large jaw in civilized life, can be named as having caused the more frequent survival of small-jawed individuals. The only advantage accompanying smallness of jaw, is the advantage of economized nutrition; and this cannot be great enough to further the preservation of those distinguished by it. The decrease of weight in the jaw and co-operative parts, which has arisen in the course of thousands of years, does not amount to more than a few ounces. This decrease has to be divided among the many generations which have lived and died in the interval. Let us admit that the weight of these parts diminished to the extent of an ounce in a single generation (which is a large admission); it still cannot be contended that the having to carry an ounce less in weight, and to keep in repair an ounce less of tissue, could sensibly affect any man's fate. And if it never did this—nay, if it did not cause a *frequent* survival of small-jawed individuals where large-jawed individuals died; natural selection could neither cause nor aid diminution of the jaw and its appendages. Here, therefore, the decreased action which has accompanied the growth of civilized habits (the use of tools and the disuse of coarse food), must have been the sole cause at work. Through direct equilibration, diminished external stress on these parts has resulted in diminution of the internal forces by which this stress is met. From generation to generation, this lessening of the parts consequent on functional decline has been inherited. And since the survival of individuals must always have been determined by more important structural traits, this trait can have neither been facilitated nor retarded by natural selection.

§ 167. Returning from these extensive classes of facts for which Mr. Darwin's hypothesis does not account, to the still more extensive classes of facts for which it does account, and which are unaccountable on any other hypothesis; let us consider in what way this hypothesis is expressible in terms of the general doctrine of evolution. Already it has been pointed out that the evolving of modified types by "natural selection or the preservation of favoured races in the struggle for life," must be a process of equilibration; since it results in the production of organisms which are in equilibrium with their environments. At the outset of this chapter, something was done towards showing how this continual survival of the fittest may be understood as the progressive establishment of a balance between inner and outer forces. Here, however, we must consider the matter more closely.

On previous occasions we have contemplated the assemblage of individuals composing a species, as an aggregate in a state of moving equilibrium. We have seen that its powers of multiplication give it an expansive energy which is antagonized by other energies; and that through the rhythmical variations in these two sets of energies there is maintained an oscillating limit to its habitat, and an oscillating limit to its numbers. On another occasion (§ 96) it was shown that the aggregate of individuals constituting a species, has a kind of general life which, "like the life of an individual, is maintained by the unequal and ever-varying actions of incident forces on its different parts." We saw that "just as, in each organism, incident forces constantly produce divergences from the mean state in various directions, which are constantly balanced by opposite divergences indirectly produced by other incident forces; and just as the combination of rhythmical functions thus maintained, constitutes the life of the organism; so, in a species there is, through gamogenesis, a perpetual neutralization of those contrary deviations from the mean state, which are caused in its different parts by different sets of incident forces; and it is similarly by the rhythmical production and compensation of these contrary deviations that the species continues to live." Hence, to understand how a species is affected by causes which destroy some of its units and favour the multiplication of others, we must consider it as a whole whose parts are held together by complex forces that are ever re-balancing themselves—a whole whose moving equilibrium is continually disturbed and continually rectified. Thus much premised, let us next call to mind how moving equilibria in general are changed. In the first place, a new incident force falling on any part of an aggregate with balanced motions, produces a new motion in the direction of least resistance. In the second place, the new incident force is gradually used up in overcoming the opposing forces, and when it is all expended the opposing forces produce a recoil—a reverse deviation which counter-balances the original deviation. Consequently, to consider whether the moving equilibrium of a species is modified in the same way as moving equilibria in general, is to consider whether, when exposed to a new force, a species yields in the direction of least resistance; and whether, by its thus yielding, there is generated in the species a compensating change in the opposite direction. We shall find that it does both these things.

For what, expressed in mechanical terms, is the effect wrought on a species by some previously-unknown enemy, that kills such of its members as fail in defending themselves? The disappearance of those individuals which meet the destroying forces by the smallest preserving forces, is tantamount to the yielding of the species as a whole at the places where the resistances are the least. Or if by some general influence, such as alteration of climate, the members of a species are subject to increase of external actions which are ever tending to overthrow their equilibria, and which they are ever counter-balancing by certain physiological actions, which are the first to die? Those least able to generate the internal energies which antagonize these external energies. If the change be an increase of the winter's cold, then such members of the species as have unusual powers of getting food or of digesting food, or such as are by their constitutional aptitude for making fat, furnished with reserve stores of force, available in times of scarcity, or such as have the thickest coats and so lose least heat by radiation, survive; and their survival implies that in each of them the moving equilibrium of functions presents such an adjustment of internal forces, as prevents overthrow by the modified aggregate of external forces. Conversely, the members which die are, other things equal, those deficient in the power of meeting the new action by an equivalent counter-action. Thus, in all cases, a species considered as an aggregate in a state of moving equilibrium, has its state changed by the yielding of its fluctuating mass wherever this mass is weakest in relation to the special forces acting on it. The conclusion is, indeed, a truism. But now what must follow from the destruction of the least-resisting individuals and survival of the most-resisting individuals? On the moving equilibrium of the species as a whole, existing from generation to generation, the effect of this deviation from the mean state is to produce a compensating deviation. For if all such as are deficient of power in a certain direction are destroyed, what must be the effect on posterity? Had they lived and left offspring, the next generation would have had the same average powers as preceding generations: there would have been a like proportion of individuals less endowed with the needful power, and individuals more endowed with it. But the more-endowed individuals being alone left to continue the race, there must result a new generation characterized by a larger average endowment of this power. That is to say, on the moving equilibrium of a species, an action producing change in a given direction is followed, in the next generation, by a reaction producing an opposite change. Observe, too, that these effects correspond in their degrees of violence. If the alteration of some external factor is so great that it leaves alive only the few individuals possessing extreme endowments of the power required to antagonize it; then, in succeeding generations, there is a rapid multiplication of individuals similarly possessing extreme endowments of this power—the force impressed calls out an equivalent conflicting force. Moreover, the change is temporary where the cause is temporary, and permanent where the cause is permanent. All that are deficient in the needful attribute having been killed off, and the survivors having the needful attribute in a comparatively high degree, there will descend from them, not only some possessing equal amounts of this attribute with themselves, but also some possessing less amounts of it. If the destructive agency has not continued in action, such less-endowed individuals will multiply; and the species, after sundry oscillations, will return to its previous mean state. But if this agency be a persistent one, such less endowed individuals will be continually killed off, and eventually none but highly-endowed individuals will be produced—a new moving equilibrium, adapted to the new environing conditions, will result.

It may be objected that this mode of expressing the facts does not include the cases in which a species becomes modified in relation to surrounding agencies of a passive kind—cases like that of a plant which acquires hooked seed-vessels, by which it lays hold of the skins of passing animals, and makes them the distributors of its seeds—cases in which the outer agency has no direct tendency at first to affect the species, but in which the species so alters itself as to take advantage of the outer agency. To cases of this kind, however, the same mode of interpretation applies on simply changing the terms. While, in the aggregate of influences amid which a species exists, there are some which tend to overthrow the moving equilibria of its members, there are others which facilitate the maintenance of their moving equilibria, and some which are capable of giving their moving equilibria increased stability: instance the spread into their habitat of some new kind of prey, which is abundant at seasons when other prey is scarce. Now what is the process by which the moving equilibrium in any species becomes adapted to some additional external factor furthering its maintenance? Instead of an increased resistance to be met and counterbalanced, there is here a diminished resistance; and the diminished resistance is equilibrated in the same way as the increased resistance. As, in the one case, there is a more frequent survival of individuals whose peculiarities enable them to resist the new adverse factor; so, in the other case, there is a more frequent survival of individuals whose peculiarities enable them to take advantage of the new favourable factor. In each member of the species, the balance of functions and correlated arrangement of structures, differ slightly from those existing in other members. To say that among all its members, one is better fitted than the rest to benefit by some before-unused agency in the environment, is to say that its moving equilibrium is, in so far, more stably adjusted to the sum of surrounding influences. And if, consequently, this individual maintains its moving equilibrium when others fail, and has offspring which do the like—that is, if individuals thus characterized multiply and supplant the rest; there is, as before, a process which effects equilibration between the organism and its environment, not immediately but mediately, through the continuous intercourse between the species as a whole and the environment.

§ 168. Thus we see that indirect equilibration does whatever direct equilibration cannot do. All these processes by which organisms are refitted to their ever-changing environments, must be equilibrations of one kind or other. As authority for this conclusion, we have not simply the universal truth that change of every order is towards equilibrium; but we have also the truth that life itself is a moving equilibrium between inner and outer actions—a continuous adjustment of internal relations to external relations; or the maintenance of a balance between the forces to which an organism is subject and the forces which it evolves. Hence all changes which enable a species to live under altered conditions, are changes towards equilibrium with the altered conditions; and therefore those which do not come within the class of direct equilibrations, must come within the class of indirect equilibrations.

And now we reach an interpretation of Natural Selection regarded as a part of Evolution at large. As understood in *First Principles*, Evolution is a continuous redistribution of matter and motion; and a process of evolution which is not expressible in terms of matter and motion has not been reduced to its ultimate form. The conception of Natural Selection is manifestly one not known to physical science: its terms are not of a kind physical science can take cognisance of. But here we have found in what manner it may be brought within the realm of physical science. Rejecting metaphor we see that the process called Natural Selection is literally a survival of the fittest; and the outcome of the above argument is that survival of the fittest is a maintenance of the moving equilibrium of the functions in presence of outer actions: implying the possession of an equilibrium which is relatively stable in contrast with the unstable equilibria of those which do not survive.

CHAPTER XIII.

THE CO-OPERATION OF THE FACTORS.

§ 169. Thus the phenomena of Organic Evolution may be interpreted in the same way as the phenomena of all other Evolution. Fully to see this, it will be needful for us to contemplate in their *ensemble*, the several processes separately described in the four preceding chapters.

If the forces acting on any aggregate remain the same, the changes produced by them will presently reach a limit, at which the outer forces are balanced by the inner forces; and thereafter no further metamorphosis will take place. Hence, that there may be continuous changes of structure in organisms, there must be continuous changes in the incident forces. This condition to the evolution of animal and vegetal forms, we find to be fully satisfied. The astronomic, geologic, and meteorologic changes that have been slowly but incessantly going on, and have been increasing in the complexity of their combinations, have been perpetually altering the circumstances of organisms; and organisms, becoming more numerous in their kinds and higher in their kinds, have been perpetually altering one another's circumstances. Thus, for those progressive modifications upon modifications which organic evolution implies, we find a sufficient cause. The increasing inner changes for which we thus find a cause in the perpetual outer changes, conform, so far as we can trace them, to the universal law of the instability of the homogeneous. In organisms, as in all other things, the exposure of different parts to different kinds and amounts of incident forces, has necessitated their differentiation; and, for the like reason, aggregates of individuals have been lapsing into varieties, and species, and genera, and orders. Further, in each type of organism, as in the aggregate of types, the multiplication of effects has continually aided this transition from a more homogeneous to a more heterogeneous state. And yet again, that increasing segregation and concomitant increasing definiteness, associated with the growing heterogeneity of organisms, has been aided by the continual destruction of those which expose themselves to aggregates of external actions markedly incongruous with the aggregates of their internal actions, and the survival of those subject only to comparatively small incongruities. Finally, we have found that each change of structure, superposed on preceding changes, has been a re-equilibration necessitated by the disturbance of a preceding equilibrium. The maintenance of life being the maintenance of a balanced combination of functions, it follows that individuals and species that have continued to live, are individuals and species in which the balance of functions has not been overthrown. Hence survival through successive changes of conditions, implies successive adjustments of the balance to the new conditions.

The actions that are here specified in succession, are in reality simultaneous; and they must be so conceived before organic evolution can be rightly understood. Some aid towards so conceiving them will be given by the annexed table, representing the co-operation of the factors.

§ 170. Respecting this co-operation, it remains only to point out the respective shares of the factors in producing the total result; and the way in which the proportions of their respective shares vary as evolution progresses.

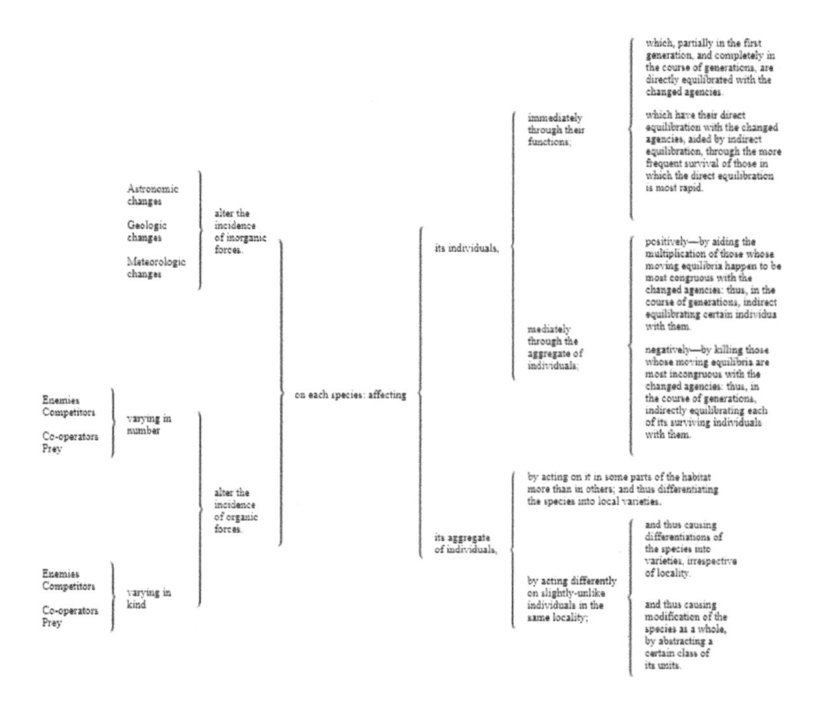

At first, changes in the amounts and combinations of inorganic forces, astronomic, geologic, and meteorologic, were the only causes of the successive modifications; and these changes have continued to be causes. But as, through the diffusion of organisms and consequent differential actions of inorganic forces, there arose unlikenesses among them, producing varieties, species, genera, orders, classes, the actions of organisms on one another became new sources of organic modifications. And as fast as types have multiplied and become more complex, so fast have the mutual actions of organisms come to be more influential factors in their respective evolutions: eventually becoming the chief factors.

Passing from the external causes of change to the internal processes of change entailed by them, we see that these, too, have varied in their proportions: that which was originally the most important and almost the sole process, becoming gradually less important, if not at last the least important. Always there must have been, and always there must continue to be, a survival of the fittest; natural selection must have been in operation at the outset, and can never cease to operate. While yet organisms had small abilities to coordinate their actions, and adjust them to environing actions, natural selection worked almost alone in moulding and remoulding organisms into fitness for their changing environments; and natural selection has remained almost the sole agency by which plants and inferior orders of animals have been modified and developed. The equilibration of organisms that are almost passive, is necessarily effected indirectly, by the action of incident forces on the species as a whole. But along with the evolution of organisms having some activity, there grows up a kind of equilibration which is in part direct. In proportion as the activity increases direct equilibration plays a more important part. Until, when the nervo-muscular apparatus becomes greatly developed, and the power of varying the actions to fit the varying requirements becomes considerable, the share taken by direct equilibration rises into co-ordinate importance or greater importance. As fast as essential faculties multiply, and as fast as the number of organs which co-operate in any given function increases, indirect equilibration through natural selection becomes less and less capable of producing specific adaptations; and remains capable only of maintaining the general fitness of constitution to conditions. The production of adaptations by direct equilibration then takes the first place: indirect equilibration serving to facilitate it. Until at length, among the civilized human races, the equilibration becomes mainly direct: the action of natural selection being limited to the destruction of those who are constitutionally too feeble to live, even with external aid. As the preservation of incapables is secured by our social arrangements; and as very few save incarcerated criminals are prevented by their inferiorities from leaving the average number of offspring; it results that survival of the fittest can scarcely at all act in such way as to produce specialities of nature, either bodily or mental. Here the specialities of nature, chiefly mental, which we see produced, and which are so rapidly produced that a few centuries show a considerable change, must be ascribed almost wholly to direct equilibration.[54]

CHAPTER XIV.

THE CONVERGENCE OF THE EVIDENCES.

§ 171. Of the three classes of evidences that have been assigned in proof of Evolution, the *à priori*, which we took first, were partly negative, partly positive.

On considering the "General Aspects of the Special-creation hypothesis," we discovered it to be worthless. Discredited by its origin, and wholly without any basis of observed fact, we found that it was not even a thinkable hypothesis; and, while thus intellectually illusive, it turned out to have moral implications irreconcilable with the professed beliefs of those who hold it.

Contrariwise, the "General Aspects of the Evolution-hypothesis" begot the stronger faith in it the more nearly they were considered. By its lineage and its kindred, it was found to be as closely allied with the proved truths of modern science, as is the antagonist hypothesis with the proved errors of ancient ignorance. We saw that instead of being a mere pseud-idea, it admits of elaboration into a definite conception: so showing its legitimacy as an hypothesis. Instead of positing a purely fictitious process, the process which it alleges proves to be one actually going on around us. To which add that, morally considered, this hypothesis presents no radical incongruities.

Thus, even were we without further means of judging, there could be no rational hesitation which of the two views should be entertained.

§ 172. Further means of judging, however, we found to be afforded by bringing the two hypotheses face to face with the general truths established by naturalists. These inductive evidences were dealt with in four chapters.

"The Arguments from Classification" were these. Organisms fall into groups within groups; and this is the arrangement which we see results from evolution, where it is known to take place. Of these groups within groups, the great or primary ones are the most unlike, the sub-groups are less unlike, the sub-sub-groups still less unlike, and so on; and this, too, is a characteristic of groups demonstrably produced by evolution. Moreover, indefiniteness of equivalence among the groups is common to those which we know have been evolved, and those here supposed to have been evolved. And then there is the further significant fact, that divergent groups are allied through their lowest rather than their highest members.

Of "the Arguments from Embryology," the first is that when developing embryos are traced from their common starting point, and their divergences and re-divergences symbolized by a genealogical tree, there is manifest a general parallelism between the arrangement of its primary, secondary, and tertiary branches, and the arrangement of the divisions and sub-divisions of our classifications. Nor do the minor deviations from this general parallelism, which look like difficulties, fail, on closer observation, to furnish additional evidence; since those traits of a common ancestry which embryology reveals, are, if modifications have resulted from changed conditions, liable to be disguised in different ways and degrees in different lines of descendants.

We next considered "the Arguments from Morphology." Apart from those kinships among organisms disclosed by their developmental changes, the kinships which their adult forms show are profoundly significant. The unities of type found under such different externals, are inexplicable except as results of community of descent with non-community of modification. Again, each organism analyzed apart, shows, in the likenesses obscured by unlikenesses of its component parts, a peculiarity which can be ascribed only to the formation of a more heterogeneous organism out of a more homogeneous one. And once more, the existence of rudimentary organs, homologous with organs that are developed in allied animals or plants, while it admits of no other rational interpretation, is satisfactorily interpreted by the hypothesis of evolution.

Last of the inductive evidences, came "the Arguments from Distribution." While the facts of distribution in Space are unaccountable as results of designed adaptation of organisms to their habitats, they are accountable as results of the competition of species, and the spread of the more fit into the habitats of the less fit, followed by the changes which new conditions induce. Though the facts of distribution in Time are so fragmentary that no positive conclusion can be drawn, yet all of them are reconcilable with the hypothesis of evolution, and some of them yield it strong support: especially the near relationship existing between the living and extinct types in each great geographical area.

Thus of these four groups, each furnished several arguments which point to the same conclusion; and the conclusion pointed to by the arguments of any one group, is that pointed to by the arguments of every other group. This coincidence of coincidences would give to the induction a very high degree of probability, even were it not enforced by deduction. But the conclusion deductively reached, is in harmony with the inductive conclusion.

§ 173. Passing from the evidence that evolution has taken place, to the question—How has it taken place? we find in known agencies and known processes, adequate causes of its phenomena.

In astronomic, geologic, and meteorologic changes, ever in progress, ever combining in new and more involved ways, we have a set of inorganic factors to which all organisms are exposed; and in the varying and complicating actions of organisms on one another, we have a set of organic factors that alter with increasing rapidity. Thus, speaking generally, all members of the Earth's Flora and Fauna experience perpetual re-arrangements of external forces.

Each organic aggregate, whether considered individually or as a continuously-existing species, is modified afresh by each fresh distribution of external forces. To its pre-existing differentiations new differentiations are added; and thus that lapse to a more heterogeneous state, which would have a fixed limit were the circumstances fixed, has its limit perpetually removed by the perpetual change of the circumstances.

These modifications upon modifications which result in evolution structurally considered, are the accompaniments of those functional alterations continually required to re-equilibrate inner with outer actions. That moving equilibrium of inner actions corresponding with outer actions, which constitutes the life of an organism, must either be overthrown by a change in the outer actions, or must undergo perturbations that cannot end until there is a re-adjusted balance of functions and correlative adaptation of structures.

But where the external changes are either such as are fatal when experienced by the individuals, or such as act on the individuals in ways that do not affect the equilibrium of their functions; then the re-adjustment results through the effects produced on the species as a whole—there is indirect equilibration. By the preservation in successive generations of those whose moving equilibria are least at variance with the requirements, there is produced a changed equilibrium completely in harmony with the requirements.

§ 174. Even were this the whole of the evidence assignable for the belief that organisms have been gradually evolved, it would have a warrant higher than that of many beliefs which are regarded as established. But the evidence is far from exhausted.

At the outset it was remarked that the phenomena presented by the organic world as a whole, cannot be properly dealt with apart from the phenomena presented by each organism, in the course of its growth, development, and decay. The interpretation of either implies interpretation of the other; since the two are in reality parts of one process. Hence, the validity of any hypothesis respecting the one class of phenomena, may be tested by its congruity with phenomena of the other class. We are now about to pass to the more special phenomena of development, as displayed in the structures and functions of individual organisms. If the hypothesis that plants and animals have been progressively evolved be true, it must furnish us with keys to these phenomena. We shall find that it does this; and by doing it gives numberless additional vouchers for its truth.

CHAPTER XIVA.

RECENT CRITICISMS AND HYPOTHESES.

§ 174*a*. Since the first edition of this work was published, and more especially since the death of Mr. Darwin, an active discussion of the Evolution hypothesis has led to some significant results.

That organic evolution has been going on from the dawn of life down to the present time, is now a belief almost universally accepted by zoologists and botanists—"almost universally," I say, because the surviving influence of Cuvier prevents acceptance of it by some of them in France. Omitting the ideas of these, all biological interpretations, speculations, and investigations, tacitly assume that organisms of every kind in every era and in every region have come into existence by the process of descent with modification.

But while concerning the fact of evolution there is agreement, concerning its causes there is disagreement. The ideas of naturalists have, in this respect, undergone a differentiation increasingly pronounced; which has ended in the production of two diametrically opposed beliefs. The cause which Mr. Darwin first made conspicuous has come to be regarded by some as the sole cause; while, on the part of others there has been a growing recognition of the cause which he at first disregarded but afterwards admitted. Prof. Weismann and his supporters contend that natural selection suffices to explain everything. Contrariwise, among many who recognize the inheritance of functionally-produced changes, there are a few, like the Rev. Prof. Henslow, who regard it as the sole factor.

The foregoing chapters imply that the beliefs of neither extreme are here adopted. Agreeing with Mr. Darwin that both factors have been operative, I hold that the inheritance of functionally-caused alterations has played a larger part than he admitted even at the close of his life; and that, coming more to the front as evolution has advanced, it has played the chief part in producing the highest types. I am not now about to discuss afresh these questions, but to deal with certain further questions.

For while there has been taking place in the biological world the major differentiation above indicated, there have been taking place certain minor differentiations—there have been arising special views respecting the process of organic evolution. Concerning each of these it is needful to say something.

§ 174*b*. Among the implied controversies the most conspicuous one has concerned the alleged process called by Prof. Weismann *Panmixia*—a process which Dr. Romanes had foreshadowed under the name of "the Cessation of Selection." Dr. Romanes says:—"At that time it appeared to me, as it now appears to Weismann, entirely to supersede the necessity of supposing that the effect of disuse is ever inherited in any degree at all."[55] The alleged mode of action is exemplified by Prof. Weismann as follows:—

"A goose or a duck must possess strong powers of flight in the natural state, but such powers are no longer necessary for obtaining food when it is brought into the poultry-yard, so that a rigid selection of individuals with well-developed wings, at once ceases among its descendants. Hence in the course of generations, a deterioration of the organs of flight must necessarily ensue, and the other members and organs of the bird will be similarly affected."[56]

Here, and throughout the arguments of those who accept the hypothesis of Panmixia, there is an unwarranted assumption—nay, an assumption at variance with the doctrine in support of which it is made. It is contended that in such cases as the one given there will, apart from any effects of disuse, be decrease in the disused organs because, not being kept by Natural Selection up to the level of strength previously needed, they will vary in the direction of decrease; and that variations in the direction of decrease, occurring in some individuals, will, by interbreeding, produce an average decrease throughout the species. But why will the disused organs vary in the direction of decrease more than in the direction of increase? The hypothesis of Natural Selection postulates indeterminate variations—deviations no more in one direction than in the opposite direction: implying that increases and decreases of size will occur to equal extents and with equal frequencies. With any other assumption the hypothesis lapses; for if the variations in one direction exceed those in another the question arises—What makes them do this? And whatever makes them do this becomes the essential cause of the modification: the selection of favourable variations is tacitly admitted to be an insufficient explanation. But if the hypothesis of Natural Selection itself implies the occurrence of equal variations on all sides of the mean, how can Panmixia produce decrease? *Plus* deviations will cancel *minus* deviations, and the organ will remain where it was.[57]

"But you have forgotten the tendency to economy of growth," will be the reply—"you have forgotten that in Mr. Darwin's words 'natural selection is continually trying to economize in every part of the organization;' and that this is a constant cause favouring *minus* variations." I have not forgotten it;

but have remembered it as showing how, to support the hypothesis of Panmixia, there is invoked the aid of that very hypothesis which it is to replace. For this principle of economy is but another aspect of the principle of functionally-produced modifications. Nearly forty years ago I contended that "the different parts of ... an individual organism compete for nutriment; and severally obtain more or less of it according as they are discharging more or less duty:"[58] the implication being that as all other organs are demanding blood, decrease of duty in any one, entailing decreased supply of blood, brings about decreased size. In other words, the alleged economy is nothing else than the abstraction, by active parts, of nutriment from an inactive part; and is merely another name for functionally-produced decrease. So that if the variations are supposed to take place predominantly in the direction of decrease, it can only be by silently assuming the cause which is overtly denied.

But now we come to the strange fact that the particular case in which panmixia is assigned in disproof of alleged inheritance of functionally-produced modifications, is a case in which it would be inapplicable even were its assumption legitimate—the case of disused organs in domestic animals. For since nutrition is here abundant, the principle of economy under the form alleged does not come into play. Contrariwise, there even occurs a partial re-development of rudimentary organs: instances named by Mr. Darwin being the supplementary mammæ in cows, fifth toes on the hind feet of dogs, spurs and comb in hens, and canine teeth in mares. Now clearly, if organs disused for innumerable generations may thus vary in the direction of increase, it must, *a fortiori*, be so with recently disused organs, and there disappears all plea (even the illegitimate plea) for assuming that in the wing of a wild duck which has become domesticated, the *minus* variations will exceed the *plus* variations: the hypothesis of panmixia loses its postulate.

If it be said that Mr. Darwin's argument is based on the changed ratio between the weights of leg-bones and wing-bones, and that this changed ratio may result not from decrease of the wing-bones but from increase of the leg-bones, then there comes a fatal reply. Such, increase cannot be ascribed to selection of varieties, since there is no selective breeding to obtain larger legs, and as it is not pretended that panmixia accounts for increase the case is lost: there remains no cause for such increase save increase of function.

§ 174*c*. The doctrine of determinate evolution or definitely-directed evolution, which appears to be in one form or other entertained by sundry naturalists, has been set forth by the late Prof. Eimer under the title "Orthogenesis." A distinct statement of his conception is not easily made for the reason that, as I think, the conception itself is indistinct. Here are some extracts from a translation of his paper published at Chicago. Out of these the reader may form a notion of the theory:

"Orthogenesis shows that organisms develop in definite directions without the least regard for utility through purely physiological causes as the result of *organic growth*, as I term the process."

"I am concerned in this paper with definitely directed evolution as the cause of transmutation, and not with the effects of the use and activity of organs which with Lamarck I adopted as the second main explanatory cause thereof."

"The causes of definitely directed evolution are contained, according to my view, in the effects produced by outward circumstances and influences such as climate and nutrition upon the constitution of a given organism."

"At variance with all the facts of definitely directed evolution ... is also the contention of my opponent [Weismann] ... that the variations demonstrably oscillate to and fro in the most diverse directions about a given zero-point. There is no oscillation in the direction of development, but simply an advance forwards in a straight line with occasional lateral divergences whereby the forkings of the ancestral tree are produced."[59]

These sentences contain one of those explanations which explain nothing; for we are not enabled to see how the "outward circumstances and influences" produce the effects ascribed to them. We are not shown in what way they cause organic evolution in general, still less in what way they cause the infinitely-varied forms in which organic evolution results. The assertion that evolution takes definitely-directed lines is accompanied by no indication of the reasons why particular lines are followed rather than others. In short, we are simply taken a step back, and for further interpretation referred to a cause said to be adequate, but the operations of which we are to imagine as best we may.

This is a re-introduction of supernaturalism under a disguise. It may pair off with the conception made popular by the *Vestiges of the Natural History of Creation*, in which it was contended that there exists a persistent tendency towards the birth of a higher form of creature; or it may be bracketed with the idea entertained by the late Prof. Owen, who alleged an "ordained becoming" of living things.

§ 174*d*. An objection to the Darwinian doctrine which has risen into prominence, is that Natural Selection does not explain that which it professes to explain. In the words of Mr. J. T. Cunningham:—

"Everybody knows that the theory of natural selection was put forward by Darwin as a theory of the origin of species, and yet it is only a theory of the origin of adaptations. The question is: Are the differences between species differences of adaptation? If so, then the origin of species and the origin of adaptations are equivalent terms. But there is scarcely a single instance in which a specific character has been shown to be useful, to be adaptive."[60]

To illustrate this last statement Mr. Cunningham names the plaice, flounder, and dab as three flat fishes in which, along with the adaptive characters related to the mode of life common to them all, each has specific characters which are not adaptive. No evidence is forthcoming that these in any way conduce to the welfare of the species. Two propositions are here involved which should be separately dealt with.

The first is that the adaptive modifications which survival of the fittest is able to produce, do not become specific traits: they are traits separate in kind from those which mark off groups proved to be specifically distinct by their inability to breed together. Such evidence as we at present have seems to warrant this statement. Out of the many varieties of dogs most, if not all, have been rendered distinct by adaptive modifications, mostly produced by selection. But, notwithstanding the immense divergences of structure so produced, the varieties inter-breed. To this, however, it may be replied that sufficient time has not elapsed—that the process by which a structural adaptation so reacts on the constitution as to make it a distinct one, possibly, or probably, takes many thousands of years. Let us accept for the moment Lord Kelvin's low estimate of the geologic time during which life has existed—one hundred million years. Suppose we divide that time into as many parts as there are hours occupied in the development of a human fœtus. And suppose that during these hundred million years there has been going on with some uniformity the evolution of the various organic types now existing. Then the amount of change undergone by the fœtus in an hour, will be equivalent to the amount of change undergone by an evolving organic form in fifteen thousand years. That is to say, during general evolution it may have taken fifteen thousand years to establish, as distinct, two species differing from one another no more than the fœtus differs from itself after the lapse of an hour. Hence, though we lack proof that adaptive modifications become specific traits, it is quite possible that they are in course of becoming specific traits.

The converse proposition, that the traits by which species are ordinarily distinguished are non-adaptive traits is well sustained; and the statement that, if not themselves useful they are correlated with those which are useful, is, to say the least, unproved. For the instances given by Mr. Darwin of correlated traits are not those between adaptive traits and the traits regarded as specific, but between traits none of which are specific; as between skull and limbs in swine, tusks and bristles in swine, horns and wool in sheep, beak and feet in pigeons.

If we seek a clue in those processes by which correlations are brought about—the physiological actions and reactions—we may at once see that any organic modification, be it adaptive or not, must entail secondary modifications throughout the rest of the organism, most of them insensible but some of them sensible. The competition for blood among organs, referred to above, necessitates that, other things remaining the same, the extra growth of any one tells on all others, in variable degrees according to conditions, and may cause appreciable diminutions of some. This is not all. While the quantity of blood supplied to other organs is affected, its quality also is in some cases affected. Each organ, or at any rate each class of organs, has special nutrition—abstracts from the blood a proportion of ingredients different from that abstracted by other organs or classes of organs. Hence may result a deficiency or a surplus of some element: instance the change in the blood which must be caused by growth of a stag's antlers. Now if such effects are always produced, and if, further, a change of general nutrition caused by a new food or by a difference of ability to utilize certain components of food, similarly operates (instance the above named correlation between horns and wool), then every modification must entail throughout the organism multitudinous alterations of structure. Such alterations will ordinarily be neither in themselves useful nor necessarily correlated with those which are useful; since they must arise as concomitants of any change, whether adaptive or not. There will consequently arise the innumerable minute differences presented by allied species in addition to the differences called specific.

On joining with recognition of this general process a recognition of the tendency towards localization of deposit, one possible origin of specific marks is suggested. When in an organism the circulating fluids contain useless matter, normal or abnormal, the excretion of it, once determined towards a certain place, continues at that place. Trees furnish examples in the casting out of gums and resins. Animal life yields evidence in gouty concretions and such morbid products as tubercle. A place of enfeebled nutrition is commonly chosen—not unfrequently a place where a local injury has occurred. Now if we extend this principle, well recognized in pathological processes, to physiological processes, we may infer that where an adaptive modification has so reacted on the blood as to leave some matter to be got rid of, the deposit of this, initiated at some place of least resistance, may produce a local structure which eventually becomes a species-mark. A relevant inquiry suggests itself—What proportion of species-marks are formed out of inanimate tissue or tissue of low vitality—tissue which, like hair, feathers, horns, teeth, is composed of by-products unfit for carrying on vital actions.

§ 174*e*. In the days when, not having been better instructed by Mr. Darwin, I believed that all changes of structure in organisms result from changes of function, I held that the cause of such changes of function is migration. Assuming as the antecedent of migration a great geologic change, such as upheaval of the East Indian Archipelago step by step into a continent, it was argued, in an essay I then wrote, that, subjected primarily to new influences in its original habitat, each kind of plant and animal would secondarily be subjected to the altered conditions consequent on spreading over the upheaved regions.

"Each species being distributed over an area of some extent, and tending continually to colonize the new area exposed, its different members would be subject to different sets of changes. Plants and animals spreading towards the equator would not be affected in the same way with others spreading from it. Those spreading towards the new shores would undergo changes unlike the changes undergone by those spreading into the mountains. Thus, each original race of organisms would become the root from which diverged several races differing more or less from it and from one another."

It was further argued that, beyond modifications caused by change of physical conditions and food, others would be caused by contact of the Flora and Fauna of each island with the Floras and Faunas of other islands: bringing experience of animals and plants before unknown.[61]

While this conception was wrong in so far as it ascribed the production of new species entirely to inheritance of functionally-wrought alterations (thus failing to recognize Natural Selection, which was not yet enunciated), it was right in so far as it ascribed organic changes to changes of conditions. And it was, I think, also right in so far as it implied that isolation is a condition precedent to such changes. Apparently it did not occur to me as needful to specify this isolation as making possible the differentiation of species; since it goes without saying that members of a species spreading east, west, north, south, and forming groups hundreds of miles apart, must, while breeding with those of the same group be prevented from breeding with those of other groups—prevented from having their locally-caused modifications mutually cancelled.

The importance of isolation has of late been emphasized by Dr. Romanes and others, who, to that isolation consequent on geographical diffusion, have added that isolation which results from difference of station in the same habitat, and also that due to differences in the breeding periods arising in members of the same species. Doubtless in whatever way effected, the isolation of a group subject to new conditions and in course of being changed, is requisite as a means to permanent differentiation.

Doubtless also, as contended by Mr. Gulick and Dr. Romanes, there is a difference between the case in which an entire species being subject to the same conditions is throughout modified in character, thus illustrating what Mr. Gulick calls "monotypic evolution," and the case in which different parts of the species, leading different lives, will, if they are by any means prevented from inter-breeding with other parts, form divergent varieties: thus illustrating "polytypic evolution."

§ 174*f*. Beyond geographical and topographical isolation, there is an isolation of another kind regarded by some as having had an important share in organic evolution. Foreshadowed by Mr. Belt, subsequently enunciated by Mr. Catchpool, fully thought out by Mr. Gulick, and more recently elaborated by Dr. Romanes, "Physiological Selection" is held to account for the genesis of marked varieties side by side with their parents. It is contended that without the kind of isolation implied by it, variations will be swamped by inter-crossing, and divergence prevented; but that by the aid of this kind of isolation, a uniform species may be differentiated into two or more species, though its members continue to live in the same area.

Facts are assigned to show that slightly unlike varieties may become unable to inter-breed either with the parent-species or with one another. This mutual inferiority is not of the kind we might expect. We might reasonably suppose that when varieties had diverged widely, crossing would be impracticable, because their constitutions had become so far unlike as to form an unworkable mixture. But there seems evidence that the infertility arises long before such a cause could operate, and that instead of failure to produce a workable constitution, there is failure to produce any constitution at all—failure to fertilize. Some change in the sexual system is suggested as accounting for this. That a minute difference in the reproductive elements may suffice, plants prove by the fact that when two members of slightly-divergent varieties are fertilized by each other's pollen, the fertility is less than if each were fertilized by the pollen of its own variety; and where the two kinds of pollen are both used, that derived from members of the same variety is prepotent in its effect over that derived from members of the other variety.

The writers above named contend that variations must occur in the reproductive organs as well as in other organs; that such variations may produce relative infertility in particular directions; and that such relative infertility may be the first step towards prevention of crossing and establishment of isolation: so making possible the accumulation of such differences as mark off new species. Without doubt we have here a legitimate supposition and a legitimate inference. Necessarily there must happen variations of the kind alleged, and considering how sensitive the reproductive system is to occult influences (witness among ourselves the frequent infertility of healthy people while feeble unhealthy ones are fertile), it is reasonable to infer that minute and obscure alterations of this kind may make slightly-different varieties unable to inter-breed.

Granting that there goes on this "physiological selection," we must recognize it as one among the causes by which isolation is produced, and the differentiating influence of natural selection in the same locality made possible.

§ 174*g*. The foregoing criticisms and hypotheses do not, however, affect in any essential way the pre-existing conceptions. If, as in the foregoing chapters, we interpret the facts in terms of that redistribution of matter and motion constituting Evolution at large, we shall see that the general theory, as previously held, remains outstanding.

It is indisputable that to maintain its life an organism must maintain the moving equilibrium of its functions in presence of environing actions. This is a truism: overthrow of the equilibrium is death. It is a corollary that when the environment is changed, the equilibrium of functions is disturbed, and there must follow one of two results—either the equilibrium is overthrown or it is re-adjusted: there is a re-equilibration. Only two possible ways of effecting the re-adjustment exist—the direct and the indirect. In the one case the changed outer action so alters the moving equilibrium as to call forth an equivalent reaction which balances it. If re-equilibration is not thus effected in the individual it is effected in the succession of individuals. Either the species altogether disappears, or else there disappear, generation after generation, those members of it the equilibria of whose functions are least congruous with the changed actions in the environment; and this is the survival of the fittest or natural selection.

If now we persist in thus contemplating the problem as a statico-dynamical one, we shall see that much of the discussion commonly carried on is beside the question. The centre around which the collision of arguments has taken place, is the question of the formation of species. But here we see that this question is a secondary and, in a sense, irrelevant one. We are concerned with the production of evolving and diverging organic forms; and whether these are or are not marked off by so-called specific traits, and whether they will or will not breed together, matters little to the general argument. If two divisions of a species, falling into unlike conditions and becoming re-equilibrated with them, eventually acquire the differences of nature called specific, this is but a collateral result. The *essential* result is the formation of divergent organic forms. The biologic atmosphere, so to speak, has been vitiated by the conceptions of past naturalists, with whom the identification and classification of species was the be-all and end-all of their science, and who regarded the traits which enabled them to mark off their specimens from one another, as the traits of cardinal importance in Nature. But after ignoring these technical ideas it becomes manifest that the distinctions, morphological or physiological, taken as tests of species, are merely incidental phenomena.

Moreover, on continuing thus to look at the facts, we shall better understand the relation between adaptive and specific characters, and between specific characters and those many small differences which always accompany them. For during re-equilibration there must, beyond those changes of structure required to balance outer actions by inner actions, be numerous minor changes. In any complex moving equilibrium alterations of larger elements inevitably cause alterations of elements immediately dependent on them, and these again of others: the effects reverberate and re-reverberate throughout the entire aggregate of actions down to the most minute. Of resulting structural changes a few will be conspicuous, more will be less conspicuous, and so on continuously multiplying in number and decreasing in amount.

Here seems a fit place for remarking that there are certain processes which do not enter into these re-equilibrations but in a sense interfere with them. One example must suffice. Among dogs may be observed the trick of rolling on some mass having a strong animal smell: commonly a decaying carcase. This trick has probably been derived from the trick of rolling on the body of an animal caught and killed, and so gaining a tempting odour. A male dog which first did this, and left a trail apt to be mistaken for that of prey, would be more easily found by a female, and would be more likely than others to leave posterity. Now such a trick could have no relation to better maintenance of the moving equilibrium, and might very well arise in a dog having no superiority. If it arose in one of the worst it would be eliminated from the species, but if it arose in one of medium constitution, fairly capable of self-preservation, it would tend to produce survival of certain of the less fit rather than the fittest. Probably there are many such minor traits which are in a sense accidental, and are neither adaptive nor specific in the ordinary sense.

§ 174*b*. But now let it be confessed that though all phenomena of organic evolution must fall within the lines above indicated, there remain many unsolved problems.

Take as an instance the descent of the testes in the *Mammalia*. Neither direct nor indirect equilibration accounts for this. We cannot consider it an adaptive change, since there seems no way in which the production of sperm-cells, internally carried on in a bird, is made external by adjustment to the changed requirements of mammalian life. Nor can we ascribe it to survival of the fittest; for it is incredible that any mammal was ever advantaged in the struggle for life by this changed position of these organs. Contrariwise, the removal of them from a place of safety to a place of danger, would seem to be negatived by natural selection. Nor can we regard the transposition as a concomitant of re-equilibration; since it can hardly be due to some change in the general physiological balance.

An example of another order is furnished by the mason-wasp. Several instincts, capacities, peculiarities, which are in a sense independent though they cooperate to the same end, are here displayed. There is the instinct to build a cell of grains of sand, and the ability to do this, which though in a sense separate may be regarded as an accompaniment; and there is the secretion of a cement—a physiological process not directly connected with the psychological process. After oviposition there comes into play the instinct to seek, carry home, and pack into the cell, the small caterpillars, spiders, &c., which are to serve as food for the larva; and then there is the instinct to sting each of them at a spot where the injected hypnotic poison keeps the creature insensible though alive till it is wanted. These cannot be regarded as parts of a whole developed in simultaneous coordination. There is no direct connexion between the building instinct and the hypnotizing instinct; still less between these instincts and the associated appliances. What were the early stages they passed through imagination fails to suggest. Their usefulness depends on their combination; and this combination would seem to have been useless until they had all reached something like their present completeness. Nor can we in this case ascribe anything to the influence of teaching by imitation, supposed to explain the doings of social insects; for the mason-wasp is solitary.

Thus the process of organic evolution is far from being fully understood. We can only suppose that as there are devised by human beings many puzzles apparently unanswerable till the answer is given, and many necromantic tricks which seem impossible till the mode of performance is shown; so there are apparently incomprehensible results which are really achieved by natural processes. Or, otherwise, we must conclude that since Life itself proves to be in its ultimate nature inconceivable, there is probably an inconceivable element in its ultimate workings.

END OF VOL. I.

APPENDICES.

APPENDIX A.

THE GENERAL LAW OF ANIMAL FERTILITY.

[*In the* Westminster Review *for April, 1852, I published an essay under the title "A Theory of Population deduced from the General Law of Animal Fertility." That essay was the germ of Part VI of this work, "The Laws of Multiplication," in which its essential theses are fully developed. When developing them, I omitted some portions of the original essay—one which was not directly relevant, and another which contained a speculation open to criticism. As indicated in § 74f, I find that this speculation has an unexpected congruity with recent results of inquiry. I therefore decide to reproduce it here along with the definition of Life propounded in that essay, which, though subsequently replaced by the definition elaborated in Part I, contains an element of truth.*]

* * * * *

Some clear idea of the nature of Life itself, must, indeed, form a needful preliminary. We may be sure that a search for the influences determining the maintenance and multiplication of living organisms, cannot be successfully carried out unless we understand what is the peculiar property of a living organism—what is the widest generalization of the phenomena that indicate life. By way of preparation, therefore, for the Theory of Population presently to be developed, we propose devoting a brief space to this prior question.

* * * * *

Employing the term, then, in its usual sense, as applicable only to organisms, Life may be defined as—*the co-ordination of actions.* The growth of a crystal, which is the highest inorganic process we are acquainted with, involves but one action—that of accretion. The growth of a cell, which is the lowest organic process, involves two actions—accretion and disintegration—repair and waste—assimilation and oxidation. Wholly deprive a cell of oxygen, and it becomes inert—ceases to manifest vital phenomena; or, as we say, dies. Give it no matter to assimilate, and it wastes away and disappears, from continual oxidation. Evidently, then, it is in the balance of these two actions that the life consists. It is not in the assimilation alone; for the crystal assimilates: neither is it in the oxidation alone; for oxidation is common to inorganic matter: but it is in the joint maintenance of these—the *co-ordination* of them. So long as the two go on together, life continues: suspend either of them, and the result is—death.

The attribute which thus distinguishes the lowest organic from the highest inorganic bodies, similarly distinguishes the higher organisms from the lower ones. It is in the greater complexity of the co-ordination—that is, in the greater number and variety of the co-ordinated actions—that every advance in the scale of being essentially consists. And whether we regard the numerous vital processes carried on in a creature of complex structure as so many additional processes, or whether, more philosophically, we regard them as subdivisions of the two fundamental ones—oxidation and accretion—the co-ordination of them is still the life. Thus turning to what is physiologically classified as the *vegetative system*, we see that stomach, lungs, heart, liver, skin, and the rest, must work in concert. If one of them does too much or too little—that is, if the co-ordination be imperfect—the life is disturbed; and if one of them ceases to act—that is, if the co-ordination be destroyed—the life is destroyed. So likewise is it with the *animal system*, which indirectly assists in co-ordinating the actions of the viscera by supplying food and oxygen. Its component parts, the limbs, senses, and instruments of attack or defence must perform their several offices in proper sequence; and further, must conjointly minister to the periodic demands of the viscera, that these may in turn supply blood. How completely the several attributes of animal life come within the definition, we shall best see on going through them *seriatim*.

Thus *Strength* results from the co-ordination of actions; for it is produced by the simultaneous contraction of many muscles and many fibres of each muscle; and the strength is great in proportion to the number of these acting together—that is, in proportion to the co-ordination. *Swiftness* also, depending partly on strength, but requiring also the rapid alternation of movements, equally comes under the expression; seeing that, other things equal, the more quickly sequent actions can be made to follow each other, the more completely are they co-ordinated. So, too, is it with *Agility*; the power of a chamois to spring with safety from crag to crag implies accurate co-ordination in the movements of many different muscles, and a due subordination of them all to the perceptions. The definition similarly includes *Instinct*, which consists in the uniform succession of certain actions or series of actions after certain sensations or groups of sensations; and that which surprises us in instinct is the accuracy with which these compound actions respond to these compound sensations; that is—the completeness of their co-ordination. Thus, likewise, is it with *Intelligence*, even in its highest manifestations. That which we call rationality is the power to combine, or co-ordinate a great number and a great variety of complex actions for the achievement of a desired result. The husbandman has in the course of years, by drainage and manuring, to bring his ground into a fertile state; in the autumn he must plough, harrow, and sow, for his next year's crop; must subsequently hoe and weed, keep out cattle, and scare away birds; when harvest comes, must adapt the mode and time of getting in his produce to the weather and the labour market; he must afterwards decide when, and where, and how to sell to the best advantage; and must do all this that he may get food and clothing for his family. By properly coordinating these various processes (each of which involves many others)—by choosing right modes, right times, right quantities, right qualities, and performing his acts in right order, he attains his end. But if he have done too little of this, or too much of that; or have done one thing when he should have done another—if his proceedings have been badly co-ordinated—that is, if he have lacked intelligence—he fails.

We find, then, that *the co-ordination of actions* is a definition of Life, which includes alike its highest and its lowest manifestations; and not only so, but expresses likewise the degree of Life, seeing that the Life is high in proportion as the co-ordination is great. Proceeding upwards, from the simplest organic cell in which there are but two interdependent actions, on through the group in which many such cells are acting in concert, on through the higher group in which some of these cells assume mainly the respiratory and others the assimilative function—proceeding still higher to organisms in which these two functions are subdivided into many others, and in which some cells begin to act together as contractile fibres; next to organisms in which the visceral division of labour is carried yet further, and in which many contractile fibres act together as muscles—ascending again to creatures that combine the movements of several limbs and many bones and muscles in one action; and further, to creatures in which complex impressions are followed by the complex acts we term instinctive—and arriving finally at man, in whom not only are the separate acts complex, but who achieves his ends by combining together an immense number and variety of acts often extending through years—we see that the progress is uniformly towards greater co-ordination of actions. Moreover, this co-ordination of actions unconsciously constitutes the essence of our common notion of life; for we shall find, on inquiry, that when we infer the death of an animal, which does not move on being touched, we infer it because we miss the usual co-ordination of a sensation and a motion: and we shall also find, that the test by which we habitually rank creatures high or low in the scale of vitality is the degree of co-ordination their actions exhibit.

* * * * *

There remains but to notice the objection which possibly may be raised, that the co-ordination of actions is not life, but the ability to maintain life. Lack of space forbids going into this at length. It must suffice to say, that life and the ability to maintain life will be found the same. We perpetually expend the vitality we have that we may continue our vitality. Our power to breathe a minute hence depends upon our breathing now. We must digest during this week that we may have strength to digest next. That we may get more food, we must use the force which the food we have eaten gives us.

Everywhere vigorous life is the strength, activity, and sagacity whereby life is maintained; and equally in descending the scale of being, or in watching the decline of an invalid, we see that the ebbing away of life is the ebbing away of the ability to preserve life.[62]

[Only on now coming to re-read the definition of Life enunciated at the commencement of this essay with the arguments used in justification of it, does it occur to me that its essential thought ought to have been incorporated in the definition of Life given in Part I. The idea of co-ordination is there implied in the idea of correspondence, but the idea of co-ordination is so cardinal a one that it should be expressed not by implication but overtly. It is too late to make the required amendment in the proper place, for the first part of this work is already stereotyped and printed. Being unable to do better I make the amendment here. The formula as completed will run:—The definite combination of heterogeneous changes, both simultaneous and successful, *co-ordinated into* correspondence with external co-existences and sequences.]

* * * * *

Ending here this preliminary dissertation, let us now proceed to our special subject.

§ 1. On contemplating its general circumstances, we perceive that any race of organisms is subject to two sets of conflicting influences. On the one hand by natural death, by enemies, by lack of food, by atmospheric changes, &c., it is constantly being destroyed. On the other hand, partly by the strength, swiftness and sagacity of its members, and partly by their fertility, it is constantly being maintained. These conflicting sets of influences may be conveniently generalized as—the forces destructive of race, and the forces preservative of race.

§ 2. Whilst any race continues to exist, the forces destructive of it and the forces preservative of it must perpetually tend towards equilibrium. If the forces destructive of it decrease, the race must gradually become more numerous, until, either from lack of food or from increase of enemies, the destroying forces again balance the preserving forces. If, reversely, the forces destructive of it increase, then the race must diminish, until, either from its food becoming relatively more abundant, or from its enemies dying of hunger, the destroying forces sink to the level of the preserving forces. Should the destroying forces be of a kind that cannot be thus met (as great change of climate), the race, by becoming extinct, is removed out of the category. Hence this is necessarily the *law of maintenance* of all races; seeing that when they cease to conform to it they cease to be.

Now the forces preservative of race are two—ability in each member of the race to preserve itself, and ability to produce other members—power to maintain individual life, and power to propagate the species. These must vary inversely. When, from lowness of organization, the ability to contend with external dangers is small, there must be great fertility to compensate for the consequent mortality; otherwise the race must die out. When, on the contrary, high endowments give much capacity of self-preservation, there needs a correspondingly low degree of fertility. Given the dangers to be met as a constant quantity; then, as the ability of any species to meet them must be a constant quantity too, and as this is made up of the two factors—power to maintain individual life and power to multiply—these cannot do other than vary inversely.

§ 3. To show that observed phenomena harmonise with this *à priori* principle seems scarcely needful But, though axiomatic in its character, and therefore incapable of being rendered more certain, yet illustrations of the conformity to it which nature everywhere exhibits, will facilitate the general apprehension of it.

In the vegetable kingdom we find that the species consisting of simple cells, exhibit the highest reproductive power. The yeast fungus, which in a few hours propagates itself throughout a large mass of wort, offers a familiar example of the extreme rapidity with which these lowly organisms multiply. In the *Protococcus nivalis*, a microscopic plant which in the course of a night reddens many square miles of snow, we have a like example; as also in the minute *Algæ*, which colour the waters of stagnant pools. The sudden appearance of green films on damp decaying surfaces, the spread of mould over stale food, and the rapid destruction of crops by mildew, afford further instances. If we ascend a step to plants of appreciable size, we still find that in proportion as the organization is low the fertility is great. Thus of the common puff-ball, which is little more than a mere aggregation of cells, Fries says, "in a single individual of *Reticularia maxima*, I have counted (calculated?) 10,000,000 sporules." From this point upwards, increase of bulk and greater complexity of structure are still accompanied by diminished reproductive power; instance the *Macrocystis pyrifera*, a gigantic sea-weed, which sometimes attains a length of 1500 feet, of which Carpenter remarks, "This development of the nutritive surface takes place at the expense of the fructifying apparatus, which is here quite subordinate."[63] And when we arrive at the highly-organized exogenous trees, we find that not only are they many years before beginning to bear with any abundance, but that even then they produce, at the outside, but a few thousand seeds in a twelvemonth. During its centuries of existence, an oak does not develop as many acorns as a fungus does spores in a single night.

Still more clearly is this truth illustrated throughout the animal kingdom. Though not so great as the fertility of the Protophyta, which, as Prof. Henslow says, in some cases passes comprehension, the fertility of the Protozoa is yet almost beyond belief. In the polygastric animalcules spontaneous fission takes place so rapidly that "it has been calculated by Prof. Ehrenberg that no fewer than 268 millions might be produced in a month from a single *Paramecium*;"[64] and even this astonishing rate of increase is far exceeded in another species, one individual of which, "only to be perceived by means of a high magnifying power, is calculated to generate 170 billions in four days."[65] Amongst the larger organisms exhibiting this lowest mode of reproduction under a modified form—that of gemmation—we see that, though not nearly so rapid as in the Infusoria, the rate of multiplication is still extremely high. This fact is well illustrated by the polypes; and in the apparent suddenness with which whole districts are blighted by the Aphis (multiplying by internal gemmation), we have a familiar instance of the startling results which the parthenogenetic process can achieve. Where reproduction becomes occasional instead of continuous, as it does amongst higher creatures, the fertility equally bears an inverse ratio to the development. "The queen ant of the African *Termites* lays 80,000 eggs in twenty-four hours; and the common hairworm (*Gordius*) as many as 8,000,000 in less than one day."[66] Amongst the *Vertebrata* the lowest are still the most prolific. "It has been calculated," says Carpenter, "that above a million of eggs are produced at once by a single codfish."[67] In the strong and sagacious shark comparatively few are found. Still less fertile are the higher reptiles. And amongst the Mammalia, beginning with small Rodents, which quickly reach maturity, produce large litters, and several litters in the year; advancing step by step to the higher mammals, some of which are long in attaining the reproductive age, others of which produce but one litter in a year, others but one young one at a time, others who unite these peculiarities; and ending with the elephant and man, the least prolific of all, we find that throughout this class, as throughout the rest, ability to multiply decreases as ability to maintain individual life increases.

§ 4. The *à priori* principle thus exemplified has an obverse of a like axiomatic character. We have seen that for the continuance of any race of organisms it is needful that the power of self-preservation and the power of reproduction should vary inversely.

We shall now see that, quite irrespective of such an end to be subserved, these powers could not do otherwise than vary inversely. In the nature of things species can subsist only by conforming to this law; and equally in the nature of things they cannot help conforming to it.

Reproduction, under all its forms, may be described as the separation of portions of a parent plant or animal for the purpose of forming other plants or animals. Whether it be by spontaneous fission, by gemmation, or by gemmules; whether the detached products be bulbels, spores or seeds, ovisacs, ova or spermatozoa; or however the process of multiplication be modified, it essentially consists in the throwing off of parts of adult organisms for the purpose of making new organisms. On the other hand, self preservation is fundamentally a maintenance of the organism in undiminished bulk. Amongst the lowest forms of life, aggregation of tissue is the only mode in which the self-preserving power is shown. Even in the highest, sustaining the body in its integrity is that in which self-preservation most truly consists—is the end which the widest intelligence is indirectly made to subserve. Whilst, on the one side, it cannot be denied that the increase of tissue constituting growth is self-preservation both in essence and in result; neither can it, on the other side, be denied that a diminution of tissue, either from injury, disease, or old age, is in both essence and result the reverse.

Hence the maintenance of the individual and the propagation of the race being respectively aggregative and separative, *necessarily* vary inversely. Every generative product is a deduction from the parental life; and, as already pointed out, to diminish life is to diminish the ability to preserve life. The portion thrown off is organised matter; vital force has been expended in the organisation of it, and in the assimilation of its component elements; which vital force, had no such portion been made and thrown off, *would have been available for the preservation of the parent.*

Neither of these forces, therefore, can increase, save at the expense of the other. The one draws in and incorporates new material; the other throws off material previously incorporated. The one adds to; the other takes from. Using a convenient expression for describing the facts (though one that must not be construed into an hypothesis), we may say that the force which builds up and repairs the individual is an attractive force, whilst that which throws off germs is a repulsive force. But whatever may turn out to be the true nature of the two processes, it is clear that they are mutually destructive; or, stating the proposition in its briefest form—Individuation and Reproduction are antagonistic.

Again, illustrating the abstract by reference to the concrete, let us now trace throughout the organic world the various phases of this antagonism.

§ 5. All the lowest animal and vegetable forms—*Protozoa* and *Protophyta*—consist essentially of a single cell containing fluid, and having usually a solid nucleus. This is true of the Infusoria, the simplest Entozoa, and the microscopic Algæ and Fungi. The organisms so constituted uniformly multiply by spontaneous fission. The nucleus, originally spherical, becomes elongated, then constricted across its smallest diameter, and ultimately separates, when "its divisions," says Prof. Owen, describing the process in the Infusoria, "seem to repel each other to positions equidistant from each other, and from the pole or end of the body to which they are nearest. The influence of these distinct centres of assimilation is to divert the flow of the plasmatic fluid from a common course through the body of the polygastrian to two special courses about those centres. So much of the primary developmental process is renewed, as leads to the insulation of the sphere of the influence of each assimilative centre from that of the other by the progressive formation of a double party wall of integument, attended by progressive separation of one party wall from the other, and by concomitant constriction of the body of the polygastrian, until the vibratile action of the superficial cilia of each separating moiety severs the narrowed neck of union, and they become two distinct individuals."[68] Similar in its general view is Dr. Carpenter's description of the multiplication of vegetable cells, which he says divide, "in virtue, it may be surmised, of a sort of mutual repulsion between the two halves of the endochrome (coloured cell-contents) which leads to their spontaneous separation."[69] Under a modified form of this process, the cell-contents, instead of undergoing bisection, divide into numerous parts, each of which ultimately becomes a separate individual. In some of the Algæ "a whole brood of young cells may thus be at once generated in the cavity of the parent-cell, which subsequently bursts and sets them free."[70] The *Achlya prolifera* multiplies after this fashion. Amongst the Fungi, too, the same mode of increase is exemplified by the *Protococcus nivalis*. And "it would appear that certain Infusoria, especially the *Kolpodinæ*, propagate by the breaking-up of their own mass into reproductive particles."[71]

Now in this fissiparous mode of multiplication, which "is amazingly productive, and indeed surpasses in fertility any other with which we are acquainted,"[72] we see most clearly the antagonism between individuation and reproduction. We see that the reproductive process involves destruction of the individual; for in becoming two, the parent fungus or polygastrian must be held to lose its own proper existence; and when it breaks up into a numerous progeny, does so still more completely. Moreover, this rapid mode of multiplication not only destroys the individuals in whom it takes place, but also involves that their individualities, whilst they continue, shall be of the lowest kind. For assume a protozoon to be growing by imbibition at a given rate, and it follows that the oftener it divides the smaller must be the size it attains to; that is, the smaller the development of its individuality. And a further manifestation of the same truth is seen in the fact that the more frequent the spontaneous fission the shorter the existence of each individual. So that alike by preventing anything beyond a microscopic bulk being attained, by preventing the continuance of this in its integrity beyond a few hours, and by being fatal when it occurs, this most active mode of reproduction shows the strongest antagonism to individual life.

§ 6. Whether or not we regard reproduction as resulting from a repulsive force (and, as seen above, both Owen and Carpenter lean to some such view), and whether or not we consider the formation of the individual as due to the reverse of this—an attractive force—we cannot, on studying the phenomena, help admitting that two opposite activities thus generalized are at work; we cannot help admitting that the aggregative and separative tendencies do in each case determine the respective developments of the individual and the race. On ascending one degree in the scale of organic life, we shall find this truth clearly exemplified.

For if these single-celled organisms which multiply so rapidly be supposed to lose some of their separative tendency, what must be the result? They now not only divide frequently, but the divided portions fly apart. How, then, will a diminution of this separative tendency first show itself? May we not expect that it will show itself in the divided portions *not* flying apart, but remaining near each other, and forming a group? This we find in nature to be the first step in advance. The lowest compound organisms are "*simple aggregations of vesicles without any definite arrangement, sometimes united, but capable of existing separately.*"[73] In these cases, "every component cell of the aggregate mass that springs from a single germ, being capable of existing independently of the rest, may be regarded as a distinct individual."[74] The several stages of this aggregation are very clearly seen in both the animal and vegetable kingdoms. In the *Hæmatococcus binalis*, the plant producing the reddish slime seen on damp surfaces, not only does each of the cells retain its original sphericity, but each is separated from its neighbour by a wide interval filled with mucus; so that it is only as being diffused through a mass of mucus common to them all, that these cells can be held to constitute one individual. We find, too, that "the component cells, even in the highest Algæ, are generally separated from each other by a large quantity of mucilaginous intercellular substance."[75] And, again, the tissue of the simpler Lichens, "in consequence of the very slight adhesion of its component cells, is said to be pulverulent."[76] Similarly the Protozoa, by their feeble union, constitute the organisms next above them. Amongst the Polygastrica there are many cases "in which the individuals produced by fission or gemmation do not become completely detached from each other."[77] The *Ophrydium*, for instance, "exists under the form of a motionless jelly-like mass ... made up of millions of distinct and similar individuals imbedded in a gelatinous connecting substance;"[78] and again, the *Uvella*, or "grape monad," consists of a cluster "which strongly resembles a transparent mulberry rolling itself across the field of view by the ciliary action of its component individuals."[79] The parenchyma of the Sponge, too, is made up of cells "each of which has the character of a distinct animalcule, having a certain power of spontaneous motion, obtaining and assimilating its own food, and altogether living *by* and *for* itself;" and so small is the cohesion of these individual cells, that the tissue they constitute "drains away when the mass is removed from the water, like white of egg."[80]

Of course in proportion as the aggregate tendency leading to the formation of these groups of monads is strong, we may expect that, other things equal, the groups will be large. Proceeding upwards from the yeast fungus, whose cells hold together in groups of four, five, and six,[81] there must be found in each species of these composite organisms a size of group determined by the strength of the aggregative tendency in that species. Hence we may expect that, when this limit is passed, the group no longer remains united, but divides. Such we find to be the fact. These groups of cells undergo the same process that the cells themselves do. They increase up to a certain point, and then multiply either by simple spontaneous fission or by that modification of it called gemmation. The *Volvox globator*, which is made up of a number of monads associated together in the form of a hollow sphere, develops within itself a number of smaller spheres similarly constituted; and after these, swimming freely in its interior, have reached a certain size, the parent group of animalcules bursts and sets the interior groups free. And here we may observe how this compound individuality of the Volvox is destroyed in the act of reproduction as the simple individuality of the monad is. Again, in the higher forms of grouped cells, where something like organisation begins to show itself, the aggregations are not only larger, but the separative process, now carried on by the method of gemmation, no longer wholly destroys the individual. And in fact, this gemmation may be regarded as the form which spontaneous fission must assume in ceasing to be fatal; seeing that gemmation essentially consists in the separation, not into halves, but into a larger part and a smaller part; the larger part continuing to represent the original individual. Thus in the common *Hydra* or fresh-water polype, "little bud-like processes are developed from the external surface, which are soon observed to resemble the parent in character, possessing a digestive sac, mouth, and tentacula; for a long time, however, their cavity is connected with that of the parent; but at last the communication is cut off, and the young polype quits its attachment, and goes in quest of its own maintenance."[82]

§ 7. Progress from these forms of organisation to still higher forms is similarly characterized by increase of the aggregative tendency or diminution of the separative, and similarly exhibits the necessary antagonism between the development of the individual and the increase of the race. That process of grouping which constitutes the first step towards the production of complex organisms, we shall now find repeated in the formation of series of groups. Just as a diminution of the separative tendency is shown in the aggregation of divided monads, so is a further diminution of it shown in the aggregation of the divided groups of monads. The first instance that occurs is afforded by the compound polypes. "Some of the simpler forms of the composite *Hydroida*," says Carpenter, "may be likened to a *Hydra*, whose gemmæ, instead of becoming detached, remain permanently connected with the parent; and as these in their turn may develop gemmæ from their own bodies, a structure of more or less arborescent character may be produced."[83] A similar species of combination is observable amongst the *Bryozoa*, and the compound *Tunicata*. Every degree of union may be found amongst these associated organisms; from the one extreme in which the individuals can exist as well apart as together, to the other extreme in which the individuals are lost in the general mass. Whilst each *Bryozoon* is tolerably independent of its neighbour, "in the compound *Hydroida*, the lives of the polypes are subordinate to that of the polypdom."[84] Of the *Salpidæ* and *Pyrosomidæ*, Carpenter says:—"Although closely attached to one another, these associated animals are capable of being separated by a smart shock applied to the sides of the vessel in which they are swimming.... In other species, however, the separate animals are imbedded in a gelatinous mass," and in one kind "there is an absolute union between the vascular systems of the different individuals."[85]

In the same manner that with a given aggregative tendency there is a limit to the size of groups, so is there a similarly-determined limit to the size of series of groups; and that spontaneous fission which we have seen in cells and groups of cells we here find repeated. In the lower *Annelida*, for example, "after the number of segments in the body has been greatly multiplied by gemmation, a separation of those of the posterior portion begins to take place; a constriction forms itself about the beginning of the posterior third of the body, in front of which the alimentary canal undergoes a dilatation, whilst on the segment behind it a proboscis and eyes are developed, so as to form the head of the young animal which is to be budded off; and in due time, by the narrowing of the constriction, a complete separation is effected."[86] Not unfrequently in the *Nais* this process is repeated in the young one before it becomes independent of the parent. The higher *Annelida* are distinguished by the greater number of segments held in continuity; an obvious result of comparatively infrequent fission. In the class *Myriapoda*, which stands next above, "there is no known instance of multiplication by fission."[87] Yet even here the law may be traced both in the number and structure of the segments. The length of the body is still increased after birth "by gemmation from (or partial fission of) the penultimate segment." The lower members of the class are distinguished from the higher by the greater extent to which this gemmation is carried. Moreover, the growing aggregative tendency is seen in the fact, that each segment of the Julus "is formed by the coalescence of two original segments,"[88] whilst in the *Scolopendridæ*, which are the highest of this class, "the head, according to Mr. Newport, is composed of eight segments, which are often consolidated into one piece;"[89] both of which phenomena may be understood as arrests of that process of fission, which, if allowed to go a little further, would have produced distinct segments; and, if allowed to go further still, would have separated these segments into groups.

§ 8. Remarking, first, how gradually this mode of multiplication disappears—how there are some creatures that spontaneously divide or not according to circumstances; others that divide when in danger (the several parts being capable of growing into complete individuals); others which, though not self-dividing, can live on in each half if artificially divided; and others in which only one of the divided halves can live—how, again, in the Crustaceans the power is limited to the reproduction of lost limbs; how there are certain reptiles that can re-supply a lost tail, but only imperfectly; and how amongst the higher *Vertebrata* the ability to repair small injuries is all that remains—remarking thus much, let us now, by way of preparation for what is to follow, consider the significance of the foregoing facts taken in connection with the definition of Life awhile since given.

This spontaneous fission, which we have seen to be, in all cases, more or less destructive of individual life, is simply a cessation in the co-ordination of actions. From the single cell, the halves of whose nucleus, instead of continuing to act together, begin to repel each other, fly apart, establish distinct centres of assimilation, and finally cause the cell to divide; up to the Annelidan, whose string of segments separates, after reaching a certain length; we everywhere see the phenomenon to be fundamentally this. The tendency to separate is the tendency not to act together, probably arising from inability to act together any longer; and the process of separation is the process of ceasing to act together. How truly non-co-ordination is the essence of the matter will be seen on observing that fission takes place more or less rapidly, according as the co-ordinating apparatus is less or more developed. Thus, "the capability of spontaneous division is one of the most distinctive attributes of the acrite type of structure;"[90] the acrite type of structure being that in which the neurine or nervous matter is supposed to be diffused through the tissues in a molecular state, and in which, therefore, there exists no distinct nervous or co-ordinating system. From this point upwards the gradual disappearance of spontaneous fission is clearly related to the gradual appearance of nerves and ganglia—a fact well exemplified by the several grades of *Annelida* and *Myriapoda.* And when we remember that in the embryotic development of these classes, the nervous system does not make its appearance until after the rest of the organism has made great progress, we may even suspect that that coalescence of segments characteristic of the *Myriapoda*, exhibits the co-ordinating power of the rapidly-growing nervous system overtaking and arresting the separative tendency; and doing this most where it (the nervous system) is most developed, namely, in the head.

And here let us remark, in passing, how, from this point of view, we still more clearly discern the antagonism of individuation and reproduction. We before saw that the propagation of the race is at the expense of the individual: in the above facts we may contemplate the obverse of this—may see that the formation of the individual is at the expense of the race. This combination of parts that are tending to separate and become distinct beings—this union of many incipient minor individualities into one large individuality—is an arrest of reproduction—a diminution in the number produced. Either these units may part and lead independent lives, or they may remain together and have their actions co-ordinated. Either they may, by their diffusion, form a small, simple, and prolific race, or, by their aggregation, a large, complex, and infertile one. But manifestly the aggregation involves the infertility; and the fertility involves the smallness.

§ 9. The ability to multiply by spontaneous fission, and the ability to maintain individual life, are opposed in yet another mode. It is not in respect of size only, but still more in respect of structure, that the antagonism exists.

Higher organisms are distinguished from lower ones partly by bulk, and partly by complexity. This complexity essentially consists in the mutual dependence of numerous different organs, each subserving the lives of the rest, and each living by the help of the rest. Instead of being made up of many like parts, performing like functions, as the Crinoid, the Star-fish, or the Millipede, a vertebrate animal is made up of many unlike parts, performing unlike functions. From that initial form of a compound organism, in which a number of minor individuals are simply grouped together, we may, more or less distinctly, trace not only the increasing closeness of their union, and the gradual disappearance of their individualities in that of the mass, but the gradual assumption by them of special duties. And this "physiological division of labour," as it has been termed, has the same effect as the division of labour amongst men. As the preservation of a number of persons is better secured when, uniting into a society, they severally undertake different kinds of work, than when they are separate and each performs for himself every kind of work; so the preservation of a congeries of parts, which, combining into one organism, respectively assume nutrition, respiration, circulation, locomotion, as separate functions, is better secured than when those parts are independent, and each fulfils for itself all these functions.

But the condition under which this increased ability to maintain life becomes possible is, that the parts shall cease to separate. While they are perpetually separating, it is clear that they cannot assume mutually subservient duties. And it is further clear that the more the tendency to separate diminishes, that is, the larger the groups that remain connected, *the more minutely and perfectly can that subdivision of functions which we call organization be carried out.*

Thus we see that in its most active form the ability to multiply is antagonistic to the ability to maintain individual life, not only as preventing increase of bulk, but also as preventing organization—not only as preventing homogeneous co-ordination, but as preventing heterogeneous co-ordination.

§ 10. To establish the unbroken continuity of this law of fertility, it will be needful, before tracing its results amongst the higher animals, to explain in what manner spontaneous fission is now understood, and what the cessation of it essentially means. Originally, naturalists supposed that creatures which multiply by self-division, under any of its several forms, continue so to multiply perpetually. In many cases, however, it has latterly been shown that they do not do this; and it is now becoming a received opinion that they do not, and cannot, do this, in any case. A fertilised germ appears here, as amongst higher organisms, to be the point of departure; and that constant formation of new tissue implied in the production of a great number of individuals by fission, seems gradually to exhaust the germinal capacity in the same way that the constant formation of new tissue, during the development of a single mammal, exhausts it. The phenomena classified by Steenstrup as "Alternate Generation," and since generalised by Professor Owen in his work "On Parthenogenesis," illustrate this. The egg of a *Medusa* (jellyfish) develops into a polypoid animal called the *Strobila.* This *Strobila* lives as the polype does, and, like it, multiplies rapidly by gemmation. After a great number of individuals has been thus produced, and when, as we must suppose, the germinal capacity is approaching exhaustion, each *Strobila* begins to exhibit a series of constrictions, giving it some resemblance to a rouleau of coin or a pile of saucers. These constrictions deepen; the segments gradually develop tentacula; the terminal segment finally separates itself, and swims away in the form of a young *Medusa*; the other segments, in succession, do the same; and from the eggs which these *Medusæ* produce, other like series of polypoid animals, multiplying by gemmation, originate. In the compound Polypes, in the *Tunicata*, in the *Trematoda*, and in the Aphis, we find repeated, under various modifications, the same phenomenon.

Understanding then, this lowest and most rapid mode of multiplication to consist essentially in the production of a great number of individuals from a single germ—perceiving, further, that diminished activity of this mode of multiplication consists essentially in the aggregation of the germ-product into larger masses—and seeing, lastly, that the disappearance of this mode of multiplication consists essentially in the aggregation of the germ-product into *one* mass—we shall be in a position to comprehend, amongst the higher animals, that new aspect of the law, under which increased individuation still involves diminished reproduction. Progressing from those lowest forms of life in which a single ovum originates countless organisms, through the successive stages in which the number of organisms so originated becomes smaller and smaller; and finally arriving at a stage in which one ovum produces but one organism; we have now, in our further ascent, to observe the modified mode in which this same necessary antagonism between the ability to multiply, and the ability to preserve individual life, is exhibited.

§ 11. Throughout both the animal and vegetable kingdoms, generation is effected "by the union of the contents of a 'sperm-cell' with those of a 'germ-cell;' the latter being that from within which the embryo is evolved, whilst the former supplies some material or influence necessary to its evolution."[91] Amongst the lowest vegetable organisms, as in the *Desmideæ*, the *Diatomaceæ*, and other families of the inferior *Algæ*, those cells do not appreciably differ; and the application to them of the terms "sperm-cell" and "germ-cell" is hypothetical. From this point upwards, however, distinctions become visible. As we advance to higher and higher types of structure, marked differences arise in the character of these cells, in the organs evolving them, and in the position of these organs, which are finally located in separate sexes. Doubtless a separation in the *functions* of "sperm-cell" and "germ-cell" has simultaneously arisen. That change from homogeneity of function to heterogeneity of function which essentially constitutes progress in organization may be assumed to take place here also; and, indeed, it is probable that the distinction gradually established between these cells, in origin and appearance, is merely significant of, and consequent upon, the distinction that has arisen between them in constitution and office. Let us now inquire in what this distinction consists.

If the foundation of every new organism be laid by the combination of two elements, we may reasonably suspect that these two elements are typical of some two fundamental divisions of which the new organism is to consist. As nothing in nature is without meaning and purpose, we may be sure that the universality of this binary origin, signifies the universality of a binary structure. The simplest and broadest division of which an organism is capable must be that signified. What, then, must this division be?

The proposed definition of organic life supplies an answer. If organic life be the co-ordination of actions, then an organism may be primarily divided into parts whose actions are co-ordinated, and parts which co-ordinate them—organs which are made to work in concert, and the apparatus which makes them so work—or, in other words, the assimilative, vascular, excretory, and muscular systems on the one hand, and the nervous system on the other. The justness of this classification will become further apparent, when it is remembered that by the nervous system alone is the individuality established. By it all parts are made one in purpose, instead of separate; by it the organism is rendered a conscious whole—is enabled to recognise its own extent and limits; and by it are all injuries notified, repairs directed, and the general conservation secured. The more the nervous system is developed, the more reciprocally subservient do the components of the body become—the less can they bear separating. And that which thus individuates many parts into one whole, must be considered as more broadly distinguished from the parts individuated, than any of these parts from each other. Further evidence in support of this position may be drawn from the fact, that as we ascend in the scale of animal life, that is, as the co-ordination of actions becomes greater, we find the co-ordinating or nervous system becoming more and more definitely separated from the rest; and in the vertebrate or highest type of structure we find the division above insisted on distinctly marked. The co-ordinating parts and the parts co-ordinated are placed on opposite sides of the vertebral column. With the exception of a few ganglia, the whole of the nervous masses are contained within the neural arches of the vertebræ; whilst all the viscera and limbs are contained within, or appended to, the hæmal arches—the terms neural and hæmal having, indeed, been chosen to express this fundamental division.

If, then, there be truth in the assumption that the two elements, which, by their union, give origin to a new organism, typify the two essential constituents of such new organism, we must infer that the sperm-cell and germ-cell respectively consist of co-ordinating matter and matter to be co-ordinated—neurine and nutriment. That apparent identity of sperm-cell and germ-cell seen in the lowest forms of life may thus be understood as significant to the fact that no extended co-ordination of actions exists in the generative product—each cell being a separate individual; and the dissimilarity seen in higher organic types may, conversely, be understood as expressive of, and consequent upon, the increasing degree of co-ordination exhibited.[92]

That the sperm-cell and germ-cell are thus contrasted in nature and function may further be suspected on considering the distinctive characteristics of the sexes. Of the two elements they respectively contribute to the formation of a fertile germ, it may be reasonably supposed that each furnishes that which it possesses in greatest abundance and can best spare. Well, in the greater size of the nervous centres in the male, as well as in the fact that during famines men succumb sooner than women, we see that in the male the co-ordinating system is relatively predominant. From the same evidence, as well as from the greater abundance of the cellular and adipose tissues in women, we may infer that the nutritive system predominates in the female.[93] Here, then, is additional support for the hypothesis that the sperm-cell, which is supplied by the male, contains co-ordinating matter, and the germ-cell, which is supplied by the female, contains matter to be co-ordinated.

The same inference may, again, be drawn from a general view of the maternal function. For if, as we see, it is the office of the mother to afford milk to the infant, and during a previous period to afford blood to the fœtus, it becomes probable that during a yet earlier stage it is still the function to supply nutriment, though in another form. Indeed when, ascending gradually the scale of animal life, we perceive that this supplying of milk, and before that of blood, is simply a continuation of the previous process, we may be sure that, with Nature's usual consistency, this process is essentially one from the beginning.

Quite in harmony with this hypothesis concerning the respective natures of the sperm-cell and germ-cell is a remark of Carpenter's on the same point:—

"Looking," he says, "to the very equal mode in which the characters of the two parents are mingled in *hybrid* offspring, and to the certainty that the *material* conditions which determine the development of the germ are almost exclusively female, it would seem probable that the *dynamical* conditions are, in great part, furnished by the male."[94]

§ 12. Could nothing but the foregoing indirect evidence be adduced in proof of the proposition that the spermatozoon is essentially a neural element, and the ovum essentially a hæmal element, we should scarcely claim for it anything more than plausibility. On finding, however, that this indirect evidence is merely introductory to evidence of a quite direct nature, its significance will become apparent. Adding to their weight taken separately the force of their mutual confirmation, these two series of proofs will be seen to give the hypothesis a high degree of probability. The direct evidence now to be considered is of several kinds.

On referring to the description of the process of multiplication in monads, quoted some pages back (§ 5), from Professor Owen, the reader will perceive that it is by the pellucid nucleus that the growth and reproduction of these single-celled creatures are regulated. The nucleus controls the circulation of the plasmatic fluid; the fission of the nucleus is the first step towards the formation of another cell; each half of the divided nucleus establishes round itself an independent current; and, apparently, it is by the repulsion of the nuclei that the separation into two individuals is finally effected. All which facts, when generalised, imply that the nucleus is the governing or *co-ordinating* part. Now, Professor Owen subsequently points out that the matter of the sperm-cell performs in the fertilised germ-cell just this same function which the nucleus performs in a single-celled animal. We find the absorption by a germ-cell of the contents of a sperm-cell "followed by the appearance of a pellucid nucleus in the centre of the opaque and altered germ-cell; we further see its successive fissions governed by the preliminary division of the pellucid centre;" and, led by these and other facts, Professor Owen thinks that "one cannot reasonably suppose that the nature and properties of the nucleus of the impregnated germ-cell and that of the monad can be different."[95] And hence he further infers that "the nucleus of the monad is of a nature similar to, if not identical with," the matter of the spermatozoon. But we have seen that in the monad the nucleus is the co-ordinating part; and hence to say that the sperm-cell is, in nature, identical with it, is to say that the sperm-cell consists of co-ordinating matter.

Chemical analysis affords further evidence, though, from the imperfect data at present obtained, less conclusive evidence than could be wished. Partly from the white and gray nervous substances having been analysed together instead of separately, and partly from the difficulty of isolating the efficient contents of the sperm-cells, a satisfactory comparison cannot be made. Nevertheless, possessing in common, as they do, one element, by which they are specially characterised, the analysis, as far as it goes, supports our argument. The following table, which has been made up from data given in the *Cyclopædia of Anatomy and Physiology, Art.* NERVOUS SYSTEM, gives the proportion of this element in the brain in different conditions, and shows how important is its presence.

	In Infants.	In Youth.	In Adults.	In Old Men.	In Idiots.
Solid constituents in a hundred parts of the	17.21	25.74	27.49	26.15	29.07

brain					
Of these solid constituents the phosphorus amounts to	0.8	1.65	1.80	1.00	0.85
Which gives a percentage of phosphorus in the solid constituents of	4.65	6.41	6.54	3.82	2.92

This connection between the quantity of phosphorus present and the degree of mental power exhibited, is sufficiently significant; and the fact that in the same individual the varying degrees of cerebral activity are indicated by the varying quantities of alkaline phosphates excreted by the kidneys,[96] still more clearly shows the essentialness of phosphorus as a constituent of nervous matter. Respecting the constitution of sperm-cells chemists do not altogether agree. One thing, however, is certain—that they contain unoxidized phosphorus; and also a fatty acid, that is not improbably similar to the fatty acid contained in neurine.[97] In fact, there would seem to be present the constituents of that oleophosphoric acid which forms so distinctive an element of the brain. That a large quantity of binoxide of protein is also present, may be ascribed to the fact that a great part of the sperm-cell consists merely of the protective membrane and its locomotive appendage; the really efficient portion being but the central contents.[98]

Evidence of a more conclusive nature—evidence, too, which will show in what direction our argument tends—is seen in the marked antagonism of the nervous and generative systems. Thus, the fact that intense mental application, involving great waste of the nervous tissues, and a corresponding consumption of nervous matter for their repair, is accompanied by a cessation in the production of sperm-cells, gives strong support to the hypothesis that the sperm-cells consist essentially of neurine. And this becomes yet clearer on finding that the converse fact is true—that undue production of sperm-cells involves cerebral inactivity. The first result of a morbid excess in this direction is headache, which may be taken to indicate that the brain is out of repair; this is followed by stupidity; should the disorder continue, imbecility supervenes, ending occasionally in insanity.

That the sperm-cell is co-ordinating matter, and the germ-cell matter to be co-ordinated, is, therefore, an hypothesis not only having much *à priori* probability, but one supported by numerous facts.

§ 13. This hypothesis alike explains, and is confirmed by, the truth, that throughout the vertebrate tribes the degree of fertility varies inversely as the development of the nervous system.

The necessary antagonism of Individuation and Reproduction does indeed show itself amongst the higher animals, in some degree in the manner hitherto traced; namely, as determining the total bulk. Though the parts now thrown off, being no longer segments or gemmæ, are not obvious diminutions of the parent, yet they must be really such. Under the form of internal fission, the separative tendency is as much opposed to the aggregative tendency as ever; and, *other things equal*, the greater or less development of the individual depends upon the less or greater production of new individuals or germs of new individuals. As in groups of cells, and series of groups of cells, we saw that there was in each species a limit, passing which, the germ product would not remain united; so in each species of higher animal there is a limit, passing which, the process of cell-multiplication results in the throwing off of cells, instead of resulting in the formation of more tissue. Hence, taking an average view, we see why the smaller animals so soon arrive at a reproductive age, and produce large and frequent broods; and why, conversely, increased size is accompanied by retarded and diminished fertility.

But, as above implied, it is not so much to the bulk of the body as a whole, as to the bulk of the nervous system, that fertility stands related amongst the higher animals. Probably, indeed, it stands thus related in all cases; the difference simply arising from the fact, that whereas in the lower organisms, where the nervous system is not concentrated, its bulk varies as the bulk of the body, in the higher organisms it does not do so. Be this as it may, however, we see clearly that, amongst the vertebrata, the bodily development is not the determining circumstance. In a fish, a reptile, a bird, and a mammal of the same weight, there is nothing like equality of fecundity. Cattle and horses, arriving as they do so soon at a reproductive age, are much more prolific than the human race, at the same time that they are much larger. And whilst, again, the difference in size between the elephant and man is far greater, their respective powers of multiplication are less unlike. Looking in these cases at the nervous systems, however, we find no such discrepancy. On learning that the average ratio of the brain to the body is—in fishes, 1 to 5668; in reptiles, 1 to 1321; in birds, 1 to 212; and in mammals, 1 to 186;[99] their different degrees of fecundity are accounted for. Though an ox will outweigh half-a-dozen men, yet its brain and spinal cord are far less than those of one man; and though in bodily development the elephant so immensely exceeds the human being, yet the elephant's cerebro-spinal system is only thrice the size attained by that of civilized men.[100] Unfortunately, it is impossible to trace throughout the animal kingdom this inverse relationship between the nervous and reproductive systems with any accuracy. Partly from the fact that, in each case, the degree of fertility depends on three variable elements—the age at which reproduction begins, the number produced at a birth, and the frequency of the births; partly from the fact that, in respect to most animals, these data are not satisfactorily attainable, and that, when they are attainable, they are vitiated by the influence of domesticity; and partly from the fact that no precise measurement of the respective nervous systems has been made, we are unable to draw any but general and somewhat vague comparisons. These, however, as far as they go, are in our favour. Ascending from beings of the acrite nerveless type, which are the most prolific of all, through the various invertebrate sub-kingdoms, amongst which spontaneous fission disappears as the nervous system becomes developed; passing again to the least nervous and most fertile of the vertebrate series—Fishes, of which, too, the comparatively large-brained cartilaginous kinds multiply much less rapidly than the others; progressing through the more highly endowed and less prolific Reptiles to the Mammalia, amongst which the Rodents, with their unconvoluted brains, are noted for their fecundity; and ending with man and the elephant, the least fertile and largest-brained of all—there seems to be throughout a constant relationship between these attributes.

And indeed, on turning back to our *à priori* principle, no other relationship appears possible. We found it to be the necessary law of maintenance of races, that the ability to maintain individual life and the ability to multiply vary inversely. But the ability to maintain individual life *is in all cases measured by the development of the nervous system.* If it be in good visceral organization that the power of self-preservation is shown, this implies some corresponding nervous apparatus to secure sufficient food. If it be in strength, there must be a provision of nerves and nervous centres answering to the number and size of the muscles. If it be in swiftness and agility, a proportionate development of the cerebellum is presupposed. If it be in intelligence, this varies with the size of the cerebrum. As in all cases co-ordination of actions constitutes the life, or, what is the same thing, the ability to maintain life; and as throughout the animal kingdom this co-ordination, under all its forms, is effected by nervous agents of some kind or other; and as each of these nervous agents performs but one function; it follows that in proportion to the number of the actions co-ordinated must be the number of nervous agents. Hence the nervous system becomes the universal measure of the degree of co-ordination of actions; that is, of the life, or ability to maintain life. And if the nervous system varies directly as the ability to maintain life, it *must* vary inversely as the ability to multiply.[101]

And here, assuming the constitution of the sperm-cell above inferred to be the true one, we see how the obverse *à priori* principle is fulfilled. Where, as amongst the lowest organisms, bulk is expressive of life, the antagonism of individuation and reproduction was broadly exhibited in the fact that the making of two or more new individuals was the *un*making of the original individual. And now, amongst the higher organisms, where bulk is no longer the measure of life, we see that this antagonism is between the neural elements thrown off, and that internal neural mass whose bulk *is* the measure of life. The production of co-ordinating cells must be at the expense of the co-ordinating apparatus; and the aggregation of the co-ordinating apparatus must be at the expense of co-ordinating cells. How the antagonism affects the female economy is not so clear. Possibly the provision required to be made for supplying nervous as well as other nutriment to the embryo, involves an arrest in the development of the nervous system; and if so, probably this arrest takes place early in proportion as the number of the coming offspring makes the required provision great: or rather, to put the facts in their right sequence, an early arrest renders the production of a numerous offspring possible.

§ 14. The law which we have thus traced throughout the animal kingdom, and which must alike determine the different fertilities of different species, and the variations of fertility in the same species, we have now to consider in its application to mankind.

[*The remainder of the essay, which as implied, deals with the application of this general principle to the multiplication of the human race, need not be here reproduced. The subject is treated in full in Part VI.*]

APPENDIX B.

THE INADEQUACY OF NATURAL SELECTION, ETC., ETC.

[*In this Appendix are included four essays originally published in the* Contemporary Review *and subsequently republished as pamphlets. The first appeared under the above title in February and March, 1893; the second in May of that year under the title "Prof. Weismann's Theories;" the third in December of that year under the title "A Rejoinder to Prof. Weismann;" and the fourth in October, 1894, under the title "Weismannism Once More." As these successive essays practically form parts of one whole, I have thought it needless to keep them separate by repeating their titles, and have simply marked them off from one another by the numbers I, II, III, IV. Of course, as they are components of a controversy, some incompleteness arises from the absence of the essays to which portions of them were replies; but in each the course of the argument sufficiently indicates the counter-arguments which were met.*]

I.

Students of psychology are familiar with the experiments of Weber on the sense of touch. He found that different parts of the surface differ widely in their ability to give information concerning the things touched. Some parts, which yielded vivid sensations, yielded little or no knowledge of the sizes or forms of the things exciting them; whereas other parts, from which there came sensations much less acute, furnished clear impressions respecting the tangible characters, even of relatively small objects. These unlikenesses of tactual discriminativeness he ingeniously expressed by actual measurements. Taking a pair of compasses, he found that if they were closed so nearly that the points were less than one-twelfth of an inch apart, the end of the forefinger could not perceive that there were two points: the two points seemed one. But when the compasses were opened so that the points were one-twelfth of an inch apart, then the end of the forefinger distinguished the two points. At the same time, he found that the compasses must be opened to the extent of two and a half inches, before the middle of the back could distinguish between two points and one. That is to say, as thus measured, the end of the forefinger has thirty times the tactual discriminativeness which the middle of the back has.

Between these extremes he found gradations. The inner surfaces of the second joints of the fingers can distinguish separateness of positions only half as well as the tip of the forefinger. The innermost joints are still less discriminating, but have powers of discrimination equal to that of the tip of the nose. The end of the great toe, the palm of the hand, and the cheek, have alike one-fifth of the perceptiveness which the tip of the forefinger has; and the lower part of the forehead has but one-half that possessed by the cheek. The back of the hand and the crown of the head are nearly alike in having but a fourteenth or a fifteenth of the ability to perceive positions as distinct, which is possessed by the finger-end. The thigh, near the knee, has rather less, and the breast less still; so that the compasses must be opened more than an inch and a half before the breast distinguishes the two points from one another.

What is the meaning of these differences? How, in the course of evolution, have they been established? If "natural selection," or survival of the fittest, is the assigned cause, then it is required to show in what way each of these degrees of endowment has advantaged the possessor to such extent that not infrequently life has been directly or indirectly preserved by it. We might reasonably assume that in the absence of some differentiating process, all parts of the surface would have like powers of perceiving relative positions. They cannot have become widely unlike in perceptiveness without some cause. And if the cause alleged is natural selection, then it is necessary to show that the greater degree of the power possessed by this part than by that, has not only conduced to the maintenance of life, but has conduced so much that an individual in whom a variation has produced better adjustment to needs, thereby maintained life when some others lost it; and that among the descendants inheriting this variation, there was a derived advantage such as enabled them to multiply more than the descendants of individuals not possessing it. Can this, or anything like this, be shown?

That the superior perceptiveness of the forefinger-tip has thus arisen, might be contended with some apparent reason. Such perceptiveness is an important aid to manipulation, and may have sometimes given a life-saving advantage. In making arrows or fish-hooks, a savage possessing some extra amount of it may have been thereby enabled to get food where another failed. In civilized life, too, a sempstress with well-endowed finger-ends might be expected to gain a better livelihood than one with finger-ends which were obtuse; though this advantage would not be so great as appears. I have found that two ladies whose finger-ends were covered with glove-tips, reducing their sensitiveness from one-twelfth of an inch between compass-points to one-seventh, lost nothing appreciable of their quickness and goodness in sewing. An experience of my own here comes in evidence. Towards the close of my salmon-fishing days I used to observe what a bungler I had become in putting on and taking off artificial flies. As the tactual discriminativeness of my finger-ends, recently tested, comes up to the standard specified by Weber, it is clear that this decrease of manipulative power, accompanying increase of age, was due to decrease in the delicacy of muscular co-ordination and sense of pressure—not to decrease of tactual discriminativeness. But not making much of these criticisms, let us admit the conclusion that this high perceptive power possessed by the forefinger-end may have arisen by survival of the fittest; and let us limit the argument to the other differences.

How about the back of the trunk and its face? Is any advantage derived from possession of greater tactual discriminativeness by the last than the first? The tip of the nose has more than three times the power of distinguishing relative positions which the lower part of the forehead has. Can this greater power be shown to have any advantage? The back of the hand has scarcely more discriminative ability than the crown of the head, and has only one-fourteenth of that which the finger-tip has. Why is this? Advantage might occasionally be derived if the back of the hand could tell us more than it does about the shapes of the surfaces touched. Why should the thigh near the knee be twice as perceptive as the middle of the thigh? And, last of all, why should the middle of the forearm, middle of the thigh, middle of the back of the neck, and middle of the back, all stand on the lowest level, as having but one-thirtieth of the perceptive power which the tip of the forefinger has? To prove that these differences have arisen by natural selection, it has to be shown that such small variation in one of the parts as might occur in a generation—say one-tenth extra amount—has yielded an appreciably greater power of self-preservation; and that those inheriting it have continued to be so far advantaged as to multiply more than those who, in other respects equal, were less endowed with this trait. Does any one think he can show this?

But if this distribution of tactual perceptiveness cannot be explained by survival of the fittest, how can it be explained? The reply is that, if there has been in operation a cause which it is now the fashion among biologists to ignore or deny, these various differences are at once accounted for. This cause is the inheritance of acquired characters. As a preliminary to setting forth the argument showing this, I have made some experiments.

It is a current belief that the fingers of the blind, more practised in tactual exploration than the fingers of those who can see, acquire greater discriminativeness: especially the fingers of those blind who have been taught to read from raised letters. Not wishing to trust to this current belief, I recently tested two youths, one of fifteen and the other younger, at the School for the Blind in Upper Avenue Road, and found the belief to be correct. I found that instead of being unable to distinguish between points of the compasses until they were opened to one-twelfth of an inch apart, both of them could distinguish between points when only one-fourteenth of an inch apart. They had thick and coarse skins; and doubtless, had the intervening obstacle, so produced, been less, the discriminative power would have been greater. It afterwards occurred to me that a better test would be furnished by those whose finger-ends are exercised in tactual perceptions, not occasionally, as by the blind in reading, but all day long in pursuit of their occupations. The facts answered expectation. Two skilled compositors, on whom I experimented, were both able to distinguish between points when they were only one-seventeenth of an inch apart. Thus we have clear proof that constant exercise of the tactual nervous structure leads to further development.[102]

Now if acquired structural traits are inheritable, the various contrasts above set down are obvious consequences; for the gradations in tactual perceptiveness correspond with the gradations in the tactual exercises of the parts. Save by contact with clothes, which present only broad surfaces having but slight and indefinite contrast, the trunk has scarcely any converse with external bodies, and it has but small discriminative power; but what discriminative power it has is greater on its face than on its back, corresponding to the fact that the chest and abdomen are much more frequently explored by the hands: this difference being probably in part inherited from inferior creatures; for, as we may see in dogs and cats, the belly is far more accessible to feet and tongue than the back. No less obtuse than the back are the middle of the back of the neck, the middle of the forearm, and the middle of the thigh; and these parts have but rare experiences of irregular foreign bodies. The crown of the head is occasionally felt by the fingers, as also the back of one hand by the fingers of the other; but neither of these surfaces, which are only twice as perceptive as the back, is used with any frequency for touching objects, much less for examining them. The lower part of the forehead, though more perceptive than the crown of the head, in correspondence with a somewhat greater converse with the hands, is less than one-third as perceptive as the tip of the nose; and manifestly, both in virtue of its relative prominence, in virtue of its contacts with things smelt at, and in virtue of its frequent acquaintance with the handkerchief, the tip of the nose has far greater tactual experience. Passing to the inner surfaces of the hands, which, taken as wholes, are more constantly occupied in touching than are the back, breast, thigh, forearm, forehead, or back of the hand, Weber's scale shows that they are much more perceptive, and that the degrees of perceptiveness of different parts correspond with their tactual activities. The palms have but one-fifth the perceptiveness possessed by the forefinger-ends; the inner surfaces of the finger-joints next the palms have but one-third; while the inner surfaces of the second joints have but one-half. These abilities correspond with the facts that whereas the inner parts of the hand are used only in grasping things, the tips of the fingers come into play not only when things are grasped, but when such things, as well as smaller things, are felt at or manipulated. It needs but to observe the relative actions of these parts in writing, in sewing, in judging textures, &c.,

to see that above all other parts the finger-ends, and especially the forefinger-ends, have the most multiplied experiences. If, then, it be that the extra perceptiveness acquired from actual tactual activities, as in a compositor, is inheritable, these gradations of tactual perceptiveness are explained.

Doubtless some of those who remember Weber's results, have had on the tip of the tongue the argument derived from the tip of the tongue. This part exceeds all other parts in power of tactual discrimination: doubling, in that respect, the power of the forefinger-tip. It can distinguish points that are only one-twenty-fourth of an inch apart. Why this unparalleled perceptiveness? If survival of the fittest be the ascribed cause, then it has to be shown what the advantages achieved have been; and, further, that those advantages have been sufficiently great to have had effects on the maintenance of life.

Besides tasting, there are two functions conducive to life, which the tongue performs. It enables us to move about food during mastication, and it enables us to make many of the articulations constituting speech. But how does the extreme discriminativeness of the tongue-tip aid these functions? The food is moved about, not by the tongue-tip, but by the body of the tongue; and even were the tip largely employed in this process, it would still have to be shown that its ability to distinguish between points one-twenty-fourth of an inch apart, is of service to that end, which cannot be shown. It may, indeed, be said that the tactual perceptiveness of the tongue-tip serves for detection of foreign bodies in the food, as plum-stones or as fish-bones. But such extreme perceptiveness is needless for the purpose. A perceptiveness equal to that of the finger-ends would suffice. And further, even were such extreme perceptiveness useful, it could not have caused survival of individuals who possessed it in slightly higher degrees than others. It needs but to observe a dog crunching small bones, and swallowing with impunity the sharp-angled pieces, to see that but a very small amount of mortality would be prevented.

But what about speech? Well, neither here can there be shown any advantage derived from this extreme perceptiveness. For making the *s* and *z*, the tongue has to be partially applied to a portion of the palate next the teeth. Not only, however, must the contact be incomplete, but its place is indefinite—may be half an inch further back. To make the *sh* and *zh*, the contact has to be made, not with the tip, but with the upper surface of the tongue; and must be an incomplete contact. Though, for making the liquids, the tip of the tongue and the sides of the tongue are used, yet the requisite is not any exact adjustment of the tip, but an imperfect contact with the palate. For the *th*, the tip is used along with the edges of the tongue; but no perfect adjustment is required, either to the edges of the teeth, or to the junction of the teeth with the palate, where the sound may equally well be made. Though for the *t* and *d* complete contact of the tip and edges of the tongue with the palate is required, yet the place of contact is not definite, and the tip takes no more important share in the action than the sides. Any one who observes the movements of his tongue in speaking, will find that there occur no cases in which the adjustments must have an exactness corresponding to the extreme power of discrimination which the tip possesses: for speech, this endowment is useless. Even were it useful, it could not be shown that it has been developed by survival of the fittest; for though perfect articulation is an aid, yet imperfect articulation has rarely such an effect as to impede a man in the maintenance of his life. If he is a good workman, a German's interchanges of *b's* and *p's* do not disadvantage him. A Frenchman who, in place of the sound of *th*, always makes the sound of *z*, succeeds as a teacher of music or dancing, no less than if he achieved the English pronunciation. Nay, even such an imperfection of speech as that which arises from cleft palate, does not prevent a man from getting on if he is capable. True, it may go against him as a candidate for Parliament, or as an "orator" of the unemployed (mostly not worth employing). But in the struggle for life he is not hindered by the effect to the extent of being less able than others to maintain himself and his offspring. Clearly, then, even if this unparalleled perceptiveness of the tongue-tip is required for perfect speech, such use is not sufficiently important to have been developed by natural selection.

How, then, is this remarkable trait of the tongue-tip to be accounted for? Without difficulty, if there is inheritance of acquired characters. For the tongue-tip has, above all other parts of the body, unceasing experiences of small irregularities of surface. It is in contact with the teeth, and either consciously or unconsciously is continually exploring them. There is hardly a moment in which impressions of adjacent but different positions are not being yielded to it by either the surfaces of the teeth or their edges; and it is continually being moved about from some of them to others. No advantage is gained. It is simply that the tongue's position renders perpetual exploration almost inevitable; and by perpetual exploration is developed this unique power of discrimination. Thus the law holds throughout, from this highest degree of perceptiveness of the tongue-tip to its lowest degree on the back of the trunk; and no other explanation of the facts seems possible.

"Yes, there is another explanation," I hear some one say: "they may be explained by *panmixia*." Well, in the first place, as the explanation by *panmixia* implies that these gradations of perceptiveness have been arrived at by the dwindling of nervous structures, there lies at the basis of the explanation an unproved and improbable assumption; and, in the second place, even were there no such difficulty, it may with certainty be denied that *panmixia* can furnish an explanation. Let us look at its pretensions.

* * * * *

It was not without good reason that Bentham protested against metaphors. Figures of speech in general, valuable as they are in poetry and rhetoric, cannot be used without danger in science and philosophy. The title of Mr. Darwin's great work furnishes us with an instance of the misleading effects produced by them. It runs:—*The Origin of Species by means of Natural Selection, or the Preservation of favoured Races in the Struggle for Life.* Here are two figures of speech which conspire to produce an impression more or less erroneous. The expression "natural selection" was chosen as serving to indicate some parallelism with artificial selection—the selection exercised by breeders. Now selection connotes volition, and thus gives to the thoughts of readers a wrong bias. Some increase of this bias is produced by the words in the second title, "favoured races;" for anything which is favoured implies the existence of some agent conferring a favour. I do not mean that Mr. Darwin himself failed to recognize the misleading connotations of his words, or that he did not avoid being misled by them. In chapter iv of the *Origin of Species*, he says that, considered literally, "natural selection is a false term," and that the personification of Nature is objectionable; but he thinks that readers, and those who adopt his views, will soon learn to guard themselves against the wrong implications. Here I venture to think that he was mistaken. For thinking this, there is the reason that even his disciple, Mr. Wallace—no, not his disciple, but his co-discoverer, ever to be honoured—has apparently been influenced by them. When, for example, in combating a view of mine, he says that "the very thing said to be impossible by variation and natural selection has been again and again effected, by variation and artificial selection," he seems clearly to imply that the processes are analogous, and operate in the same way. Now this is untrue. They are analogous only within certain narrow limits; and, in the great majority of cases, natural selection is utterly incapable of doing that which artificial selection does.

To see this it needs only to de-personalise Nature, and to remember that, as Mr. Darwin says, Nature is "only the aggregate action and product of many natural laws [forces]." Observe its relative shortcomings. Artificial selection can pick out a particular trait, and, regardless of other traits of the individuals displaying it, can increase it by selective breeding in successive generations. For, to the breeder or fancier, it matters little whether such individuals are otherwise well constituted. They may be in this or that way so unfit for carrying on the struggle for life, that were they without human care, they would disappear forthwith. On the other hand, if we regard Nature as that which it is, an assemblage of various forces, inorganic and organic, some favourable to the maintenance of life and many at variance with its maintenance—forces which operate blindly—we see that there is no such selection of this or that trait; but that there is a selection only of individuals which are, by the aggregate of their traits, best fitted for living. And here I may note an advantage possessed by the expression "survival of the fittest;" since this does not tend to raise the thought of any one character which, more than others, is to be maintained or increased; but tends rather to raise the thought of a general adaptation for all purposes. It implies the process which Nature can alone carry on—the leaving alive of those which are best able to utilize surrounding aids to life, and best able to combat or avoid surrounding dangers. And while this phrase covers the great mass of cases in which there are preserved well-constituted individuals, it also covers those special cases which are suggested by the phrase "natural selection," in which individuals succeed beyond others in the struggle for life, by the help of particular characters which conduce in important ways to prosperity and multiplication. For now observe the fact which here chiefly concerns us, that survival of the fittest can increase any serviceable trait, only if that trait conduces to prosperity of the individual, or of posterity, or of both, *in an important degree.* There can be no increase of any structure by natural selection unless, amid all the slightly varying structures constituting the organism, increase of this particular one is so advantageous as to cause greater multiplication of the family in which it arises than of other families. Variations which, though advantageous, fail to do this, must disappear again. Let us take a case.

Keenness of scent in a deer, by giving early notice of approaching enemies, subserves life so greatly that, other things equal, an individual having it in an unusual degree is more likely than others to survive; and, among descendants, to leave some similarly endowed or more endowed, who again transmit the variation with, in some cases, increase. Clearly this highly useful power may be developed by natural selection. So also, for like reasons, may quickness of vision and delicacy of hearing; though it may be remarked in passing that since this extra sense-endowment, serving to give early alarm, profits the herd as a whole, which takes the alarm from one individual, selection of it is not so easy, unless it occurs in a conquering stag. But now suppose that one member of the herd—perhaps because of more efficient teeth, perhaps by greater muscularity of stomach, perhaps by secretion of more appropriate gastric juices—is enabled to eat and digest a not uncommon plant which the others refuse. This peculiarity may, if food is scarce, conduce to better self-maintenance, and better fostering of young if the individual is a hind. But unless this plant is abundant, and the advantage consequently great, the advantages which other members of the herd gain from other slight variations may be equivalent. This one has unusual agility, and leaps a chasm which others balk at. That one develops longer hair in winter, and resists the cold better. Another has a skin less irritated by flies, and can graze without so much interruption. Here is one which has an unusual power of detecting food under the snow; and there is one which shows extra sagacity in the choice of a shelter from wind and rain. That the variation giving ability to eat a plant before unutilized, may become a trait of the herd, and eventually of a variety, it is needful that the individual in which it occurs shall have more descendants, or better descendants, or both, than have the various other individuals severally having their small superiorities. If these other individuals severally profit by their small superiorities, and transmit them to equally large numbers of offspring, no increase of the variation in question can take place: it must soon be cancelled. Whether in the *Origin of Species* Mr. Darwin has recognized this fact, I do not remember, but he has certainly done it by implication in his *Animals and Plants under Domestication.* Speaking of variations in domestic animals, he there says that "any particular variation would generally be lost by crossing, reversion, and the accidental destruction of the varying individuals, unless carefully preserved by man." (Vol. II, p. 292.) That which survival of the fittest does in cases like the one I have instanced, is to keep all faculties up to the mark, by destroying such individuals as have faculties in some respect below the mark; and it can produce development of some one faculty only if that faculty is predominantly important. It seems to me that many naturalists have practically lost sight of this, and assume that natural selection will increase *any* advantageous trait. Certainly a view now held by some assumes as much.

The consideration of this view, to which the foregoing paragraph is introductory, may now be entered upon. This view concerns, not direct selection, but what has been called, in questionable logic, "reversed selection"—the selection which effects, not increase of an organ, but decrease of it. For as, under some conditions, it is of advantage to an individual and its descendants to have some structure of larger size, it may be, under other conditions—namely, when the organ becomes useless—of advantage to have it of smaller size; since, even if it is not in the way, its weight and the cost of its nutrition are injurious taxes on the organism. But now comes the truth to be emphasized. Just as direct selection can increase an organ only in certain cases, so can reversed selection decrease it only in certain cases. Like the increase produced by a variation, the decrease produced by one must be such as will sensibly conduce to preservation and multiplication. It is, for instance, conceivable that were the long and massive tail of the kangaroo to become useless (say by the forcing of the species into a mountainous and rocky habitat filled with brushwood), a variation which considerably reduced the tail might sensibly profit the individual in which it occurred; and, in seasons when food was scarce, might cause survival when individuals with large tails died. But the economy of nutrition must be considerable before any such result could occur. Suppose that in this new habitat the kangaroo had no enemies; and suppose that, consequently, quickness of hearing not being called for, large ears gave no greater advantage than small ones. Would an individual with smaller ears than usual, survive and propagate better than other individuals, in consequence of the economy of nutrition achieved? To suppose this is to suppose that the saving of a grain or two of protein per day would determine the kangaroo's fate.

Long ago I discussed this matter in the *Principles of Biology* (§ 166), taking as an instance the decrease of the jaw implied by the crowding of the teeth, and now proved by measurement to have taken place. Here is the passage:—

"No functional superiority possessed by a small jaw over a large jaw, in civilized life, can be named as having caused the more frequent survival of small-jawed individuals. The only advantage which smallness of jaw might be supposed to give, is the advantage of economized nutrition; and this could not be great enough to further the preservation of men possessing it. The decrease of weight in the jaw and co-operative parts that has arisen in the course of many thousands of years, does not amount to more than a few ounces. This decrease has to be divided among the many generations that have lived and died in the interval. Let us admit that the weight of these parts diminished to the extent of an ounce in a single generation (which is a large admission); it still cannot be contended that the having to carry an ounce less in weight, or having to keep in repair an ounce less of tissue, could sensibly affect any man's fate. And if it never did this—nay, if it did not cause a *frequent* survival of small-jawed individuals where large-jawed individuals died, natural selection could neither cause nor aid diminution of the jaw and its appendages."

When writing this passage in 1864, I never dreamt that a quarter of a century later, the supposable cause of degeneration here examined and excluded as impossible, would be enunciated as an actual cause and named "reversed selection."

One of the arguments used to show the adequacy of natural selection under its direct or indirect form consists of a counter-argument to the effect that inheritance of functionally-wrought changes, supposing it to be operative, does not explain certain of the facts. This is alleged by Prof. Weismann as a part justification for his doctrine of Panmixia. Concerning the "blind fish and amphibia" found in dark places, which have but rudimentary eyes "hidden under the skin," he argues that "it is difficult to reconcile the facts of the case with the ordinary theory that the eyes of these animals have simply degenerated through disuse." After giving instances of rapid degeneration of disused organs, he argues that if "the effects of disuse are so striking in a single life, we should certainly expect, if such effects can be transmitted, that all traces of an eye would soon disappear from a species which lives in the dark." Doubtless this is a reasonable conclusion. To explain the facts on the hypothesis that acquired characters are inheritable, seems very difficult. One possible explanation may, indeed, be named. It appears to be a general law of organization that structures are stable in proportion to their antiquity—that while organs of relatively modern origin have but a comparatively superficial root in the constitution, and readily disappear if the conditions do not favour their maintenance, organs of ancient origin have deep-seated roots in the constitution, and do not readily disappear. Having been early elements in the type, and having continued to be reproduced as parts of it during a period extending throughout many geological epochs, they are comparatively persistent. Now the eye answers to this description as being a very early organ. But waiving possible explanations, let us take the particular instance cited by Prof. Weismann and see what is to be made of it. He writes:—

"The caverns in Carniola and Carinthia, in which the blind *Proteus* and so many other blind animals live, belong geologically to the Jurassic formation; and although we do not exactly know when for example the *Proteus* first entered them, the low organization of this amphibian certainly indicates that it has been sheltered there for a very long period of time, and that thousands of generations of this species have succeeded one another in the caves.

"Hence there is no reason to wonder at the extent to which the degeneration of the eye has been already carried in the *Proteus*; even if we assume that it is merely due to the cessation of the conserving influence of natural selection."[103]

Let me first note a strange oversight on the part of Prof. Weismann. He points out that the caverns in question belong to the Jurassic formation: apparently intending to imply that they have an antiquity related to that of the formation. But there is no such relation, except that the caverns cannot be older than the formation. They may have originated at any period since the containing strata were deposited; and they may be therefore relatively modern. But passing over this, and admitting that the *Proteus* has inhabited the caverns for an enormous period, what is to be said of the fact that their eyes have not disappeared entirely, as Prof. Weismann contends they should have done had the inheritance of the effects of disuse been all along operative? There is a very sufficient answer—the rudimentary eyes are not entirely useless. It seems that when the underground streams it inhabits are unusually swollen, some individuals of the species are carried out of the caverns into the open (being then sometimes captured). It is also said that the creatures shun the light; this trait being, I presume, observed when it is in captivity. Now obviously, among individuals carried out into the open, those which remain visible are apt to be carried off by enemies; whereas, those which, appreciating the difference between light and darkness, shelter themselves in dark places, survive. Hence the tendency of natural selection is to prevent the decrease of the eyes beyond that point at which they can distinguish between light and darkness. Thus the apparent anomaly is explained.

Let me suggest, as another possible reason for persistence of rudimentary organs, that the principle of economy of growth will cause diminution of them only in proportion as their constituents are of value for other uses in the organism; and that in many cases their constituents are practically valueless. Hence probably the reason why, in the case of stalk-eyed crustaceans, the eye is gone but the pedicle remains, or to use Mr. Darwin's simile, the telescope has disappeared but not its stand.

* * * * *

Along with that inadequacy of natural selection to explain changes of structure which do not aid life in important ways, alleged in § 166 of *The Principles of Biology*, a further inadequacy was alleged. It was contended that the relative powers of co-operative parts cannot be adjusted solely by survival of the fittest; and especially where the parts are numerous and the co-operation complex. In illustration it was pointed out that immensely developed horns, such as those of the extinct Irish elk, weighing over a hundred-weight, could not, with the massive skull bearing them, be carried at the extremity of the outstretched neck without many and great modifications of adjacent bones and muscles of the neck and thorax; and that without strengthening of the fore-legs, too, there would be failure alike in fighting and in locomotion. And it was argued that while we cannot assume spontaneous increase of all these parts proportionate to the additional strains, we cannot suppose them to increase by variations, one at once, without supposing the creature to be disadvantaged by the weight and nutrition of parts that were for the time useless—parts, moreover, which would revert to their original sizes before the other needful variations occurred.

When, in reply to me, it was contended that co-operative parts vary together, I named facts conflicting with this assertion—the fact that the blind cray-fish of the Kentucky caves have lost their eyes but not the foot-stalks carrying them; the fact that the normal proportion between tongue and beak in certain selected varieties of pigeons is lost; the fact that lack of concomitance in decrease of jaws and teeth in sundry kinds of pet dogs, has caused great crowding of the teeth ("The Factors of Organic Evolution," *Essays*, i, 401-402). And I then argued that if co-operative parts, small in number and so closely associated as these are, do not vary together, it is unwarrantable to allege that co-operative parts which are very numerous and remote from one another vary together. After making this rejoinder I enforced my argument by a further example—that of the giraffe. Tacitly recognizing the truth that the unusual structure of this creature must have been, in its most conspicuous traits, the result of survival of the fittest (since it is absurd to suppose that efforts to reach high branches could lengthen the legs), I illustrated afresh the obstacles to co-adaptation. Not dwelling on the objection that increase of any components of the fore-quarters out of adjustment to the others, would cause evil rather than good, I went on to argue that the co-adaptation of parts required to make the giraffe's structure useful, is much greater than at first appears. This animal has a grotesque gallop, necessitated by the great difference in length between the fore and the hind limbs. I pointed out that the mode of action of the hind limbs shows that the bones and muscles have all been changed in their proportions and adjustments; and I contended that, difficult as it is to believe that all parts of the fore-quarters have been co-adapted by the appropriate variations, now of this part now of that, it becomes impossible to believe that all the parts in the hind-quarters have been simultaneously co-adapted to one another and to all the parts of the fore-quarters: adding that want of co-adaptation, even in a single muscle, would cause fatal results when high speed had to be maintained while escaping from an enemy.

Since this argument, repeated with this fresh illustration, was published in 1886, I have met with nothing to be called a reply; and might, I think, if convictions usually followed proofs, leave the matter as it stands. It is true that, in his *Darwinism*, Mr. Wallace has adverted to my renewed objection, and, as already said, contended that changes such as those instanced can be effected by natural selection, since such changes can be effected by artificial selection: a contention which, as I have pointed out, assumes a parallelism that does not exist. But now, instead of pursuing the argument further along the same line, let me take a somewhat different line.

If there occurs some change in an organ, say by increase of its size, which adapts it better to the creature's needs, it is admitted that when, as commonly happens, the use of the organ demands the co-operation of other organs, the change in it will generally be of no service unless the co-operative organs are changed. If, for instance, there takes place such a modification of a rodent's tail as that which, by successive increases, produces the trowel-shaped tail of the beaver, no advantage will be derived unless there also take place certain modifications in the bulks and shapes of the adjacent vertebræ and their attached muscles, as well as, probably, in the hind limbs; enabling them to withstand the reactions of the blows given by the tail. And the question is, by what process these many parts, changed in different degrees, are co-adapted to the new requirements—whether variation and natural selection alone can effect the readjustment. There are three conceivable ways in which the parts may simultaneously change:—(1) they may all increase or decrease together in like degree; (2) they may all simultaneously increase or decrease independently, so as not to maintain their previous proportions, or assume any other special proportions; (3) they may vary in such ways and degrees as to make them jointly serviceable for the new end. Let us consider closely these several conceivabilities.

And first of all, what are we to understand by co-operative parts? In a general sense, all the organs of the body are co-operative parts, and are respectively liable to be more or less changed by change in any one. In a narrower sense, more directly relevant to the argument, we may, if we choose to multiply difficulties, take the entire framework of bones and muscles as formed of co-operative parts; for these are so related that any considerable change in the actions of some entails change in the actions of most others. It needs only to observe how, when putting out an effort, there goes, along with a deep breath, an expansion of the chest and a bracing up of the abdomen, to see that various muscles beyond those directly concerned are strained along with them. Or, when suffering from lumbago, an effort to lift a chair will cause an acute consciousness that not the arms only are brought into action, but also the muscles of the back. These cases show how the motor organs are so tied together that altered actions of some implicate others quite remote from them.

But without using the advantage which this interpretation of the words would give, let us take, as co-operative organs, those which are obviously such—the organs of locomotion. What, then, shall we say of the fore limbs and hind limbs of terrestrial mammals, which co-operate closely and perpetually? Do they vary together? If so, how have there been produced such contrasted structures as that of the kangaroo, with its large hind limbs and small fore limbs, and that of the giraffe, in which the hind limbs are small and the fore limbs large—how does it happen that, descending from the same primitive mammal, these creatures have diverged in the proportions of their limbs in opposite directions? Take, again, the articulate animals. Compare one of the lower types, with its rows of almost equal-sized limbs, and one of the higher types, as a crab or a lobster, with limbs some very small and some very large. How came this contrast to arise in the course of evolution, if there was the equality of variation supposed?

But now let us narrow the meaning of the phrase still further, giving it a more favourable interpretation. Instead of considering separate limbs as co-operative, let us consider the component parts of the same limb as co-operative, and ask what would result, from varying together. It would in that case happen that, though the fore and hind limbs of a mammal might become different in their sizes, they would not become different in their structures. If so, how have there arisen the unlikenesses between the hind legs of the kangaroo and those of the elephant? Or if this comparison is objected to, because the creatures belong to the widely different divisions of implacental and placental mammals, take the cases of the rabbit and the elephant, both belonging to the last division. On the hypothesis of evolution these are both derived from the same original form; but the proportions of the parts have become so widely unlike that the corresponding joints are scarcely recognized as such by the unobservant: at what seem corresponding places the legs bend in opposite ways. Equally marked, or more marked, is the parallel fact among the *Articulata.* Take that limb of the lobster which bears the claw and compare it with the corresponding limb in an inferior articulate animal, or the corresponding limb of its near ally, the rock lobster, and it becomes obvious that the component segments of the limb have come to bear to one another in the one case, proportions immensely different from those they bear in the other case. Undeniably, then, on contemplating the general facts of organic structure, we see that the concomitant variations in the parts of limbs, have not been of a kind to produce equal amounts of change in them, but quite the opposite—have been everywhere producing inequalities. Moreover, we are reminded that this production of inequalities among co-operative parts, is an essential principle of development. Had it not been so, there could not have been that progress from homogeneity of structure to heterogeneity of structure which constitutes evolution.

We pass now to the second supposition:—that the variations in co-operative parts occur irregularly, or in such independent ways that they bear no definite relations to one another—miscellaneously, let us say. This is the supposition which best corresponds with the facts. Glances at the faces around yield conspicuous proofs. Many of the muscles of the face and some of the bones, are distinctly co-operative; and these respectively vary in such ways as to produce in each person a different combination. What we see in the face we have reason to believe holds in the limbs and in all other parts. Indeed, it needs but to compare people whose arms are of the same lengths, and observe how stumpy are the fingers of one and how slender those of another; or it needs but to note the unlikenesses of gait of passers-by, implying small unlikenesses of structure; to be convinced that the relations among the variations of co-operative parts are anything but fixed. And now, confining our attention to limbs, let us consider what must happen if, by variations taking place miscellaneously, limbs have to be partially changed from fitness for one function to fitness for another function—have to be re-adapted. That the reader may fully comprehend the argument, he must here have patience while a good many anatomical details are set down.

Let us suppose a species of quadruped of which the members have, for immense past periods, been accustomed to locomotion over a relatively even surface, as, for instance, the "prairie-dogs" of North America; and let us suppose that increase of numbers has driven part of them into a region full of obstacles to easy locomotion—covered, say, by the decaying stems of fallen trees, such as one sees in portions of primeval forest. Ability to leap must then become a useful trait; and, according to the hypothesis we are considering, this ability will be produced by the selection of favourable variations. What are the variations required? A leap is effected chiefly by the bending of the hind limbs so as to make sharp angles at the joints, and then suddenly straightening them; as any one may see on watching a cat leap on to the table. The first required change, then, is increase of the large extensor muscles, by which the hind limbs are straightened. Their increases must be duly proportioned; for if those which straightened one joint become much stronger than those which straightened the other joint, the result must be collapse of the other joint when the muscles are contracted together. But let us make a large admission, and suppose these muscles to vary together; what further muscular change is next required? In a plantigrade mammal the metatarsal bones chiefly bear the reaction of the leap, though the toes may have a share. In a digitigrade mammal, however, the toes form almost exclusively the fulcrum, and if they are to bear the reaction of a higher leap, the flexor muscles which depress and bend them must be proportionately enlarged: if not, the leap will fail from want of a firm *point d'appui.* Tendons as well as muscles must be modified; and, among others, the many tendons which go to the digits and their phalanges. Stronger muscles and tendons imply greater strains on the joints; and unless these are strengthened, one or other, dislocation will be caused by a more vigorous spring. Not only the articulations themselves must be so modified as to bear greater stress, but also the numerous ligaments which hold the parts of each in place. Nor can the bodies of the bones remain unstrengthened; for if they have no more than the strengths needed for previous movements they will fail to bear more violent movements. Thus, saying nothing of the required changes in the pelvis, as well as in the nerves and blood-vessels, there are, counting bones, muscles, tendons, ligaments, at least fifty different parts in each hind leg which have to be enlarged. Moreover they have to be enlarged in unlike degrees. The muscles and tendons of the outer toes, for example, need not be added to so much as those of the median toes. Now, throughout their successive stages of growth, all these parts have to be kept fairly well balanced; as any one may infer on remembering sundry of the accidents he has known. Among my own friends I could name one who, when playing lawn-tennis, snapped the Achilles tendon; another who, while swinging his children, tore some of the muscular fibres in the calf of his leg; another who, in getting over a fence, tore a ligament of one knee. Such facts, joined with every one's experience of sprains, show that during the extreme exertions to which limbs are now and then subject, there is a giving way of parts not quite up to the required level of strength. How, then, is this balance to be maintained? Suppose the extensor muscles have all varied appropriately; their variations are useless unless the other co-operative parts have also varied appropriately. Worse than this. Saying nothing of the disadvantage caused by extra weight and cost of nutrition, they will be causes of mischief—causes of derangement to the rest by contracting with undue force. And then, how long will it take for the rest to be brought into adjustment? As Mr. Darwin says concerning domestic animals:—"Any particular variation would generally be lost by crossing, reversion, &c. ... unless carefully preserved by man." In a state of nature, then, favourable variations of these muscles would disappear again long before one or a few of the co-operative parts could be appropriately varied, much more before all of them could.

With this insurmountable difficulty goes a difficulty still more insurmountable—if the expression may be allowed. It is not a question of increased sizes of parts only, but of altered shapes of parts, too. A glance at the skeletons of mammals shows how unlike are the forms of the corresponding bones of their limbs; and shows that they have been severally re-moulded in each species to the different requirements entailed by its different habits. The change from the structures of hind limbs fitted only for walking and trotting to hind limbs fitted also for leaping, implies, therefore, that, along with strengthenings of bones there must go alterations in their forms. Now the fortuitous alterations of form which may take place in any bone are countless. How long, then, will it be before there takes place that particular alteration which will make the bone fitter for its new action? And what is the probability that the many required changes of shape, as well as of size, in bones will each of them be effected before all the others are lost again? If the probabilities against success are incalculable, when we take account only of changes in the sizes of parts, what shall we say of their incalculableness when differences of form also are taken into account?

"Surely this piling up of difficulties has gone far enough"; the reader will be inclined to say. By no means. There is a difficulty immeasurably transcending those named. We have thus far omitted the second half of the leap, and the provisions to be made for it. After ascent of the animal's body comes descent; and the greater the force with which it is projected up, the greater is the force with which it comes down. Hence, if the supposed creature has undergone such changes in the hind limbs as will enable them to propel it to a greater height, without having undergone any changes in the fore limbs, the result will be that on its descent the fore limbs will give way, and it will come down on its nose. The fore limbs, then, have to be changed simultaneously with the hind. How changed? Contrast the markedly bent hind limbs of a cat with its almost straight fore limbs, or contrast the silence of the spring on to the table with the thud which the fore paws make as it jumps off the table. See how unlike the actions of the hind and fore limbs are, and how unlike their structures. In what way, then, is the required co-adaptation to be effected? Even were it a question of relative sizes only, there would be no answer; for facts already given show that we may not assume simultaneous increases of size to take place in the hind and fore limbs; and, indeed, a glance at the various human races, which differ considerably in the ratios of their legs to their arms, shows us this. But it is not simply a question of sizes. To bear the increased shock of descent the fore limbs must be changed throughout in their structures. Like those in the hind limbs, the changes must be of many parts in many proportions; and they must be both in sizes and in shapes. More than this. The scapular arch and its attached muscles must also be strengthened and re-moulded. See, then, the total requirements. We must suppose that by natural selection of miscellaneous variations, the parts of the hind limbs will be co-adapted to one another, in sizes, shapes, and ratios; that those of the fore limbs will undergo co-adaptation similar in their complexity, but dissimilar in their kinds; and that the two sets of co-adaptations will be effected *pari passu.* If, as may be held, the probabilities are millions to one against the first set of changes being achieved, then it may be held that the probabilities are billions to one against the second being simultaneously achieved, in progressive adjustment to the first.

There remains only to notice the third conceivable mode of adjustment. It may be imagined that though, by the natural selection of miscellaneous variations, these adjustments cannot be effected, they may nevertheless be made to take place appropriately. How made? To suppose them so made is to suppose that the prescribed end is somewhere recognized; and that the changes are step by step simultaneously proportioned for achieving it—is to suppose a designed production of these changes. In such case, then, we have to fall back in part upon the primitive hypothesis; and if we do this in part, we may as well do it wholly—may as well avowedly return to the doctrine of special creations.

What, then, is the only defensible interpretation? If such modifications of structure produced by modifications of function as we see take place in each individual, are in any measure transmissible to descendants, then all these co-adaptations, from the simplest up to the most complex, are accounted for. In some cases this inheritance of acquired characters suffices by itself to explain the facts; and in other cases it suffices when taken in combination with the selection of favourable variations. An example of the first class is furnished by the change just considered; and an example of the second class is furnished by the case, before named, of development in a deer's horns. If, by some extra massiveness spontaneously arising, or by formation of an additional "point," an advantage is gained either for attack or defence, then, if the increased muscularity and strengthened structure of the neck and thorax, which wielding of these somewhat heavier horns produces, are in a greater or less degree inherited, and in several successive generations are by this process brought up to the required extra strength, it becomes possible and advantageous for a further increase of the horns to take place, and a further increase in the apparatus for wielding them, and so on continuously. By such processes only, in which each part gains strength in proportion to function, can co-operative parts be kept in adjustment, and be re-adjusted to meet new requirements. Close contemplation of the facts impresses me more strongly than ever with the two alternatives—either there has been inheritance of acquired characters, or there has been no evolution.

This very pronounced opinion will be met, on the part of some, by a no less pronounced demurrer, which involves a denial of possibility. It has been of late asserted, and by many believed, that inheritance of acquired characters cannot occur. Weismann, they say, has shown that there is early established in the evolution of each organism such a distinctness between those component units which carry on the individual life and those which are devoted to maintenance of the species, that changes in the one cannot affect the other. We will look closely into his doctrine.

Basing his argument on the principle of the physiological division of labour, and assuming that the primary division of labour is that between such part of an organism as carries on individual life and such part as is reserved for the production of other lives, Weismann, starting with "the first multicellular organism," says that—"Hence the single group would come to be divided into two groups of cells, which may be called somatic and reproductive—the cells of the body as opposed to those which are concerned with reproduction." (*Essays upon Heredity*, i, p. 27.)

Though he admits that this differentiation "was not at first absolute, and indeed is not always so to-day," yet he holds that the differentiation eventually becomes absolute in the sense that the somatic cells, or those which compose the body at large, come to have only a limited power of cell-division, instead of an unlimited power which the reproductive cells have; and also in the sense that eventually there ceases to be any communication between the two further than that implied by the supplying of nutriment to the reproductive cells by the somatic cells. The outcome of this argument is that, in the absence of communication, changes induced in the somatic cells, constituting the individual, cannot influence the natures of the reproductive cells, and cannot therefore be transmitted to posterity. Such is the theory. Now let us look at a few facts—some familiar, some unfamiliar.

His investigations led Pasteur to the positive conclusion that the silkworm diseases are inherited. The transmission from parent to offspring resulted, not through any contamination of the surface of the egg by the body of the parent while being deposited, but resulted from infection of the egg itself—intrusion of the parasitic organism. Generalized observations concerning the disease called *pébrine*, enabled him to decide, by inspection of the eggs, which were infected and which were not: certain modifications of form distinguishing the diseased ones. More than this; the infection was proved by microscopical examination of the contents of the egg; in proof of which he quotes as follows from Dr. Carlo Vittadini:—

"Il résulte de mes recherches sur les graines, à l'époque où commence le développement du germe, que les corpuscules, une fois apparus dans l'œuf, augmentent graduellement en nombre, à mesure que l'embryon se développe; que, dans les derniers jours de l'incubation, l'œuf en est plein, au point de faire croire que la majeure partie des granules du jaune se sont transformés en corpuscules.

"Une autre observation importante est que l'embryon aussi est souillé de corpuscules, et à un degré tel qu'on peut soupçonner que l'infection du jaune tire son origine du germe lui-même; en d'autres termes que le germe est primordialement infecté, et porte en lui-même ces corpuscules tout comme les vers adultes, frappés du même mal."[104]

Thus, then the substance of the egg and even its innermost vital part, is permeable by a parasite sufficiently large to be microscopically visible. It is also of course permeable by the invisible molecules of protein, out of which its living tissues are formed, and by absorption of which they subsequently grow. But, according to Weismann, it is *not* permeable by those invisible units of protoplasm out of which the vitally active tissues of the parent are constituted: units composed, as we must assume, of variously arranged molecules of protein. So that the big thing may pass, and the little thing may pass, but the intermediate thing may not pass!

A fact of kindred nature, unhappily more familiar, may be next brought in evidence. It concerns the transmission of a disease not infrequent among those of unregulated lives. The highest authority concerning this disease, in its inherited form, is Mr. Jonathan Hutchinson; and the following are extracts from a letter I have received from him, and which I publish with his assent:—

"I do not think that there can be any reasonable doubt that a very large majority of those who suffer from inherited syphilis take the taint from the male parent.... It is the rule when a man marries who has no remaining local lesion, but in whom the taint is not eradicated, for his wife to remain apparently well, whilst her child may suffer. No doubt the child infects its mother's blood, but this does not usually evoke any obvious symptoms of syphilis.... I am sure I have seen hundreds of syphilitic infants whose mothers had not, so far as I could ascertain, ever displayed a single symptom."

See, then, to what we are committed if we accept Weismann's hypothesis. We must conclude, that whereas the reproductive cell may be effectually invaded by an abnormal living element in the parental organism, those normal living elements which constitute the vital protoplasm of the parental organism, cannot invade it. Or if it be admitted that both intrude, then the implication is that, whereas the abnormal element can so modify the development as to cause changes of structure (as of the teeth), the normal element can cause no changes of structure![105]

We pass now to evidence not much known to the world at large, but widely known in the biological world, though known in so incomplete a manner as to be undervalued in it. Indeed, when I name it, probably many will vent a mental pooh-pooh. The fact to which I refer is one of which record is preserved in the museum of the College of Surgeons, in the shape of paintings of a foal borne by a mare not quite thoroughbred, to a sire which was thoroughbred—a foal which bears the markings of the quagga. The history of this remarkable foal is given by the Earl of Morton, F.R.S., in a letter to the President of the Royal Society (read November 23, 1820). In it he states that wishing to domesticate the quagga, and having obtained a male but not a female, he made an experiment.

"I tried to breed from the male quagga and a young chestnut mare of seven-eighths Arabian blood, and which had never been bred from; the result was the production of a female hybrid, now five years old, and bearing, both in her form and in her colour, very decided indications of her mixed origin. I subsequently parted with the seven-eighths Arabian mare to Sir Gore Ouseley, who has bred from her by a very fine black Arabian horse. I yesterday morning examined the produce, namely, a two-year-old filly and a year-old colt. They have the character of the Arabian breed as decidedly as can be expected, where fifteen-sixteenths of the blood are Arabian; and they are fine specimens of that breed; but both in their colour and in the hair of their manes, they have a striking resemblance to the quagga. Their colour is bay, marked more or less like the quagga in a darker tint. Both are distinguished by the dark line along the ridge of the back, the dark stripes across the forehead, and the dark bars across the back part of the legs."[106]

Lord Morton then names sundry further correspondences. Dr. Wollaston, at that time President of the Royal Society, who had seen the animals, testified to the correctness of his description, and, as shown by his remarks, entertained no doubt about the alleged facts. But good reason for doubt may be assigned. There naturally arises the question—How does it happen that parallel results are not observed in other cases? If in any progeny certain traits not belonging to the sire, but belonging to a sire of preceding progeny, are reproduced, how is it that such anomalously inherited traits are not observed in domestic animals, and indeed in mankind? How is it that the children of a widow by a second husband do not bear traceable resemblances to the first husband? To these questions nothing like satisfactory replies seem forthcoming; and, in the absence of replies, scepticism, if not disbelief, may be held reasonable.

There is an explanation, however. Forty years ago I made acquaintance with a fact which impressed me by its significant implications, and has, for this reason I suppose, remained in my memory. It is set forth in the *Journal of the Royal Agricultural Society*, Vol. XIV (1853), pp. 214 *et seq.*, and concerns certain results of crossing French and English breeds of sheep. The writer of the translated paper, M. Malingie-Nouel, Director of the Agricultural School of La Charmoise, states that when the French breeds of sheep (in which were included "the *mongrel* Merinos") were crossed with an English breed, "the lambs present the following results. Most of them resemble the mother more than the father; some show no trace of the father." Joining the admission respecting the mongrels with the facts subsequently stated, it is tolerably clear that the cases in which the lambs bore no traces of the father were cases in which the mother was of pure breed. Speaking of the results of these crossings in the second generation, "having 75 per cent. of English blood," M. Nouel says:—"The lambs thrive, wear a beautiful appearance, and complete the joy of the breeder.... No sooner are the lambs weaned than their strength, their vigour, and their beauty begin to decay.... At last the constitution gives way ... he remains stunted for life:" the constitution being thus proved unstable or unadapted to the requirements. How, then, did M. Nouel succeed in obtaining a desirable combination of a fine English breed with the relatively poor French breeds?

He took an animal from "flocks originally sprung from a mixture of the two distinct races that are established in those two provinces [Berry and La Sologne]," and these he "united with animals of another mixed breed ... which blended the Tourangelle and native Merino blood of" La Beauce and

Touraine, and obtained a mixture of all four races "without decided character, without fixity ... but possessing the advantage of being used to our climate and management."

Putting one of these "mixed blood ewes to a pure New-Kent ram ... one obtains a lamb containing fifty-hundredths of the purest and most ancient English blood, with twelve and a half hundredths of four different French races, which are individually lost in the preponderance of English blood, and disappear almost entirely, leaving the improving type in the ascendant.... All the lambs produced strikingly resembled each other, and even Englishmen took them for animals of their own country."

M. Nouel goes on to remark that when this derived breed was bred with itself, the marks of the French breeds were lost. "Some slight traces" could be detected by experts, but these "soon disappeared."

Thus we get proof that relatively pure constitutions predominate in progeny over much mixed constitutions. The reason is not difficult to see. Every organism tends to become adapted to its conditions of life; and all the structures of a species, accustomed through multitudinous generations to the climate, food, and various influences of its locality, are moulded into harmonious co-operation favourable to life in that locality: the result being that in the development of each young individual, the tendencies conspire to produce the fit organization. It is otherwise when the species is removed to a habitat of different character, or when it is of mixed breed. In the one case its organs, partially out of harmony with the requirements of its new life, become partially out of harmony with one another; since, while one influence, say of climate, is but little changed, another influence, say of food, is much changed; and, consequently, the perturbed relations of the organs interfere with their original stable equilibrium. Still more in the other case is there a disturbance in equilibrium. In a mongrel, the constitution derived from each source repeats itself as far as possible. Hence a conflict of tendencies to evolve two structures more or less unlike. The tendencies do not harmoniously conspire, but produce partially incongruous sets of organs. And evidently where the breed is one in which there are united the traits of various lines of ancestry, there results an organization so full of small incongruities of structure and action, that it has a much-diminished power of maintaining its balance; and while it cannot withstand so well adverse influences, it cannot so well hold its own in the offspring. Concerning parents of pure and mixed breeds respectively, severally tending to reproduce their own structures in progeny, we may therefore say, figuratively, that the house divided against itself cannot withstand the house of which the members are in concord.

Now if this is shown to be the case with breeds the purest of which have been adapted to their habitats and modes of life during some few hundred years only, what shall we say when the question is of a breed which has had a constant mode of life in the same locality for ten thousand years or more, like the quagga? In this the stability of constitution must be such as no domestic animal can approach. Relatively stable as may have been the constitutions of Lord Morton's horses, as compared with the constitutions of ordinary horses, yet, since Arab horses, even in their native country, have probably in the course of successive conquests and migrations of tribes become more or less mixed, and since they have been subject to the conditions of domestic life, differing much from the conditions of their original wild life, and since the English breed has undergone the perturbing effects of change from the climate and food of the East to the climate and food of the West, the organizations of the horse and mare in question could have had nothing like that perfect balance produced in the quagga by a hundred centuries of harmonious co-operation. Hence the result. And hence at the same time the interpretation of the fact that analogous phenomena are not obvious among most domestic animals, or among ourselves; since both have relatively mixed, and generally extremely mixed, constitutions, which, as we see in ourselves, have been made generation after generation, not by the formation of a mean between two parents, but by the jumbling of traits of the one with traits of the other; until there exist no such conspiring tendencies among the parts as cause repetition of combined details of structure in posterity.

Expectation that scepticism might be felt respecting this alleged anomaly presented by the quagga-marked foal, had led me to think over the matter; and I had reached this interpretation before sending to the College of Surgeons Museum (being unable to go myself) to obtain the particulars and refer to the records. When there was brought to me a copy of the account as set forth in the *Philosophical Transactions*, it was joined with the information that there existed an appended account of pigs, in which a parallel fact had been observed. To my immediate inquiry—"Was the male a wild pig?" there came the reply—"I did not observe." Of course I forthwith obtained the volume, and there found what I expected. It was contained in a paper communicated by Dr. Wollaston from Daniel Giles, Esq., concerning his "sow and her produce," which said that—

"she was one of a well-known black and white breed of Mr. Western, the Member for Essex. About ten years since I put her to a boar of the wild breed, and of a deep chestnut colour which I had just received from Hatfield House, and which was soon afterwards drowned by accident. The pigs produced (which were her first litter) partook in appearance of both boar and sow, but in some the chestnut colour of the boar strongly prevailed.

"The sow was afterwards put to a boar of Mr. Western's breed (the wild boar having been long dead). The produce was a litter of pigs, some of which, we observed with much surprise, to be stained and clearly marked with the chestnut colour which had prevailed in the former litter."

Mr. Giles adds that in a second litter of pigs, the father of which was of Mr. Western's breed, he and his bailiff believe there was a recurrence, in some, of the chestnut colour, but admits that their "recollection is much less perfect than I wish it to be." He also adds that, in the course of many years' experience, he had never known the least appearance of the chestnut colour in Mr. Western's breed.

What are the probabilities that these two anomalous results should have arisen, under these exceptional conditions, as a matter of chance? Evidently the probabilities against such a coincidence are enormous. The testimony is in both cases so good that, even apart from the coincidence, it would be unreasonable to reject it; but the coincidence makes acceptance of it imperative. There is mutual verification, at the same time that there is a joint interpretation yielded of the strange phenomenon, and of its non-occurrence under ordinary circumstances.

And now, in presence of these facts, what are we to say? Simply that they are fatal to Weismann's hypothesis. They show that there is none of the alleged independence of the reproductive cells; but that the two sets of cells are in close communion. They prove that while the reproductive cells multiply and arrange themselves during the evolution of the embryo, some of their germ-plasm passes into the mass of somatic cells constituting the parental body, and becomes a permanent component of it. Further, they necessitate the inference that this introduced germ-plasm, everywhere diffused, is some of it included in the reproductive cells subsequently formed. And if we thus get a demonstration that the somewhat different units of a foreign germ-plasm permeating the organism, permeate also the subsequently formed reproductive cells, and affect the structures of the individuals arising from them, the implication is that the like happens with those native units which have been made somewhat different by modified functions: there must be a tendency to inheritance of acquired characters.

One more step only has to be taken. It remains to ask what is the flaw in the assumption with which Weismann's theory sets out. If, as we see, the conclusions drawn from it do not correspond to the facts, then, either the reasoning is invalid, or the original postulate is untrue. Leaving aside all questions concerning the reasoning, it will suffice here to show the untruth of the postulate. Had his work been written during the early years of the cell-doctrine, the supposition that the multiplying cells of which the *Metazoa* and *Metaphyta* are composed, become completely separate, could not have been met by a reasonable scepticism; but now, not only is scepticism justifiable, but denial is called for. Some dozen years ago it was discovered that in many cases vegetal cells are connected with one another by threads of protoplasm—threads which unite the internal protoplasm of one cell with the internal protoplasms of cells around It is as though the pseudopodia of imprisoned rhizopods were fused with the pseudopodia of adjacent imprisoned rhizopods. We cannot reasonably suppose that the continuous network of protoplasm thus constituted has been produced after the cells have become adult. These protoplasmic connections must have survived the process of fission. The implication is that the cells forming the embryo-plant retained their protoplasmic connections while they multiplied, and that such connections continued throughout all subsequent multiplications—an implication which has, I believe, been established by researches upon germinating palm-seeds. But now we come to a verifying series of facts which the cell-structures of animals in their early stages present. In his *Monograph of the Development of Peripatus Capensis*, Mr. Adam Sedgwick, F.R.S., Reader in Animal Morphology at Cambridge, writes as follows:—

"All the cells of the ovum, ectodermal as well as endodermal, are connected together by a fine protoplasmic reticulum." (p. 41)

"The continuity of the various cells of the segmenting ovum is primary, and not secondary; *i. e.*, in the cleavage the segments do not completely separate from one another. But are we justified in speaking of cells at all in this case? *The fully segmented ovum is a syncytium, and there are not and have not been at any stage cell limits.*" (p. 41)

"It is becoming more and more clear every day that the cells composing the tissues of animals are not isolated units, but that they are connected with one another. I need only refer to the connection known to exist between connective tissue cells, cartilage cells, epithelial cells, &c. And not only may the cells of one tissue be continuous with each other, but they may also be continuous with the cells of other tissues." (pp. 47-8)

"Finally, if the protoplasm of the body is primitively a syncytium, and the ovum until maturity a part of that syncytium, the separation of the generative products does not differ essentially from the internal gemmation of a Protozoon, and the inheritance by the offspring of peculiarities first appearing in the parent, though not explained, is rendered less mysterious; for the protoplasm of the whole body being continuous, change in the molecular constitution of any part of it would naturally be expected to spread, in time, through the whole mass." (p. 49)

Mr. Sedgwick's subsequent investigations confirm these conclusions. In a letter of December 27, 1892, passages which he allows me to publish run as follows:—

"All the embryological studies that I have made since that to which you refer confirm me more and more in the view that the connections between the cells of adults are not secondary connections, but primary, dating from the time when the embryo was a unicellular structure.... My own investigations on this subject have been confined to the Arthropoda, Elasmobranchii, and Aves. I have thoroughly examined the development of at least one kind of each of these groups, and I have never been able to detect a stage in which the cells were not continuous with each other; and I have studied innumerable stages from the beginning of cleavage onwards."

So that the alleged independence of the reproductive cells does not exist. The *soma*—to use Weismann's name for the aggregate of cells forming the body—is, in the words of Mr. Sedgwick, "a continuous mass of vacuolated protoplasm;" and the reproductive cells are nothing more than portions of it separated some little time before they are required to perform their functions.

Thus the theory of Weismann is doubly disproved. Inductively we are shown that there *does* take place that communication of characters from the somatic cells to the reproductive cells, which he says cannot take place; and deductively we are shown that this communication is a natural sequence of connections between the two which he ignores; his various conclusions are deduced from a postulate which is untrue.

* * * * *

From the title of this essay, and from much of its contents, nine readers out of ten will infer that it is directed against the views of Mr. Darwin. They will be astonished on being told that, contrariwise, it is directed against the views of those who, in a considerable measure, dissent from Mr. Darwin. For the inheritance of acquired characters, which it is now the fashion in the biological world to deny, was, by Mr. Darwin, fully recognized and often insisted on. Such of the foregoing arguments as touch Mr. Darwin's views, simply imply that the cause of evolution which at first he thought unimportant, but the importance of which he increasingly perceived as he grew older, is more important than he admitted, even at the last. The neo-Darwinists, however, do not admit this cause at all.

Let it not be supposed that this explanation implies any disapproval of the dissentients, considered as such. Seeing how little regard for authority I have myself usually shown, it would be absurd in me to reflect in any degree upon those who have rejected certain of Mr. Darwin's teachings, for reasons which they have held sufficient. But while their independence of thought is to be applauded rather than blamed, it is, I think, to be regretted that they have not guarded themselves against a long-standing bias. It is a common trait of human nature to seek some excuse when found in the wrong. Invaded self-esteem sets up a defence, and anything is made to serve. Thus it happened that when geologists and biologists, previously holding that all kinds of organisms arose by special creations, surrendered to the battery opened upon them by *The Origin of Species*, they sought to minimise their irrationality by pointing to irrationality on the other side. "Well, at any rate, Lamarck was in the wrong." "It is clear that we were right in rejecting *his* doctrine." And so, by duly emphasizing the fact that he overlooked "Natural Selection" as the chief cause, and by showing how erroneous were some of his interpretations, they succeeded in mitigating the sense of their own error. It is true their creed was that at successive periods in the Earth's history, old Floras and Faunas had been abolished and others introduced; just as though, to use Professor Huxley's figure, the table had been now and again kicked over and a new pack of cards brought out. And it is true that Lamarck, while he rejected this absurd creed, assigned for the facts reasons some of which are absurd. But in consequence of the feeling described, his defensible belief was forgotten and only his indefensible ones remembered. This one-sided estimate has become traditional; so that there is now often shown a subdued contempt for those who suppose that there can be any truth in the reasonings of a man whose general conception was partly sense, at a time when the general conceptions of his contemporaries were wholly nonsense. Hence results unfair treatment—hence result the different dealings with the views of Lamarck and of Weismann.

"Where are the facts proving the inheritance of acquired characters?" ask those who deny it. Well, in the first place, there might be asked the counter-question—Where are the facts which disprove it? Surely if not only the general structures of organisms, but also many of the modifications arising in them, are inheritable, the natural implication is that all modifications are inheritable; and if any say that the inheritableness is limited to those arising in a certain way, the *onus* lies on them of proving that those otherwise arising are not inheritable.[107] Leaving this counter-question aside, however, it will suffice if we ask another counter-question. It is asserted that the dwindling of organs from disuse is due to the successive survivals in posterity of individuals in which the organs have varied in the direction of decrease. Where now are the facts supporting this assertion? Not one has been assigned or can be assigned. Not a single case can be named in which *panmixia* is a proved cause of diminution. Even had the deductive argument for *panmixia* been as valid as we have found it to be invalid, there would still have been required, in pursuance of scientific method, some verifying inductive evidence. Yet, though not a shred of such evidence has been given, the doctrine is accepted with acclamation, and adopted as part of current biological theory. Articles are written and letters published in which it is assumed that this mere speculation, justified by not a tittle of proof, displaces large conclusions previously drawn. And then, passing into the outer world, this unsupported belief affects opinions there too; so that we have recently had a Right Honourable lecturer who, taking for granted its truth, represents the inheritance of acquired characters as an exploded hypothesis, and proceeds to give revised views of human affairs.

Finally, there comes the reply that there *are* facts proving the inheritance of acquired characters. All those assigned by Mr. Darwin, together with others such, remain outstanding when we find that the interpretation by *panmixia* is untenable. Indeed, even had that hypothesis been tenable, it would have been inapplicable to these cases; since in domestic animals, artificially fed and often overfed, the supposed advantage from economy cannot be shown to tell; and since, in these cases, individuals are not naturally selected during the struggle for life, in which certain traits are advantageous, but are artificially selected by man without regard to such traits. Should it be urged that the assigned facts are not numerous, it may be replied that there are no persons whose occupations and amusements incidentally bring out such facts; and that they are probably as numerous as those which would have been available for Mr. Darwin's hypothesis, had there been no breeders and fanciers and gardeners who, in pursuit of their profits and hobbies, furnished him with evidence. It may be added that the required facts are not likely to be numerous, if biologists refuse to seek for them.

See, then, how the case stands. Natural selection, or survival of the fittest, is almost exclusively operative throughout the vegetal world and throughout the lower animal world, characterized by relative passivity. But with the ascent to higher types of animals, its effects are in increasing degrees involved with those produced by inheritance of acquired characters; until, in animals of complex structures, inheritance of acquired characters becomes an important, if not the chief, cause of evolution. We have seen that natural selection cannot work any changes in organisms save such as conduce in considerable degrees, directly or indirectly, to the multiplication of the stirp; whence failure to account for various changes ascribed to it. And we have seen that it yields no explanation of the co-adaptation of co-operative parts, even when the co-operation is relatively simple, and still less when it is complex. On the other hand, we see that if, along with the transmission of generic and specific structures, there tend to be transmitted modifications arising in a certain way, there is a strong *a priori* probability that there tend to be transmitted modifications arising in all ways. We have a number of facts confirming this inference, and showing that acquired characters are inherited—as large a number as can be expected, considering the difficulty of observing them and the absence of search. And then to these facts may be added the facts with which this essay set out, concerning the distribution of tactual discriminativeness. While we saw that these are inexplicable by survival of the fittest, we saw that they are clearly explicable as resulting from the inheritance of acquired characters. And here let it be added that this conclusion is conspicuously warranted by one of the methods of inductive logic, known as the method of concomitant variations. For throughout the whole series of gradations in perceptive power, we saw that the amount of the effect is proportionate to the amount of the alleged cause.

II.

Apart from those more special theories of Professor Weismann I lately dealt with, the wide acceptance of which by the biological world greatly surprises me, there are certain more general theories of his—fundamental theories—the acceptance of which surprises me still more. Of the two on which rests the vast superstructure of his speculations, the first concerns the distinction between the reproductive elements of each organism and the non-reproductive elements. He says:—

"Let us now consider how it happened that the multicellular animals and plants, which arose from unicellular forms of life, came to lose this power of living for ever.

"The answer to this question is closely bound up with the principle of division of labour which appeared among multicellular organisms at a very early stage....

"The first multicellular organism was probably a cluster of similar cells, but these units soon lost their original homogeneity. As the result of mere relative position, some of the cells were especially fitted to provide for the nutrition of the colony, while others undertook the work of reproduction." (*Essays upon Heredity*, i, p. 27)

Here, then, we have the great principle of the division of labour, which is the principle of all organization, taken as primarily illustrated in the division between the reproductive cells and the non-reproductive or somatic cells—the cells devoted to the continuance of the species, and the cells which subserve the life of the individual. And the early separation of reproductive cells from somatic cells, is alleged on the ground that this primary division of labour is that which arises between elements devoted to species-life and elements devoted to individual life. Let us not be content with words but look at the facts.

When Milne-Edwards first used the phrase "physiological division of labour," he was obviously led to do so by perceiving the analogy between the division of labour in a society, as described by political economists, and the division of labour in an organism. Every one who reads has been familiarized with the first as illustrated in the early stages, when men were warriors while the cultivation and drudgery were done by slaves and women; and as illustrated in the later stages, when not only are agriculture and manufactures carried on by separate classes, but agriculture is carried on by landlords, farmers, and labourers, while manufactures, multitudinous in their kinds, severally involve the actions of capitalists, overseers, workers, &c., and while the great function of distribution is carried on by wholesale and retail dealers in different commodities. Meanwhile students of biology, led by Milne-Edwards's phrase, have come to recognize a parallel arrangement in a living creature; shown, primarily, in the devoting of the outer parts to the general business of obtaining food and escaping from enemies, while the inner parts are devoted to the utilization of food, and supporting themselves and the outer parts; and shown, secondarily, by the subdivision of these great functions into those of various limbs and senses in the one case, and in the other case into those of organs for digestion, respiration, circulation, excretion, &c. But now let us ask what is the essential nature of this division of labour. In both cases it is an *exchange of services*—an arrangement under which, while one part devotes itself to one kind of action and yields benefits to all the rest, all the rest, jointly and severally performing their special actions, yield benefits to it in exchange. Otherwise described, it is a system of *mutual* dependence: A depends for its welfare upon B, C, and D; B upon A, C, and D; and so with the rest: all depend upon each and each upon all. Now let us apply this true conception of the division of labour, to that which Professor Weismann calls a division of labour. Where is the *exchange of services* between somatic cells and reproductive cells? There is none. The somatic cells render great services to the reproductive cells, by furnishing them with materials for growth and multiplication; but the reproductive cells render no services at all to the somatic cells. If we look for the *mutual* dependence we look in vain. We find entire dependence on the one side and none on the other. Between the parts devoted to individual life and the part devoted to species-life, there is no division of labour whatever. The individual works for the species; but the species works not for the individual. Whether at the stage when the species is represented by reproductive cells, or at the stage when it is represented by eggs, or at the stage when it is represented by young, the parent does everything for it, and it does nothing for the parent. The essential part of the conception is gone: there is no giving and receiving, no exchange, no mutuality.

But now suppose we pass over this fallacious interpretation, and grant Professor Weismann his fundamental assumption and his fundamental corollary. Suppose we grant that because the primary division of labour is that between somatic cells and reproductive cells, these two groups are the first to be differentiated. Having granted this corollary, let us compare it with the facts. As the alleged primary division of labour is universal, so the alleged primary differentiation should be universal too. Let us see whether it is so. Already, in the paragraph from which I have quoted above, a crack in the doctrine is admitted: it is said that "this differentiation was not at first absolute, and indeed it is not always so to-day." And then, on turning to page 74, we find that the crack has become a chasm. Of the reproductive cells it is stated that—"In Vertebrata they do not become distinct from the other cells of the body until the embryo is completely formed." That is to say, in this large and most important division of the animal kingdom, the implied universal law does not hold. Much more than this is confessed. Lower down the page we read—"There may be in fact cases in which such separation does not take place until after the animal is completely formed, and others, as I believe that I have shown, in which it first arises one or more generations later, viz., in the buds produced by the parent."

So that in other great divisions of the animal kingdom the alleged law is broken; as among the *Cœlenterata* by the *Hydrozoa*, as among the *Mollusca* by the Ascidians, and as among the *Platyhelminthes* by the Trematode worms.

Following this admission concerning the *Vertebrata*, come certain sentences which I partially italicize:—

"Thus, as their development shows, a marked antithesis exists between the substance of the undying reproductive cells and that of the perishable body-cells. We cannot explain this fact except *by the supposition* that each reproductive cell potentially contains two kinds of substance, which at a variable time after the commencement of embryonic development, separate from one another, and finally produce two sharply contrasted groups of cells." (p. 74)

And a little lower down the page we meet with the lines:—

"*It is therefore quite conceivable* that the reproductive cells might separate from the somatic cells much later than in the examples mentioned above, without changing the hereditary tendencies of which they are the bearers."

That is to say, it is "quite conceivable" that after sexless *Cercariæ* have gone on multiplying by internal gemmation for generations, the "two kinds of substance" have, notwithstanding innumerable cell-divisions, preserved their respective natures, and finally separate in such ways as to produce reproductive cells. Here Professor Weismann does not, as in a case before noted, assume something which it is "easy to imagine," but he assumes something which it is difficult to imagine; and apparently thinks that a scientific conclusion may be thereon safely based.

* * * * *

Associated with the assertion that the primary division of labour is between the somatic cells and the reproductive cells, and associated with the corollary that the primary differentiation is that which arises between them, there goes another corollary. It is alleged that there exists a fundamental distinction of nature between these two classes of cells. They are described as respectively mortal and immortal, in the sense that those of the one class are limited in their powers of multiplication, while those of the other class are unlimited. And it is contended that this is due to inherent unlikeness of nature.

Before inquiring into the truth of this proposition, I may fitly remark upon a preliminary proposition set down by Professor Weismann. Referring to the hypothesis that death depends "upon causes which lie in the nature of life itself," he says:—

"I do not however believe in the validity of this explanation: I consider that death is not a primary necessity, but that it has been secondarily acquired as an adaptation. I believe that life is endowed with a fixed duration, not because it is contrary to its nature to be unlimited, but because the unlimited existence of individuals would be a luxury without any corresponding advantage." (p. 24)

This last sentence has a teleological sound which would be appropriate did it come from a theologian, but which seems strange as coming from a man of science. Assuming, however, that the implication was not intended, I go on to remark that Professor Weismann has apparently overlooked a universal law of evolution—not organic only, but inorganic and super-organic—which implies the necessity of death. The changes of every aggregate, no matter of what kind, inevitably end in a state of equilibrium. Suns and planets die, as well as organisms. The process of integration, which constitutes the fundamental trait of all evolution, continues until it has brought about a state which negatives further alterations, molar or molecular—a state of balance among the forces of the aggregate and the forces which oppose them.[108] In so far, therefore, as Professor Weismann's conclusions imply the non-necessity of death, they cannot be sustained.

But now let us consider the above-described antithesis between the immortal *Protozoa* and the mortal *Metazoa*. An essential part of the theory is that the *Protozoa* can go on dividing and subdividing without limit, so long as the fit external conditions are maintained. But what is the evidence for this? Even by Professor Weismann's own admission there is no proof. On p. 285 he says:—

"I could only consent to adopt the hypothesis of rejuvenescence [achieved by conjugation], if it were rendered absolutely certain that reproduction by division could never under any circumstances persist indefinitely. But this cannot be proved with any greater certainty than the converse proposition, and hence, as far as direct proof is concerned, the facts are equally uncertain on both sides."

But this is an admission which seems to be entirely ignored when there is alleged the contrast between the immortal *Protozoa* and the mortal *Metazoa*. Following Professor Weismann's method, it would be "easy to imagine" that occasional conjugation is in all cases essential; and this easily imagined conclusion might fitly be used to bar out his own. Indeed, considering how commonly conjugation is observed, it may be held difficult to imagine that it can in any cases be dispensed with. Apart from imaginations of either kind, however, here is an acknowledgment that the immortality of *Protozoa* is not proved; that the allegation has no better basis than the failure to observe cessation of fission; and that thus one term of the above antithesis is not a fact, but is only an assumption.

And now what about the other term of the antithesis—the alleged inherent mortality of the somatic cells? This we shall, I think, find is no more defensible than the other. Such plausibility as it possesses disappears when, instead of contemplating the vast assemblage of familiar cases which animals present, we contemplate certain less familiar and unfamiliar cases. By these we are shown that the usual ending of multiplication among somatic cells is due, not to an intrinsic cause, but to extrinsic causes. Let us, however, first look at Professor Weismann's own statements:—

"I have endeavoured to explain death as the result of restriction in the powers of reproduction possessed by the somatic cells, and I have suggested that such restriction may conceivably follow from a limitation in the number of cell-generations possible for the cells of each organ and tissue." (p. 28)

"The above-mentioned considerations show us that the degree of reproductive activity present in the tissues is regulated by internal causes while the natural death of an organism is the termination—the hereditary limitation—of the process of cell-division, which began in the segmentation of the ovum." (p. 30)

Now, though, in the above extracts there is mention of "internal causes" determining "the degree of reproductive activity" of tissue cells, and though, on page 28, the "causes of the loss" of the power of unlimited cell-production "must be sought outside the organism, that is to say, in the external conditions of life," yet the doctrine is that somatic cells have become constitutionally unfitted for continued cell-multiplication.

"The somatic cells have lost this power to a gradually increasing extent, so that at length they became restricted to a fixed, though perhaps very large, number of cell-generations." (p. 28)

Examination will soon disclose good reasons for denying this inherent restriction. We will look at the various causes which affect their multiplication, and usually put a stop to increase after a certain point is reached.

There is first the amount of vital capital given by the parent; partly in the shape of a more or less developed structure, and partly in the shape of bequeathed nutriment. Where this vital capital is small, and the young creature, forthwith obliged to carry on physiological business for itself, has to expend effort in obtaining materials for daily consumption as well as for growth, a rigid restraint is put on that cell-multiplication required for a large size. Clearly, the young elephant, starting with a big and well-organized body, and supplied *gratis* with milk during early stages of growth, can begin physiological business on his own account on a great scale; and by its large transactions his system is enabled to supply nutriment to its multiplying somatic cells until they have formed a vast aggregate—an aggregate such as it is impossible for a young mouse to reach, obliged as it is to begin physiological business in a small way. Then there is the character of the food in respect of its digestibility and its nutritiveness. Here, that which the creature takes in requires much grinding-up, or, when duly prepared, contains but a small amount of available matter in comparison with the matter that has to be thrown away; while there, the prey seized is almost pure nutriment, and requires but little trituration. Hence, in some cases, an unprofitable physiological business, and in other cases a profitable one; resulting in small or large supplies to the multiplying somatic cells. Further, there has to be noted the grade of visceral development, which, if low, yields only crude nutriment slowly distributed, but which, if high, serves by its good appliances for solution, depuration, absorption, and circulation, to yield to the multiplying somatic cells a rich and pure blood. Then we come to an all-important factor, the cost of obtaining food. Here large expenditure of energy in locomotion is necessitated, and there but little—here great efforts for small portions of food, and there small efforts for great portions: again resulting in physiological poverty or physiological wealth. Next, beyond the cost of nervo-muscular activities in foraging, there is the cost of maintaining bodily heat. So much heat implies so much consumed nutriment, and the loss by radiation or conduction, which has perpetually to be made good, varies according to many circumstances—climate, medium (as air or water), covering, size of body (small cooling relatively faster than large); and in proportion to the cost of maintaining heat is the abstraction from the supplies for cell-formation. Finally, there are three all-important co-operative factors, or rather laws of factors, the effects of which vary with the size of the animal. The first is that, while the mass of the body varies as the cubes of its dimensions (*proportions* being supposed constant), the absorbing surface varies as the squares of its dimensions; whence it results that, other things equal, increase of size implies relative decrease of nutrition, and therefore increased obstacles to cell-multiplication.[109] The second is a further sequence from these laws—namely, that while the weight of the body increases as the cubes of the dimensions, the sectional areas of its muscles and bones increase as their squares; whence follows a decreasing power of resisting strains, and a relative weakness of structure. This is implied in the ability of a small animal to leap many times its own length, while a great animal, like the elephant, cannot leap at all: its bones and muscles being unable to bear the stress which would be required to propel its body through the air. What increasing cost of keeping together the bodily fabric is thus entailed, we cannot say; but that there is an increasing cost, which diminishes the available, materials for increase of size, is beyond question.[110] And then, in the third place, we have augmented expense of distribution of nutriment. The greater the size becomes, the more force must be exerted to send blood to the periphery; and this once more entails deduction from the cell-forming matters.

Here, then, we have nine factors, several of them involving subdivisions, which co-operate in aiding or restraining cell-multiplication. They occur in endlessly varied proportions and combinations; so that every species differs more or less from every other in respect of their effects. But in all of them the co-operation is such as eventually arrests that multiplication of cells which causes further growth; continues thereafter to entail slow decrease in cell-multiplication, accompanying decline of vital activities; and eventually brings cell-multiplication to an end. Now a recognized principle of reasoning—the Law of Parsimony—forbids the assumption of more causes than are needful for explanation of phenomena; and since, in all such living aggregates as those above supposed, the causes named inevitably bring about arrest of cell-multiplication, it is illegitimate to ascribe this arrest to some inherent property in the cells. Inadequacy of the other causes must be shown before an inherent property can be rightly assumed.

For this conclusion we find ample justification when we contemplate types of animals which lead lives that do not put such decided restraints on cell-multiplication. First let us take an instance of the extent to which (irrespective of natures of cells as reproductive or somatic) cell-multiplication may go, where the conditions render nutrition easy and reduce expenditure to a minimum. I refer to the case of the *Aphides*. Though it is early in the season (March), the hothouses at Kew have furnished a sufficient number of these to show that twelve of them weigh a grain—a larger number than would be required were they full-sized. Citing Professor Owen, who adopts the calculations of Tougard to the effect that by agamic multiplication "a single impregnated ovum of *Aphis* may give rise, without fecundation, to a quintillion of *Aphides*," Professor Huxley says:—

"I will assume that an Aphis weighs 1/1000 of a grain, which is certainly vastly under the mark. A quintillion of *Aphides* will, on this estimate, weigh a quatrillion of grains. He is a very stout man who weighs two million grains; consequently the tenth brood alone, if all its members survive the perils to which they are exposed, contains more substance than 500,000,000 stout men—to say the least, more than the whole population of China!"[111]

And had Professor Huxley taken the actual weight, one-twelfth of a grain, the quintillion of *Aphides* would evidently far outweigh the whole human population of the globe: five billions of tons being the weight, as brought out by my own calculation! Of course I do not cite this in proof of the extent to which multiplication of somatic cells, descending from a single ovum, may go; because it will be contended, with some reason, that each of the sexless *Aphides*, viviparously produced, arose by fission of a cell which had descended from the original reproductive cell. I cite it merely to show that when the cell-products of a fertilized ovum are perpetually divided and subdivided into small groups, distributed over an unlimited nutritive area, so that they can get materials for growth at no cost, and expend nothing appreciable in motion or maintenance of temperature, cell-production may go on without limit. For the agamic multiplication of *Aphides* has been shown to continue for four years, and to all appearance would be ceaseless were the temperature and supply of food continued without break. But now let us pass to analogous illustrations of cause and consequence, open to no criticism of the kind just indicated. They are furnished by various kinds of *Entozoa*, of which take the *Trematoda*, infesting molluscs and fishes. Of one of them we read:—"*Gyrodactylus* multiplies agamically by the development of a young Trematode within the body, as a sort of internal bud. A second generation appears within the first, and even a third within the second, before the young *Gyrodactylus* is born."[112] And the drawings of Steenstrup, in his *Alternation of Generations*, show us, among creatures of this group, a sexless individual the whole interior of which is transformed into smaller sexless individuals, which severally, before or after their emergence, undergo similar transformations—a multiplication of somatic cells without any sign of reproductive cells. Under what circumstances do such modes of agamic multiplication, variously modified among parasites, occur? They occur where there is no expenditure whatever in motion or maintenance of temperature, and where nutriment surrounds the body on all sides. Other instances are furnished by groups in which, though the nutriment is not abundant, the cost of living is almost unappreciable. Among the *Cœlenterata* there are the Hydroid Polyps, simple and compound; and among the *Mollusca* we have various types of Ascidians, fixed and floating, *Botryllidæ* and *Salpæ*.

But now from these low animals in which sexless reproduction, and continued multiplication of somatic cells, is common, and one class of which is named "zoophytes," because its form of life simulates that of plants, let us pass to plants themselves. In these there is no expenditure in effort, there is no expenditure in maintaining temperature, and the food, some of it supplied by the earth, is the rest of it supplied by a medium which everywhere bathes the outer surface: the utilization of its contained material being effected *gratis* by the Sun's rays. Just as was to be expected, we here find that agamogenesis may go on without end. Numerous plants and trees are propagated to an unlimited extent by cuttings and buds; and we have sundry plants which cannot be otherwise propagated. The most familiar are the double roses of our gardens: these do not seed, and yet have been distributed everywhere by grafts and buds. Hothouses furnish many cases, as I learn from an authority second to none. Of "the whole host of tropical orchids, for instance, not one per cent. has ever seeded, and some have been a century under cultivation." Again, we have the *Acorus calamus*, "that has hardly been known to seed anywhere, though it is found wild all over the north temperate hemisphere." And then there is the conspicuous and conclusive case of *Eloidea Canadensis* (alias *Anacharis*,) introduced no one knows how (probably with timber), and first observed in 1847, in several places; and which, having since spread over nearly all England, now everywhere infests ponds, canals, and slow rivers. The plant is diœcious, and only the female exists here. Beyond all question, therefore, this vast progeny of the first slip or fragment introduced, sufficient to cover many square miles were it put together, is constituted entirely of somatic cells. Hence, as far as we can judge, these somatic cells are immortal in the sense given to the word by Professor Weismann; and the evidence that they are so is immeasurably stronger than the evidence which leads him to assert immortality for the fissiparously-multiplying *Protozoa.* This endless multiplication of somatic cells has been going on under the eyes of numerous observers for forty odd years. What observer has watched for forty years to see whether the fissiparous multiplication of *Protozoa* does not cease? What observer has watched for one year, or one month, or one week?[113]

Even were not Professor Weismann's theory disposed of by this evidence, it might be disposed of by a critical examination of his own evidence, using his own tests. Clearly, if we are to measure relative mortalities, we must assume the conditions to be the same and must use the same measure. Let us do this with some appropriate animal—say Man, as the most open to observation. The mortality of the somatic cells constituting the mass of the human body, is, according to Professor Weismann, shown by the decline and final cessation of cell-multiplication in its various organs. Suppose we apply this test to all the organs: not to those only in which there continually arise bile-cells, epithelium-cells, &c., but to those also in which there arise reproductive cells. What do we find? That the multiplication of these last comes to an end long before the multiplication of the first. In a healthy woman, the cells which constitute the various active tissues of the body, continue to grow and multiply for many years after germ-cells have died out. If similarly measured, then, these cells of the last class prove to be more mortal than those of the first. But Professor Weismann uses a different measure for the two classes of cells. Passing over the illegitimacy of this proceeding, let us accept his other mode of measurement, and see what comes of it. As described by him, absence of death among the *Protozoa* is implied by that unceasing division and subdivision of which they are said to be capable. Fission continued without end, is the definition of the immortality he speaks of. Apply this conception to the reproductive cells in a *Metazoon.* That the immense majority of them do not multiply without end, we have already seen: with very rare exceptions they die and disappear without result, and they cease their multiplication while the body as a whole still lives. But what of those extremely exceptional ones which, as being actually instrumental to the maintenance of the species, are alone contemplated by Professor Weismann? Do these continue their fissiparous multiplications without end? By no means. The condition under which alone they preserve a qualified form of existence, is that, instead of one becoming two, two become one. A member of series A and a member of series B, coalesce; and so lose their individualities. Now, obviously, if the immortality of a series is shown if its members divide and subdivide perpetually, then the opposite of immortality is shown when, instead of division, there is union. Each series ends, and there is initiated a new series, differing more or less from both. Thus the assertion that the reproductive cells are immortal, can be defended only by changing the conception of immortality otherwise implied.

Even apart from these last criticisms, however, we have clear disproof of the alleged inherent difference between the two classes of cells. Among animals, the multiplication of somatic cells is brought to an end by sundry restraining conditions; but in various plants, where these restraining conditions are absent, the multiplication is unlimited. It may, indeed, be said that the alleged distinction should be reversed; since the fissiparous multiplication of reproductive cells is necessarily interrupted from time to time by coalescence, while that of the somatic cells may go on for a century without being interrupted.

* * * * *

In the essay to which this is a postscript, conclusions were drawn from the remarkable case of the horse and the quagga, there narrated, along with an analogous case observed among pigs. These conclusions have since been confirmed. I am much indebted to a distinguished correspondent who has drawn my attention to verifying facts furnished by the offspring of whites and negroes in the United States. Referring to information given him many years ago, he says:—"It was to the effect that the children of white women by a white father, had been *repeatedly* observed to show traces of black blood, in cases when the woman had previous connection with [*i. e.* a child by] a negro." At the time I received this information, an American was visiting me; and, on being appealed to, answered that in the United States there was an established belief to this effect. Not wishing, however, to depend upon hearsay, I at once wrote to America to make inquiries. Professor Cope of Philadelphia has written to friends in the South, but has not yet sent me the results. Professor Marsh, the distinguished palæontologist, of Yale, New Haven, who is also collecting evidence, sends a preliminary letter in which he says:—"I do not myself know of such a case, but have heard many statements that make their existence probable. One instance, in Connecticut, is vouched for so strongly by an acquaintance of mine, that I have good reason to believe it to be authentic."

That cases of the kind should not be frequently seen in the North, especially nowadays, is of course to be expected. The first of the above quotations refers to facts observed in the South during slavery days; and even then, the implied conditions were naturally very infrequent. Dr. W. J. Youmans of New York has, on my behalf, interviewed several medical professors, who, though they have not themselves met with instances, say that the alleged result, described above, "is generally accepted as a fact." But he gives me what I think must be regarded as authoritative testimony. It is a quotation from the standard work of Professor Austin Flint, and runs as follows:—

"A peculiar and, it seems to me, an inexplicable fact is, that previous pregnancies have an influence upon offspring. This is well known to breeders of animals. If pure-blooded mares or bitches have been once covered by an inferior male, in subsequent fecundations the young are likely to partake of the character of the first male, even if they be afterwards bred with males of unimpeachable pedigree. What the mechanism of the influence of the first conception is, it is impossible to say; but the fact is incontestable. The same influence is observed in the human subject. A woman may have, by a second husband, children who resemble a former husband, and this is particularly well marked in certain instances by the colour of the hair and eyes. A white woman who has had children by a negro may subsequently bear children to a white man, these children presenting some of the unmistakable peculiarities of the negro race."[114]

Dr. Youmans called on Professor Flint, who remembered "investigating the subject at the time his larger work was written [the above is from an abridgment], and said that he had never heard the statement questioned."

Some days before I received this letter and its contained quotation, the remembrance of a remark I heard many years ago concerning dogs, led to the inquiry whether they furnished analogous evidence. It occurred to me that a friend who is frequently appointed judge of animals at agricultural shows, Mr. Fookes, of Fairfield, Pewsey, Wiltshire, might know something about the matter. A letter to him brought various confirmatory statements. From one "who had bred dogs for many years" he learnt that—

"It is a well known and admitted fact that if a bitch has two litters by two different dogs, the character of the first father is sure to be perpetuated in any litters she may afterwards have, no matter how pure-bred a dog may be the begetter."

After citing this testimony, Mr. Fookes goes on to give illustrations known to himself.

"A friend of mine near this had a very valuable Dachshund bitch, which most unfortunately had a litter by a stray sheep-dog. The next year her owner sent her on a visit to a pure Dachshund dog, but the produce took quite as much of the first father as the second, and the next year he sent her to another Dachshund with the same result. Another case:—A friend of mine in Devizes had a litter of puppies, unsought for, by a setter from a favourite pointer bitch, and after this she never bred any true pointers, no matter of what the paternity was."

[Since the publication of this article additional evidences have come to hand. One is from the late Prof. Riley, State Entomologist at Washington, who says that telegony is an "established principle among well-educated farmers" in the United States, and who gives me a case in horse-breeding to which he was himself witness.

Mr. W. P. Smith, writing from Stoughton Grange, Guildford, but giving the results of his experiences in America, says that "the fact of a previous conception influencing subsequent offspring was so far recognised among American cattle-breeders" that it was proposed to raise the rank of any heifer that had borne a first calf by a thoroughbred bull, and though this resolution when brought before one of the chief societies was not carried, yet on all sides it was admitted that previous conceptions had effects of the kind alleged. Mr. Smith in another letter says:—"When I had a large mule and horse ranche in America I noticed that the foals of mares by horse stallions had a mulish appearance in those cases where the mare had previously given birth to a mule foal. Common heifers who have had calves by a thoroughbred bull are apt thereafter to have well-bred calves even from the veriest scrubs."

Yet another very interesting piece of evidence is furnished by Mr. W. Sedgwick, M.R.C.S., in an article on "The Influence of Heredity in Disease," published in the *British Medical Journal* for Feb. 22, 1896, pp. 460-2. It concerns the transmission of a malformation known among medical men as hypospadias. Referring to a man belonging to a family in which this defect prevailed, he writes:—"The widow of the man from whom these three generations of hypospadians were descended married again, after an interval of eighteen months; and in this instance the second husband was not only free from the defect, but there was no history of it in his family. By this second marriage she had four hypospadiac sons and four hypospadiac grandsons; whilst there were seven grandsons and three great-grandsons who were not malformed."]

Coming from remote places, from those who have no theory to support, and who are some of them astonished by the unexpected phenomena, the agreement dissipates all doubt. In four kinds of mammals, widely divergent in their natures—man, horse, dog, and pig—we have this same seemingly-anomalous kind of heredity, made visible under analogous conditions. We must take it as a demonstrated fact that, during gestation, traits of constitution inherited from the father produce effects upon the constitution of the mother; and that these communicated effects are transmitted by her to subsequent offspring. We are supplied with an absolute disproof of Professor Weismann's doctrine that the reproductive cells are independent of, and uninfluenced by, the somatic cells; and there disappears absolutely the alleged obstacle to the transmission of acquired characters.

* * * * *

Notwithstanding experiences showing the futility of controversy for the establishment of truth, I am tempted here to answer opponents at some length. But even could the editor allow me the needful space, I should be compelled, both by lack of time and by ill-health, to be brief. I must content myself with noticing a few points which most nearly concern me.

Referring to my argument respecting tactual discriminativeness, Mr. Wallace thinks that I—

"afford a glaring example of taking the unessential in place of the essential, and drawing conclusions from a partial and altogether insufficient survey of the phenomena. For this 'tactual discriminativeness,' which is alone dealt with by Mr. Spencer, forms the least important, and probably only an incidental portion of the great vital phenomenon of skin-sensitiveness, which is at once the watchman and the shield of the organism against imminent external dangers." (*Fortnightly Review*, April, 1893, p. 497)

Here Mr. Wallace assumes it to be self-evident that skin-sensitiveness is due to natural selection, and assumes that this must be admitted by me. He supposes it is only the unequal distribution of skin-discriminativeness which I contend is not thus accounted for. But I deny that either the general sensitiveness or the special sensitiveness results from natural selection; and I have years ago justified the first disbelief as I have recently the second. In "The Factors of Organic Evolution" (*Essays*, 454-8), I have given various reasons for inferring that the genesis of the nervous system cannot be due to survival of the fittest; but that it is due to the direct effects of converse between the surface and the environment; and that thus only is to be explained the strange fact that the nervous centres are originally superficial, and migrate inwards during development. These conclusions I have, in the essay Mr. Wallace criticizes, upheld by the evidence which blind boys and skilled compositors furnish; proving, as this does, that increased nervous development is peripherally initiated. Mr. Wallace's belief that skin-sensitiveness arose by natural selection, is unsupported by a single fact. He assumes that it *must* have been so produced because it is all-important to self-preservation. My belief that it is directly initiated by converse with the environment, is supported by facts; and I have given proof that the assigned cause is now in operation. Am I called upon to abandon my own supported belief and accept Mr. Wallace's unsupported belief? I think not.

Referring to my argument concerning blind cave-animals, Professor Lankester, in *Nature* of February 23, 1893, writes:—

"Mr. Spencer shows that the saving of ponderable material in the suppression of an eye is but a small economy: he loses sight of the fact, however, that possibly, or even probably, the saving to the organism in the reduction of an eye to a rudimentary state is not to be measured by mere bulk, but by the non-expenditure of special materials and special activities which are concerned in the production of an organ so peculiar and elaborate as is the vertebrate eye."

It seems to me that a supposition is here made to do duty as a fact; and that I might with equal propriety say that "possibly, or even probably," the vertebrate eye is physiologically cheap: its optical part, constituting nearly its whole bulk, consisting of a low order of tissue. There is, indeed, strong reason for considering it physiologically cheap. If any one remembers how relatively enormous are the eyes of a fish just out of the egg—a pair of eyes with a body and head attached; and if he then remembers that every egg contains material for such a pair of eyes; he will see that eye-material constitutes a very considerable part of the fish's roe; and that, since the female fish provides this quantity every year, it cannot be expensive. My argument against Weismann is strengthened rather than weakened by contemplation of these facts.

Professor Lankester asks my attention to a hypothesis of his own, published in the *Encyclopædia Britannica*, concerning the production of blind cave-animals. He thinks it can—

"be fully explained by natural selection acting on congenital fortuitous variations. Many animals are thus born with distorted or defective eyes whose parents have not had their eyes submitted to any peculiar conditions. Supposing a number of some species of Arthropod or Fish to be swept into a cavern or to be carried from less to greater depths in the sea, those individuals with perfect eyes would follow the glimmer of light and eventually escape to the outer air or the shallower depths, leaving behind those with imperfect eyes to breed in the dark place. A natural selection would thus be effected" in successive generations.

First of all, I demur to the words "many animals." Under the abnormal conditions of domestication, congenitally defective eyes may be not very uncommon; but their occurrence under natural conditions is, I fancy, extremely rare. Supposing, however, that in a shoal of young fish, there occur some with eyes seriously defective. What will happen? Vision is all-important to the young fish, both for obtaining food and for escaping from enemies. This is implied by the immense development of eyes just referred to; and the obvious conclusion to be drawn is that the partially blind would disappear. Considering that out of the enormous number of young fish hatched with perfect eyes, not one in a hundred reaches maturity, what chance of surviving would there be for those with imperfect eyes? Inevitably they would be starved or be snapped up. Hence the chances that a matured or partially matured semi-blind fish, or rather two such, male and female, would be swept into a cave and left behind are extremely remote. Still more remote must the chances be in the case of cray-fish. Sheltering themselves as these do under stones, in crevices, and in burrows which they make in the banks, and able quickly to anchor themselves to weeds or sticks by their claws, it seems scarcely supposable that any of them could be carried into a cave by a flood. What, then, is the probability that there will be two nearly blind ones, and that these will be thus carried? Then, after this first extreme improbability, there comes a second, which we may, I think, rather call an impossibility. How would it be possible for creatures subject to so violent a change of habitat to survive? Surely death would quickly follow the subjection to such utterly unlike conditions and modes of life. The existence of these blind cave-animals can be accounted for only by supposing that their remote ancestors began making excursions into the cave, and, finding it profitable, extended them, generation after generation, further in: undergoing the required adaptations little by little.[115]

Between Dr. Romanes and myself the first difference concerns the interpretation of "Panmixia." Clearer conceptions of these matters would be reached if, instead of thinking in abstract terms, the physiological processes concerned were brought into the foreground. Beyond the production of changes in the sizes of parts by the selection of fortuitously-arising variations, I can see but one other cause for the production of them—the competition among the parts for nutriment. This has the effect that active parts are well-supplied and grow, while inactive parts are ill-supplied and dwindle.[116] This competition is the cause of "economy of growth"; this is the cause of decrease from disuse; and this is the only conceivable cause of that decrease which Dr. Romanes contends follows the cessation of selection. The three things are aspects of the same thing. And now, before leaving this question, let me remark on the strange proposition which has to be defended by those who deny the dwindling of organs from disuse. Their proposition amounts to this:—that for a hundred generations an inactive organ may be partially denuded of blood all through life, and yet in the hundredth generation will be produced of just the same size as in the first!

There is one other passage in Dr. Romanes' criticism—that concerning the influence of a previous sire on progeny—which calls for comment. He sets down what he supposes Weismann will say in response to my argument. "First, he may question the fact." Well, after the additional evidence given above, I think he is not likely to do that; unless, indeed, it be that along with readiness to base conclusions on things "it is easy to imagine" there goes reluctance to accept testimony which it is difficult to doubt. Second, he is supposed to reply that "the Germ-plasm of the first sire has in some way or another become partly commingled with that of the immature ova"; and Dr. Romanes goes on to describe how there may be millions of spermatozoa and "thousands of millions" of their contained "ids" around the ovaries, to which these secondary effects are due. But, on the one hand, he does not explain why in such cases each subsequent ovum, as it becomes matured, is not fertilized by the sperm-cells present, or their contained germ-plasm, rendering all subsequent fecundations needless; and, on the other hand, he does not explain why, if this does not happen, the potency of this remaining germ-plasm is nevertheless such as to affect not only the next succeeding offspring, but all subsequent offspring. The irreconcilability of these two implications would, I think, sufficiently dispose of the supposition, even had we not daily multitudinous proofs that the surface of a mammalian ovarium is not a spermatheca. The third reply Dr. Romanes urges, is the inconceivability of the process by which the germ-plasm of a preceding male parent affects the constitution of the female and her subsequent offspring. In response, I have to ask why he piles up a mountain of difficulties based on the assumption that Mr. Darwin's explanation of heredity by "Pangenesis" is the only available explanation preceding that of Weismann? and why he presents these difficulties to me, more especially; deliberately ignoring my own hypothesis of physiological units? It cannot be that he is ignorant of this hypothesis, since the work in which it is variously set forth (*Principles of Biology*, §§ 66-97) is one with which he is well acquainted: witness his *Scientific Evidences of Organic Evolution*; and he has had recent reminders of it in Weismann's *Germ-plasm*, where it is repeatedly referred to. Why, then, does he assume that I abandon my own hypothesis and adopt that of Darwin; thereby entangling myself in difficulties which my own hypothesis avoids? If, as I have argued, the germ-plasm consists of substantially similar units (having only those minute differences expressive of individual and ancestral differences of structure), none of the complicated requirements which Dr. Romanes emphasizes exist; and the alleged inconceivability disappears.

Here I must end: not intending to say more, unless for some very urgent reason; and leaving others to carry on the discussion. I have, indeed, been led to suspend for a short time my proper work, only by consciousness of the transcendent importance of the question at issue. As I have before contended, a right answer to the question whether acquired characters are or are not inherited, underlies right beliefs, not only in Biology and Psychology, but also in Education, Ethics, and Politics.

III.

As a species of literature, controversy is characterised by a terrible fertility. Each proposition becomes the parent of half a dozen; so that a few replies and rejoinders produce an unmanageable population of issues, old and new, which end in being a nuisance to everybody. Remembering this, I shall refrain from dealing with all the points of Professor Weismann's answer. I must limit myself to a part; and that there may be no suspicion of a selection convenient to myself, I will take those contained in his first article.

Before dealing with his special arguments, let me say something about the general mode of argument which Professor Weismann adopts.

The title of his article is "The All-Sufficiency of Natural Selection."[117] Very soon, however, as on p. 322, we come to the admission, which he has himself italicised, "that *it is really very difficult to imagine this process of natural selection in its details*; and to this day it is impossible to demonstrate it in any one point." Elsewhere, as on pp. 327 and 336 *à propos* of other cases, there are like admissions. But now if the sufficiency of an assigned cause cannot in any case be demonstrated, and if it is "really very difficult to imagine" in what way it has produced its alleged effects, what becomes of the "all-sufficiency" of the cause? How can its all-sufficiency be alleged when its action can neither be demonstrated nor easily imagined? Evidently to fit Professor Weismann's argument the title of the article should have been "The Doubtful Sufficiency of Natural Selection."

Observe, again, how entirely opposite are the ways in which he treats his own interpretation and the antagonist interpretation. He takes the problem presented by certain beautifully adapted structures on the anterior legs of "very many insects," which they use for cleansing their antennæ. These, he argues, cannot have resulted from the inheritance of acquired characters; since any supposed changes produced by function would be changes in the chitinous exo-skeleton, which, being a dead substance, cannot have had its changes transmitted. He then proceeds, very candidly, to point out the extreme difficulties which lie in the way of supposing these structures to have resulted from natural selection: admitting that an opponent might "say that it was absurd" to assume that the successive small variations implied were severally life-saving in their effects. Nevertheless, he holds it unquestionable that natural selection has been the cause. See then the difference. The supposition that the apparatus has been produced by the inheritance of acquired characters is rejected *because* it presents insuperable difficulties. But the supposition that the apparatus has been produced by natural selection is accepted, *though* it presents insuperable difficulties. If this mode of reasoning is allowable, no fair comparison between diverse hypotheses can be made.

With these remarks on Professor Weismann's method at large, let me now pass to the particular arguments he uses, taking them *seriatim.*

* * * * *

The first case he deals with is that of the progressive degradation of the human little toe. This he considers a good test case; and he proceeds to discuss an assigned cause—the inherited and accumulated effects of boot-pressure. Without much difficulty he shows that this interpretation is inadequate; since fusion of the phalanges, which constitutes in part the progressive degradation, is found among peoples who go barefoot, and has been found also in Egyptian mummies. Having thus disposed of Mr. Buckman's interpretation, Professor Weismann forthwith concludes that the ascription of this anatomical change to the inheritance of acquired characters is disposed of, and assumes, as the only other possible interpretation, a dwindling "through panmixia": "the hereditary degeneration of the little toe is thus quite simply explained from my standpoint."

It is surprising that Professor Weismann should not have seen that there is an explanation against which his criticism does not tell. If we go back to the genesis of the human type from some lower type of *primates*, we see that while the little toe has ceased to be of any use for climbing purposes, it has not come into any considerable use for walking and running. A glance at the feet of the sub-human *primates* in general, shows that the inner digits are, as compared with those of men, quite small, have no such relative length and massiveness as the human great toes. Leaving out the question of cause, it is manifest that the great toes have been immensely developed, since there took place the change from arboreal habits to terrestrial habits. A study of the mechanics of walking shows why this has happened. Stability requires that the "line of direction" (the vertical line let fall from the centre of gravity) shall fall within the base, and, in walking, shall be brought at each step within the area of support, or so near it that any tendency to fall may be checked at the next step. A necessary result is that if, at each step, the chief stress of support is thrown on the outer side of the foot, the body must be swayed so that the "line of direction" may fall within the outer side of the foot, or close to it; and when the next step is taken it must be similarly swayed in an opposite way, so that the outer side of the other foot may bear the weight. That is to say, the body must oscillate from side to side, or waddle. The movements of a duck when walking or running show what happens when the points of support are wide apart. Clearly this kind of movement conflicts with efficient locomotion. There is a waste of muscular energy in making these lateral movements, and they are at variance with the forward movement. We may infer, then, that the developing man profited by throwing the stress as much as possible on the inner sides of the feet; and was especially led to do this when going fast, which enabled him to abridge the oscillations: as indeed we now see in a drunken man. Thus there was thrown a continually increasing stress upon the inner digits as they progressively developed from the effects of use; until now that the inner digits, so large compared with the others, bear the greater part of the weight, and being relatively near one another, render needless any marked swayings from side to side. But what has meanwhile happened to the outer digits? Evidently as fast as the great toes have come more and more into play and developed, the little toes have gone more and more out of play and have been dwindling for—how long shall we say?—perhaps a hundred thousand years.

So far, then, am I from feeling that Professor Weismann has here raised a difficulty in the way of the doctrine I hold, that I feel indebted to him for having drawn attention to a very strong evidence in its support. This modification in the form of the foot, which has occurred since arboreal habits have given place to terrestrial habits, shows the effects of use and disuse simultaneously. The inner digits have increased by use while the outer digits have decreased by disuse.

* * * * *

Saying that he will not "pause to refute other apparent proofs of the transmission of acquired characters," Professor Weismann proceeds to deal with the argument which, with various illustrations, I have several times urged—the argument that the natural selection of fortuitously-arising variations cannot account for the adjustment of co-operative parts. Very clearly and very fairly he summarises this argument as used in *The Principles of Biology* in 1864. Admitting that in this case there are "enormous difficulties" in the way of any other interpretation than the inheritance of acquired characters, Professor Weismann before proceeding to assault this "last bulwark of the Lamarckian principle," premises that the inheritance of acquired characters cannot be a cause of change because inactive as well as active parts degenerate when they cease to be of use: instancing the "skin and skin-armature of crabs and insects." On this I may remark in the first place that an argument derived from degeneracy of passive structures scarcely meets the case of development of active structures; and I may remark in the second place that I have never dreamt of denying the efficiency of natural selection as a cause of degeneracy in passive structures when the degeneracy is such as aids the prosperity of the stirp.

Making this parenthetical reply to his parenthetical criticism I pass to his discussion of this particular argument which he undertakes to dispose of.

His *cheval de bataille* is furnished him by the social insects—not a fresh one, however, as might be supposed from the way in which he mounts it. From time to time it has carried other riders, who have couched their lances with fatal effects as they supposed. But I hope to show that no one of them has unhorsed an antagonist, and that Professor Weismann fails to do this just as completely as his predecessors. I am, indeed, not sorry that he has afforded me the opportunity of criticising the general discussion concerning the peculiarities of these interesting creatures, which it has often seemed to me sets out with illegitimate assumptions. The supposition always is that the specialities of structures and instincts in the unlike classes of their communities, have arisen during the period in which the communities have existed in something like their present forms. This cannot be. It is doubtless true that association without differentiations of classes may pre-exist for co-operative purposes, as among wolves, and as among various insects which swarm under certain circumstances. Hence we may suppose that there arise in some cases permanent swarms—that survival of the fittest will establish these constant swarms where they are advantageous. But admitting this, we have also to admit a gradual rise of the associated state out of the solitary state. Wasps and bees present us with gradations. If, then, we are to understand how the organized societies have arisen, either out of the solitary state or out of undifferentiated swarms, we must assume that the differences of structure and instinct among the members of them arose little by little, as the social organization arose little by little. Fortunately we are able to trace the greater part of the process in the annually-formed communities of the common wasp; and we shall recognize in it an all-important factor (ignored by Professor Weismann) to which the phenomena, or at any rate the greater part of them, are due.

But before describing the wasp's annual history, let me set down certain observations made when, as a boy, I was given to angling, and, in July or August, sometimes used for bait "wasp-grubs," as they were called. After having had two or three days the combs or "cakes" of these, full of unfed larvæ in all stages of growth, I often saw some of them devouring the edges of their cells to satisfy their appetites; and saw others, probably the most advanced in growth, which were spinning the little covering caps to their cells, in preparation for assuming the pupa state. It is to be inferred that if, after a certain stage of growth has been reached, the food-supply becomes inadequate or is stopped altogether, the larva undergoes its transformation prematurely; and, as we shall presently see, this premature transformation has several natural sequences.

Let us return now to the wasp's family history. In the spring, a queen-wasp or mother-wasp which has survived the winter, begins to make a small nest containing four or more cells in which she lays eggs, and as fast as she builds additional cells, she lays an egg in each. Presently, to these activities, is added the feeding of the larvæ: one result being that the multiplication of larvæ involves a restriction of the food that can be given to each. If we suppose that the mother-wasp rears no more larvæ than she can fully feed, there will result queens or mothers like herself, relatively few in number. But if we suppose that, laying more numerous eggs she produces more larvæ than she can fully feed, the result will be that when these have reached a certain stage of growth, inadequate supply of food will be followed by premature retirement and transformation into pupæ. What will be the characters of the developed insects? The first effect of arrested nutrition will be smaller size. This we find. A second effect will be defective development of parts that are latest formed and least important for the survival of the individual. Hence we may look for arrested development of the reproductive organs—non-essential to individual life. And this expectation is in accord with what we see in animal development at large; for (passing over entirely sexless individuals) we see that though the reproductive organs may be marked out early in the course of development, they are not made fit for action until after the structures for carrying on individual life are nearly complete. The implication is, then, that an inadequately-fed and small larva will become a sterile imago. Having noted this, let us pass to a remarkable concomitant. In the course of development, organs are formed not alone in the order of their original succession, but partly in the order of importance and the share they have to take in adult activities—a change of order called by Haeckel "heterochrony." Hence the fact that we often see the maternal instinct precede the sexual instinct. Every little girl with her doll shows us that the one may become alive while the other remains dormant. In the case of wasps, then, premature arrest of development may result in incompleteness of the sexual traits, along with completeness of the maternal traits. What happens? Leave out the laying of eggs, and the energies of the mother-wasp are spent wholly in building cells and feeding larvæ, and the worker-wasp forthwith begins to spend its life in building cells and feeding larvæ. Thus interpreting the facts, we have no occasion to assume any constitutional difference between the eggs of worker-wasps and the eggs of queens; and that, their eggs are not different we see, first, in the fact that occasionally the worker-wasp is fertile and lays drone-producing eggs, and we see secondly that (if in this respect they are like the bees, of which, however, we have no proof) the larva of a worker-wasp can be changed into the larva of a queen-wasp by special feeding. But be this as it may, we have good evidence that the feeding determines everything. Says Dr. Ormerod, in his *British Social Wasps*:—

"When the swarm is strong and food plentiful ... the well fed larvæ develop into females, full, large, and overflowing with fat. There are all gradations of size, from the large fat female to the smallest worker.... The larger the wasp, the larger and better developed, as the rule, are the female organs, in all their details. In the largest wasps, which are to be the queens of another year, the ovaries differ to all appearances in nothing but their size from those of the larger worker wasps.... Small feeble swarms produce few or no perfect females; but in large strong swarms they are found by the score." (pp. 248-9)

To this evidence add the further evidence that queens and workers pass through certain parallel stages in respect of their maternal activities. At first the queen, besides laying eggs, builds cells and feeds larvæ, but after a time ceases to build cells, and feeds larvæ only, and eventually doing neither one nor the other, only lays eggs, and is supplied with food by the workers. So it is in part with the workers. While the members of each successive brood, when in full vigour, build cells and feed larvæ, by-and-by they cease to build cells, and only feed larvæ: the maternal activities and instincts undergo analogous changes. In this case, then, we are not obliged to assume that only by a process of natural selection can the differences of structure and instinct between queens and workers be produced. The only way in which natural selection here comes into play is in the better survival of the families of those queens which made as many cells, and laid as many eggs, as resulted in the best number of half-fed larvæ, producing workers; since by a rapid multiplication of workers the family is advantaged, and the ultimate production of more queens surviving into the next year insured.

The differentiation of classes does not go far among the wasps, because the cycle of processes is limited to a year, or rather to the few months of the summer. It goes further among the hive-bees, which, by storing food, survive from one year into the next. Unlike the queen-wasp, the queen-bee neither builds cells nor gathers food, but is fed by the workers: egg laying has become her sole business. On the other hand the workers, occupied exclusively in building and nursing, have the reproductive organs more dwarfed than they are in wasps. Still we see that the worker-bee occasionally lays drone-producing eggs, and that, by giving extra nutriment and the required extra space, a worker-larva can be developed into a queen-larva. In respect to the leading traits, therefore, the same interpretation holds. Doubtless there are subsidiary instincts which are apparently not thus interpretable. But before it can be assumed that an interpretation of another kind is necessary, it must be shown that these instincts cannot be traced back to those pre-social types and semi-social types which must have preceded the social types we now see. For unquestionably existing bees must have brought with them from the pre-social state an extensive endowment of instincts, and, acquiring other instincts during the unorganized social state, must have brought these into the present organized social state. It is clear, for instance, that the cell-building instinct in all its elaboration was mainly developed in the pre-social stage; for the transition from species building solitary cells to those building combs is traceable. We are similarly enabled to account for swarming as being an inheritance from remote ancestral types. For just in the same way that, with under-feeding of larvæ, there result individuals with imperfectly developed reproductive systems, so there will result individuals with imperfect sexual instincts; and just as the imperfect reproductive system partially operates upon occasion, so will the imperfect sexual instinct. Whence it will result that on the event which causes a queen to undertake a nuptial flight which is effectual, the workers may take abortive nuptial flights: so causing a swarm.

And here, before going further, let us note an instructive class of facts related to the class of facts above set forth. Summing up, in a chapter on "The Determination of Sex," an induction from many cases, Professor Geddes and Mr. Thompson remark that "such conditions as deficient or abnormal food," and others causing "preponderance of waste over repair ... tend to result in production of males;" while "abundant and rich nutrition" and other conditions which "favour constructive processes ... result in the production of females."[118] Among such evidences of this as immediately concern us, are these:—J. H. Fabre found that in the nests of *Osmia tricornis*, eggs at the bottom, first laid, and accompanied by much food, produced females, while those at the top, last laid, and accompanied by one-half or one-third the quantity of food, produced males,[119] Huber's observations on egg-laying by the honey-bee, show that in the normal course of things, the queen lays eggs of workers for eleven months, and only then lays eggs of drones: that is, when declining nutrition or exhaustion has set in. Further, we have the above-named fact, shown by wasps and bees, that when workers lay eggs these produce drones only.[120] Special evidence, harmonizing with general evidence, thus proves that among the social insects the sex is determined by degree of nutrition while the egg is being formed. See then how congruous this evidence is with the conclusion above drawn; for it is proved that after an egg, predetermined as a female, has been laid, the character of the produced insect as a perfect female or imperfect female is determined by the nutrition of the larva. *That is, one set of differences in structures and instincts is determined by nutrition before the egg is laid, and a further set of differences in structures and instincts is determined by nutrition after the egg is laid.*

We come now to the extreme case—that of the ants. Is it not probable that the process of differentiation has been similar? There are sundry reasons for thinking so. With ants as with wasps and bees—the workers occasionally lay eggs; and an ant-community can, like a bee-community, when need be, produce queens out of worker-larvæ: presumably in the same manner by extra feeding. But here we have to add special evidence of great significance. For observe that the very facts concerning ants, which Professor Weismann names as exemplifying the formation of the worker type by selection, serve, as in the case of wasps, to exemplify its formation by arrested nutrition. He says that in several species the egg-tubes in the ovaries show progressive decrease in number; and this, like the different degrees of arrest in the ovaries of the worker-wasps, indicates arrest of larva-feeding at different stages. He gives cases showing that, in different degrees, the eyes of workers are less developed in the number of their facets than those of the perfect insects; and he also refers to the wings of workers as not being developed: remarking, however, that the rudiments of their wings show that the ancestral forms had wings. Are not these traits also results of arrested nutrition? Generally among insects the larvæ are either blind or have but rudimentary eyes; that is to say, visual organs are among the latest organs to arise in the genesis of the perfect organism. Hence early arrest of nutrition will stop formation of these, while various more ancient structures have become tolerably complete. Similarly with wings. Wings are late organs in insect phylogeny, and therefore will be among those most likely to abort where development is prematurely arrested. And both these traits will, for the same reason, naturally go along with arrested development of the reproductive system. Even more significant, however, is some evidence assigned by Mr. Darwin respecting the caste-gradations among the driver ants of West Africa. He says:—

"But the most important fact for us is, that, though the workers can be grouped into castes of different sizes, yet they graduate insensibly into each other, as does the widely-different structure of their jaws."[121]

"Graduate insensibly," he says; implying that there are very numerous intermediate forms. This is exactly what is to be expected if arrest of nutrition be the cause; for unless the ants have definite measures, enabling them to stop feeding at just the same stages, it must happen that the stoppage of feeding will be indefinite; and that, therefore, there will be all gradations between the extreme forms—"insensible gradations," both in size and in jaw-structure.

In contrast with this interpretation, consider now that of Professor Weismann. From whichever of the two possible suppositions he sets out, the result is equally fatal. If he is consistent, he must say that each of these intermediate forms of workers must have its special set of "determinants," causing its special set of modifications of organs; for he cannot assume that while perfect females and the extreme types of workers have their different sets of determinants, the intermediate types of workers have not. Hence we are introduced to the strange conclusion that besides the markedly-distinguished sets of determinants there must be, to produce these intermediate forms, many other sets slightly distinguished from one another—a score or more kinds of germ-plasm in addition to the four chief kinds. Next comes an introduction to the still stranger conclusion, that these numerous kinds of germ-plasm, producing these numerous intermediate forms, are not simply needless but injurious—produce forms not well fitted for either of the functions discharged by the extreme forms: the implication being that natural selection has originated these disadvantageous forms! If to escape from this necessity for suicide, Professor Weismann accepts the inference that the differences among these numerous intermediate forms are caused by arrested feeding of the larvæ at different stages, then he is bound to admit that the differences between the extreme forms, and between these and perfect females, are similarly caused.

But if he does this, what becomes of his hypothesis that the several castes are constitutionally distinct, and result from the operation of natural selection? Observe, too, that his theory does not even allow him to make this choice; for we have clear proof that unlikenesses among the forms of the same species cannot be determined this way or that way by differences of nutrition. English greyhounds and Scotch greyhounds do not differ from one another so much as do the Amazon-workers from the inferior workers, or the workers from the queens. But no matter how a pregnant Scotch greyhound is fed, or her pups after they are born, they cannot be changed into English greyhounds: the different germ-plasms assert themselves spite of all treatment. But in these social insects the different structures of queens and workers *are* determinable by differences of feeling. Therefore the production of their various castes does not result from the natural selection of varying germ-plasm.

Before dealing with Professor Weismann's crucial case—that co-adaptation of parts, which, in the soldier-ants, has, he thinks, arisen without inheritance of acquired characters—let me deal with an ancillary case which he puts forward as explicable by "panmixia alone." This is the "degeneration, in the warlike Amazon-ants, of the instinct to search for food."[122] Let us first ask what have been the probable antecedents of these Amazon-ants; for, as I have above said, it is absurd to speculate about the structures and instincts the species possesses in its existing organized social state without asking what structures and instincts it brought with it from its original solitary state and its unorganized social state. From the outset these ants were predatory. Some variety of them led to swarm—probably at the sexual season—did not again disperse so soon as other varieties. Those which thus kept together derived advantages from making simultaneous attacks on prey, and prospered accordingly. Of descendants the varieties which carried on longest the associated state prospered most; until, at length, the associated state became permanent. All which social progress took place while there existed only perfect males and females. What was the next step? Ants utilize other insects, and, among other ways of doing this, sometimes make their nests where there are useful insects ready to be utilized. Giving an account of certain New Zealand species of *Tetramorium*, Mr. W. W. Smith says they seek out underground places where there are "root-feeding aphides and coccids," which they begin to treat as domestic animals; and further he says that when, after the pairing season, new nests are being formed, there are "a few ants of both sexes ... from two up to eight or ten."[123] Carrying with us this fact as a key, let us ask what habits will be fallen into by the conquering species of ants. They, too, will seek places where there are creatures to be utilized; and, finding it profitable, will invade the habitations not of defenceless creatures only, but of creatures whose powers of defence are inadequate—weaker species of their own order. A very small modification will affiliate their habits on habits of their prototypes. Instead of being supplied with sweet substance excreted by the aphides they are supplied with sweet substance by the ants among which they parasitically settle themselves. How easily the subjugated ants may fall into the habit of feeding them, we shall see on remembering that already they feed not only larvæ but adults—individuals bigger than themselves. And that attentions kindred to these paid to parasitic ants may be established without difficulty, is shown us by the small birds which continue to feed a young cuckoo in their nest when it has outgrown them. This advanced form of parasitism grew up while there were yet only perfect males and females, as happens in the initial stage with these New Zealand ants. What further modifications of habits were probably then acquired? From the practice of settling themselves where there already exist colonies of aphides, which they carry about to suitable places in the nest, like *Tetramorium*, other ants pass to the practice of making excursions to get aphides, and putting them in better feeding places where they become more productive of saccharine matter. By a parallel step these soldier-ants pass from the stage of settling themselves among other ants which feed them, to the stage of fetching the pupæ of such ants to the nest: a transition like that which occurs among slave-making human beings. Thus by processes analogous to those we see going on, these communities of slave-making ants may be formed. And since the transition from an unorganized social state to a social state characterized by castes, must have been gradual, there must have been a long interval during which the perfect males and females of these conquering ants could acquire habits and transmit them to progeny. A small modification accounts for that seemingly-strange habit which Professor Weismann signalizes. For if, as is observed, those ants which keep aphides solicit them to excrete a supply of ant-food by stroking them with the antennæ, they come very near to doing that which Professor Weismann says the soldier-ants do towards a worker—"they come to it and beg for food:" the food being put into their mouths in this last case as almost or quite in the first. And evidently this habit of passively receiving food, continued through many generations of perfect males and females, may result in such disuse of the power of self-feeding that this is eventually lost. The behaviour of young birds, during, and after, their nest-life, gives us the clue. For a week or more after they are full-grown and fly about with their parents, they may be seen begging for food and making no efforts to recognize and pick up food for themselves. If, generation after generation, feeding of them in full measure continued, they would not learn to feed themselves: the perceptions and instincts implied in self-feeding would be later and later developed, until, with entire disuse of them, they would disappear altogether by inheritance. Thus self-feeding may readily have ceased among these soldier-ants before the caste-organization arose among them.

With this interpretation compare the interpretation of Professor Weismann. I have before protested against arguing in abstracts without descending to concretes. Here let us ask what are the particular changes which the alleged explanation by survival of the fittest involves. Suppose we make the very liberal supposition that an ant's central ganglion bears to its body the same ratio as the human brain bears to the human body—say, one-fortieth of its weight. Assuming this, what shall we assume to be the weight of those ganglion-cells and fibres in which are localized the perceptions of food and the suggestion to take it? Shall we say that these amount to one-tenth of the central ganglion? This is a high estimate considering all the impressions which this ganglion has to receive, and all the operations which it has to direct. Still we will say one-tenth. Then it follows that this portion of nervous substance is one-400th of the weight of its body. By what series of variations shall we say that it is reduced from full power to entire incapacity? Shall we say five? This is a small number to assume. Nevertheless we will assume it. What results? That the economy of nerve-substance achieved by each of these five variations will amount to one-2000th of the entire mass. Making these highly favourable assumptions, what follows:—The queen-ant lays eggs that give origin to individuals in each of which there is achieved an economy in nerve-substance of one-2000th of its weight; and the implication of the hypothesis is that such an economy will so advantage this ant-community that in the competition with other ant-communities it will conquer. For here let me recall the truth before insisted upon, that natural selection can operate only on those variations which appreciably benefit the stirp. Bearing in mind this requirement, is any one now prepared to say that survival of the fittest can cause this decline of the self-feeding faculty?[124]

Not limiting himself to the Darwinian interpretation, however, Professor Weismann says that this degradation may be accounted for by "panmixia alone." Here I will not discuss the adequacy of this supposed cause, but will leave it to be dealt with by implication a few pages in advance, where the general hypothesis of panmixia will be reconsidered.

And now, at length, we are prepared for dealing with Professor Weismann's crucial case—with his alleged disproof that co-adaptation of co-operative parts results from inheritance of acquired characters, because in the case of the Amazon-ants, it has arisen where the inheritance of acquired characters is impossible. For after what has been said, it will be manifest that the whole question is begged when it is assumed that this co-adaptation has arisen since there existed among these ants an organized social state. Unquestionably this organized social state pre-supposes a series of modifications through which it has been reached. It follows, then, that there can be no rational interpretation without a preceding inquiry concerning that earlier state in which there were no castes, but only males and females. What kinds of individuals were the ancestral ants—at first solitary, and then semi-social? They must have had marked powers of offence and defence. Of predacious creatures, it is the more powerful which form societies, not the weaker. Instance human races. Nations originate from the relatively warlike tribes, not from the relatively peaceful tribes. Among the several types of individuals forming the existing ant community, to which, then, did the ancestral ants bear the greatest resemblance? They could not have been like the queens, for these, now devoted to egg-laying, are unfitted for conquest. They could not have been like the inferior class of workers, for these, too, are inadequately armed and lack strength. Hence they must have been most like these Amazon-ants or soldier-ants, which now make predatory excursions—which now do, in fact, what their remote ancestors did. What follows? Their co-adapted parts have not been produced by the selection of variations within the ant-community, such as we now see it. They have been inherited from the pre-social and early social types of ants, in which the co-adaptation of parts had been effected by inheritance of acquired characters. It is not that the soldier-ants have gained these traits; it is that the other castes have lost them. Early arrest of development causes absence of them in the inferior workers; and from the queens they have slowly disappeared by inheritance of the effects of disuse. For, in conformity with ordinary facts of development, we may conclude that in a larva which is being so fed as that the development of the reproductive organs is becoming pronounced, there will simultaneously commence arrest in the development of those organs which are not to be used. There are abundant proofs that along with rapid growth of some organs others abort. And if these inferences are true, then Professor Weismann's argument falls to the ground. Nay, it falls to the ground even if conclusions so definite as these be not insisted upon; for before he can get a basis for his argument he must give good reasons for concluding that these traits of the Amazon-ants have *not* been inherited from remote ancestors.

One more step remains. Let us grant him his basis, and let us pass from the above negative criticism to a positive criticism. As before, I decline to follow the practice of talking in abstracts instead of in concretes, and contend that, difficult as it may be to see how natural selection has in all cases operated, we ought, at any rate, to trace out its operation whenever we can, and see where the hypothesis lands us. According to Professor Weismann's admission, for production of the Amazon-ant by natural selection, "*many parts must have varied simultaneously and in harmony with one another*;"[125] and he names as such, larger jaws, muscles to move them, larger head, and thicker chitin for it, bigger nerves for the muscles, bigger motor centres in the brain, and, for the support of the big head, strengthening of the thorax, limbs, and skeleton generally. As he admits, all these parts must have varied simultaneously in due proportion to one another. What must have been the proximate causes of their variations? They must have been variations in what he calls the "determinants." He says:—

"We have, however, to deal with the transmission of parts which are *variable* and this necessitates the assumption that just as many independent and variable parts exist in the germ-plasm as are present in the fully formed organism."[126]

Consequently to produce simultaneously these many variations of parts, adjusted in their sizes and shapes, there must have simultaneously arisen a set of corresponding variations in the "determinants" composing the germ-plasm. What made them simultaneously vary in the requisite ways? Professor Weismann will not say that there was somewhere a foregone intention. This would imply supernatural agency. He makes no attempt to assign a physical cause for these simultaneous appropriate variations in the determinants: an adequate physical cause being inconceivable. What, then, remains as the only possible interpretation? Nothing but *a fortuitous concourse of variations*; reminding us of the old "fortuitous concourse of atoms." Nay, indeed, it is the very same thing. For each of the "determinants," made up of "biophors," and these again of protein-molecules, and these again of simpler chemical molecules, must have had its molecular constitution changed in the required way; and the molecular constitutions of all the "determinants," severally modified differently, but in adjustment to one another, must have been thus modified by "a fortuitous concourse of atoms." Now if this is an allowable supposition in respect of the "determinants," and the varying organs arising from them, why is it not an allowable supposition in respect of the organism as a whole? Why not assume "a fortuitous concourse of atoms" in its broad, simple form? Nay, indeed, would not this be much the easier? For observe, this co-adaptation of numerous co-operative parts is not achieved by one set of variations, but is achieved gradually by a series of such sets. That is to say, the "fortuitous concourse of atoms" must have occurred time after time in appropriate ways. We have not one miracle, but a series of miracles!

* * * * *

Of the two remaining points in Professor Weismann's first article which demand notice, one concerns his reply to my argument drawn from the distribution of tactual discriminativeness. In what way does he treat this argument? He meets it by an argument derived from hypothetical evidence—not actual evidence. Taking the case of the tongue-tip, I have carefully inquired whether its extreme power of tactual discrimination can give any life-saving advantage in moving about the food during mastication, in detecting foreign bodies in it, or for purposes of speech; and have, I think, shown that the ability to distinguish between points one twenty-fourth of an inch apart is useless for such purposes. Professor Weismann thinks he disposes of this by observing that among the apes the tongue is used as an organ of touch. But surely a counter-argument equivalent in weight to mine should have given a case in which power to discriminate between points one twenty-fourth of an inch apart instead of one-twentieth of an inch apart (a variation of one-sixth) had a life-saving efficacy; or, at any rate, should have suggested such a case. Nothing of the kind is done or even attempted. But now note that his reply, accepted even as it stands, is suicidal. For what has the trusted process of panmixia been doing ever since the human being began to evolve from the ape? Why during thousands of generations has not the nervous structure giving this extreme discriminativeness dwindled away? Even supposing it had been proved of life-saving efficacy to our simian ancestors, it ought, according to Professor Weismann's own hypothesis, to have disappeared in us. Either there was none of the assumed special capacity in the ape's tongue, in which case his reply fails, or panmixia has not operated, in which case his theory of degeneracy fails.

All this, however, is but preface to the chief answer. The argument drawn from the case of the tongue-tip, with which alone Professor Weismann deals, is but a small part of my argument, the remainder of which he does not attempt to touch—does not even mention. Had I never referred to the tongue-tip at all, the various contrasts in discriminativeness which I have named, between the one extreme of the forefinger-tip and the other extreme of the middle of the back, would have abundantly sufficed to establish my case—would have sufficed to show the inadequacy of natural selection as a key and the adequacy of the inheritance of acquired characters.

It seems to me, then, that judgment must go against him by default. Practically he leaves the matter standing just where it did.[127]

The other remaining point concerns the vexed question of panmixia. Confirming the statement of Dr. Romanes, Professor Weismann says that I have misunderstood him. Already (*Contemporary Review*, May, 1893, p. 758, and Reprint, p. 66) I have quoted passages which appeared to justify my interpretation, arrived at after much seeking.[128] Already, too, in this review (July, 1893, p. 54) I have said why I did not hit upon the interpretation now said to be the true one: I never supposed that any one would assume, without assigned cause, that (apart from the excluded influence of disuse) the *minus* variations of a disused organ are greater than the *plus* variations.

This was a tacit challenge to produce reasons for the assumption. Professor Weismann does not accept the challenge, but simply says:—"In my opinion all organs are maintained at the height of their development only through uninterrupted selection" (p. 332): in the absence of which they decline. Now it is doubtless true that as a naturalist he may claim for his "opinion" a relatively great weight. Still, in pursuance of the methods of science, it seems to me that something more than an opinion is required as the basis of a far-reaching theory.[129]

Though the counter-opinion of one who is not a naturalist (as Professor Weismann points out) may be of relatively small value, yet I must here again give it, along with a final reason for it. And this reason shall be exhibited, not in a qualitative form, but in a quantitative form. Let us quantify the terms of the hypothesis by weights; and let us take as our test case the rudimentary hind-limbs of the whale. Zoologists are agreed that the whale has been evolved from a mammal which took to aquatic habits, and that its disused hind-limbs have gradually disappeared. When they ceased to be used in swimming, natural selection played a part—probably an important part—in decreasing them; since, being then impediments to movement through the water, they diminished the attainable speed. It may be, too, that for a period after disappearance of the limbs beneath the skin, survival of the fittest had still some effect. But during the latter stages of the process it had no effect; since the rudiments caused no inconvenience and entailed no appreciable cost. Here, therefore, the cause, if Professor Weismann is right, must have been panmixia. Dr. Struthers, Professor of Anatomy at Aberdeen, whose various publications show him to be a high, if not the highest, authority on the anatomy of these great cetaceans, has kindly taken much trouble in furnishing me with the needful data, based upon direct weighing and measuring and estimation of specific gravity. In the Black Whale (*Balænoptera borealis*) there are no rudiments of hind-limbs whatever: rudiments of the pelvic bones only remain. A sample of the Greenland Right Whale, estimated to weigh 44,800 lbs., had femurs weighing together 3½ ozs.; while a sample of the Razor-back Whale (*Balænoptera musculus*), 50 feet long, and estimated to weigh 56,000 lbs., had rudimentary femurs weighing together one ounce; so that these vanishing remnants of hind-limbs weighed but one-896,000th part of the animal. Now in considering the alleged degeneration by panmixia, we have first to ask why these femurs must be supposed to have varied in the direction of decrease rather than in the direction of increase. During its evolution from the original land-mammal, the whale has grown enormously, implying habitual excess of nutrition. Alike in the embryo and in the growing animal, there must have been a chronic plethora. Why, then, should we suppose these rudiments to have become smaller? Why should they not have enlarged by deposit in them of superfluous materials? But let us grant the unwarranted assumption of predominant *minus* variations. Let us say that the last variation was a reduction of one-half—that in some individuals the joint weight of the femurs was suddenly reduced from two ounces to one ounce—a reduction of one-900,000th of the creature's weight. By inter-crossing with those inheriting the variation, the reduction, or a part of the reduction, was made a trait of the species. Now, in the first place, a necessary implication is that this *minus* variation was maintained in posterity. So far from having reason to suppose this, we have reason to suppose the contrary. As before quoted, Mr. Darwin says that "unless carefully preserved by man," "any particular variation would generally be lost by crossing, reversion, and the accidental destruction of the varying individuals."[130] And Mr. Galton, in his essay on "Regression towards Mediocrity,"[131] contends that not only do deviations of the whole organism from the mean size tend to thus disappear, but that deviations in its components do so. Hence the chances are against such *minus* variation being so preserved as to affect the species by panmixia. In the second place, supposing it to be preserved, may we reasonably assume that, by inter-crossing, this decrease, amounting to about a millionth part of the creature's weight, will gradually affect the constitutions of all Razor-back Whales distributed over the Arctic seas and the North Atlantic Ocean, from Greenland to the Equator? Is this a credible conclusion? For three reasons, then, the hypothesis must be rejected.

Thus, the only reasonable interpretation is the inheritance of acquired characters. If the effects of use and disuse, which are known causes of change in each individual, influence succeeding individuals—if functionally-produced modifications of structure are transmissible, as well as modifications of structure otherwise arising—then this reduction of the whale's hind limbs to minute rudiments is accounted for. The cause has been unceasingly operative on all individuals of the species ever since the transformation began.

In one case see all. If this cause has thus operated on the limbs of the whale, it has thus operated in all creatures on all parts having active functions.

* * * * *

At the outset I intimated that I must limit my replies to those arguments of Professor Weismann which are contained in his first article. That those contained in his second might be dealt with no less effectually, did time and space permit, is manifest to me; but about the probability of this the reader must form his own judgment. My replies thus far may be summed up as follows:—

Professor Weismann says he has disproved the conclusion that degeneration of the little toe has resulted from inheritance of acquired characters. But his reasoning fails against an interpretation he overlooks. A profound modification of the hind limbs and their appendages must have taken place during the transition from arboreal habits to terrestrial habits; and dwindling of the little toe is an obvious consequence of disuse, at the same time that enlargement of the great toe is an obvious consequence of increased use.

The entire argument based on the unlike forms and instincts presented by castes of social insects is invalidated by an omission. Until probable conclusions are reached respecting the characters which such insects brought with them into the organized social state, no valid inferences can be drawn respecting characters developed during that state.

A further large error of interpretation is involved in the assumption that the different caste-characters are transmitted to them in the eggs laid by the mother insect. While we have evidence that the unlike structures of the sexes are determined by nutrition of the germ before egg-laying, we have evidence that the unlike structures of classes are caused by unlikenesses of nutrition of the larvæ. That these varieties of forms do not result from varieties of germ-plasms, is demonstrated by the fact that where there are varieties of germ-plasms, as in varieties of the same species of mammal, no deviations in feeding prevent display of their structural results.

For such caste-modifications as those of the Amazon-ants, which are unable to feed themselves, there is a feasible explanation other than Professor Weismann's. The relation of common ants to their domestic animals—aphides and coccids—which yield them food on solicitation, does not differ widely from this relation between these Amazon-ants and their domestic animals—the slave-ants. And the habit of being fed, contracted during the first stages of their parasitic life, when there were perfect males and females, may, during that stage, have become established by inheritance. Meanwhile the opposed interpretation—that this incapacity has resulted from the selection of those ant-communities the queens of which laid eggs that had so varied as to entail this incapacity—implies that a scarcely appreciable economy of nerve-matter advantaged the stirp so greatly as to cause it to spread more than other stirps: an incredible supposition.

As the outcome of these alternative interpretations we saw that the argument respecting the co-adaptation of co-operative parts, which Professor Weismann thinks is furnished to him by the Amazon-ants, disappears. The ancestral ants were conquering ants. These founded the communities; and hence those members of the present communities which are most like them are the Amazon-ants. If so, the co-adaptation of the co-operative parts was effected by inheritance during the solitary and semi-social stages. Even were there no such solution, the opposed solution will be unacceptable. These simultaneous appropriate variations of the co-operative parts in sizes, shapes, and proportions, are supposed to be effected by simultaneous variations in the "determinants" of the germ-plasms; and in the absence of an assigned physical cause, this implies a fortuitous concourse of appropriate variations, which carries us back to a "fortuitous concourse of atoms." This may just as well be extended to the entire organism. The old hypothesis of special creations is more consistent and comprehensible.

To rebut my inference drawn from the distribution of discriminativeness, Professor Weismann uses not an argument but the blank form of an argument. The ability to discriminate one twenty-fourth of an inch by the tongue-tip *may* have been useful to the ape: no conceivable use being even suggested. And then the great body of my argument derived from the distribution of discriminativeness over the skin, which amply suffices, is wholly ignored.

The tacit challenge I gave to name some facts in support of the hypothesis of panmixia—or even a solitary fact—is passed by. It remains a pure speculation having no basis but Professor Weismann's "opinion." When from the abstract statement of it we pass to a concrete test, in the case of the whale, we find that it necessitates an unproved and improbable assumption respecting *plus* and *minus* variations; that it ignores the unceasing tendency to reversion; and that it implies an effect out of all proportion to the cause.

It is curious what entirely opposite conclusions men may draw from the same evidence. Professor Weismann thinks he has shown that the "last bulwark of the Lamarckian principle is untenable." Most readers will hold with me that he is, to use the mildest word, premature in so thinking. Contrariwise my impression is that he has not shown either this bulwark or any other bulwark to be untenable; but rather that while his assault has failed it has furnished opportunity for strengthening sundry of the bulwarks.

IV.

Among those who follow a controversy to its close, not one in a hundred turns back to its beginning to see whether its chief theses have been dealt with. Very often the leading arguments of one disputant, seen by the other to be unanswerable, are quietly ignored, and attention is concentrated on subordinate arguments to which replies, actually or seemingly valid, can be made. The original issue is thus commonly lost sight of.

More than once I have pointed out that, as influencing men's views about Education, Ethics, Sociology, and Politics, the question whether acquired characters are inherited is the most important question before the scientific world. Hence I cannot allow the discussion with Professor Weismann to end in so futile a way as it will do if no summary of results is made. Here, therefore, I propose to recapitulate the whole case in brief. Primarily my purpose is to recall certain leading propositions which, having been passed by unnoticed, remain outstanding. I will turn, in the second place, to such propositions as have been dealt with; hoping to show that the replies given are invalid, and consequently that these propositions also remain outstanding.

But something beyond a summing-up is intended. A few pages at the close will be devoted to setting forth new evidence which has come to light since the controversy commenced—evidence which many will think sufficient in itself to warrant a positive conclusion.

* * * * *

The fact that the tip of the fore finger has thirty times the power of discrimination possessed by the middle of the back, and that various intermediate degrees of discriminative power are possessed by various parts of the skin, was set down as a datum for my first argument. The causes which might be assigned for these remarkable contrasts were carefully examined under all their aspects. I showed in detail that the contrasts could not in any way be accounted for by natural selection. I further showed that no interpretation of them is afforded by the alleged process of panmixia: this has no *locus standi* in the case. Having proved experimentally, that ability of the fingers to discriminate is increased by practice, and having pointed out that gradations of discriminativeness in different parts correspond with gradations in the activities of the parts as used for tactual exploration, I argued that these contrasts have arisen from the organized and inherited effects of tactual converse with surrounding things, varying in its degrees according to the positions of the parts—in other words, that they are due to the inheritance of acquired characters. As a crowning proof I instanced the case of the tongue-tip, which has twice the discriminativeness of the forefinger-tip: pointing out that consciously, or semi-consciously, or unconsciously, the tongue-tip is perpetually exploring the inner surfaces of the teeth.

Singling out this last case, Professor Weismann made, or rather adopted from Dr. Romanes, what professed to be a reply but was nothing more than the blank form of a reply. It was said that though this extreme discriminativeness of the tongue-tip is of no use to mankind, it may have been of use to certain ancestral *primates*. No evidence of any such use was given; no imaginable use was assigned. It was simply suggested that there perhaps was a use.

In my rejoinder, after indicating the illusory nature of this proceeding (which is much like offering a cheque on a bank where no assets have been deposited to meet it), I pointed out that had the evidence furnished by the tongue tip never been mentioned, the evidence otherwise furnished amply sufficed. I then drew attention to the fact that this evidence had been passed over, and tacitly inquired why.

No reply.[132]

* * * * *

In his essay on "The All-Sufficiency of Natural Selection," Professor Weismann set out, not by answering one of the arguments I had used, but by importing into the discussion an argument used by another writer, which it was easy to meet. It had been contended that the smallness and deformity of the little toe are consequent upon the effects of boot-pressure, inherited from generation to generation. To this Professor Weismann made the sufficient reply that the fusion of the phalanges and otherwise degraded structure of the little toe, exist among peoples who go barefoot.

In my "Rejoinder" I said that though the inheritance of acquired characters does not explain this degradation in the way alleged, it explains it in a way which Professor Weismann overlooks. The cause is one which has been operating ever since the earliest anthropoid creatures began to decrease their life in trees and increase their life on the earth's surface. The mechanics of walking and running, in so far as they concern the question at issue, were analyzed; and it was shown that effort is economized and efficiency increased in proportion as the stress is thrown more and more on the inner digits of the foot and less and less on the outer digits. So that thus the foot furnishes us simultaneously with an instance of increase from use and of decrease from disuse; a further disproof being yielded of the allegation that co-operative parts vary together, since we have here co-operative parts of which one grows while the other dwindles.

I ended by pointing out that, so far from strengthening his own case, Professor Weismann had, by bringing into the controversy this changed structure of the foot, given occasion for strengthening the opposite case.

No reply.

* * * * *

We come now to Professor Weismann's endeavour to disprove my second thesis—that it is impossible to explain by natural selection alone the co-adaptation of co-operative parts. It is thirty years since this was set forth in *The Principles of Biology*. In § 166 I instanced the enormous horns of the extinct Irish elk, and contended that in this, and in kindred cases, where for the efficient use of some one enlarged part many other parts have to be simultaneously enlarged, it is out of the question to suppose that they can have all spontaneously varied in the required proportions. In "The Factors of Organic Evolution," by way of enforcing this argument, which had, so far as I know, never been met, I dwelt upon the aberrant structure of the giraffe. And then, in the essay which initiated this controversy, I brought forward yet a third case—that of an animal which, previously accustomed only to walking, acquires the power of leaping.

In the first of his articles in the *Contemporary Review* (September, 1893), Professor Weismann made no direct reply, but he made an indirect reply. He did not attempt to show how there could have taken place in the stag the "harmonious variation of the different parts that co-operate to produce one physiological result" (p. 311); but he contended that such harmonious variation *must* have taken place, because the like has taken place in "the neuters of state-forming insects"—"animal forms which do not reproduce themselves, but are always propagated anew by parents which are unlike them" (p. 313), and which therefore cannot have transmitted acquired characters. Singling out those soldier-neuters which exist among certain kinds of ants, he described (p. 318) the many co-ordinated parts required to make their fighting organs efficient. He then argued that the required simultaneous changes can "only have arisen by a selection of the parent-ants dependent on the fact that those parents which produced the best workers had always the best prospect of the persistence of their colony. No other explanation is conceivable; *and it is just because no other explanation is conceivable, that it is necessary for us to accept the principle of natural selection*" (pp. 318-9).

[This passage initiated a collateral controversy, which, as continually happens, has greatly obscured the primary controversy. It became a question whether these forms of neuter insects have arisen as Professor Weismann assumes, or whether they have arisen from arrested development consequent upon innutrition. To avoid entanglements I must for the present pass over this collateral controversy, intending to resume it presently, when the original issues have been dealt with.]

No one will suspect me of thinking that the inconceivability of the negation is not a valid criterion, since, in "The Universal Postulate," published in the *Westminster Review* in 1852 and afterwards in *The Principles of Psychology*, I contended that it is the ultimate test of truth. But then in every case there has to be determined the question—Is the negation inconceivable; and in assuming that it is so in the case named, lies the fallacy of the above-quoted passage. The three separate ways in which I dealt with this position of Professor Weismann are as follows:—

If we admit the assumption that the form of the soldier-ant has been developed since the establishment of the organized ant-community in which it exists, Professor Weismann's assertion that no other process than that which he alleges is conceivable, is true. But I pointed out that this assumption is inadmissible; and that no valid conclusion respecting the genesis of the soldier-ant can be drawn without postulating either the ascertained, or the probable, structure of those pre-social, or semi-social, ants from which the organized social ants have descended. I went on to contend that the pre-social type must have been a conquering type, and that therefore in all probability the soldier-ants represent most nearly the structures of those ancestral ants which existed when the society had perfect males and females and could transmit acquired characters, while the other members of the existing communities are degraded forms of the type.

No reply.

A further argument I used was that where there exist different castes among the neuter-ants, as those seen in the soldiers and workers of the Driver ants of West Africa, "they graduate insensibly into each other" alike in their sizes and in their structures; and that Professor Weismann's hypothesis implies a special set of "determinants" for each intermediate form. Or if he should say that the intermediate forms result from mixtures of the determinants of the two extreme forms, there still remains the further difficulty that natural selection has maintained, for innumerable generations, these intermediate forms which are injurious deviations from the useful extreme forms.

No reply.

One further reason—fatal it seems to me—was urged in bar of his interpretation. No physical cause has been, or can be, assigned, why in the germ-plasm of any particular queen-ant, the "determinants" initiating these various co-operative organs, all simultaneously vary in fitting ways and degrees, and still less why there occur such co-ordinated variations generation after generation, until by their accumulated results these efficient co-operative structures have been evolved. I pointed out that in the absence of any assigned or assignable physical cause, it is necessary to assume a fortuitous concurrence of favourable variations, which means "a fortuitous concourse of atoms;" and that it would be just as rational, and much more consistent, to assume that the structure of the entire organism thus resulted.

No reply.

*****

It is reasonable to suspect that Professor Weismann recognized these difficulties as insuperable, for, in his Romanes Lecture on "The Effect of External Influences upon Development," instead of his previous indirect reply, he makes a direct reply. Reverting to the stag and its enlarging horns, he alleges a process by which, as he thinks, we may understand how, by variation and selection, all the bones and muscles of the neck, of the thorax, and of the fore-legs, are step by step adjusted in their sizes to the increasing sizes of the horns. He ascribes this harmonization to the internal struggle for nutriment, and that survival of the fittest which takes place among the parts of an organism: a process which he calls "*intra-individual-*selection, or more briefly—*intra-selection*" (p. 12).

"Wilhelm Roux has given an explanation of the cause of these wonderfully fine adaptations by applying the principle of selection to the parts of the organism. Just as there is a struggle for survival among the individuals of a species, and the fittest are victorious, so also do even the smallest living particles contend with one another, and those that succeed best in securing food and place grow and multiply rapidly, and so displace those that are less suitably equipped" (p. 12).[133]

That I do not explain as he does the co-adaptation of co-operative parts, Professor Weismann ascribes to my having overlooked this "principle of intra-selection"—an unlucky supposition, as we see. But I do not think that when recognizing it a generation ago, I should have seen its relevancy to the question at issue, had that issue then been raised, and I certainly do not see it now. Full reproduction of Professor Weismann's explanation is impracticable, for it occupies several pages, but here are the essential sentences from it:—

"The great significance of intra-selection appears to me not to depend on its producing structures that are directly transmissible,—it cannot do that,—but rather consists in its causing a development of the germ-structure, acquired by the selection of individuals, which will be suitable to varying conditions.... We may therefore say that intra-selection effects the adaptation of the individual to its chance developmental conditions,—the suiting of the hereditary primary constituents to fresh circumstances" (p. 16).... "But as the primary variations in the phyletic metamorphosis occurred little by little, the secondary adaptations would probably as a rule be able to keep pace with them. Time would thus be gained till, in the course of generations, by constant selection of those germs the primary constituents of which are best suited to one another, the greatest possible degree of harmony may be reached, and consequently a definitive metamorphosis of the species involving all the parts of the individual may occur" (p. 19).

The connecting sentences, along with those which precede and succeed, would not, if quoted, give to the reader clearer conceptions than these by themselves give. But when disentangled from Professor Weismann's involved statements, the essential issues are, I think, clear enough. In the case of the stag, that daily working together of the numerous nerves, muscles, and bones concerned, by which they are adjusted to the carrying and using of somewhat heavier horns, produces on them effects which, as I hold, are inheritable, but which, as Professor Weismann holds, are not inheritable. If they are not inheritable, what must happen? A fawn of the next generation is born with no such adjustment of nerves, muscles and bones as had been produced by greater exercise in the parent, and with no tendency to such adjustment. Consequently if, in successive generations, the horns go on enlarging, all these nerves, muscles, and bones, remaining of the original sizes, become utterly inadequate. The result is loss of life: the process of adaptation fails. "No," says Professor Weismann, "we must conclude that the germ-plasm has varied in the needful manner." How so? The process of "intra-individual selection," as he calls it, can have had no effect, since the cells of the soma cannot influence the reproductive cells. In what way, then, has the germ-plasm gained the characters required for producing simultaneously all these modified co-operative parts. Well, Professor Weismann tells us merely that we must suppose that the germ-plasm acquires a certain sensitiveness such as gives it a proclivity to development in the requisite ways. How is such proclivity obtainable? Only by having a multitude of its "determinants" simultaneously changed in fit modes. Emphasizing the fact that even a small failure in any one of the co-operative parts may be fatal, as the sprain of an over-taxed muscle shows us, I alleged that the chances are infinity to one against the needful variations taking place at the same time. Divested of its elaboration, its abstract words and technical phrases, the outcome of Professor Weismann's explanation is that he accepts this, and asserts that the infinitely improbable thing takes place!

Either his argument is a disguised admission of the inheritableness of acquired characters (the effects of "intra-selection") or else it is, as before, the assumption of a fortuitous concourse of favourable variations in the determinants—"a fortuitous concourse of atoms."

* * * * *

Leaving here this main issue, I return now to that collateral issue named on a preceding page as being postponed—whether the neuters among social insects result from specially modified germ-plasms or whether they result from the treatment received during their larval stages.

For the substantiation of his doctrine Professor Weismann is obliged to adopt the first of these alternatives; and in his Romanes Lecture he found it needful to deal with the evidence I brought in support of the second alternative. He says that "poor feeding is not the *causa efficiens* of sterility among bees, but is merely the stimulus which *not only results in the formation of rudimentary ovaries, but at the same time calls forth all the other distinctive characters of the workers*" (pp. 29-30); and he says this although he has in preceding lines admitted that it is "true of all animals that they reproduce only feebly or not at all when badly and insufficiently nourished:" a known cause being thus displaced by a supposed cause. But Professor Weismann proceeds to justify his interpretation by experimentally-obtained evidence.

He "reared large numbers of the eggs of a female blow-fly"; the larvæ of some he fed abundantly, but the larvæ of others sparingly; and eventually he obtained, from the one set flies of full size, and from the other small flies. Nevertheless the small flies were fertile, as well as the others. Here, then, was proof that innutrition had not produced infertility; and he contends that therefore among the neuter social insects, infertility has not resulted from innutrition. The argument seems strong, and to many will appear conclusive; but there are two differences which entirely vitiate the comparison Professor Weismann institutes.

One of them has been pointed out by Mr. Cunningham. In the case of the blow-fly the food supplied to the larvæ though different in quantity was the same in quality; in the case of the social insects the food supplied, whether or not different in quantity, differs in quality. Among bees, wasps, ants, &c., the larvæ of the reproductive forms are fed upon a more nitrogenous food than are the larvæ of the workers; whereas the two sets of larvæ of the blow-fly, as fed by Professor Weismann, were alike supplied with highly nitrogenous food. Hence there did not exist the same cause for non-development of the reproductive organs. Here, then, is one vitiation of the supposed parallel. There is a second.

While the development of an embryo follows in a rude way the phyletic metamorphoses passed through by its ancestry, the order of development of organs is often gradually modified by the needs of particular species: the structures being developed in such order as conduces to self-sustentation and the welfare of offspring. Among other results there arise differences in the relative dates of maturity of the reproductive system and of the other systems. It is clear, *à priori*, that it must be fatal to a species if offspring are habitually produced before the conditions requisite for their survival are fulfilled. And hence, if the life is a complex one, and the care taken of offspring is great, reproduction must be much longer delayed than where the life is simple and the care of offspring absent or easy. The contrast between men and oxen sufficiently illustrates this truth. Now the subordination of the order of development of parts to the needs of the species, is conspicuously shown in the contrast between these two kinds of insects which Professor Weismann compares as though their requirements were similar. What happens with the blow fly? If it is able to suck up some nutriment, to fly tolerably, and to scent out dead flesh, various of its minor organs may be more or less imperfect without appreciable detriment to the species: the eggs can be laid in a fit place, and that is all that is wanted. Hence it profits the species to have the reproductive system developed comparatively early—in advance, even, of various less essential parts. Quite otherwise is it with social insects, which take such remarkable care of their young; or rather to make the case parallel—quite otherwise is it with those types from which the social insects have descended, bringing into the social state their inherited instincts and constitutions. Consider the doings of the mason-wasp, or mason-bee, or those of the carpenter-bee. What, in these cases, must the female do that she may rear members of the next generation? There is a fit place for building or burrowing to be chosen; there is the collecting together of grains of sand and cementing them into a strong and water-proof cell, or there is the burrowing into wood and there building several cells; there is the collecting of food to place along with the eggs deposited in these cells, solitary or associated, including that intelligent choice of small caterpillars which, discovered and carried home, are carefully packed away and hypnotized by a sting, so that they may live until the growing larva has need of them. For all these proceedings there have to be provided the fit external organs—cutting instruments, &c., and the fit internal organs—complicated nerve-centres in which are located these various remarkable instincts, and ganglia by which these delicate operations have to be guided. And these special structures have, some if not all of them, to be made perfect and brought into efficient action before egg-laying takes place. Ask what would happen if the reproductive system were active in advance of these ancillary appliances. The eggs would have to be laid without protection or food, and the species would forthwith disappear. And if that full development of the reproductive organs which is marked by their activity, is not needful until these ancillary organs have come into play, the implication, in conformity with the general law above indicated, is that the perfect development of the reproductive organs will take place later than that of these ancillary organs, and that if innutrition checks the general development, the reproductive organs will be those which chiefly suffer. Hence, in the social types which have descended from these solitary types, this order of evolution of parts will be inherited, and will entail the results I have inferred.

If only deductively reached, this conclusion would, I think, be fully justified. But now observe that it is more than deductively reached. It is established by observation. Professor Riley, Ph.D., late Government Entomologist of the United States, in his annual address as President of the Biological Society of Washington,[134] on January 29, 1894, said:—

"Among the more curious facts connected with these Termites, because of their exceptional nature, is the late development of the internal sexual organs in the reproductive forms." (p. 34.)

Though what has been shown of the Termites has not been shown of the other social insects, which belong to a different order, yet, considering the analogies between their social states and between their constitutional requirements, it is a fair inference that what holds in the one case holds partially, if not fully, in the other. Should it be said that the larval forms do not pass into the pupa state in the one case as they do in the other, the answer is that this does not affect the principle. The larva carries into the pupa state a fixed quantity of tissue-forming material for the production of the imago. If the material is sufficient, then a complete imago is formed. If it is not sufficient, then, while the earlier formed organs are not affected by the deficiency, the deficiency is felt when the latest formed organs come to be developed, and they are consequently imperfect.

Even if left without reply, Professor Weismann's interpretation commits him to some insuperable difficulties, which I must now point out. Unquestionably he has "the courage of his opinions;" and it is shown throughout this collateral discussion as elsewhere. He is compelled by accumulated evidence to admit "that there is only *one* kind of egg from which queens and workers as well as males arise."[135] But if the production of one or other form from the same germ does not result from speciality of feeding, what does it result from? Here is his reply:—

"We must rather suppose that the primary constituents of two distinct reproductive systems—*e. g.* those of the queen and worker—are contained in the germ-plasm of the egg."[136]

"The courage of his opinions," which Professor Weismann shows in this assumption, is, however, quite insufficient. For since he himself has just admitted that there is only one kind of egg for queens, workers, and males, he must at any rate assume three sets of "determinants." (I find that on a subsequent page he does so.) But this is not enough, for there are, in many cases, two if not more kinds of workers, which implies that four sets of determinants must co-exist in the same egg. Even now we have not got to the extent of the assumption required. In the address above referred to on "Social Insects from Psychical and Evolutional Points of View," Professor Riley gives us (p. 33) the—

Forms in a Termes Colony under Normal Conditions.

1. Youngest larvæ.

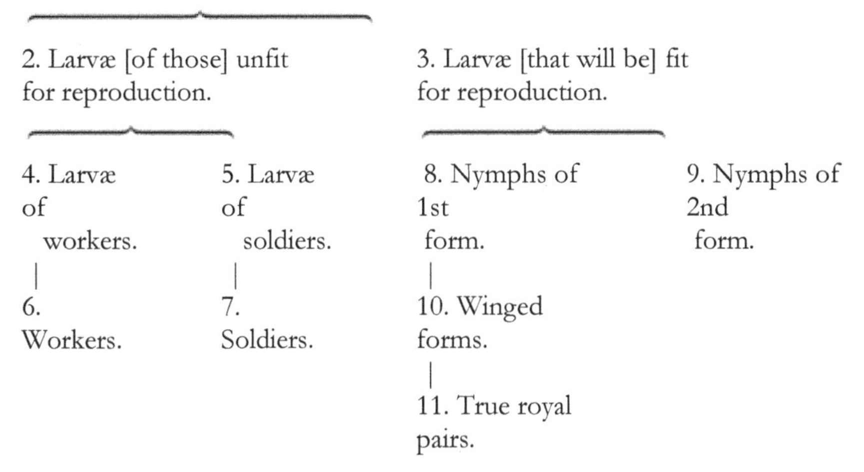

Hence as, in this family tree, the royal pair includes male and female, it results that there are *five* different adult forms (Grassi says there are two others) arising from like eggs or larvæ; and Professor Weismann's hypothesis becomes proportionately complicated. Let us observe what the complications are.

It often happens in controversy—metaphysical controversy more than any other—that propositions are accepted without their terms having been mentally represented. In public proceedings documents are often "taken as read," sometimes with mischievous results; and in discussions propositions are often taken as thought when they have not been thought and cannot be thought. It sufficiently taxes imagination to assume, as Professor Weismann does, that two sets of "ids" or of "determinants" in the same egg are, throughout all the cell-divisions which end in the formation of the *morula*, kept separate, so that they may subsequently energize independently; or that if they are not thus kept separate, they have the power of segregating in the required ways. But what are we to say when three, four, and even five sets of "ids" or bundles of "determinants" are present? How is dichotomous division to keep these sets distinct; or if they are not kept distinct, what shall we say to the chaos which must arise after many fissions, when each set in conflict with the others strives to produce its particular structure? And how are the conquering determinants to find they ways out of the *mêlée* to the places where they are to fulfil their organizing functions? Even were they all intelligent beings and each had a map by which to guide his movements, the problem would be sufficiently puzzling. Can we assume it to be solved by unconscious units?

Thus even had Professor Weismann shown that the special structures of the different individuals in an insect-community are not due to differences in the nurtures they receive, which he has failed to do, he would still be met by this difficulty in the way of his own view, in addition to the three other insuperable difficulties grouped together in a preceding section.

* * * * *

The collateral issue, which has occupied the largest space in the controversy, has, as commonly happens, begotten a second generation of collateral issues. Some of these are embodied in the form of questions put to me, which I must here answer, lest it should be supposed that they are unanswerable and my view therefore untenable.

In the notes he appends to his Romanes Lecture, Professor Weismann writes:—

"One of the questions put to Spencer by Ball is quite sufficient to show the utter weakness of the position of Lamarckism:—if their characteristics did not arise among the workers themselves, but were transmitted from the pre-social time, how does it happen that the queens and drones of every generation can give anew to the workers the characteristics which they themselves have long ago lost?" (p. 68).

It is curious to see put forward in so triumphant a manner, by a professed naturalist, a question so easily disposed of. I answer it by putting another. How does it happen that among those moths of which the female has but rudimentary wings, she continues to endow the males of her species with wings? How does it happen, for example, that among the *Geometridæ*, the peculiar structures and habits of which show that they have all descended from a common ancestor, some species have winged females and some wingless females; and that though they have lost the wings the ancestral females had, these wingless females convey to the males the normal developments of wings? Or, still better, how is it that in the *Psychidæ* there are apterous worm-like females, which lay eggs that bring forth winged males of the ordinary imago form? If for males we read workers, the case is parallel to the cases of those social insects, the queens of which bequeath characteristics they have themselves lost. The ordinary facts of embryonic evolution yield us analogies. What is the most common trait in the development of the sexes? When the sexual organs of either become pronounced, the incipient ancillary organs belonging to the opposite sex cease to develop and remain rudiments, while the organs special to the sex, essential and nonessential, become fully developed. What, then, must happen with the queen-ant, which, through countless generations, has ceased to use certain structures and has lost them from disuse? If one of the eggs which she lays, capable, as Professor Weismann admits, of becoming queen, male, or worker of one or other kind, does not at a certain stage begin actively to develop its reproductive system, then those organs of the ancestral or pre-social type which the queen has lost begin to develop, and a worker results.

Another difficulty in the way of my view, supposed to be fatal, is that presented by the Honey-ants—aberrant members of certain ant-colonies which develop so enormously the pouch into which the food is drawn, that the abdomen becomes little else than a great bladder out of which the head, thorax, and legs protrude. This, it is thought, cannot be accounted for otherwise than as a consequence of specially endowed eggs, which it has become profitable to the community for the queen to produce. But the explanation fits in quite easily with the view I have set forth. No one will deny that the taking in of food is the deepest of vital requirements, and the correlative instinct a dominant one; nor will any one deny that the instinct of feeding young is less deeply seated—comes later in order of time. So, too, every one will admit that the worker-bee or worker-ant before regurgitating food into the mouth of a larva must first of all take it in. Hence, alike in order of time and necessity, it is to be assumed that development of the nervous structures which guide self-nutrition, precedes development of the nervous structures which guide the feeding of larvæ. What, then, will in some cases happen, supposing there is an arrested development consequent on innutrition? It will in some cases happen that while the nervous centres prompting and regulating deglutition are fully formed, the formation of those prompting and regulating the regurgitation of the food into the mouths of larvæ are arrested. What will be the consequence? The life of the worker is mainly passed in taking in food and putting it out again. If the putting out is stopped its life will be mainly passed in taking in food. The receptacle will go on enlarging and it will eventually assume the monstrous form that we see.[137]

Here, however, to exclude misinterpretations, let me explain. I by no means deny that variation and selection have produced, in these insect-communities, certain effects such as Mr. Darwin suggested. Doubtless ant-queens vary; doubtless there are variations in their eggs; doubtless differences of structure in the resulting progeny sometimes prove advantageous to the stirp, and originate slight modifications of the species. But such changes, legitimately to be assumed, are changes in single parts—in single organs or portions of organs. Admission of this does not involve admission that there can take place numerous correlated variations in different and often remote parts, which must take place simultaneously or else be useless. Assumption of this is what Professor Weismann's argument requires, and assumption of this we have seen to be absurd.

Before leaving the general problem presented by the social insects, let me remark that the various complexities of action not explained by inheritance from pre-social or semi-social types, are probably due to accumulated and transmitted knowledge. I recently read an account of the education of a butterfly, carried to the extent that it became quite friendly with its protector and would come to be fed. If a non-social and relatively unintelligent insect is capable of thus far consciously adjusting its actions, then it seems a reasonable supposition that in a community of social insects there has arisen a mass of experience and usage into which each new individual is initiated; just as happens among ourselves. We have only to consider the chaos which would result were we suddenly bereft of language, and if the young were left to grow up without precept and example, to see that very probably the polity of an insect community is made possible by the addition of intelligence to instinct, and the transmission of information through sign-language.

* * * * *

There remains now the question of *panmixia*, which stands exactly where it did when I published the "Rejoinder to Professor Weismann."

After showing that the interpretation I put upon his view was justified by certain passages quoted; and after pointing out that one of his adherents had set forth the view which I combated—if not as his view yet as supplementary to it; I went on to criticize the view as set forth afresh by Professor Weismann himself. I showed that as thus set forth the actuality of the supposed cause of decrease in disused organs, implies that *minus* variations habitually exceed *plus* variations—in degree or in number, or in both. Unless it can be proved that such an excess ordinarily occurs, the hypothesis of *panmixia* has no place; and I asked, where is the proof that it occurs.

No reply.

Not content with this abstract form of the question I put it also in a concrete form, and granted for the nonce Professor Weismann's assumption: taking the case of the rudimentary hind limbs of the whale. I said that though, during those early stages of decrease in which the disused limbs were external, natural selection probably had a share in decreasing them, since they were then impediments to locomotion, yet when they became internal, and especially when they had dwindled to nothing but remnants of the femurs, it is impossible to suppose that natural selection played any part: no whale could have survived and initiated a more prosperous stirp in virtue of the economy achieved by such a decrease. The operation of natural selection being out of the question, I inquired whether such a decrease, say of one-half when the femurs weighed a few ounces, occurring in one individual, could be supposed in the ordinary course of reproduction to affect the whole of the whale species inhabiting the Arctic Seas and the North Atlantic Ocean; and so on with successive diminutions until the rudiments had reached their present minuteness. I asked whether such an interpretation could be rationally entertained.

No reply.

Now in the absence of replies to these two questions it seems to me that the verdict must go against Professor Weismann by default. If he has to surrender the hypothesis of *panmixia*, what results? All that evidence collected by Mr. Darwin and others, regarded by them as proof of the inheritance of acquired characters, which was cavalierly set aside on the strength of this alleged process of panmixia, is reinstated. And this reinstated evidence, joined with much evidence since furnished, suffices to establish the repudiated interpretation.

In the printed report of his Romanes Lecture, after fifty pages of complicated speculations which we are expected to accept as proofs, Professor Weismann ends by saying, in reference to the case of the neuter insects:—

"This case is of additional interest, as it may serve to convince those naturalists who are still inclined to maintain that acquired characters are inherited, and to support the Lamarckian principle of development, that their view cannot be the right one. It has not proved tenable in a single instance" (p. 54).

Most readers of the foregoing pages will think that since Professor Weismann has left one after another of my chief theses without reply, this is rather a strong assertion; and they will still further raise their eyebrows on remembering that, as I have shown, where he has given answers his answers are invalid.

* * * * *

And now we come to the additions which I indicated at the outset as having to be made—certain evidences which have come to light since this controversy commenced.

When, by a remembered observation made in boyhood, joined with the familiar fact that worker-larvæ can be changed into the larvæ of queens by feeding, I was led to suggest that probably all the variations of form in the social insects are consequent on differences of nurture, I was unaware that observations and experiments were being made which have justified this suggestion. Professor Grassi has recently published accounts of the food-habits of two European species of Termites, shewing that the various forms are due to feeding. He is known to be a most careful observer, and some of the most curious of his facts are confirmed by the collection of white ants exhibited by Dr. David Sharp, F.R.S., at the *soirée* of the Royal Society in May last. He has favoured me with the following account of Grassi's results, which I publish with his assent:—

"There is great variety as to the constituents of the community and economy of the species in White Ants. One of the simplest conditions known is that studied by Grassi in the case of the European species Calotermes flavicollis. In this species there is no worker caste; the adult forms are only of two kinds, viz., soldiers, and the males and females; the sexes are externally almost indistinguishable, and there are males and females of soldiers as well as of the winged forms, though the sexual organs do not undergo their full development in any soldier whether male or female.

"The soldier is not however a mere instance of simple arrested development. It is true that there is in it arrested development of the sexual organs, but this is accompanied by change of form of other parts—changes so extreme that one would hardly suppose the soldier to have any connection with either the young or the adult of the winged forms.

"Now according to Grassi the whole of the individuals when born are undifferentiated forms (except as to sex), and each one is capable of going on the natural course of development and thus becoming a winged insect, or can be deviated from this course and made into a soldier; this is accomplished by the White Ants by special courses of feeding.

"The evidence given by Grassi is not conclusive as to the young being all born alike; and it may be that there are some individuals born that could not be deviated from the natural course and made into soldiers. But there is one case which seems to show positively that the deviation Grassi believes to occur is real, and not due to the selection by the ants of an individual that though appearing to our eyes undifferentiated is not really so. This is that an individual can be made into a soldier after it has visibly undergone one half or more of the development into a winged form. The Termites can in fact operate on an individual that has already acquired the rudiments of wings and whose head is totally destitute of any appearance of the shape of the armature peculiar to the soldier, and can turn it into a soldier; the rudiments of the wings being in such a case nearly entirely re-absorbed."

Grassi has been for many years engaged in investigating these phenomena, and there is no reason for rejecting his statement. We can scarcely avoid accepting it, and if so, Professor Weismann's hypothesis is conclusively disposed of. Were there different sets of "determinants" for the soldier-form and for the winged sexual form, those "determinants" which had gone a long way towards producing the winged sexual form, would inevitably go on to complete that form, and could not have their proclivity changed by feeding.

[Yet more evidence to the like effect has since become known. At the meeting of the Entomological Society, on March 14, 1894 (reported in *Nature*, March 29):—

"Dr. D. Sharp, F.R.S., exhibited a collection of white ants (*Termites*), formed by Mr. G. D. Haviland in Singapore, which comprised about twelve species, of most of which the various forms were obtained. He said that Prof. Grassi had recently made observations on the European species, and had brought to light some important particulars; and also that in the discussion that had recently been carried on between Mr. Herbert Spencer and Prof. Weismann, the former had stated that in his opinion the different forms of social insects were produced by nutrition. Prof. Grassi's observations showed this view to be correct, and the specimens now exhibited confirmed one of the most important points in his observations. Dr. Sharp also stated that Mr. Haviland found in one nest eleven neoteinic queens—that is to say, individuals having the appearance of the queen in some respects, while in others they are still immature."

Another similarly conclusive verification I published in *Nature* for December 6, 1894, under the title "The Origin of Classes among the 'Parasol' Ants." The letter ran as follows:—

"Mr. J. H. Hart is Superintendent of the Royal Botanic Gardens in Trinidad. He has sent me a copy of his report presented to the Legislative Council in March, 1893, and has drawn my attention to certain facts contained in it concerning the 'Parasol' ants—the leaf-cutting ants which feed on the fungi developed in masses of the cut leaves carried to their nests. Both Mr. Bates and Mr. Belt described these ants, but described, it seems, different, though nearly allied, species, the habits of which are partially unlike. As they are garden-pests, Mr. Hart was led to examine into the development and social arrangements of these ants; establishing, to that end, artificial nests, after the manner adopted by Sir John Lubbock. Several of the facts set down have an important bearing on a question now under discussion. The following extracts, in which they are named, I abridge by omitting passages not relevant to the issue:—

"'The history of my nests is as follows: Nos. 1 and 2 were both taken (August 9) on the same day, while destroying nests in the Gardens, and were portions of separate nests but of the same species. No. 3 was procured on September 5, and is evidently a different although an allied species to Nos. 1 and 2.

"'Finding neither of my nests had a queen, I procured one from another nest about to be destroyed, and placed it with No. 1 nest. It was received by the workers, and at once attended by a numerous retinue in royal style. On August 30 I removed the queen from No. 1 and placed it with No. 2, when it was again received in a most loyal manner....

"'Ants taken from Nos. 1 and 2 and placed with No. 3 were immediately destroyed by the latter, and even the soldiers of No. 3, as well as workers or nurses, were destroyed when placed with Nos. 1 and 2.

"'In nest No. 2, from which I removed the queen on August 30, there are now in the pupa stage several queens and several males. The forms of ant in nests Nos. 1 and 2 are as follows: (*a*) queen, (*b*) male (both winged, but the queen loses its wings after marital flight), (*c*) large workers, (*d*) small workers, and (*e*) nurses. In nest No. 3 I have not yet seen the queen or male, but it possesses—(*a*) soldier, (*b*) larger workers, (*c*) smaller workers, and (*d*) nurses; but these are different in form to those of nests No. 1 and No. 2. Probably we might add a third form of worker, as there are several sizes in the nest....

"'It is curious that in No. 1 nest, from which the queen was removed on August 30, new queens and males are now being developed, while in No. 2 nest, where the queen is at present, nothing but workers have been brought out, and if a queen larva or pupa is placed there it is at once destroyed, while worker larvæ or pupæ are amicably received. In No. 3 all the eggs, larvæ, and pupæ collected with the nest have been hatched, and no eggs have since made their appearance to date. There is no queen with this nest.... On November 14 I attempted to prove by experiment how small a number of "parasol" ants it required to form a new colony. I placed two dozen of ants (one dozen workers and one dozen nurses) in two separate nests, No. 4 and No. 5. With No. 4 I placed a few larvæ with a few rose petals for them to manipulate. With No. 5 I gave a small piece of nest covered with mycelium. On the 16th these nests were destroyed by small foraging ants, known as the "sugar" or "meat" ant, and I had to remove them and replace with a new colony. My notes on these are not sufficiently lengthy to be of much importance. But I noted four eggs laid on the 16th, or two days after being placed in their new quarters; no queen being present. The experiment is being continued. I may mention that in No. 4 nest, in which no fungus was present, the larvæ of all sizes appeared to change into the pupæ stage at once for want of food [a fact corresponding with the fact I have named as observed by myself sixty years ago in the case of wasp larvæ]. The circumstance tends to show that the development of the insect is influenced entirely by the feeding it gets in the larva stage.

"'In nest No. 2 before the introduction of a queen there were no eggs or larvæ. The first worker was hatched on October 27, or fifty-seven days afterwards, and a continual succession has since been maintained, but as yet (November 19) no males or queens have made their appearance.'

"In a letter accompanying the report, Mr. Hart says:—

"'Since these were published, my notes go to prove that ants can practically manufacture at will, male, female, soldier, worker, or nurse. Some of the workers are capable of laying eggs, and from these can be produced all the various forms as well as from a queen's egg.

"'There does not, however, appear to be any difference in the character of the food; as I cannot find that the larger larvæ are fed with anything different to that given to the smaller.'

"These results were obtained before the recent discussion of the question commenced, and joined with the other evidence entirely dispose of those arguments which Prof. Weismann bases on facts furnished by the social insects."]

The other piece of additional evidence I have referred to, is furnished by two papers contributed to *The Journal of Anatomy and Physiology* for October 1893 and April 1894, by R. Havelock Charles, M. D., &c. &c., Professor of Anatomy in the Medical College, Lahore. These papers set forth the differences between the leg-bones of Europeans and those of the Punjaub people—differences caused by their respective habits of sitting in chairs and squatting on the ground. He enumerates more than twenty such differences, chiefly in the structures of the knee-joint and ankle-joint. From the *résumé* of his second paper I quote the following passages, which sufficiently show the data and the inferences:—

"7. The habits as to sitting postures of Europeans differ from those of their prehistoric ancestors, the Cave-dwellers, &c., who probably squatted on the ground.

"8. The sitting postures of Orientals are the same now as ever. They have retained the habits of their ancestors. The Europeans have not done so.

"9. Want of use would induce changes in form and size, and so, gradually, small differences would be integrated till there would be total disappearance of the markings on the European skeleton, as no advantage would accrue to him from the possession of facets on his bones fitting them for postures not practised by him.

"10. The facets seen on the bones of the Panjabi infant or fœtus have been transmitted to it by the accumulation of peculiarities gained by habit in the evolution of its racial type—in which an acquisition having become a permanent possession, 'profitable to the individual under its conditions of life,' is transmitted as a useful inheritance.

"11. These markings are due to the influence of certain positions, which are brought about by the use of groups of muscles, and they are the definite results produced by actions of these muscles.

"12. The effects of the use of the muscles mentioned in No. 11 are transmitted to the offspring, for the markings are present in the *fœtus-in-utero*, in the child at birth, and in the infant.

"13. The markings are instances of the transmission of acquired characters, which heritage in the individual, function subsequently develops."

No other conclusion appears to me possible. *Panmixia*, even were it not invalidated by its unwarranted assumption as above shown, would be out of court: the case is not a case of either increase or decrease of size but of numerous changes of form. Simultaneous variation of co-operative parts cannot be alleged, since these co-operative parts have not changed in one way but in various ways and degrees. And even were it permissible to suppose that the required different variations had taken place simultaneously, natural selection cannot be supposed to have operated. The assumption would imply that in the struggle for existence, individuals of the European races who were less capable than others of crouching and squatting, gained by those minute changes of structure which incapacitated them, such advantages that their stirps prevailed over other stirps—an absurd supposition.

And now I must once more point out that a grave responsibility rests on biologists in respect of the general question; since wrong answers lead, among other effects, to wrong beliefs about social affairs and to disastrous social actions. In me this conviction has unceasingly strengthened. Though *The Origin of Species* proved to me that the transmission of acquired characters cannot be the sole factor in organic evolution, as I had assumed in *Social Statics* and in *The Principles of Biology*, published in pre-Darwinian days, yet I have never wavered in the belief that it is a factor and an all-important factor. And I have felt more and more that since all the higher sciences are dependent on the science of life, and must have their conclusions vitiated if a fundamental datum given to them by the teachers of this science is erroneous, it behoves these teachers not to let an erroneous datum pass current: they are called on to settle this vexed question one way or other. The times give proof. The work of Mr. Benjamin Kidd on *Social Evolution*, which has been so much lauded, takes Weismannism as one of its data; and if Weismannism be untrue, the conclusions Mr. Kidd draws must be in large measure erroneous and may prove mischievous.

POSTSCRIPT.—Since the foregoing pages have been put in type there has appeared in *Natural Science* for September, an abstract of certain parts of a pamphlet by Professor Oscar Hertwig, setting forth facts directly bearing on Professor Weismann's doctrine respecting the distinction between reproductive cells and somatic cells. In *The Principles of Biology*, § 77, I contended that reproductive cells differ from other cells composing the organism, only in being unspecialized. And in support of the hypothesis that tissue-cells in general have a reproductive potentiality, I instanced the cases of the *Begonia phyllomaniaca* and *Malaxis paludosa.* In the thirty years which have since elapsed, many facts of like significance have been brought to light, and various of these are given by Professor Hertwig. Here are some of them:—

"Galls are produced under the stimulus of the insect almost anywhere on the surface of a plant. Yet in most cases these galls, in a sense grown at random on the surface of a plant, when placed in damp earth will give rise to a young plant. In the hydroid *Tubularia mesembryanthemum*, when the polyp heads are cut off, new heads arise. But if both head and root be cut off, and the upper end be inserted in the mud, then from the original upper end not head-polyps but root filaments will arise, while from the original lower end not root filaments but head-polyps will grow.... Driesch, by separating the first two and the first four segmentation spheres of an *Echinus* ovum, obtained two or four normal plutei, respectively one half and a quarter of the normal size.... So, also, in the case of *Amphioxus*, Wilson obtained a normal, but proportionately diminished embryo with complete nervous system from a separated sphere of a two- or four- or eight celled stage.... Chabry obtained normal embryos in cases where some of the segmentation-spheres had been artificially destroyed."

These evidences, furnished by independent observers, unite in showing, firstly, that all the multiplying cells of the developing embryo are alike; and, secondly, that the soma-cells of the adult severally retain, in a latent form, all the powers of the original embryo-cell. If these facts do not disprove absolutely Professor Weismann's hypothesis, we may wonderingly ask what facts would disprove it?

Since Hertwig holds that all the cells forming an organism of any species primarily consist of the same components, I at first thought that his hypothesis was identical with my own hypothesis of "physiological units," or, as I would now call them, constitutional units. It seems otherwise, however; for he thinks that each cell contains "only those material particles which are bearers of cell-properties," and that organs "are the functions of cell-complexes." To this it may be replied that the ability to form the appropriate cell-complexes, itself depends upon the constitutional units contained in the cells.

APPENDIX C.

THE INHERITANCE OF FUNCTIONALLY-WROUGHT MODIFICATIONS: A SUMMARY.

The assertion that changes of structure caused by changes of function are transmitted to descendants is continually met by the question—Where is the evidence? When some facts are assigned in proof, they are pooh-poohed as insufficient. If after a time the question is raised afresh and other facts are named, there is a like supercilious treatment of them. Successively rejected in this way, the evidences do not accumulate in the minds of opponents; and hence produce little or no effect. When they are brought together, however, it turns out that they are numerous and weighty. We will group them into negative and positive.

* * * * *

Negative evidence is furnished by those cases in which traits otherwise inexplicable are explained if the structural effects of use and disuse are transmitted. In the foregoing chapters and appendices three have been given.

(1) Co-adaptation of co-operative parts comes first. This has been exemplified by the case of enlarged horns in a stag, by the case of an animal led into the habit of leaping, and in the case of the giraffe (cited in "The Factors of Organic Evolution"); and it has been shown that the implied co-adaptations of parts cannot possibly have been effected by natural selection.

(2) The possession of unlike powers of discrimination by different parts of the human skin, was named as a problem to be solved on the hypothesis of natural selection or the hypothesis of panmixia; and it was shown that neither of these can by any twisting yield a solution. But the facts harmonize with the hypothesis that the effects of use are inherited.

(3) Then come the cases of those rudimentary organs which, like the hind limbs of the whale, have nearly disappeared. Dwindling by natural selection is here out of the question; and dwindling by panmixia, even were its assumptions valid, would be incredible. But as a sequence of disuse the change is clearly explained.

Failure to solve any *one* of these three problems would, I think, alone prove the Neo-Darwinian doctrines untenable; and the fact that we have *three* unsolved problems seems to me fatal.

* * * * *

From this negative evidence, turn now to the positive evidence. This falls into several groups.

There are first the facts collected by Mr. Darwin, implying functionally-altered structures in domestic animals. The hypothesis of panmixia is, as we have seen, out of court; and therefore Mr. Darwin's groups of evidences are reinstated. There is the changed ratio of wing-bones and leg-bones in the duck; there are the drooping ears of cats in China, of horses in Russia, of sheep in Italy, of guinea-pigs in Germany, of goats and cattle in India, of rabbits, pigs, and dogs in all long-civilized countries. Though artificial selection has come into play where drooping has become a curious trait (as in rabbits), and has probably caused the greater size of ears which has in some cases gone along with diminished muscular power over them; yet it could not have been the initiator, and has not been operative on animals bred for profit. Again there are the changes produced by climate; as instance, among plants, the several varieties of maize established in Germany and transformed in the course of a few generations.

Facts of another class are yielded by the blind inhabitants of caverns. One who studies the memoir by Mr. Packard on *The Cave Fauna of North America*, &c., will be astonished at the variety of types in which degeneration or loss of the eyes has become a concomitant of life passed in darkness. A great increase in the force of this evidence will be recognized on learning that absence or extreme imperfection of visual organs is found also in creatures living in perpetual night at the bottoms of deep oceans. Endeavours to account for these facts otherwise than by the effects of disuse we have seen to be futile.

Kindred evidence is yielded by decrease of the jaws in those races which have had diminished use of them—mankind and certain domestic animals. Relative smallness in the jaws of civilized men, manifest enough on comparison, has been proved by direct measurement. In pet dogs—pugs, household spaniels—we find associated the same cause with the same effect. Though there has been artificial selection, yet this did not operate until the diminution had become manifest. Moreover there has been diminution of the other structures concerned in biting: there are smaller muscles, feeble zygomata, and diminished areas for insertion of muscles—traits which cannot have resulted from selection, since they are invisible in the living animal.

In abnormal vision produced by abnormal use of the eyes we have evidence of another kind. That the Germans, among whom congenital short sight is notoriously prevalent, have been made shortsighted by inheritance of modifications due to continual reading of print requiring close attention, is by some disputed. It is strange, however, that if there exists no causal connexion between them, neither trait occurs without the other elsewhere. But for the belief that there is a causal connexion we have the verifying testimony of oculists. From Dr. Lindsay Johnson I have cited cases within his professional experience of functionally-produced myopia transmitted to children; and he asserts that other oculists have had like experiences.

Development of the musical faculty in the successive members of families from which the great composers have come, as well as in the civilized races at large, is not to be explained by natural selection. Even when it is great, the musical faculty has not a life-saving efficiency as compared with the average of faculties; for the most highly gifted have commonly passed less prosperous lives and left fewer offspring than have those possessed of ordinary abilities. Still less can it be said that the musical faculty in mankind at large has been developed by survival of the fittest. No one will assert that men in general have been enabled to survive and propagate in proportion as their musical appreciation was great.

The transmission of nervous peculiarities functionally produced is alleged by the highest authorities—Dr. Savage, president of the Neurological Society, and Dr. Hughlings Jackson. The evidence they assign confirms, and is confirmed by, that which the development of the musical faculty above named supplies.

Here, then, we have sundry groups of facts directly supporting the belief that functionally-wrought modifications descend from parents to offspring.

* * * * *

Now let us consider the position of those Darwinians who dissent from Darwin, and who make light of all this evidence. We might naturally suppose that their own hypothesis is unassailable. Yet, strange to say, they admit that there is no direct proof that any species has been established by natural selection. The proof is inferential only.

The certainty of an axiom does not give certainty to the deductions drawn from it. That natural selection is, and always has been, operative is incontestable. Obviously I should be the last person to deny that survival of the fittest is a necessity: its negation is inconceivable. The Neo-Darwinians, however, judging from their attitude, apparently assume that firmness of the basis implies firmness of the superstructure. But however high may be the probability of some of the conclusions drawn, none of them can have more than probability; while some of them remain, and are likely to remain, very questionable. Observe the difficulties.

(1) The general argument proceeds upon the analogy between natural selection and artificial selection. Yet all know that the first cannot do what

the last does. Natural selection can do nothing more than preserve those of which the *aggregate* characters are most favourable to life. It cannot pick out those possessed of one particular favourable character, unless this is of extreme importance.

(2) In many cases a structure is of no service until it has reached a certain development; and it remains to account for that increase of it by natural selection which must be supposed to take place before it reaches the stage of usefulness.

(3) Advantageous variations, not preserved in nature as they are by the breeder, are liable to be swamped by crossing or to disappear by atavism.

Now whatever replies are made, their component propositions cannot be necessary truths. So that the conclusion in each case, however reasonable, cannot claim certainty: the fabric can have no stability like that of its foundation.

When to uncertainties in the arguments supporting the hypothesis we add its inability to explain facts of cardinal significance, as proved above, there is I think ground for asserting that natural selection is less clearly shown to be a factor in the origination of species than is the inheritance of functionally-wrought changes.

* * * * *

If, finally, it is said that the mode in which functionally-wrought changes, especially in small parts, so affect the reproductive elements as to repeat themselves in offspring, cannot be imagined—if it be held inconceivable that those minute changes in the organs of vision which cause myopia can be transmitted through the appropriately-modified sperm-cells or germ-cells; then the reply is that the opposed hypothesis presents a corresponding inconceivability. Grant that the habit of a pointer was produced by selection of those in which an appropriate variation in the nervous system had occurred; it is impossible to imagine how a slightly-different arrangement of a few nerve-cells and fibres could be conveyed by a spermatozoon. So too it is impossible to imagine how in a spermatozoon there can be conveyed the 480,000 independent variables required for the construction of a single peacock's feather, each having a proclivity towards its proper place. Clearly the ultimate process by which inheritance is effected in either case passes comprehension; and in this respect neither hypothesis has an advantage over the other.

APPENDIX D.

ON ALLEGED "SPONTANEOUS GENERATION," AND ON THE HYPOTHESIS OF PHYSIOLOGICAL UNITS.

[*The following letter, originally written for publication in the* North American Review, *but declined by the Editor in pursuance of a general rule, and eventually otherwise published in the United States, I have thought well to append to this first volume of the* Principles of Biology. *I do this because the questions which it discusses are dealt with in this volume; and because the further explanations it furnishes seem needful to prevent misapprehensions.*]

The Editor of the North American Review.

SIR,

It is in most cases unwise to notice adverse criticisms. Either they do not admit of answers or the answers may be left to the penetration of readers. When, however, a critic's allegations touch the fundamental propositions of a book, and especially when they appear in a periodical having the position of the *North American Review*, the case is altered. For these reasons the article on "Philosophical Biology," published in your last number, demands from me an attention which ordinary criticisms do not.

It is the more needful for me to notice it, because its two leading objections have the one an actual fairness and the other an apparent fairness; and in the absence of explanations from me, they will be considered as substantiated even by many, or perhaps most, of those who have read the work itself—much more by those who have not read it. That to prevent the spread of misapprehensions I ought to say something, is further shown by the fact that the same two objections have already been made in England—the one by Dr. Child, of Oxford, in his *Essays on Physiological Subjects*, and the other by a writer in the *Westminster Review* for July, 1865.

* * * * *

In the note to which your reviewer refers, I have, as he says, tacitly repudiated the belief in "spontaneous generation;" and that I have done this in such a way as to leave open the door for the interpretation given by him is true. Indeed the fact that Dr. Child, whose criticism is a sympathetic one, puts the same construction on this note, proves that your reviewer has but drawn what seems to be a necessary inference. Nevertheless, the inference is one which I did not intend to be drawn.

In explanation, let me at the outset remark that I am placed at a disadvantage in having had to omit that part of the System of Philosophy which deals with Inorganic Evolution. In the original programme will be found a parenthetic reference to this omitted part, which should, as there stated, precede the *Principles of Biology*. Two volumes are missing. The closing chapter of the second, were it written, would deal with the evolution of organic matter—the step preceding the evolution of living forms. Habitually carrying with me in thought the contents of this unwritten chapter, I have, in some cases, expressed myself as though the reader had it before him; and have thus rendered some of my statements liable to misconstructions. Apart from this, however, the explanation of the apparent inconsistency is very simple, if not very obvious. In the first place, I do not believe in the "spontaneous generation" commonly alleged, and referred to in the note; and so little have I associated in thought this alleged "spontaneous generation" which I disbelieve, with the generation by evolution which I do believe, that the repudiation of the one never occurred to me as liable to be taken for repudiation of the other. That creatures having *quite specific structures* are evolved in the course of a few hours, without antecedents calculated to determine their specific forms, is to me incredible. Not only the established truths of Biology, but the established truths of science in general, negative the supposition that organisms having structures definite enough to identify them as belonging to known genera and species, can be produced in the absence of germs derived from antecedent organisms of the same genera and species. If there can suddenly be imposed on simple protoplasm the organization which constitutes it a *Paramœcium*, I see no reason why animals of greater complexity, or indeed of any complexity, may not be constituted after the same manner. In brief, I do not accept these alleged facts as exemplifying Evolution, because they imply something immensely beyond that which Evolution, as I understand it, can achieve. In the second place, my disbelief extends not only to the alleged cases of "spontaneous generation," but to every case akin to them. The very conception of spontaneity is wholly incongruous with the conception of Evolution. For this reason I regard as objectionable Mr. Darwin's phrase "spontaneous variation" (as indeed he does himself); and I have sought to show that there are always assignable causes of variation. No form of Evolution, inorganic or organic, can be spontaneous; but in every instance the antecedent forces must be adequate in their quantities, kinds, and distributions, to work the observed effects. Neither the alleged cases of "spontaneous generation," nor any imaginable cases in the least allied to them, fulfil this requirement.

If, accepting these alleged cases of "spontaneous generation," I had assumed, as your reviewer seems to do, that the evolution of organic life commenced in an analogous way; then, indeed, I should have left myself open to a fatal criticism. This supposed "spontaneous generation" habitually occurs in menstrua that contain either organic matter, or matter originally derived from organisms; and such organic matter, proceeding in all known cases from organisms of a higher kind, implies the pre-existence of such higher organisms. By what kind of logic, then, is it inferrible that organic life was initiated after a manner like that in which *Infusoria* are said to be now spontaneously generated? Where, before life commenced, were the superior organisms from which these lowest organisms obtained their organic matter? Without doubting that there are those who, as the reviewer says, "can penetrate deeper than Mr. Spencer has done into the idea of universal evolution," and who, as he contends, prove this by accepting the doctrine of "spontaneous generation"; I nevertheless think that I can penetrate deep enough to see that a tenable hypothesis respecting the origin of organic life must be reached by some other clue than that furnished by experiments on decoction of hay and extract of beef.

From what I do not believe, let me now pass to what I do believe. Granting that the formation of organic matter, and the evolution of life in its lowest forms, may go on under existing cosmical conditions; but believing it more likely that the formation of such matter and such forms, took place at a time when the heat of the Earth's surface was falling through those ranges of temperature at which the higher organic compounds are unstable; I conceive that the moulding of such organic matter into the simplest types, must have commenced with portions of protoplasm more minute, more indefinite, and more inconstant in their characters, than the lowest Rhizopods—less distinguishable from a mere fragment of albumen than even the *Protogenes* of Professor Haeckel. The evolution of specific shapes must, like all other organic evolution, have resulted from the actions and reactions between such incipient types and their environments, and the continued survival of those which happened to have specialities best fitted to the specialities of their environments. To reach by this process the comparatively well-specialized forms of ordinary *Infusoria*, must, I conceive, have taken an enormous period of time.

To prevent, as far as may be, future misapprehension, let me elaborate this conception so as to meet the particular objections raised. The reviewer takes for granted that a "first organism" must be assumed by me, as it is by himself. But the conception of a "first organism," in anything like the current sense of the words, is wholly at variance with conception of evolution; and scarcely less at variance with the facts revealed by the microscope. The lowest living things are not properly speaking organisms at all; for they have no distinctions of parts—no traces of organization. It is almost a misuse of language to call them "forms" of life: not only are their outlines, when distinguishable, too unspecific for description, but they change from moment to moment and are never twice alike, either in two individuals or in the same individual. Even the word "type" is applicable in but a loose way; for there is little constancy in their generic characters: according as the surrounding conditions determine, they undergo transformations now of one kind and now of another. And the vagueness, the inconstancy, the want of appreciable structure, displayed by the simplest of living things as we now see them, are characters (or absences of characters) which, on the hypothesis of Evolution, must have been still more decided when, as at first, no "forms," no "types," no "specific shapes," had been moulded. That "absolute commencement of organic life on the globe," which the reviewer says I "cannot evade the admission of," I distinctly deny. The affirmation of universal evolution is in itself the negation of an "absolute commencement" of anything. Construed in terms of evolution, every kind of being is conceived as a product of modifications wrought by insensible gradations on a pre-existing kind of being; and this holds as fully of the supposed "commencement of organic life" as of all subsequent developments of organic life. It is no more needful to suppose an "absolute commencement of organic life" or a "first organism," than it is needful to suppose an absolute commencement of social life and a first social organism. The assumption of such a necessity in this last case, made by early speculators with their theories of "social contracts" and the like, is disproved by the facts; and the facts, so far as they are ascertained, disprove the assumption of such a necessity in the first case. That organic matter was not produced all at once, but was reached through steps, we are well warranted in believing by the experiences of chemists. Organic matters are produced in the laboratory by what we may literally call *artificial evolution.* Chemists find themselves unable to form these complex combinations directly from their elements; but they succeed in forming them indirectly, by successive modifications of simpler combinations. In some binary compound, one element of which is present in several equivalents, a change is made by substituting for one of these equivalents an equivalent of some other element; so producing a ternary compound. Then another of the equivalents is replaced, and so on. For instance, beginning with ammonia, $N H_3$, a higher form is obtained by replacing one of the atoms of hydrogen by an atom of methyl, so producing methyl-amine, $N (C H_3 H_2)$; and then, under the further action of methyl, ending in a further substitution, there is reached the still more compound substance dimethyl-amine, $N (C H_3) (C H_3) H$. And in this manner highly complex substances are eventually built up. Another characteristic of their method is no less significant. Two complex compounds are employed to generate, by their action upon one another, a compound of still greater complexity: different heterogeneous molecules of one stage, become parents of a molecule a stage higher in heterogeneity. Thus, having built up acetic acid out of its elements, and having by the process of substitution described above, changed the acetic acid into propionic acid, and propionic into butyric, of which the formula is

$$\left\{ \begin{matrix} C(CH_3)(CH_3)H \\ CO(HO) \end{matrix} \right\}$$

this complex compound, by operating on another complex compound, such as the dimethyl-amine named above, generates one of still greater complexity, butyrate of dimethyl-amine

$$\left\{ \begin{matrix} C(CH_3)(CH_3)H \\ CO(HO) \end{matrix} \right\} N(CH_3)(CH_3)H.$$

See, then, the remarkable parallelism. The progress towards higher types of organic molecules is effected by modifications upon modifications; as throughout Evolution in general. Each of these modifications is a change of the molecule into equilibrium with its environment—an adaptation, as it were, to new surrounding conditions to which it is subjected; as throughout Evolution in general. Larger, or more integrated, aggregates (for compound molecules are such) are successively generated; as throughout Evolution in general. More complex or heterogeneous aggregates are so made to arise, one out of another; as throughout Evolution in general. A geometrically-increasing multitude of these larger and more complex aggregates so produced, at the same time results; as throughout Evolution in general. And it is by the action of the successively higher forms on one another, joined with the action of environing conditions, that the highest forms are reached; as throughout Evolution in general.

When we thus see the identity of method at the two extremes—when we see that the general laws of evolution, as they are exemplified in known organisms, have been unconsciously conformed to by chemists in the artificial evolution of organic matter; we can scarcely doubt that these laws were conformed to in the natural evolution of organic matter, and afterwards in the evolution of the simplest organic forms. In the early world, as in the modern laboratory, inferior types of organic substances, by their mutual actions under fit conditions, evolved the superior types of organic substances, ending in organizable protoplasm. And it can hardly be doubted that the shaping of organizable protoplasm, which is a substance modifiable in multitudinous ways with extreme facility, went on after the same manner. As I learn from one of our first chemists, Prof. Frankland, *protein* is capable of existing under probably at least a thousand isomeric forms; and, as we shall presently see, it is capable of forming, with itself and other elements, substances yet more intricate in composition, that are practically infinite in their varieties of kind. Exposed to those innumerable modifications of conditions which the Earth's surface afforded, here in amount of light, there in amount of heat, and elsewhere in the mineral quality of its aqueous medium, this extremely changeable substance must have undergone now one, now another, of its countless metamorphoses. And to the mutual influences of its metamorphic forms under favouring conditions, we may ascribe the production of the still more composite, still more sensitive, still more variously-changeable portions of organic matter, which, in masses more minute and simpler than existing *Protozoa*, displayed actions verging little by little into those called vital—actions which protein itself exhibits in a certain degree, and which the lowest known living things exhibit only in a greater degree. Thus, setting out with inductions from the experiences of organic chemists at the one extreme, and with inductions from the observations of biologists at the other extreme, we are enabled deductively to bridge the interval—are enabled to conceive how organic compounds were evolved, and how, by a continuance of the process, the nascent life displayed in these became gradually more pronounced. And this it is which has to be explained, and which the alleged cases of "spontaneous generation" would not, were they substantiated, help us in the least to explain.

It is thus manifest, I think, that I have not fallen into the alleged inconsistency. Nevertheless, I admit that your reviewer was justified in inferring this inconsistency; and I take blame to myself for not having seen that the statement, as I have left it, is open to misconstruction.

* * * * *

I pass now to the second allegation—that in ascribing to certain specific molecules, which I have called "physiological units," the aptitude to build themselves into the structure of the organism to which they are peculiar, I have abandoned my own principle, and have assumed something beyond the re-distribution of Matter and Motion. As put by the reviewer, his case appears to be well made out; and that he is not altogether unwarranted in so putting it, may be admitted. Nevertheless, there does not in reality exist the supposed incongruity.

Before attempting to make clear the adequacy of the conception which I am said to have tacitly abandoned as insufficient, let me remove that excess of improbability the reviewer gives to it, by the extremely-restricted meaning with which he uses the word mechanical. In discussing a proposition of mine he says:—

"He then cites certain remarks of Mr. Paget on the permanent effects wrought in the blood by the poison of scarlatina and small-pox, as justifying the belief that such a 'power' exists, and attributes the repair of a wasted tissue to 'forces analogous to those by which a crystal reproduces its lost apex.' (Neither of which phenomena, however, is explicable by mechanical causes.)"

Were it not for the deliberation with which this last statement is made, I should take it for a slip of the pen. As it is, however, I have no course left but to suppose the reviewer unaware of the fact that molecular actions of all kinds are now not only conceived as mechanical actions, but that calculations based on this conception of them, bring out the results that correspond with observation. There is no kind of re-arrangement among molecules (crystallization being one) which the modern physicist does not think of. and correctly reason upon, in terms of forces and motions like those of sensible masses. Polarity is regarded as a resultant of such forces and motions; and when, as happens in many cases, light changes the molecular structure of a crystal, and alters its polarity, it does this by impressing, in conformity with mechanical laws, new motions on the constituent molecules. That the reviewer should present the mechanical conception under so extremely limited a form, is the more surprising to me because, at the outset of the very work he reviews, I have, in various passages, based inferences on those immense extensions of it which he ignores; indicating, for example, the interpretation it yields of the inorganic chemical changes effected by heat, and the organic chemical changes effected by light (*Principles of Biology*, § 13).

Premising, then, that the ordinary idea of mechanical action must be greatly expanded, let us enter upon the question at issue—the sufficiency of the hypothesis that the structure of each organism is determined by the polarities of the special molecules, or physiological units, peculiar to it as a species, which necessitate tendencies towards special arrangements. My proposition and the reviewer's criticism upon it, will be most conveniently presented if I quote in full a passage of his from which I have already extracted some expressions. He says:—

"It will be noticed, however, that Mr. Spencer attributes the possession of these 'tendencies,' or 'proclivities,' to natural inheritance from ancestral organisms; and it may be argued that he thus saves the mechanist theory and his own consistency at the same time, inasmuch as he derives even the 'tendencies' themselves ultimately from the environment. To this we reply, that Mr. Spencer, who advocates the nebular hypothesis, cannot evade the admission of an absolute commencement of organic life on the globe, and that the 'formative tendencies,' without which he cannot explain the evolution of a single individual, could not have been inherited by the first organism. Besides, by his virtual denial of spontaneous generation, he denies that the first organism was evolved out of the inorganic world, and thus shuts himself off from the argument (otherwise plausible) that its 'tendencies' were ultimately derived from the environment."

This assertion is already in great measure disposed of by what has been said above. Holding that, though not "spontaneously generated," those minute portions of protoplasm which first displayed in the feeblest degree that changeability taken to imply life, were evolved, I am *not* debarred from the argument that the "tendencies" of the physiological units are derived from the inherited effects of environing actions. If the conception of a "first organism" were a necessary one, the reviewer's objection would be valid. If there were an "absolute commencement" of life, a definite line parting organic matter from the simplest living forms, I should be placed in the predicament he describes. But as the doctrine of Evolution itself tacitly negatives any such distinct separation; and as the negation is the more confirmed by the facts the more we know of them; I do not feel that I am entangled in the alleged difficulty. My reply might end here; but as the hypothesis in question is one not easily conceived, and very apt to be misunderstood, I will attempt a further elucidation of it.

Much evidence now conspires to show that molecules of the substances we call elementary are in reality compound; and that, by the combination of these with one another, and re-combinations of the products, there are formed systems of systems of molecules, unimaginable in their complexity. Step by step as the aggregate molecules so resulting, grow larger and increase in heterogeneity, they become more unstable, more readily transformable by small forces, more capable of assuming various characters. Those composing organic matter transcend all others in size and intricacy of structure; and in them these resulting traits reach their extreme. As implied by its name *protein*, the essential substance of which organisms are built, is remarkable alike for the variety of its metamorphoses and the facility with which it undergoes them: it changes from one to another of its thousand isomeric forms on the slightest change of conditions. Now there are facts warranting the belief that though these multitudinous isomeric forms of protein will not unite directly with one another, yet they admit of being linked together by other elements with which they combine. And it is very significant that there are habitually present two other elements, sulphur and phosphorus, which have quite special powers of holding together many equivalents—the one being pentatomic and the other hexatomic. So that it is a legitimate supposition (justified by analogies) that an atom of sulphur may be a bond of union among half-a-dozen different isomeric forms of protein; and similarly with phosphorus. A moment's thought will show that, setting out with the thousand isomeric forms of protein, this makes possible a number of these combinations almost passing the power of figures to express. Molecules so produced, perhaps exceeding in size and complexity those of protein as those of protein exceed those of inorganic matter, may, I conceive, be the special units belonging to special kinds of organisms. By their constitution they must have a plasticity, or sensitiveness to modifying forces, far beyond that of protein; and bearing in mind not only that their varieties are practically infinite in number, but that closely allied forms of them, chemically indifferent to one another as they must be, may coexist in the same aggregate, we shall see that they are fitted for entering into unlimited varieties of organic structures.

The existence of such physiological units, peculiar to each species of organism, is not unaccounted for. They are evolved simultaneously with the evolution of the organisms they compose—they differentiate as fast as these organisms differentiate; and are made multitudinous in kind by the same actions which make the organism they compose multitudinous, in kind. This conception is clearly representable in terms of the mechanical hypothesis. Every physicist will endorse the proposition that in each aggregate there tends to establish itself an equilibrium between the forces exercised by all the units upon each and by each upon all. Even in masses of substance so rigid as iron and glass, there goes on a molecular re-arrangement, slow or rapid according as circumstances facilitate, which ends only when there is a complete balance between the actions of the parts on the whole and the actions of the whole on the parts: the implications being that every change in the form or size of the whole, necessitates some redistribution of the parts. And though in cases like these, there occurs only a polar re-arrangement of the molecules, without changes in the molecules themselves; yet where, as often happens, there is a passage from the colloid to the crystalloid state, a change of constitution occurs in the molecules themselves. These truths are not limited to inorganic matter: they unquestionably hold of organic matter. As certainly as molecules of alum have a form of equilibrium, the octahedron, into which they fall when the temperature of their solvent allows them to aggregate, so certainly must organic molecules of each kind, no matter how complex, have a form of equilibrium in which, when they aggregate, their complex forces are balanced—a form far less rigid and definite, for the reason that they have far less definite polarities, are far more unstable, and have their tendencies more easily modified by environing conditions. Equally certain is it that the special molecules having a special organic structure as their form of equilibrium, must be reacted upon by the total forces of this organic structure; and that, if environing actions lead to any change in this organic structure, these special molecules, or physiological units, subject to a changed distribution of the total forces acting upon them will undergo modification—modification which their extreme plasticity will render easy. By this action and reaction I conceive the physiological units peculiar to each kind of organism, to have been moulded along with the organism itself. Setting out with the stage in which protein in minute aggregates, took on those simplest differentiations which fitted it for differently-conditioned parts of its medium, there must have unceasingly gone on perpetual re-adjustments of balance between aggregates and their units—actions and reactions of the two, in which the units tended ever to establish the typical form produced by actions and reactions in all antecedent generations, while the aggregate, if changed in form by change of surrounding conditions, tended ever to impress on the units a corresponding change of polarity, causing them in the next generation to reproduce the changed form—their new form of equilibrium.

This is the conception which I have sought to convey, though it seems unsuccessfully, in the *Principles of Biology*; and which I have there used to interpret the many involved and mysterious phenomena of Genesis, Heredity, and Variation. In one respect only am I conscious of having so inadequately explained myself, as to give occasion for a misinterpretation—the one made by the *Westminster* reviewer above referred to. By him, as by your own critic, it is alleged that in the idea of "inherent tendencies" I have introduced, under a disguise, the conception of "the archæus, vital principle, *nisus formativus*, and so on." This allegation is in part answered by the foregoing explanation. That which I have here to add, and did not adequately explain in the *Principles of Biology*, is that the proclivity of units of each order towards the specific arrangement seen in the organism they form, is not to be understood as resulting from their own structures and actions only; but as the product of these and the environing forces to which they are exposed. Organic evolution takes place only on condition that the masses of protoplasm formed of the physiological units, and of the assimilable materials out of which others like themselves are to be multiplied, are subject to heat of a given degree—are subject, that is, to the unceasing impacts of undulations of a certain strength and period; and, within limits, the rapidity with which the physiological units pass from their indefinite arrangement to the definite arrangement they presently assume, is proportionate to the strengths of the ethereal undulations falling upon them. In its complete form, then, the conception is that these specific molecules, having the immense complexity above described, and having correspondently complex polarities which cannot be mutually balanced by any simple form of aggregation, have, for the form of aggregation in which all their forces are equilibrated, the structure of the adult organism to which they belong; and that they are compelled to fall into this structure by the co-operation of the environing forces acting on them, and the forces they exercise on one another—the environing forces being the source of the *power* which effects the re-arrangement, and the polarities of the molecules determining the *direction* in which that power is turned. Into this conception there enters no trace of the hypothesis of an "archæus or vital principle;" and the principles of molecular physics fully justify it.

It is, however, objected that "the living body in its development presents a long succession of *differing* forms; a continued series of changes for the whole length of which, according to Mr. Spencer's hypothesis, the physiological units must have an 'inherent tendency.' Could we more truly say of anything, 'it is unrepresentable in thought?'" I reply that if there is taken into account an element here overlooked, the process will not be found "unrepresentable in thought." This is the element of size or mass. To satisfy or balance the polarities of each order of physiological units, not only a certain structure of organism, but a certain size of organism is needed; for the complexities of that adult structure in which the physiological units are equilibrated, cannot be represented within the small bulk of the embryo. In many minute organisms, where the whole mass of physiological units required for the structure is present, the very thing *does* take place which it is above implied *ought* to take place. The mass builds itself directly into the complete form. This is so with *Acari*, and among the nematoid *Entozoa*. But among higher animals such direct transformations cannot happen. The mass of physiological units required to produce the size as well as the structure that approximately equilibrates them, is not all present, but has to be formed by successive additions—additions which in viviparous animals are made by absorbing, and transforming into these special molecules, the organizable materials directly supplied by the parent, and which in oviparous animals are made by doing the like with the organizable materials in the "food-yelk," deposited by the parent in the same envelope with the germ. Hence it results that, under such conditions, the physiological units which first aggregate into the rudiment of the future organism, do not form a structure like that of the adult organism, which, when of such small dimensions, does not equilibrate them. They distribute themselves so as partly to satisfy the chief among their complex polarities. The vaguely-differentiated mass thus produced cannot, however, be in equilibrium. Each increment of physiological units formed and integrated by it, changes the distribution of forces; and this has a double effect. It tends to modify the differentiations already made, bringing them a step nearer to the equilibrating structure; and the physiological units next integrated, being brought under the aggregate of polar forces exercised by the whole mass, which now approaches a step nearer to that ultimate distribution of polar forces which exists in the adult organism, are coerced more directly into the typical structure. Thus there is necessitated a series of compromises. Each successive form assumed is unstable and transitional: approach to the typical structure going on hand in hand with approach to the typical bulk.

Possibly I have not succeeded by this explanation, any more than by the original explanation, in making this process "representable in thought." It is manifestly untrue, however, that I have, as alleged, re-introduced under a disguise the conception of a "vital principle." That I interpret embryonic development in terms of Matter and Motion, cannot, I think, be questioned. Whether the interpretation is adequate, must be a matter of opinion; but it is clearly a matter of fact, that I have not fallen into the inconsistency asserted by your reviewer. At the same time I willingly admit that, in the absence of certain statements which I have now supplied, he was not unwarranted in representing my conception in the way that he has done.

NOTES

[1]

Gross misrepresentations of this statement, which have been from time to time made, oblige me, much against my will, to add here an explanation of it. The last of these perversions, uttered in a lecture delivered at Belfast by the Rev. Professor Watts, D.D., is reported in the *Belfast Witness* of December 18, 1874; just while a third impression of this work is being printed from the plates. The report commences as follows:—"Dr. Watts, after showing that on his own confession Spencer was indebted for his facts to Huxley and Hooker, who," &c., &c.

Wishing in this, as in other cases, to acknowledge indebtedness when conscious of it, I introduced the words referred to, in recognition of the fact that I had repeatedly questioned the distinguished specialists named, on matters beyond my knowledge, which were not dealt with in the books at my command. Forgetting the habits of antagonists, and especially theological antagonists, it never occurred to me that my expression of thanks to my friends for "information where my own was deficient," would be turned into the sweeping statement that I was indebted to them for my facts.

Had Professor Watts looked at the preface to the second volume (the two having been published separately, as the prefaces imply), he would have seen a second expression of my indebtedness "for their valuable criticisms, and for the trouble they have taken in *checking* the numerous statements of fact on which the arguments proceed"—no further indebtedness being named. A moment's comparison of the two volumes in respect of their accumulations of facts, would have shown him what kind of warrant there was for his interpretation.

Doubtless the Rev. Professor was prompted to make this assertion by the desire to discredit the work he was attacking; and having so good an end in view, thought it needless to be particular about the means. In the art of dealing with the language of opponents, Dr. Watts might give lessons to Monsignor Capel and Archbishop Manning.

December 28th, 1874.

[2]

In this passage as originally written (in 1862) they were described as incondensible; since, though reduced to the density of liquids, they had not been liquefied.

[3]

Here and hereafter the word "atom" signifies a unit of something classed as an element, because thus far undecomposed by us. The word must not be supposed to mean that which its derivation implies. In all probability it is not a simple unit but a compound one.

[4]

The name hydro-carbons was here used when these pages were written, thirty-four years ago. It was the name then current. In this case, as in multitudinous other cases, the substitution of newer words and phrases for older ones, is somewhat misleading. Putting the thoughts of 1862 in the language of 1897 gives an illusive impression of recency.

[5]

It will perhaps seem strange to class oxygen as a crystalloid. But inasmuch as the crystalloids are distinguished from the colloids by their atomic simplicity, and inasmuch as sundry gases are reducible to a crystalline state, we are justified in so classing it.

[6]

The remark made by a critic to the effect that in a mammal higher temperature diminishes the rate of molecular change in the tissues, leads me to add that the exhalation I have alleged is prevented if the heat rises above the range of variation normal to the organism; since, then, unusually rapid pulsations with consequent inefficient propulsion of the blood, cause a diminished rate of circulation. To produce the effect referred to in the text, heat must be associated with dryness; for otherwise evaporation is not aided. General evidence supporting the statement I have made is furnished by the fact that the hot and dry air of the eastern deserts is extremely invigorating; by the fact that all the energetic and conquering races of men have come from the hot and dry regions marked on the maps as rainless; and by the fact that travellers in Africa comment on the contrast between the inhabitants of the hot and dry regions (relatively elevated) and those of the hot and moist regions: active and inert respectively.

[7]

The increase of respiration found to result from the presence of light, is probably an *indirect* effect. It is most likely due to the reception of more vivid impressions through the eyes, and to the consequent nervous stimulation. Bright light is associated in our experience with many of our greatest outdoor pleasures, and its presence partially arouses the consciousness of them, with the concomitant raised vital functions.

[8]

To exclude confusion it may be well here to say that the word "atom" is, as before explained, used as the name for a unit of a substance at present undecomposed; while the word "molecule" is used as the name for a unit of a substance known to be compound.

[9]

On now returning to the subject after many years, I meet with some evidence recently assigned, in a paper read before the Royal Society by Mr. J. W. Pickering, D.Sc. (detailing results harmonizing with those obtained by Prof. Grimaux), showing clearly how important an agent in vital actions is this production of isomeric changes by slight changes of conditions. Certain artificially produced substances, simulating proteids in other of their characters and reactions, were found to simulate them in coagulability by trifling disturbances. "In the presence of a *trace of neutral salt* they coagulate on heating at temperatures very similar to proteid solutions." And it is shown that by one of these factitious organic colloids a like effect is produced in coagulating the blood, to that "produced by the intravenous injection of a nucleoproteid."

[10]

After this long interval during which other subjects have occupied me, I now find that the current view is similar to the view above set forth, in so far that a small molecular disturbance is supposed suddenly to initiate a great one, producing a change compared to an explosion. But while, of two proposed interpretations, one is that the fuse is nitrogenous and the charge a carbo-hydrate, the other is that both are nitrogenous. The relative probabilities of these alternative views will be considered in a subsequent chapter.

[11]

When writing this passage I omitted to observe the verification yielded of the conclusion contained in § 15 concerning the part played in the vital processes by the nitrogenous compounds. For these vegeto-alkalies, minute quantities of which produce such great effects in exalting the functions (*e.*

g., a sixteenth of a grain of strychnia is a dose), are all nitrogenous bodies, and, by implication, relatively unstable bodies. The small amounts of molecular change which take place in these small quantities of the vegeto-alkalies when diffused through the system, initiate larger amounts of molecular change in the nitrogenous elements of the tissues.

But the evidence furnished a generation ago by these vegeto-alkalies has been greatly reinforced by far more striking evidence furnished by other nitrogenous compounds—the various explosives. These, at the same time that they produce by their sudden decompositions violent effects outside the organism, also produce violent effects inside it: a hundredth of a grain of nitro-glycerine being a sufficient dose. Investigations made by Dr. J. B. Bradbury, and described by him in the Bradshaw Lecture on "Some New Vaso-Dilators" (see *The Lancet*, Nov. 16, 1895), details the effects of kindred bodies—methyl-nitrate, glycol-dinitrate, erythrol-tetranitrate. The first two, in common with nitro-glycerine, are stable only when cool and in the dark—sunlight or warmth decomposes them, and they explode by rapid heating or percussion. The fact which concerns us here is that the least stable—glycol-dinitrate—has the most powerful and rapid physiological effect, which is proportionately transient. In one minute the blood-pressure is reduced by one-fourth and in four minutes by nearly two-thirds: an effect which is dissipated in a quarter of an hour. So that this excessively unstable compound, decomposing in the body in a very short time, produces within that short time a vast amount of molecular change: acting, as it seems, not through the nervous system, but directly on the blood-vessels.

[12]

This interpretation is said to be disproved by the fact that the carbo-hydrate contained in muscle amounts to only about 1.5 of the total solids. I do not see how this statement is to be reconciled with the statement cited three pages back from Professor Michael Foster, that the deposits of glycogen contained in the liver and in the muscles may be compared to the deposits in a central bank and branch banks.

[13]

Before leaving the topic let me remark that the doctrine of metabolism is at present in its inchoate stage, and that the prevailing conclusions should be held tentatively. As showing this need an anomalous fact may be named. It was long held that gelatine is of small value as food, and though it is now recognized as valuable because serving the same purposes as fats and carbo-hydrates, it is still held to be valueless for structural purposes (save for some inactive tissue); and this estimate agrees with the fact that it is a relatively stable nitrogenous compound, and therefore unfit for those functions performed by unstable nitrogenous compounds in the muscular and other tissues. But if this is true, it seems a necessary implication that such substances as hair, wool, feathers, and all dermal growths chemically akin to gelatine, and even more stable, ought to be equally innutritive or more innutritive. In that case, however, what are we to say of the larva of the clothes-moth, which subsists exclusively on one or other of these substances, and out of it forms all those unstable nitrogenous compounds needful for carrying on its life and developing its tissues? Or again, how are we to understand the nutrition of the book-worm, which, in the time-stained leaves through which it burrows, finds no proteid save that contained in the dried-up size, which is a form of gelatine; or, once more, in what form is the requisite amount of nitrogenous substance obtained by the coleopterous larva which eats holes in wood a century old?

[14]

This chapter and the following two chapters originally appeared in Part III of the original edition of the *Principles of Psychology* (1855): forming a preliminary which, though indispensable to the argument there developed, was somewhat parenthetical. Having now to deal with the general science of Biology before the more special one of Psychology, it becomes possible to transfer these chapters to their proper place.

[15]

See *Westminster Review* for April, 1852.—Art. IV. "A Theory of Population." See Appendix A.

[16]

This paragraph replaces a sentence that, in *The Principles of Psychology*, referred to a preceding chapter on "Method;" in which the mode of procedure here indicated was set forth as a mode to be systematically pursued in the choice of hypotheses. This chapter on Method is now included, along with other matter, in a volume entitled *Various Fragments*.

[17]

Speaking of "the general idea of *life*" M. Comte says:—"Cette idée suppose, en effet, non-seulement celle d'un être organisé de manière à comporter l'état vital, mais aussi celle, non moins indispensable, d'un certain ensemble d'influences extérieures propres à son accomplissement. Une telle harmonie entre l'être vivant et le *milieu* correspondant, caractérise evidemment la condition fondamentale de la vie." Commenting on de Blainville's definition of life, which he adopts, he says:—"Cette lumineuse définition ne me paraît laisser rien d'important à désirer, si ce n'est une indication plus directe et plus explicite de ces deux conditions fondamentales co-relatives, nécessairement inséparables de l'état vivant, un *organisme* déterminé et un *milieu* convenable." It is strange that M. Comte should have thus recognized the necessity of a harmony between an organism and its environment, as a *condition* essential to life, and should not have seen that the continuous maintenance of such inner actions as will counterbalance outer actions, *constitutes* life.

[When the original edition was published Dr. J. H. Bridges wrote to me saying that in the *Politique Positive*, Comte had developed his conception further. On p. 413, denying "le prétendu antagonisme des corps vivants envers leurs milieux inorganiques," he says "au lieu de ce conflit, on a reconnu bientôt que cette relation nécessaire constitue une condition fondamentale de la vie réelle, dont la notion systématique consiste dans une intime conciliation permanente entre la spontanéité intérieure et la fatalité extérieure." Still, this "conciliation *permanente*" seems to be a "*condition*" to life; not that varying adjustment of changes which life consists in maintaining. In presence of an ambiguity, the interpretation which agrees with his previous statement must be chosen.]

[18]

In further elucidation of this general doctrine, see *First Principles*, § 25.

[19]

In ordinary speech Development is often used as synonymous with Growth. It hence seems needful to say that Development as here and hereafter used, means *increase of structure* and not *increase of bulk*. It may be added that the word Evolution, comprehending growth as well as Development, is to be reserved for occasions when both are implied.

[20]

This paragraph originally formed part of a review-article on "Transcendental Physiology," published in 1857.

[21]

When, in 1863, the preceding chapter was written, it had not occurred to me that there needed an accompanying chapter treating of Structure. The gap left by that oversight I now fill up. In doing this there have been included certain statements which are tacitly presupposed in the last chapter, and there may also be some which overlap statements in the next chapter. I have not thought it needful so to alter adjacent chapters as to remove these slight defects: the duplicated ideas will bear re-emphasizing.

[22]

In connexion with this matter I add here a statement made by Prof. Foster which it is difficult to understand: "Indeed it has been observed that a dormouse actually gained in weight during a hybernating period; it discharged during this period neither urine nor fæces, and the gain in weight was the excess of oxygen taken in over the carbonic acid given out." (*Text-book of Physiology*, 6th ed., Part II, page 859.)

[23]

In the account of James Mitchell, a boy born blind and deaf, given by James Wardrop, F.R.S. (Edin. 1813), it is said that he acquired a "preternatural acuteness of touch and smell." The deaf Dr. Kitto described himself as having an extremely strong visual memory: he retained "a clear impression or image of everything at which he ever looked."

[24]

Here, as in sundry places throughout this chapter, the necessities of the argument have obliged me to forestall myself, by assuming the conclusion reached in a subsequent chapter, that modifications of structure produced by modifications of function are transmitted to offspring.

[25]

Whether the *Volvox* is to be classed as animal or vegetal is a matter of dispute; but its similarity to the blastula stage of many animals warrants the claim of the zoologists.

[26]

While the proof was in my hands there was published in *Science Progress* an essay by Dr. T. G. Brodie on "The Phosphorus-containing Substances of the Cell." In this essay it is pointed out that "nucleic acid is particularly characterized by its instability.... In the process of purification it is extremely liable to decompose, with the result that it loses a considerable part of its phosphorus. In the second place it is most easily split up in another manner in which it loses a considerable part of its nitrogen.... To avoid the latter source of error he [Miescher] found that it was necessary to keep the temperature of all solutions down to 0°C., the whole time of the preparation." These facts tend strongly to verify the hypothesis that the nucleus is a source of perpetual molecular disturbance—not a regulating centre but a stimulating centre.

[27]

The writing of the above section reminded me of certain allied views which I ventured to suggest nearly 50 years ago. They are contained in the *Westminster Review* for April, 1852, in an article entitled "A Theory of Population deduced from the General Law of Animal Fertility." It is there suggested that the "spermatozoon is essentially a neural element, and the ovum essentially a hæmal element," or, as otherwise stated, that the "sperm-cell is co-ordinating matter and the germ-cell matter to be co-ordinated" (pp. 490-493). And along with this proposition there is given some chemical evidence tending to support it. Now if, in place of "neural" and "hæmal," we say—the element that is most highly phosphorized and the element that is phosphorized in a much smaller degree; or if, in place of co-ordinating matter and matter to be co-ordinated, we say—the matter which initiates action and the matter which is made to act; there is disclosed a kinship between this early view and the view just set forth. In the last part of this work, "Laws of Multiplication," which is developed from the essay referred to, I left out the portion containing the quoted sentences, and the evidence supporting the conclusion drawn. Partly I omitted them because the speculation did not form an essential link in the general argument, and partly because I did not see how the suggested interpretation could hold of plants as well as of animals. If, however, the alleged greater staining capacity of the male generative nucleus in plants implies, as in other cases, that the male cell has a larger proportion of the phosphorized matter than the other elements concerned, then the difficulty disappears.

As, along with the idea just named, the dropped portion of the original essay contains other ideas which seem to me worth preserving, I have thought it as well to reproduce it, in company with the chief part of the general argument as at first sketched out. It will be found in Appendix A to this volume.

[28]

Unfortunately the word *heterogenesis* has been already used as a synonym for "spontaneous generation." Save by those few who believe in "spontaneous generation," however, little objection will be felt to using the word in a sense that seems much more appropriate. The meaning above given to it covers both Metagenesis and Parthenogenesis.

[29]

Prof. Huxley avoids this difficulty by making every kind of Genesis a mode of development. His classification, which suggested the one given above, is as follows:—

Development	Continuous	Growth
		Metamorphosis

			Metagenesis
Discontinuous	{	Agamogenesis	{
			Parthenogenesis
		Gamogenesis	

[30]

The implication is that an essentially similar process occurs in those fragments of leaves used for artificial propagation. Besides the Begonias in general, I learn that various other plants are thus multiplied—Citron and orange trees, *Hoya carnosa*, *Aucuba japonica*, *Clianthus puniceus*, etc., etc. *Bryophyllum calicinum*, *Rochea falcata*, and *Echeveria*. I also learn that the following plants, among others, produce buds from their foliage leaves:—*Cardamine pratensis*, *Nasturtium officinale*, *Roripa palustris*, *Brassica oleracea*, *Arabis pumila*, *Chelidonium majus*, *Nymphæa guianensis*, *Episcia bicolor*, *Chirita sivensis*, *Pinguicula Backeri*, *Allium*, *Gagea*, *Tolmia*, *Fritillaria*, *Ornithogalum*, etc. In *Cardamine* and several others, a complete miniature plant is at once produced; in other cases bulbils or similar detachable buds.

[31]

Among various examples I have observed, the most remarkable were among Foxgloves, growing in great numbers and of large size, in a wood between Whatstandwell Bridge and Crich, in Derbyshire. In one case the lowest flower on the stem contained, in place of a pistil, a shoot or spike of flower-buds, similar in structure to the embryo-buds of the main spike. I counted seventeen buds on it; of which the first had three stamens, but was otherwise normal; the second had three; the third, four; the fourth, four; &c. Another plant, having more varied monstrosities, evinced excess of nutrition with equal clearness. The following are the notes I took of its structure:—1st, or lowest flower on the stem, very large; calyx containing eight divisions, one partly transformed into a corolla, and another transformed into a small bud with bract (this bud consisted of a five-cleft calyx, four sessile anthers, a pistil, and a rudimentary corolla); the corolla of the main flower, which was complete, contained six stamens, three of them bearing anthers, two others being flattened and coloured, and one rudimentary; there was no pistil but, *in place of it*, a large bud, consisting of a three-cleft calyx of which two divisions were tinted at the ends, an imperfect corolla marked internally with the usual purple spots and hairs, three anthers sessile on this mal-formed corolla, a pistil, a seed vessel with ovules, and, growing to it, another bud of which the structure was indistinct. 2nd flower, large; calyx of seven divisions, one being transformed into a bud with bract, but much smaller than the other; corolla large but cleft along the top; six stamens with anthers, pistil, and seed-vessel. 3rd flower, large; six-cleft calyx, cleft corolla, with six stamens, pistil, and seed-vessel, with a second pistil half unfolded at its apex. 4th flower, large; divided along the top, six stamens. 5th flower, large; corolla divided into three parts, six stamens. 6th flower, large; corolla cleft, calyx six cleft, the rest of the flower normal. 7th, and all succeeding flowers, normal.

While this chapter is under revision, another noteworthy illustration has been furnished to me by a wall-trained pear tree which was covered in the spring by luxuriant "foreright" shoots. As I learned from the gardener, it was pruned just as the fruit was setting. A large excess of sap was thus thrown into other branches, with the result that in a number of them the young pears were made monstrous by reversion. In some cases, instead of the dried up sepals at the top of the pear, there were produced good sized leaves; and in other cases the seed-bearing core of the pear was transformed into a growth which protruded through the top of the pear in the shape of a new shoot.

[32]

In partial verification, Mr. Tansley writes:—"Prof. Klebs of Basel has shown that in *Hydrodictyon*, gametes can only be produced by the cells of a net when these are above a certain size and age; and then only under conditions unfavourable to growth, such as a feeble light or poverty of nutritive inorganic salts or absence of oxygen, or a low temperature in the water containing the plant. The presence of organic substances, especially sugar, also acts as a stimulus to the formation of gametes, and this is also the case in *Vaucheria*. Many other *Algæ* produce gametes mainly at the end of the vegetative season, when food is certainly difficult to obtain in their natural habitat, and we may well suppose that their assimilative power is waning. Where, however, as is the case in *Vaucheria*, the plant depends for propagation mainly on the production of fertilized eggs, we find the sexual organs often produced in conditions very favourable to vegetative growth, in opposition to those cases such as *Hydrodictyon*, where the chief means of propagation is by zoospores. So that side by side with, and to some extent obscuring, the principle developed above we have a clear adaptation of the production of reproductive cells to the special circumstances of the case."

[33]

This establishment by survival of the fittest of reproductive processes adapted to variable conditions, is indirectly elucidated by the habits of salmon. As salmon thrive in the sea and fall out of condition in fresh water (having during their sea-life not exercised the art of catching fresh-water prey), the implication is that the species would profit if all individuals ran up the rivers just before spawning time in November. Why then do most of them run up during many preceding months? Contemplation of the difficulties which lie in the way to the spawning grounds, will, I think, suggest an explanation. There are falls to be leaped and shallow rapids to be ascended. These obstacles cannot be surmounted when the river is low. A fish which starts early in the season has more chances of getting up the falls and the rapids than one which starts later; and, out of condition as it will be, may spawn, though not well. On the other hand, one which starts in October, if floods occur appropriately, may reach the upper waters and then spawn to great advantage; but in the absence of adequate rains it may fail altogether to reach the spawning grounds. Hence the species profits by an irregularity of habits adapted to meet irregular contingencies.

[34]

I owe to Mr. (now Sir John) Lubbock an important confirmation of this view. After stating his belief that between Crustaceans and Insects there exists a physiological relation analogous to that which exists between water vertebrata and land-vertebrata, he pointed out to me that while among Insects there is a definite limit of growth, and an accompanying definite commencement of reproduction, among Crustaceans, where growth has no definite limit, there is no definite relation between the commencement of reproduction and the decrease or arrest of growth.

[35]

While this chapter is passing through the press, I learn from Mr. White Cooper, that not only are near sight, long sight, dull sight, and squinting, hereditary; but that a peculiarity of vision confined to one eye is frequently transmitted: re-appearing in the same eye in offspring.

[36]

An instance here occurs of the way in which those who are averse to a conclusion will assign the most flimsy reasons for rejecting it. Rather than admit that the eyes of these creatures living in darkness have disappeared from lack of use, some contend that such creatures would be liable to have their eyes injured by collisions with objects, and that therefore natural selection would favour those individuals in which the eyes had somewhat diminished and were least liable to injury: the implication being that the immunity from the inflammations due to injuries would be so important a factor in life as to cause survival. And this is argued in presence of the fact that one of the most conspicuous among these blind cave-animals is a cray-fish, and that the cray-fish in its natural habitat is in the habit of burrowing in the banks of rivers holes a foot or more deep, and has its eyes exposed to all those possible blows and frictions which the burrowing involves!

[37]

In addition to the numerous illustrations given by Mr. Sedgwick, here is one which Colonel A. T. Fraser published in *Nature* for Nov. 9, 1893, concerning two Hindoo dwarfs:—"In speech and intelligence the dwarfs were indistinguishable from ordinary natives of India. From an interrogation of one of them, it appeared that he belonged to a family all the male members of which have been dwarfs for several generations. They marry ordinary native girls, and the female children grow up like those of other people. The males, however, though they develop at the normal rate until they reach the age of six, then cease to grow, and become dwarfs."

[38]

This remarkable case appears to militate against the conclusion, drawn a few pages back, that the increase of a peculiarity by coincidence of "spontaneous variations" in successive generations, is very improbable; and that the special superiorities of musical composers cannot have thus arisen. The reply is that the extreme frequency of the occurrence among so narrow a class as that of musical composers, forbids the interpretation thus suggested.

[39]

I omitted to name here a cause which may be still more potent in producing irregularity in the results of cousin-marriages. So far as I can learn, no attempt has been made to distinguish between such results as arise when the related parents from whom the cousins descend are of the same sex and those which arise when they are of different sexes. In the one case two sisters have children who intermarry; and in the other case a brother and a sister have children who intermarry. The marriages of cousins in these two cases may be quite dissimilar in their results. If there is a tendency to limitation of heredity by sex—if daughters usually inherit more from the mother than sons do, while sons inherit more from the father than from the mother, then two sisters will on the average of cases be more alike in constitution than a sister and a brother. Consequently the descendants of two sisters will differ less in their constitutions than the descendants of a brother and a sister; and marriage in the first case will be more likely to prove injurious from absence of dissimilarity in the physiological units than marriage in the second. My own small circle of friends furnishes evidence tending to verify this conclusion. In one instance two cousins who intermarried are children of two sisters, and they have no offspring. In another the cousins who intermarried are children of two brothers, and they have no offspring. In the third case the cousins were descendants of two brothers and only one child resulted.

[40]

A propos of this sentence one of my critics writes:—"I cannot find in this book the statement as first made that the 'life of an individual is maintained by the unequal and ever-varying actions of incident forces on its different parts.' Recent physiological work offers a startling example of the statement."

To the question contained in the first sentence the answer is that I have not made the statement in the above words, but that it is implied in the chapter entitled "The Degree of Life varies as the Degree of Correspondence," and more especially in § 36, which, towards its close, definitely involves the statement. The verifying evidence my critic gives me is this:—

"Prof. Sherrington has shown that if the sensory roots of the spinal nerves are cut one by one there is at first no general effect produced. That is to say, the remainder of the nervous system continues to function as before. This condition (lack of general effect) persists until about six pairs have been cut. With the severance of the seventh pair, however, the whole central nervous system ceases to function, so that stimulation of intact sensory nerves produces no reflex action. After a variable period, but one of many hours duration, the power of functioning is recovered. That is to say, if the sensory impulses (from the skin, &c.) reaching the central nervous system are rapidly reduced in amount, there comes a point where those remaining do not suffice to keep the structure 'awake.' After a time, however, it adjusts itself to work with the diminished supply. Similarly Strumpell describes the case of a boy 'whose sensory inlets were all paralyzed except one eye and one ear.' When these were closed he instantly fell asleep."

[41]

Fifty years before the discovery of the Röntgen rays and those habitually emanating from uranium, it had been observed by Moser that under certain conditions the surfaces of metals receive permanent impressions from appropriate objects placed upon them. Such facts show that the molecules of substances propagate in all directions special ethereal undulations determined by their special constitutions.

[42]

This classification, and the three which follow it, I quote (abridging some of them) from Prof. Agassiz's "Essay on Classification."

[43]

For explanations, see "Illogical Geology," *Essays*, Vol. I. How much we may be misled by assuming that because the remains of creatures of high types have not been found in early strata, such creatures did not exist when those strata were formed, has recently (1897) been shown by the discovery of a fossil Sea-cow in the lower Miocene of Hesse-Darmstadt. The skeleton of this creature proves that it differed from such Sirenian mammals as the existing Manatee only in very small particulars: further dwindling of disused parts being an evident cause. The same is true as regards, now, we consider that since the beginning of Miocene days this aberrant type of mammal has not much increased its divergence from the ordinary mammalian type; if we then consider how long it must have taken for this large aquatic mammal (some eight or ten feet long) to be derived by modification from a land-mammal; and if then we contemplate the probable length of the period required for the evolution of that land-mammal out of a pre-mammalian type; we seem carried back in thought to a time preceding any of our geologic records. We are shown that the process of organic evolution has most likely been far slower than is commonly supposed.

[44]

Since this passage was written, in 1863, there has come to light much more striking evidence of change from a more generalized to a less generalized type during geologic time. In a lecture delivered by him in 1876, Prof. Huxley gave an account of the successive modifications of skeletal structure in animals allied to the horse. Beginning with the *Orohippus* of the Eocene formation, which had four complete toes on the front limb and three toes on the hind limb, he pointed out the successive steps by which in the *Mesohippus*, *Miohippus*, *Protohippus*, and *Pliohippus*, there was a gradual approach to the existing horse.

[45]

Several of the arguments used in this chapter and in that which follows it, formed parts of an essay on "The Development Hypothesis," originally published in 1852.

[46]

Studies from the Morphological Laboratory in the University of Cambridge, vol. vi, p. 84.

[47]

Ibid., p. 81.

[48]

Studies from the Morphological Laboratory in the University of Cambridge, vol. vi, p. 89.

[49]

Early in our friendship (about 1855) Prof. Huxley expressed to me his conviction that all the higher articulate animals have twenty segments or somites. That he adhered to this view in 1880, when his work on *The Crayfish* was published, is shown by his analysis there given of the twenty segments existing in this fluviatile crustacean; and adhesion to it had been previously shown in 1877, when his work on *The Anatomy of Invertebrated Animals* was published. On p. 398 of that work he writes:—"In the abdomen there are, at most, eleven somites, none of which, in the adult, bear ambulatory limbs. Thus, assuming the existence of six somites in the head, the normal number of somites in the body of insects will be twenty, as in the higher *Crustacea* and *Arachnida*." To this passage, however, he puts the note:—"It is open to question whether the podical plates represent a somite; and therefore it must be recollected that the total number of somites, the existence of which can be actually demonstrated in insects, is only seventeen, viz., four for the head, three for the thorax, and ten for the abdomen." I have changed the number twenty, which in the original edition occurred in the text, to the number seventeen in deference to suggestions made to me; though I find in Dr. Sharp's careful and elaborate work on the *Insecta*, that Viallanes and Cholodkovsky agree with Huxley in believing that there are six somites in the insect-head. The existence of a doubt on this point, however, does not essentially affect the argument, since there is agreement among morphologists respecting the *constancy* of the total number of somites in insects.

[50]

To avoid circumlocution I let these words stand, though they are not truly descriptive; for the prosperity of imported species is largely, if not mainly, caused by the absence of those natural enemies which kept them down at home.

[51]

While these pages are passing through the press (in 1864), Dr. Hooker has obliged me by pointing out that "plants afford many excellent examples" of analogous transitions. He says that among true "water plants," there are found, in the same species, varieties which have some leaves submerged and some floating; other varieties in which they are all floating; and other varieties in which they are all submerged. Further, that many plants characterized by floating leaves, and which have all their leaves floating when they grow in deeper water, are found with partly aerial leaves when they grow in shallower water; and that elsewhere they occur in almost dry soil with all their leaves aerial.

[52]

It will be seen that the argument naturally leads up to this expression—Survival of the Fittest—which was here used for the first time. Two years later (July, 1866) Mr. A. R. Wallace wrote to Mr. Darwin contending that it should be substituted for the expression "Natural Selection." Mr. Darwin demurred to this proposal. Among reasons for retaining his own expression he said that I had myself, in many cases, preferred it—"continually using the words Natural Selection." (*Life and Letters*, &c., vol. III, pp. 45-6.) Mr. Darwin was quite right in his statement, but not right in the motive he ascribed to me. My reason for frequently using the phrase "Natural Selection," after the date at which the phrase "Survival of the Fittest" was first used above, was that disuse of Mr. Darwin's phrase would have seemed like an endeavour to keep out of sight my own indebtedness to him, and the indebtedness of the world at large. The implied feeling has led me ever since to use the expressions Natural Selection and Survival of the Fittest with something like equal frequency.

[53]

I am indebted to Mr. [now Sir W.] Flower for the opportunity of examining the many skulls in the Museum of the College of Surgeons for verification of this. Unfortunately the absence, in most cases, of some or many teeth, prevented me from arriving at that specific result which would have been given by weighing a number of the under jaws in each race. Simple inspection, however, disclosed a sufficiently-conspicuous difference. The under jaws of Australians and Negroes, when collated with those of Englishmen, were visibly larger, not only relatively but absolutely. One Australian jaw only seemed about of the same size as an average English jaw; and this (probably the jaw of a woman), belonging as it did to a smaller skull, bore a greater ratio to the whole body of which it formed part, than did an English jaw of the same actual size. In all the other cases, the under jaws of these inferior races (containing larger teeth than our own) were *absolutely* more massive than our own—often exceeding them in all dimensions; and *relatively* to their smaller skeletons were much more massive. Let me add that the Australian and Negro jaws are thus strongly contrasted, not with all British jaws, but only with the jaws of the civilized British. An ancient British skull in the collection possesses a jaw almost or quite as massive as those of the Australian skulls. All this is in harmony with the alleged relation between greater size of jaws and greater action of jaws, involved by the habits of savages.

[In 1891 Mr. F. Howard Collins carefully investigated this matter: measuring ten Australian, ten Ancient British, and ten recent English skulls in the College of Surgeons Museum. The result proved an absolute difference of the kind above indicated, and a far greater relative difference. To ascertain this last a common standard of comparison was established—

an equal size of skull in all the cases; and then when the relative masses or cubic sizes of the jaws were calculated, the result which came out was this:—Australian jaw, 1948; Ancient British jaw, 1135; Recent English jaw, 1030. "Hence," in the words of Mr. Collins, "the mass of the Recent English jaw is, roughly speaking, half that of the Australian relatively to that of the skull, and a ninth less than that of the Ancient British." He adds verifying evidence from witnesses who have no hypothesis to support—members of the Odontological Society. The Vice-President, Mr. Mummery, remarks of the Australians that "the jaw-bones are powerfully developed, and large in proportion to the cranium."]

[54]

As bearing on the question of the varieties of Man, let me here refer to a paper on "The Origin of the Human Races" read before the Anthropological Society, March 1st, 1864, by Mr. Alfred Wallace. In this paper, Mr. Wallace shows that along with the attainment of that intelligence implied by the use of implements, clothing, &c., there arises a tendency for modifications of brain to take the place of modifications of body: still, however, regarding the natural selection of spontaneous variations as the cause of the modifications. But if the foregoing arguments be valid, natural selection here plays but the secondary part of furthering the adaptations otherwise caused. It is true that, as Mr. Wallace argues, and as I have myself briefly indicated (see *Westminster Review*, for April, 1852, pp. 496-501), the natural selection of races leads to the survival of the more cerebrally-developed, while the less cerebrally-developed disappear. But though natural selection acts freely in the struggle of one society with another; yet, among the units of each society, its action is so interfered with that there remains no adequate cause for the acquirement of mental superiority by one race over another, except the inheritance of functionally-produced modifications.

[55]

Darwin and after Darwin, Part II, p. 99.

[56]

Essays upon Heredity, vol. i, p. 90.

[57]

In a letter published by Dr. Romanes in *Nature*, for April 26, 1894, he alleges three reasons why "as soon as selection is withdrawn from an organ the *minus* variations of that organ outnumber the *plus* variations." The first is that "the survival-mean must descend to the birth-mean." The interpretation of this is that if the members of a species are on the average born with an organ of the required size, and if they are exposed to natural selection, then those in which the organ is relatively small will some of them die, and consequently the mean size of the organ at adult age will be greater than at birth. Contrariwise, if the organ becomes useless and natural selection does not operate on it, this difference between the birth-mean and the survival-mean disappears. Now here, again, the *plus* variations and their effects are ignored. Supposing the organ to be useful, it is tacitly assumed that while *minus* variations are injurious, *plus* variations are not injurious. This is untrue. Superfluous size of an organ implies several evils:—Its original cost is greater than requisite, and other organs suffer; the continuous cost of its nutrition is unduly great, involving further injury; it adds needlessly to the weight carried and so again is detrimental; and there is in some cases yet a further mischief—it is in the way. Clearly, then, those in which *plus* variations of the organ have occurred are likely to be killed off as well as those in which *minus* variations have occurred; and hence there is no proof that the survival-mean will exceed the birth-mean. Moreover the assumption has a fatal implication. To say that the survival-mean of an organ is greater than the birth-mean is to say that the organ is greater *in proportion to other organs* than it was at birth. What happens if instead of one organ we consider all the organs? If the survival-mean of a particular organ is greater than its birth-mean, the survival mean of each other organ must also be greater. Thus the proposition is that every organ has become larger in relation to every other organ!—a marvellous proposition. I need only add that Dr. Romanes' inferences with respect to the two other causes—atavism and failing heredity—are similarly vitiated by ignoring the plus variations and their effects.

[58]

Westminster Review, January, 1860. See also *Essays, &c.*, vol. i, p. 290.

[59]

"On Orthogenesis and the Impotence of Natural Selection in Species-Formation," pp. 2, 19, 22, 24.

[60]

Address to Plymouth Institution, at opening of Session 1895-6.

[61]

Westminster Review, April, 1857. "Progress: its Law and Cause." See also *Essays*, vol. i.

[62]

It may be needful to remark, that by the proposed expression it is intended to define—not Life in its essence; but, Life as manifested to us—not Life as a *noumenon*: but, Life as a *phenomenon*. The ultimate mystery is as great as ever: seeing that there remains unsolved the question—What *determines* the co-ordination of actions?

[63]

Prin. of Phys., 2nd edit., p. 77.

[64]

Ibid., 3rd edit., p 249.

[65]

Ibid., p. 124.

[66]

Agassiz and Gould, p. 274.

[67]

Prin. of Phys., 3rd edit., p. 964.

[68]

"Parthenogenesis," p. 8.

[69]

Prin. of Phys., p. 92.

[70]

Ibid., p. 93.

[71]

Ibid., p. 917.

[72]

"A General Outline of the Animal Kingdom." By Prof. T. R. Jones, F. G. S., p. 61.

[73]

Carpenter.

[74]

Prin. of Phys., p. 873.

[75]

Ibid., p. 203.

[76]

Ibid., p. 209.

[77]

Ibid., p. 249.

[78]

Ibid., p. 249.

[79]

Ibid., p. 250.

[80]

Prin. of Phys., p. 256.

[81]

Ibid., p. 212.

[82]

Ibid., p. 266.

[83]

Prin. of. Phys., p. 267.

[84]

Ibid., p. 276.

[85]

Ibid., 2nd edit., p. 115.

[86]

Prin. of Phys., p. 954.

[87]

Ibid., p. 958.

[88]

Ibid., p. 688.

[89]

Ibid., p. 958.

[90]

"A General Outline of the Animal Kingdom." By Professor T. R. Jones, p. 61.

[91]

Prin. of Phys., p. 907.

[92]

Should it be objected that in the higher plants the sperm-cell and germ-cell differ, though no distinct co-ordinating system exists, it is replied that there *is* co-ordination of actions, though of a feeble kind, and that there must be some agency by which this is carried on.

[93]

It is a significant fact that amongst the diœcious invertebrata, where the nutritive system greatly exceeds the other systems in development, the female is commonly the largest, and often greatly so. In some of the Rotifera the male has no nutritive system at all. See *Prin. of Phys.*, p. 954.

[94]

Prin. of Phys., p. 908.

[95]

"Parthenogenesis," pp. 66, 67.

[96]

"Lectures on Animal Chemistry." By Dr. Bence Jones. *Medical Times*, Sept. 13th, 1851. See also *Prin. of Phys.*, p. 171.

[97]

Cyclopædia of Anatomy and Physiology, Vol. IV, p. 506.

[98]

From a remark of Drs. Wagner and Leuckart this chemical evidence seems to have already suggested the idea that the sperm-cell becomes "metamorphosed into the central parts of the nervous system." But though they reject this assumption, and though the experiments of Mr. Newport clearly render it untenable, yet none of the facts latterly brought to light conflict with the hypothesis that the sperm-cell contains unorganized co-ordinating matter.

[99]

Quain's *Elements of Anatomy*, p. 672.

[100]

The maximum weight of the horse's brain is 1 lb. 7 ozs.; the human brain weighs 3 lbs., and occasionally as much as 4 lbs.; the brain of a whale, 75 feet long, weighed 5 lbs. 5 ozs.; and the elephant's brain reaches from 8 lbs. to 10 lbs. Of the whale's fertility we know nothing; but the elephant's quite agrees with the hypothesis. The elephant does not attain its full size until it is thirty years old, from which we may infer that it arrives at a reproductive age later than man does; its period of gestation is two years, and it produces one at a birth. Evidently, therefore, it is much less prolific than man. See Müller's *Physiology* (Baly's translation), p. 815, and Quain's *Elements of Anatomy*, p. 671.

[101]

That the size of the nervous system is the measure of the ability to maintain life, is a proposition that must, however, be taken with some qualifications. The ratio between the amounts of gray and white matter present in each case is probably a circumstance of moment. Moreover, the temperature of the blood may have a modifying influence; seeing that small nervous centres exposed to rapid oxidation will be equivalent to larger ones more slowly oxidized. Indeed, we see amongst mankind, that though, in the main, size of brain determines mental power, yet temperament exercises some control. There is reason to think, too, that certain kinds of nervous action involve greater consumption of nervous tissue than others; and this will somewhat complicate the comparisons. Nevertheless, these admissions do not affect the generalization as a whole, but merely prepare us to meet with minor irregularities.

[102]

Let me here note in passing a highly significant implication. The development of nervous structures which in such cases take place, cannot be limited to the finger-ends. If we figure to ourselves the separate sensitive areas which severally yield independent feelings, as constituting a network (not, indeed, a network sharply marked out, but probably one such that the ultimate fibrils in each area intrude more or less into adjacent areas, so that the separations are indefinite), it is manifest that when, with exercise, the structure has become further elaborated, and the meshes of the network smaller, there must be a multiplication of fibres communicating with the central nervous system. If two adjacent areas were supplied by branches of one fibre, the touching of either would yield to consciousness the same sensation: there could be no discrimination between points touching the two. That there may be discrimination, there must be a distinct connection between each area and the tract of grey matter which receives the impressions. Nay more, there must be, in this central recipient-tract, an added number of the separate elements which, by their excitements, yield separate feelings. So that this increased power of tactual discrimination implies a peripheral development, a multiplication of fibres in the trunk-nerve, and a complication of the nerve-centre. It can scarcely be doubted that analogous changes occur under analogous conditions throughout all parts of the nervous system—not in its sensory appliances only, but in all its higher co-ordinating appliances, up to the highest.

[103]

Essays upon Heredity, p. 87.

[104]

Les Maladies des Vers à soie, par L. Pasteur, Vol. I, p. 39.

[105]

Curiously enough, Weismann refers to, and recognizes, syphilitic infection of the reproductive cells. Dealing with Brown-Séquard's cases of inherited epilepsy (concerning which, let me say, that I do not commit myself to any derived conclusions), he says:—"In the case of epilepsy, at any rate, it is easy to imagine [many of Weismann's arguments are based on things 'it is easy to imagine'] that the passage of some specific organism through the reproductive cells may take place, as in the case of syphilis" (p. 82). Here is a sample of his reasoning. It is well known that epilepsy is frequently caused by some peripheral irritation (even by the lodging of a small foreign body under the skin), and that, among peripheral irritations causing it, imperfect healing is one. Yet though, in Brown-Séquard's cases, a peripheral irritation caused in the parent by local injury was the apparent origin, Weismann chooses gratuitously to assume that the progeny were infected by "some specific organism," which produced the epilepsy! And then though the epileptic virus, like the syphilitic virus, makes itself at home in the egg, the parental protoplasm is not admitted!

[106]

Philosophical Transactions of the Royal Society for the Year 1821, Part I, pp. 20-24.

[107]

It will, I suppose, be said that the non-inheritance of mutilations constitutes evidence of the kind here asked for. The first reply is that the evidence is conflicting, as it may well be. It is forgotten that to have valid evidence of non-inheritance of mutilations, it is requisite that both parents shall have undergone mutilation, and that this does not often happen. If they have not, then, assuming the inheritableness of mutilations, there would, leaving out other causes, be an equal tendency to appearance and non-appearance of the mutilation in offspring. But there is another cause—the tendency to reversion, which ever works in the direction of cancelling individual characters by the return to ancestral characters. So that even were the inheritance of mutilations to be expected (and for myself I may say that its occurrence surprises me), it could not be reasonably looked for as more than exceptional: there are two strong countervailing tendencies. But now, in the second place, let it be remarked that the inheritance or non-inheritance of mutilations is beside the question. The question is whether modifications of parts produced by modifications of functions are inheritable or not. And then, by way of disproof of their inheritableness, we are referred to cases in which the modifications of parts are not produced by modifications of functions, but are otherwise produced!

[108]

See *First Principles*, Part II, Chap. XXII, "Equilibration."

[109]

Principles of Biology, § 46, (No. 8. April, 1863).

[110]

Ibid. This must not be understood as implying that while the mass increases as the cubes, the *quantity of motion* which can be generated increases only as the squares; for this would not be true. The quantity of motion is obviously measured, not by the sectional areas of the muscles alone, but by these multiplied into their lengths, and therefore increases as the cubes. But this admission leaves untouched the conclusion that the ability to *bear stress* increases only as the squares; and thus limits the ability to generate motion, by relative incoherence of materials.

[111]

The Transactions of the Linnæan Society of London, Vol. XXII, p. 215. The estimate of Reaumur, cited by Kirby and Spence, is still higher—"in five generations one Aphis may be the progenitor of 5,904,900,000 descendants; and that it is supposed that in one year there may be twenty generations." (*Introduction to Entomology*, Vol. I, p. 175)

[112]

A Manual of the Anatomy of Invertebrated Animals, by T. H. Huxley, p. 206.

[113]

Respecting the *Eloidea* I learn that in 1879—thirty years after it had become a pest—one solitary male plant was found in a pond near Edinburgh; but "in an exhaustive inquiry on the plant made by Dr. Groenland, of

Copenhagen, he could find no trace of any male specimens having been found in Europe other than the Scotch." In waters from which the *Eloidea* has disappeared, it seems to have done so in consequence of the growth of an *Alga*, which has produced turbid water unfavourable to it. That is to say, the decreased multiplication of somatic cells in some cases, is not due to any exhaustion, but is caused by the rise of enemies or adverse conditions; as happens generally with introduced species of plants and animals which multiply at first enormously, and then, without any loss of reproductive power, begin to decrease under the antagonizing influences which grow up.

[114]

A Text Book of Human Physiology. By Austin Flint, M.D., LL.D. Fourth edition. New York: D. Appleton & Co. 1888. Page 797.

[115]

This supposition I find verified by Mr. A. S. Packard in his elaborate monograph on "The Cave Fauna of North America, &c.," as also in his article published in the *American Naturalist*, September, 1888; for he there mentions "variations in *Pseudotremia cavernarum* and *Tomocerus plumbeus*, found living near the entrance to caves in partial daylight." The facts, as accumulated by Mr. Packard, furnished a much more complete answer to Prof. Lankester than is above given, as, for example, the "blindness of *Neotoma*, or the Wood-Rat of Mammoth Cave." It seems that there are also "cave beetles, with or without rudimentary eyes," and "eyeless spiders" and Myriapods. And there are insects, as some "species of Anophthalmus and Adelops, whose larvæ are lacking in all traces of eyes and optic nerves and lobes." These instances cannot be explained as sequences of an inrush of water carrying with it the remote ancestors, some of which did not find their way out; nor can others of them be explained by supposing an inrush of air, which did the like.

[116]

See "Social Organism" in *Westminster Review* for January, 1860; also *Principles of Sociology*, § 247.

[117]

Contemporary Review, September, 1893.

[118]

Evolution of Sex, p. 50.

[119]

Souvenirs Entomologiques, 3me Série, p. 328.

[120]

Natural History of Bees, new ed., p. 33.

[121]

Origin of Species, 6th ed., p. 232.

[122]

Contemporary Review, September, 1893, p. 333.

[123]

The Entomologist's Monthly Magazine, March, 1892, p. 61.

[124]

Perhaps it will be alleged that nerve-matter is costly, and that this minute economy might be of importance. Anyone who thinks this will no longer think it after contemplating a litter of half-a-dozen young rabbits (in the wild rabbit the number varies from four to eight); and on remembering that the nerve-matter contained in their brains and spinal cords, as well as the materials for building up the bones, muscles, and viscera of their bodies, has been supplied by the doe in the space of a month; at the same time that she has sustained herself and carried on her activities: all this being done on relatively poor food. Nerve-matter cannot be so very costly then.

[125]

Loc. cit., p. 318.

[126]

The Germ Plasm, p. 54.

[127]

While Professor Weismann has not dealt with my argument derived from the distribution of discriminativeness on the skin, it has been criticized by Mr. McKeen Cattell, in the last number of *Mind* (October, 1893). His general argument, vitiated by extreme misconceptions, I need not deal with. He says:—"Whether changes acquired by the individual are hereditary, and if so to what extent, is a question of great interest for ethics no less than for biology. But Mr. Spencer's application of this doctrine to account for the origin of species [!] simply begs the question. He assumes useful variations [!]—whether of structure or habit is immaterial—without attempting to explain their origin": two absolute misstatements in two sentences! The only part of Mr. Cattell's criticism requiring reply is that which concerns the "sensation-areas" on the skin. He implies that since Weber, experimental psychologists have practically set aside the theory of sensation areas:

showing, among other things, that relatively great accuracy of discrimination can be quickly acquired by "increased interest and attention.... Practice for a few minutes will double the accuracy of discrimination, and practice on one side of the body is carried over to the other." To me it seems manifest that "increased interest and attention" will not enable a patient to discriminate two points where a few minutes before he could perceive only one. That which he can really do in this short time is to learn to discriminate between the *massiveness of a sensation* produced by two points and the massiveness of that produced by one, and to *infer* one point or two points accordingly. Respecting the existence of sensation-areas marked off from one another, I may, in the first place, remark that since the eye originates as a dermal sac, and since its retina is a highly developed part of the sensitive surface at large, and since the discriminative power of the retina depends on the division of it into numerous rods and cones, each of which gives a separate sensation-area, it would be strange were the discriminative power of the skin at large achieved by mechanism fundamentally different. In the second place I may remark that if Mr. Cattell will refer to Professor Gustav Retzius's *Biologische Untersuchungen*, New Series, vol. iv (Stockholm, 1892), he will see elaborate diagrams of superficial nerve-endings in various animals showing many degrees of separateness. I guarded myself against being supposed to think that the sensation-areas are sharply marked off from one another; and suggested, contrariwise, that probably the branching nerve-terminations intruded among the branches of adjacent nerve-terminations. Here let me add that the intrusion may vary greatly in extent; and that where the intruding fibres run far among those of adjacent areas, the discriminativeness will be but small, while it will be great in proportion as each set of branching fibres is restricted more nearly to its own area. All the facts are explicable on this supposition.

[128]

To save space and exclude needless complication I have omitted these passages from the preceding divisions of this appendix.

[129]

Though Professor Weismann does not take up the challenge, Dr. Romanes does. He says:—"When selection is withdrawn there will be no excessive *plus* variations, because so long as selection was present the efficiency of the organ was maintained at its highest level: it was only the *minus* variations which were then eliminated" (*Contemporary Review*, p. 611). In the first place, it seems to me that the phrases used in this sentence beg the question. It says that "the efficiency of the organ was maintained at its *highest* level"; which implies that the highest level (tacitly identified with the greatest size) is the best and that the tendency is to fall below it. This is the very thing I ask proof of. Suppose I invert the idea and say that the organ is maintained at its right size by natural selection, because this prevents increase beyond the size which is best for the organism. Every organ should be in due proportion, and the welfare of the creature as a whole is interfered with by excess as well as by defect. It may be directly interfered with—as for instance by too big an eyelid; and it may be indirectly interfered with, where the organ is large, by needless weight and cost of nutrition. In the second place the question which here concerns us is not what natural selection will do with variations. We are concerned with the previous question—What variations will arise? An organ varies in all ways; and, unless reason to the contrary is shown, the assumption must be that variations in the direction of increase are as frequent and as great as those in the direction of decrease. Take the case of the tongue. Certainly there are tongues inconveniently large, and probably tongues inconveniently small. What reason have we for assuming that the inconveniently small tongues occur more frequently than the inconveniently large ones? None that I can see. Dr. Romanes has not shown that when natural selection ceases to act on an organ the *minus* variations in each new generation will exceed the *plus* variations. But if they are equal the alleged process of panmixia has no place.

[130]

The Variation of Animals and Plants under Domestication, vol. ii, p. 292.

[131]

Journal of the Anthropological Institute for 1885, p. 253.

[132]

In "The All-Sufficiency of Natural Selection" (*Contemporary Review*, Sept., 1893, p. 311), Professor Weismann writes:—"I have ever contended that the acceptance of a principle of explanation is justified, if it can be shown that without it certain facts are inexplicable." Unless, then, Prof. Weismann can show that the distribution of discriminativeness is otherwise explicable, he is bound to accept the explanation I have given, and admit the inheritance of acquired characters.

[133]

Prof. Weismann is unaware that the view here ascribed to Roux, writing in 1881, is of far earlier date. In the *Westminster Review* for January, 1860, in an essay on "The Social Organism," I wrote:—"One more parallelism to be here noted, is that the different parts of a social organism, like the different parts of an individual organism, compete for nutriment; and severally obtain more or less of it according as they are discharging more or less duty." (See also *Essays*, i, 290.) And then, in 1876, in *The Principles of Sociology*, vol. i, § 247, I amplified the statement thus:—"All other organs, therefore, jointly and individually, compete for blood with each organ ... local tissue-formation (which under normal conditions measures the waste of tissue in discharging function) is itself a cause of increased supply of materials ... the resulting competition, not between units simply, but between organs, causes in a society, as in a living body, high nutrition and growth of parts called into greatest activity by the requirements of the rest." Though I did not use the imposing phrase "intra-individual-selection," the process described is the same.

[134]

Proceedings of the Biological Society of Washington, vol. ix.

[135]

Romanes Lecture, p. 29.

[136]

Ibid., p. 35.

[137]

This interpretation harmonizes with a fact which I learn from Prof. Riley, that there are gradations in this development, and that in some species the ordinary neuters swell their abdomens so greatly with food that they can hardly get home.

Milton Keynes UK
Ingram Content Group UK Ltd.
UKHW030717041024
449263UK00004B/429